174

ALFRED T. GOBLE is Professor of Physics at Union College. After receiving his Ph.D. from the University of Wisconsin, Dr. Goble was Assistant Professor at Tulsa University and at Alfred University. He is active in theoretical-spectroscopy and cosmic-ray research.

DAVID K. BAKER is Professor of Physics at Union College. He received his B.Sc. from McMaster University and his Ph.D. from the University of Pennsylvania. While in residence at St. Andrew's University, Scotland, Dr. Baker conducted research in solid-state physics, particularly in semiconductors.

Elements of
MODERN PHYSICS

ALFRED T. GOBLE

UNION COLLEGE

and

DAVID K. BAKER

UNION COLLEGE

THE RONALD PRESS COMPANY · NEW YORK

Library of Congress Catalog Card Number: 62–9761

PRINTED IN THE UNITED STATES OF AMERICA

Preface

The increasing importance of modern developments in physics makes it imperative to supplement the traditional introductory course in general physics for engineering and science students. A current trend is to offer an additional one or two semesters in atomic and nuclear physics to serve as an introduction to this field. The purpose of this book is to provide a basic text for such a course at an elementary level. It is assumed that students taking this course will have an understanding of general physics and a knowledge of introductory calculus.

The first three chapters, emphasizing the classical approach, serve as a bridge to more recent developments in the study of the atom and give students an opportunity to view general physics from a more quantitative point of view. Following a study of the nature and behavior of electrons and other particles, the student is introduced to quantum effects and quantum mechanics. The chapters on harmonic motion and wave mechanics provide much of the background needed for a discussion of the eigenvalue problem and its significance. It is hoped that this introduction to quantum mechanics will enable the student to read more advanced material with some appreciation of its significance. The earlier chapters also provide a number of illustrative examples to give the student a start in applying physical principles to particular problems.

The last half of the book is devoted almost entirely to a study of the atom and subatomic particles, including x-ray and optical spectroscopy, radioactivity, the physics of the nucleus, cosmic rays, and "strange" particles. These topics are introduced in a way that presents not only a description of their nature and characteristics but also the methods of their discovery. A feature of this book is the chapter devoted exclusively to a discussion of the laws governing the behavior of electrons in solid materials. One indication of the intense interest and importance of solid state physics today may be seen in the rapid growth in the application of semiconductors in the electronics field. This chapter will provide an introduction for engineering students who contemplate further work with solid state devices. The problems at the end of each chapter have a range of difficulty sufficient to stimulate the interest of varying levels of students. Five appendixes provide fuller treatments of the units systems, complex numbers, Fourier methods and wave packets, the wave functions of the hydrogen atom, and angular momentum and spectroscopy.

Although designed primarily for a concluding course in the general physics sequence, this text has been so organized that it can be adapted for use in other programs. For those schools which are limited in the time available, the authors suggest omitting Chapters 1, 2, 3, 10, 11, 16, 18, and 20, thus making a shorter course covering the essentials of recent developments in this field.

The authors, as physicists, believe that engineering and science students will profit from having the methods and attitudes of fundamental science explained to them. This includes the careful recognition of order and simplicity in the relationships among physical quantities, the logical proceeding from hypothesis to test, to development, to retest, and to further consequence—in short, all the orderly features of the scientific method. But the maturing student must also be aware of the almost random probing into the unknown, the quick follow-up of a promising lead, the suggestion that leads to still further discovery, the disappointing dead end, the error that accidentally leads to a new truth, and the many other features of modern research that make the term "scientific method" often hardly appropriate to the process of discovery.

The authors have followed the trend toward the use of rationalized mks units but have not clung to them slavishly. Since many readers are likely to study related works in which cgs units are used, the authors have given the appropriate cgs Gaussian formula in brackets wherever it differs from the mks formula. An appendix on units provides help on this unavoidable problem. Frankly, it would be helpful if all students could learn to use each of the several systems of units with comparative ease, since so much of the literature is to be found using different systems.

The authors wish to acknowledge their appreciation of the invaluable assistance given by their colleagues, Professors C. L. Hemenway, V. E. Pilcher, and W. M. Schwarz. Professors R. W. Christy and W. P. Davis of Dartmouth College read the original notes and made useful suggestions, and Professor Pilcher provided a number of the problems. Finally, the authors wish to acknowledge the tremendous assistance provided by their wives. The book would never have been finished without the very considerable secretarial help of one (Mrs. A. T. G.) and the understanding and patience of both.

ALFRED T. GOBLE
DAVID K. BAKER

Schenectady, New York
January, 1962

Contents

Elements of
MODERN PHYSICS

1

Conservation of Energy

Physics is the formal study of the world's experience with natural phenomena. It is a formal study that is highly organized by the *methods* of mathematics and explicitly expressed in the *language* of mathematics.

It is perhaps curious that mathematics should be the proper language for describing natural phenomena. Some superstitious individuals go so far as to say that the mathematical language cannot be valid. They hope that magic or other supernatural effects will overcome the regular laws of nature. However, the non-superstitious might very well wonder that a simple mathematics, based on the rules of algebra, should enable the physicist to describe the tremendously complicated happenings of nature. It is certainly a wonder that we have been so successful.

Physicists now realize that only a start has been made in the description of matter. It has been necessary to turn to algebras and analyses involving more complicated rules and sometimes unfamiliar quantities. This interdependence of mathematics and physics is a most interesting one. There have been times when the mathematics and its use have grown together, or times when the mathematics has been invented for the situation, but very often in the history of science the mathematics has preceded its physical application.

It is customary to use the term *laws* for the rules of behavior of nature. Physical laws are usually quantitative expressions. They are usually expressed as mathematical relations between physically measurable quantities. Part of the remarkable success that comes from the use of mathematics is that these laws are often very simple but have great generality.

Among such simple, fundamental, and often-used relations are a group of laws called *conservation laws*. A conservation law is simply one that states that a particular quantity of a system remains unchanged in the process being considered. The quantity that is *conserved* neither decreases (as is implied by the term) nor increases. Conservation laws may apply to a small limited system such as a single particle or a collection of a few particles (perhaps an atom); or it may apply to a very extensive system including many particles which interact on each other (a complicated atom, a crystal, or even the whole universe). Examples of conservation laws of especial interest are:

1. the law of conservation of charge.
2. the law of conservation of mass.
3. the law of conservation of energy.
4. the law of conservation of momentum.
5. the law of conservation of angular momentum.

It is possible that these laws will not hold for a limited system since charge, mass, energy, etc. may be transferred out of or into a limited system, but if the system is completely isolated, the conservation laws above should hold for it.

Our wide experience with these laws has tended to confirm their validity and fundamental nature. This is so firmly felt that when experimental information indicates a conflict with these laws, a physicist will go looking elsewhere for an "explanation" rather than modify the laws. One modern modification has been to lump the law of conservation of mass and the law of conservation of energy into a single law of conservation of mass and energy, since experience has confirmed the predictions of the special theory of relativity that *mass* and *energy* are interconvertible.

There are a number of other laws calling for the conservation of a quantity either in the universe or in a more limited system; these will be treated as we come to them. The purpose of this and the next two chapters will be to examine the nature of laws three, four, and five. We will do this by "deriving" them. These derivations have a somewhat limited validity; however, the laws themselves do not lack this validity. All experience confirms them.

1–1. Work, Energy, Kinetic Energy. When a force $\mathbf{F}$ moves an object through a distance from an initial point a to a final point b, it is said to do work. The amount of work done by the force is

$$W = \int_a^b \mathbf{F} \cdot \mathbf{ds} = \int_a^b F \cos \theta \, ds. \tag{1–1}$$

This expression makes use of the standard notation for vector quantities. Thus the boldface letter $\mathbf{F}$ represents a vector quantity, the force, while the plain letter F represents a scalar quantity, the magnitude of the force. The differential displacement $\mathbf{ds}$ is also a vector with both a direction and a magnitude. The use of the dot between $\mathbf{F}$ and $\mathbf{ds}$ indicates the *scalar product* (sometimes called "dot product"). The second integral in Eq. 1–1 follows from the first by definition since the scalar product of a vector **A** and a vector **B** is defined by

$$\mathbf{A} \cdot \mathbf{B} = AB \cos \theta, \tag{1-2}$$

where θ is the angle between **A** and **B** as shown in Fig. 1–1. The path does

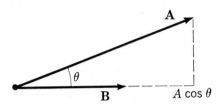

Fig. 1–1.   Diagram of scalar product.

not need to be straight, the direction of the force may change along the path from a to b, and the magnitude of the force may change as indicated in Fig. 1–2. Such an integral as that written in Eq. 1–1 is called a *line*

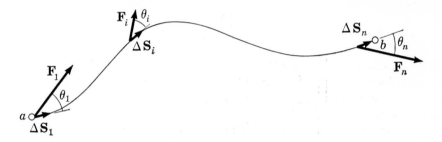

Fig. 1–2.   Calculating work by a line integral.

integral. It is essentially the same kind of integral as any other definite integral; that is, you are to think that the whole path has been broken into a large number of displacements Δs_i; at a point on each element of displacement the value of $F \cos \theta$ is to be determined; the sum

$$\sum_{i=1}^{n} F_i \cos \theta_i \, \Delta s_i$$

is to be computed; the limit of this sum as the number of displacement elements increases without limit is to be determined (this limit is the value of the integral) thus

$$\int_a^b F \cos \theta \, ds = \lim_{\substack{n \to \infty \\ \Delta s_i \to 0}} \sum_{i=1}^{n} F_i \cos \theta_i \, \Delta s_i.$$

Often this integral can be evaluated by simple processes, especially if **F** and θ are constant. In other cases it is usually necessary to express **F**, **Δs**, and θ in terms of some common parameter in order to evaluate the integral.

The units of force in the mks system are *newtons* and those of distance, *meters;* a *newton-meter* is a *joule.* In the cgs system, forces are given in *dynes* and lengths in *centimeters* and a *dyne-centimeter* is an *erg.* The British engineering system measures forces in *pounds*, distances in *feet;* so the unit of work is a *foot-pound* and bears no other name.

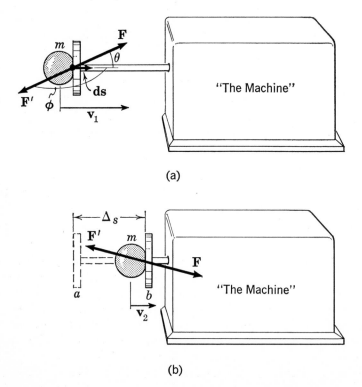

(a)

(b)

Fig. 1–3. The decrease in kinetic energy of *m* equals the work done by it on something else.

Now let us consider the case of an object having a mass *m* moving with an initial velocity $\mathbf{v}_1$. Let us suppose it comes in contact with another object (which we call "the machine"— see Fig. 1–3) so that it exerts a force **F** (not necessarily constant) on this "machine." We also assume that the angle at which this force is applied to the machine may change as the mass *m* moves against the machine and hence in Fig. 1–3b **F** appears at a different angle. In addition, we neglect the weight of *m*. As the motion proceeds, the mass does work on the "machine" while it moves from the point of initial contact

a to another point b. The amount of work done by m on the machine, since $\mathbf{F} = -\mathbf{F'}$, is

$$W = \int_a^b \mathbf{F} \cdot \mathbf{ds} = -\int_a^b \mathbf{F'} \cdot \mathbf{ds}$$

where $\mathbf{F'}$ is the reaction of the "machine" on the mass. Newton's second law of motion gives

$$\mathbf{F'} = m\mathbf{a}$$

so

$$W = -m \int_a^b \mathbf{a} \cdot \mathbf{ds} = -m \int_a^b a \cos \phi \, ds.$$

But

$$a \cos \phi = \frac{d^2s}{dt^2} = \frac{dv}{dt} ; \qquad (1\text{–}3)$$

so substituting Eq. 1–3 into the relation immediately above it gives

$$W = -m \int_a^b \frac{d^2s}{dt^2} \, ds = -m \int_{v_1}^{v_2} \frac{dv}{dt} \, ds$$

$$= -m \int_{v_1}^{v_2} v \, dv$$

$$= \tfrac{1}{2}mv_1{}^2 - \tfrac{1}{2}mv_2{}^2. \qquad (1\text{–}4)$$

In the last expression the speeds at a and b have been designated by v_1 and v_2. The direction of $\mathbf{v}$ plays no role here, only the speed v counts. Now note that the work done by m was the change in the value of the expression $\tfrac{1}{2}mv^2$. If v_2 were zero, m would have done all the work it could do. Thus $\tfrac{1}{2}mv^2$ is the measure of the ability of m to do work because of its motion v. We therefore call $\tfrac{1}{2}mv^2$ the *kinetic energy* of m. The work done by m on something else equals the decrease in kinetic energy.

Let us next imagine that the process is exactly reversed so far as the motion is concerned. The forces at each position are to stay the same both in magnitude and direction so the acceleration at each point is the same in both magnitude and direction. Since the direction of the motion is reversed, a point at which there was a slowing down becomes a point at which there is a speeding up and the motion is truly reversed in detail. The cosine in Eq. 1–3 should change sign since in Eq. 1–1, θ is the angle between the force and the direction of motion. The reversal of motion thus changes the sign of the component of force along the motion. This means that if the work done by m was positive before, it is now negative. Thus the other object has done work on m and hence has increased the kinetic energy of m.

The proof that we have just given that the decrease in $\frac{1}{2}mv^2$ is equal to the work done by m and that the work done on m is equal to the increase of $\frac{1}{2}mv^2$ is quite rigorous within the validity of Newton's laws, provided there are no internal changes within m and provided that if m is an extended body its orientation does not change (i.e., there is no rotation).

1–2. Potential Energy and the Law of Conservation of Energy. It is now time to turn our attention to the "machine" and see what has been going on in it. For our first example let us suppose that **F**, the force exerted by m, compresses a spring inside the machine. (On the reversal of motion, although the spring is now extending rather than shortening, the force **F** still is the one that the mass exerts against the spring.) The work done by m in compressing the spring increases the spring's ability to do work. This ability of the spring to do work is called its *potential energy*. For an ideal spring, the amount of compression is proportional to the force, or

$$F = kx \qquad (1\text{--}5)$$

where x is the amount of compression from the equilibrium, or uncompressed state, and k is a proportionality constant (see Fig. 1–4). In our case of the mass compressing the spring, we may make $ds = dx$ and $\cos \theta = 1$. The work done on the spring as the mass moves from x_1 to x_2 is thus

$$W = \int_{x_1}^{x_2} F \cos \theta \, ds = \int_{x_1}^{x_2} kx \, dx = \tfrac{1}{2}kx_2{}^2 - \tfrac{1}{2}kx_1{}^2. \qquad (1\text{--}6)$$

The increase in $\frac{1}{2}kx^2$ is the work done on the spring by m.

If we again think of the motion reversed, when the compressed spring is released, it will do work on m; the increase in $\frac{1}{2}mv^2$ is equal to this work; the decrease in $\frac{1}{2}kx^2$ is also equal to this work. This leads us to call $\frac{1}{2}kx^2$ the potential energy of the spring. Let us denote it by $V(x)$. (This means "the potential energy function of x.") Now we have seen that

$$\tfrac{1}{2}mv_1{}^2 - \tfrac{1}{2}mv_2{}^2 = \tfrac{1}{2}kx_2{}^2 - \tfrac{1}{2}kx_1{}^2$$

or

$$\tfrac{1}{2}mv_1{}^2 + \tfrac{1}{2}kx_1{}^2 = \tfrac{1}{2}mv_2{}^2 + \tfrac{1}{2}kx_2{}^2. \qquad (1\text{--}7)$$

It is not uncommon to denote the kinetic energy of a system by K. Using this notation we have

$$K_1 + V(x_1) = K_2 + V(x_2) = K + V \quad \text{(anywhere)}. \qquad (1\text{--}8)$$

The constancy of the sum of kinetic energy and potential energy shows the *conservation of energy* for this process.

In this process there has been a transformation of energy from one form to another (kinetic energy into potential energy or vice versa). The fact that the total energy does not change, that the decrease of one form equals the increase of the other form, is called the *law of conservation of energy*. It is believed to hold as well for all forms of energy as for kinetic and potential energy. When a process is irreversible and one cannot

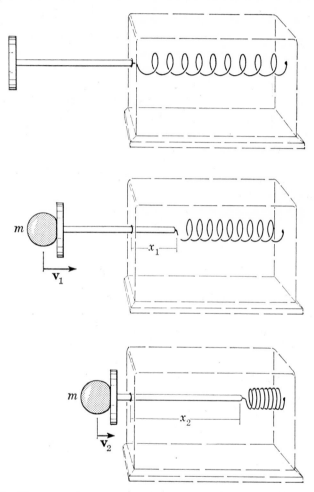

Fig. 1–4. The work done on "the machine" increases its potential energy.

reclaim as much energy of one form as was put in, we find that we can still keep the law of conservation of energy by saying that the amount of energy not returned was transformed into heat or some similar form of energy. There are usually ways of identifying and measuring this energy, and such measurements confirm the law.

The potential energy of the spring is related of course to the force which the spring exerts. Let us consider a compressed spring alone and let it extend to do work on another object as indicated in Fig. 1–5. The work done on the other body (not shown) by the spring in extending (decreasing x) from x_1 to x_2 is positive, while the potential energy of the spring decreases the same amount. We write this sentence as follows:

$$W_{sp} = V(x_1) - V(x_2) = -[V(x_2) - V(x_1)] = -\Delta V(x). \quad (1\text{–}9)$$

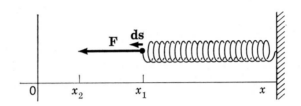

Fig. 1–5.   A compressed spring exerts a force F and does work on expansion. Its potential energy decreases.

The change in potential energy, $\Delta V(x)$, here is negative. We also have from the definition of work in Eq. 1–1,

$$W_{sp} = \int_{x_1}^{x_2} F(-dx) = -\int_{x_1}^{x_2} F\,dx \quad (1\text{–}10)$$

since $\cos \theta = +1$ and $ds = -dx$, and where F, the magnitude of $\mathbf{F}$, the force exerted by the spring, is positive. Thus

$$\Delta V = -W_{sp} = \int_{x_1}^{x_2} F\,dx. \quad (1\text{–}11)$$

Now if $x_2 - x_1 = \Delta x$ is small, we can write this as

$$\Delta V = \int_{x_1}^{x_2} F\,dx = \bar{F}(x_2 - x_1) = \bar{F}\,\Delta x. \quad (1\text{–}12)$$

where $\bar{F}$ is an average value of F in the interval Δx. As we make the interval smaller and smaller $\bar{F}$ gets closer and closer to both the values of F at x_1 and x_2, and these approach the same value F. Therefore

$$\frac{dV}{dx} = \lim_{\Delta x \to 0} \frac{\Delta V}{\Delta x} = +F. \quad (1\text{–}13)$$

Note that in the case of the spring as it is pictured in Fig. 1–5, $V(x_1) > V(x_2)$; so dV/dx is positive as it should be. But note that $dV/dx =$

$-dV/ds$. Therefore

$$F = -\frac{dV}{ds},\qquad(1\text{--}14)$$

an important relation that tells us that the force on an object is the negative of the rate of change of its potential energy with distance or that the force is the slope of the potential energy function when it is expressed in terms of the distance. The derivation was independent of the actual system, so that Eq. 1–14 is quite generally true for the component of the force along the displacement.

1–3. Other Forms of Potential Energy. Work must be done to raise a mass in the gravitational field of the earth. This provides another example of the interchange of energy from one form to another. This work can come from a decrease in the kinetic energy of a body, as we shall see.

If the object lifted has a mass m the magnitude of its weight is mg (g is the acceleration for a freely falling body). Over reasonable distances this is constant and the work required to lift it a height h is

$$W = \int_0^h mg\,dz = mgh.$$

This is the work that the object can do if lowered this distance. Thus we can define a potential energy due to position in our gravitational field. This *gravitational* potential energy $V(z)$ is proportional to the altitude z of the weight above a reference level at which $V = 0$. So,

$$V(z) = mgz.\qquad(1\text{--}15)$$

The object could be a moving mass. Such a body with a mass m will have a speed v which can be computed from the relation,

$$\tfrac{1}{2}mv^2 + mgz = \text{constant},\qquad(1\text{--}16)$$

which follows directly from the law of conservation of energy. In Fig. 1–6 is pictured a mass sliding on a surface of variable altitude. As z increases, v must decrease; while sliding downhill produces an increase in speed. Eq. 1–16 is based on the additional assumption that there are no frictional forces acting.

One other example of potential energy is that due to the proximity of two localized electric charges. The work to bring one close to the other can be calculated as follows. Assume that a positive charge of q units is carried from a point A at a distance r_1 from a second positive charge of size Q to another point B at a distance r_2 from Q. The force on q due to Q is

$$F = \frac{1}{4\pi\epsilon_0}\frac{qQ}{r^2}. \qquad \left[F = \frac{qQ}{r^2}.\right]\qquad(1\text{--}17)$$

(*Note:* Most electrical equations will be written in both mks and rationalized cgs Gaussian systems, putting the cgs form in brackets. Most mechanical equations are the same for both systems.) The units for charge in the mks system are *coulombs,* and in the Gaussian system they are *statcoulombs.* ϵ_0, the permittivity of free space, equals 8.854×10^{-12} farad per m. Since q and Q are of the same sign, the direction of the force **F** on q due to Q will be away from Q, as shown in Fig. 1–7. If q is to be carried from A to B, an external agent must exert a force equal to

$$F = \frac{1}{4\pi\epsilon_0} \frac{qQ}{r^2}$$

but in the opposite direction. The work done by this agent in carrying the charge from A to B is the *electrostatic potential energy,*

$$W = -\int_{r_1}^{r_2} \frac{1}{4\pi\epsilon_0} \frac{Qq}{r^2} \, dr \qquad \left[W = -\int_{r_1}^{r_2} \frac{Qq}{r^2} \, dr \right]$$

$$= \frac{Qq}{4\pi\epsilon_0} \left(\frac{1}{r_2} - \frac{1}{r_1} \right). \qquad \left[= Qq \left(\frac{1}{r_2} - \frac{1}{r_1} \right). \right] \qquad (1\text{–}18)$$

(The angle between the exerted force and the displacement is zero but $\mathbf{ds} = -\mathbf{dr}$, as can be seen in Fig. 1–7 where **r** points from Q toward q, hence the negative sign.) This is the amount that the potential energy will have increased. If the motion is reversed, an equal amount of work

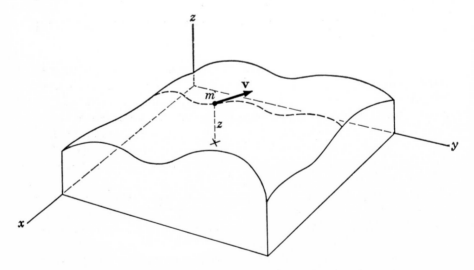

Fig. 1–6.   A mass sliding on a surface.   Its total energy is constant.

is done by the system of charges. The quantity

$$\frac{W}{q} = \frac{Q}{4\pi\epsilon_0}\frac{1}{r_2} - \frac{Q}{4\pi\epsilon_0}\frac{1}{r_1} = \Phi(B) - \Phi(A) \tag{1–19}$$

$$\left[\frac{W}{q} = \frac{Q}{r_2} - \frac{Q}{r_1} = \Phi(B) - \Phi(A)\right]$$

is the amount of work required to carry a unit charge from r_1 to r_2. This is called the *potential difference* between the two points and

$$\Phi(r) = \frac{Q}{4\pi\epsilon_0 r} \qquad \left[\Phi(r) = \frac{Q}{r}\right] \tag{1–20}$$

is the potential at a point a distance r from Q relative to a very remote point. The remote point (often referred to as infinity) makes a convenient reference point. The potential of a point could of course be referred to some other reference point. The unit of potential difference and of potential is the *volt;* thus 1 joule of work is required to carry 1 coulomb across a potential difference of 1 volt. Since the charge of atomic particles is always in multiples of the charge on an electron, $e = 1.60 \times 10^{-19}$ coulomb, it is often convenient to report energy and work in electron volts (ev). It should be clear that 1 ev $= 1.60 \times 10^{-19}$ j.

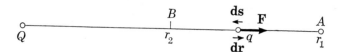

Fig. 1–7. The potential energy of similar electrical charges is increased if their separation is decreased.

We have worked out only the potential of a point charge close to another single point charge, but it is possible to do it for much more complicated sets of charges. For example, an important situation consists of two parallel plates bearing opposite charges. In this case the potential varies linearly across the space between them. Further, in the most general case, we can still find the amount of work to bring a unit positive charge to the point (x,y,z) in question from some reference point and thus can give $\Phi(x,y,z)$, the potential at the point.

Our integration of Eq. 1–18 shows that the result depends only on r_1 and r_2. In fact we could have chosen another path and would have found that the work to go from A to B is independent of the path between them. The reversal of any one path simply reverses which does work on which. In carrying q from A to B, the external agent does work on the system of charges thus increasing the system's potential energy; while if the charge q

moves from B to A, the system of charges does work and thus the system's potential energy decreases. Of course, if q and Q are of opposite sign, these statements are reversed. The independence of path and the reversibility is an important feature of this system, the other systems we have talked about, and most any idealized system. In fact it is the feature of reversibility that makes the concept of a potential a useful one.

1–4. The Force Field. It should be clear from our earlier discussions that the force $\mathbf{F}$ on an object may vary in both magnitude and direction from point to point. We now introduce the very useful concept of a *force field*. A force field exists in a region where we can use a force vector at every point in the region to describe the force on an object. An example of such a force field is the gravitational force field around the earth. Another example is the electric force field between the plates of a parallel-plate capacitor. We have been considering the case of forces and force fields such that

$$W = \oint \mathbf{F} \cdot \mathbf{ds} = 0 \qquad (1\text{–}21)$$

where the sign $\oint$ means that we are to integrate over a closed path in the field, for example, from point A to point B and then back again to point A along a different path, as shown in Fig. 1–8. In the example shown in Fig. 1–8(b) the integral from A to C is zero, from C to B it is Fl, from B to D it is zero and from D to A it is $-Fl$. Such a force field having the property of Eq. 1–21 is said to be a *conservative force field*.

For the case of electric fields of force we can introduce the concept of an *electric field intensity*. This is the measure and description of the *electric field*. It is the force that would be exerted on a unit positive charge if placed in the electric field without disturbing the other charges. That is, it is given by

$$\mathbf{E} = \frac{\mathbf{F}}{q} \qquad (1\text{–}22)$$

where $\mathbf{F}$ is the force on the charge q. In accordance with our discussion that led to the result of Eq. 1–14, we can also compute $\mathbf{E}$ from Φ. The component of $\mathbf{E}$ in a certain direction is the negative of the rate of change of Φ in that direction. In fact the direction of $\mathbf{E}$ is in the direction of most rapid decrease of Φ and E is $-d\Phi/ds$, where ds is in the direction of most rapid decrease of Φ. From this we see that E will be in volts per meter (or the equivalent, newtons per coulomb).

We have already pointed out that if there are frictional forces acting, the reversal of motion does not result in the system giving the same amount of work back and so at first sight it seems that energy is not conserved (such forces are actually called non-conservative forces), but we recognize that the work done against friction goes into kinetic energy of random motion of the molecules; that is, it goes into heat. The amount of heat developed is just equal to the work done; so energy (if we include heat) is conserved in this case. Another example in which energy appears not to

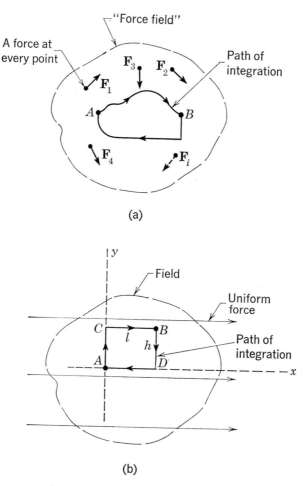

(a)

(b)

Fig. 1–8. Illustration of the concept of a line integral around a closed path. (a) General case. (b) Particular case.

be conserved is the case of electromagnetic waves. When an electromagnetic wave is radiated one can say that energy apparently lost is contained in the electromagnetic field. On absorption, it reappears in some other form. No cases of failure of the law of conservation of energy are known.

Three numerical examples may contribute to an understanding of the material in this chapter.

EXAMPLE 1. A small spring gun is used to eject a pellet horizontally. After ejection, the pellet falls freely. The mass of the pellet is 2.4×10^{-3} kg. The spring is compressed 0.06 m, which requires a final force of 1.44 newtons. With what speed is the pellet moving as it leaves the gun? What is its speed after falling a distance of 6 m?

Solution:

$$k = \frac{1.44}{0.06} = 24 \text{ newton m}^{-1}.$$

The potential energy of the compressed spring is

$$\tfrac{1}{2}kx^2 = \tfrac{1}{2} \times 24 \times 0.06^2 = 4.32 \times 10^{-2} \text{ j}.$$

This potential energy is converted into the kinetic energy of the pellet; so if v_0 is the speed as the pellet leaves the gun, we have

$$\tfrac{1}{2}mv_0{}^2 = \tfrac{1}{2} \, 2.4 \times 10^{-3}v_0{}^2 = 4.32 \times 10^{-2}$$

$$v_0{}^2 = 36$$

$$v_0 = 6 \text{ m sec}^{-1}.$$

After the pellet has fallen 6 m, its gravitational potential energy has decreased $mgh = 2.4 \times 10^{-3} \times 9.8 \times 6 = 0.14$ j. The total kinetic energy $= 0.0432 + 0.14 = 0.1832$ j and

$$v^2 = \frac{0.1832}{\tfrac{1}{2} \, 2.4 \times 10^{-3}} = 152.5$$

$$v = 12.35 \text{ m sec}^{-1}.$$

EXAMPLE 2. An electron leaves a hot filament with a very low velocity. It is then accelerated by an electric field between the filament and a cylindrical plate which is at an electric potential 250 v positive with respect to the filament. What is the kinetic energy of the electron just before it strikes the plate, and what is its velocity at that moment?

Solution: The loss in potential energy of the electron is

$$eV = 1.6 \times 10^{-19} \times 250 = 4.0 \times 10^{-17} \text{ j} = 250 \text{ ev}.$$

$$\tfrac{1}{2}mv^2 = eV = \tfrac{1}{2} \, 9.11 \times 10^{-31}v^2 = 4.0 \times 10^{-17};$$

so

$$v^2 = 87.8 \times 10^{12}$$

$$v = 9.37 \times 10^6 \text{ m sec}^{-1}.$$

EXAMPLE 3. A classical model of a hydrogen atom consists of a single electron moving in an elliptical orbit about what may be considered a fixed positive charge of 1 electronic size located at one focus of the ellipse.

For a particular elliptical orbit the electron comes to 3×10^{-10} m from the positive charge and goes as far away as 5×10^{-10} m. The total energy is $W = -2.88 \times 10^{-19}$ j. At the point of closest approach and at the most remote point (these are the two ends of the major axis) find:

    a. the kinetic energy of the electron,
    b. the velocity of the electron,
    c. the electric field intensity,
    d. the radius of curvature of the path.

Solution: Call the point of closest approach A and the remote point B.

a.   At A $V(A) = -\dfrac{9.0 \times 10^9 (1.6 \times 10^{-19})^2}{3 \times 10^{-10}} = -7.68 \times 10^{-19}$ j

$$K_A = W - V = [-2.88 - (-7.68)] \times 10^{-19}$$
$$= 4.80 \times 10^{-19} \text{ j}$$

At B $V(B) = -\dfrac{9.0 \times 10^9 (1.6 \times 10^{-19})^2}{5 \times 10^{-10}} = -4.61 \times 10^{-19}$ j

so

$$K_B = W - V = (4.61 - 2.88) \times 10^{-19}$$
$$= 1.73 \times 10^{-19} \text{ j}$$

b.   Since

$$K = \tfrac{1}{2}mv^2, \qquad v^2 = 2K/m.$$

At A $v^2 = \dfrac{2 \times 4.80 \times 10^{-19}}{9.1 \times 10^{-31}} = 1.055 \times 10^{12} \text{ m}^2 \text{ sec}^{-2},$

$v = 1.028 \times 10^6 \text{ m sec}^{-1}.$

At B $v^2 = \dfrac{2 \times 1.73 \times 10^{-19}}{9.1 \times 10^{-31}} = .380 \times 10^{12},$

$v = 6.16 \times 10^5 \text{ m sec}^{-1}.$

c.   At A $E = \dfrac{1}{4\pi\epsilon_0} \dfrac{Q}{r^2} = \dfrac{9.0 \times 10^9 \times 1.6 \times 10^{-19}}{9 \times 10^{-20}} = 1.6 \times 10^{10} \text{ v m}^{-1}$

At B $E = \dfrac{1}{4\pi\epsilon_0} \dfrac{Q}{r^2} = \dfrac{9.0 \times 10^9 \times 1.6 \times 10^{-19}}{25 \times 10^{-20}} = 5.75 \times 10^9 \text{ v m}^{-1}$

d.   The centripetal force is $Ee = mv^2/R$, where R is the radius of curvature; so

at A $R = \dfrac{mv^2}{Ee} = \dfrac{9.1 \times 10^{-31} \times 1.055 \times 10^{12}}{1.6 \times 10^{10} \times 1.6 \times 10^{-19}} = 3.75 \times 10^{-10} \text{ m}.$

at B $R = \dfrac{mv^2}{Ee} = \dfrac{9.1 \times 10^{-31} \times .380 \times 10^{12}}{5.75 \times 10^9 \times 1.6 \times 10^{-19}} = 3.75 \times 10^{-10} \text{ m}.$

Note that at the opposite ends of the major axis the radii of curvatures are equal, but not equal to the semimajor axis.

PROBLEMS

1-1. Write out the following laws of physics and critically discuss their approximations and limitations. (a) Newton's second law of motion, (b) Newton's law of cooling, (c) the law of gravitation, (d) Ampère's law, (e) Malus' law, (f) Coulomb's law.

1-2. Find the dot product of the following pairs of vectors.

A		B	
Length	Angle	Length	Angle
14.1	0°	1	45°
25	30°	25	60°
10	0°	100	180°

1-3. Prove that two vectors at right angles have a dot product of zero.

1-4. A certain force in newtons is directed along the x-axis and is given by the relation $F = 10x$, where x is in meters. Compute the work done by an agent working against this force in moving from the point (10,0) to the point (0,0).

1-5. A man pushes a mass of 15 kg up an inclined plane of height h that makes an angle of 30° with the horizontal. There is no friction between the block and plane. Using the law of conservation of energy find the force the man must exert to move the block along the plane at constant speed if the force is (a) parallel to the plane, or (b) horizontal.

1-6. Two men lower a mass of 750 kg down an inclined plane on rollers that make it virtually frictionless. They are only able to exert a horizontal force. What is this horizontal force if the incline is 4 m long and 1.6 m high?

1-7. The constant k of a spring is 0.06 newton m^{-1}. Calculate the work to stretch it 0.1 m from its unextended length; 0.1 m further; and finally for a third decimeter.

1-8. A mass of 0.4 kg when hung on a spring stretches it a distance of 0.08 m. (a) What is the value of the spring constant k? (b) How much work is done just in stretching the spring this amount?

1-9. A spring requires 1200 dynes to stretch (or compress) it 1 cm. It has a ball with a mass of 30 gm attached to it. The spring is stretched 15 cm beyond its equilibrium point and held there. It is then released. Neglect friction. (a) What force was required to stretch the spring? (b) How much work was done by the person to stretch the spring? (c) Calculate the speed of the ball as it passes the equilibrium point. (d) Calculate the speed of the ball 5 cm from the equilibrium point. (e) How far will the spring be compressed as the ball comes to rest?

1–10. A 6000 lb railway coach collides with a spring loaded buffer at the end of the railway line. If the springs are rated to compress 4 in. for a load of 80,000 lb, compute the velocity with which the car strikes the buffer if it is compressed 6 in.

1–11. Calculate the velocity of the following: (a) A mass of 5 kg with a kinetic energy of 200 j, (b) a mass of 3.6×10^{-4} kg with a kinetic energy of 0.4 j, (c) a mass of 1.4×10^{-22} kg with a kinetic energy of 0.7×10^{-12} j, (d) a mass of 3.3×10^{-8} gm with a kinetic energy of 52 erg.

1–12. The velocity of sound in air is approximately 3×10^2 m sec^{-1}. Calculate the kinetic energy of the following objects moving at that speed: (a) An electron $m = 9.11 \times 10^{-31}$ kg. (b) An oxygen molecule $m = 5.3 \times 10^{-26}$ kg. (c) A bullet $m = 10^{-3}$ kg. (d) An airplane $m = 10^4$ kg.

1–13. A $\frac{1}{2}$ lb ball is thrown upward with a velocity (at $h = 0$) of 40 ft/sec. Treat this as a problem in conservation of energy and calculate (a) the height to which it will rise; (b) the kinetic energy and velocity at the 10 ft level; (c) the kinetic energy and velocity at the 15 ft level.

1–14. (a) Using the law of gravitation and assuming that the earth is a sphere derive an expression for the potential energy of a mass m at the surface of the earth in terms of G, the universal gravitational constant, the mass M and radius R of the earth.

(b) Express this relation in terms of the acceleration of gravity at the surface of the earth, g.

1–15. (a) Find an expression for the potential energy of a satellite in a circular orbit of radius r.

(b) What is the value of this energy for a 1000 lb capsule in an orbit 400 miles above the earth?

1–16. A satellite with a mass m moves in an elliptic orbit about the earth which has a mass M. At apogee its distance from the center of the earth is R and its speed is v_a. At perigee its distance from the center of the earth is r and its speed is v_p. Write a relation showing the law of conservation of energy as it applies to the satellite at apogee and perigee.

1–17. Using the results of Problem 14 and the fact that the radius of the earth is approximately $R = 6400$ km calculate the numerical value of the initial velocity required by a rocket intended to escape from the earth's gravitational field. (Hint: use the law of conservation of energy and neglect friction.)

1–18. The radius of a nucleus is approximately 1.5×10^{-13} cm. (a) How much work must be done against gravitational forces to separate two protons originally this distance apart? (b) How much work must be done against electrical forces to separate one electron and one proton at the given distance? $G = 6.67 \times 10^{-11}$ newton-m^2 kg^{-2}.

1–19. An alpha particle has a kinetic energy of 1.6 Mev (million electron volts). It has a charge $+2e$. How close could it come to the nucleus of an atom which has a charge $+79e$?

1-20. Compute the potential energy of $+4.8 \times 10^{-19}$ coulomb when located 3×10^{-9} m from a charge of $+6.4 \times 10^{-18}$ coulomb.

1-21. An electron ($q = 1.6 \times 10^{-19}$ coulomb) is located 10^{-11} m from a charge of $+35$ electronic charges. What is its potential energy? (Give in electron volts as well as joules.) What is the force on the electron?

1-22. An electron starting from rest passes through a potential difference of 2000 v. What is its kinetic energy as a result? What is its velocity? ($m_e = 9.1 \times 10^{-31}$ kg.)

1-23. Calculate the velocity of an argon ion, $M = 6.6 \times 10^{-26}$ kg, that has passed through a potential difference of 500 v.

1-24. What will be the total energy of a particle of mass 6.65×10^{-27} kg that bears a charge of 2 electronic charges when it is 4.3×10^{-14} m from a charge of 90 electronic charges, if its velocity is 7×10^6 m sec^{-1}?

1-25. Calculate the kinetic energy and velocity of an alpha particle ($q = 3.2 \times 10^{-19}$ coulomb; $M = 6.6 \times 10^{-27}$ kg) which has an energy of 5.5 Mev when it is at a distance of 9×10^{-14} m from a charge of $+88$ electronic charges.

1-26. The energy required to remove an electron from a certain metal surface is 2 ev. What incident energy is required to produce an electron from this surface with a speed of 1×10^8 cm sec^{-1}?

1-27. A potential energy function is given by the relation $V = ax^2$ joules. Find the force derivable from this potential energy. Evaluate it at the point $x = 2$ m.

1-28. The potential energy of a particle is $V = -A \exp -kx$. What is the force as a function of position?

1-29. The potential energy between two particles separated by a distance r is

$$V' = \frac{-m_1 m_2}{r^2} \exp \frac{-r}{r_0}.$$

What is the force as a function of position?

1-30. A potential energy function is given by the relation

$$V(r) = \frac{a}{r^2} - \frac{b}{r}.$$

(a) Plot this function by plotting each term separately and adding (a, b are positive constants). (b) Find the force function corresponding to this potential. (c) Is there an equilibrium separation? If so, what is it?

1-31. At what separation will two particles exert no force on each other if $V(r) = g/r \exp +kr$?

1-32. If **i** and **j** are vectors of unit length directed along the positive x and y axes respectively, find the following dot products **i·i**, **i·j**, **j·j**, **j·i**.

If m_2 is greater than m_1, v'_1 will be negative, implying that m_1 rebounds from the spring; if m_2 is less than m_1, m_1 will follow after.

The impulse given to m_2 is

$$G_{12} = m_2 v'_2 - 0 = \frac{2m_1 m_2}{m_1 + m_2} v_1, \qquad (2\text{–}15)$$

and the impulse given to m_1 is

$$G_{21} = m_1 v'_1 - m_1 v_1 = \frac{m_1{}^2 - m_1 m_2}{m_1 + m_2} v_1 - m_1 v_1$$

$$= -\frac{2m_1 m_2}{m_1 + m_2} v_1, \qquad (2\text{–}16)$$

and $G_{12} + G_{21} = 0$, as it should.

2–2. Rockets. Although rockets, and other reaction devices, have been used for centuries, a tremendous increase in interest started during World War II. The development of jet engines for aircraft, the V-2 rocket, and smaller rockets such as the "bazooka" were responsible for this increase in interest. Space exploration is possible only through the use of such devices, so their development has been greatly accelerated recently. The reason for including a brief discussion of them is that they are such an important application of the law of conservation of linear momentum.

We shall restrict our consideration in this article to rockets only, that is, to devices which carry both fuel and oxidizer or to devices which require no material from their surroundings. In these devices, matter is ejected at high speeds from a nozzle; for momentum to be conserved, the rest of the rocket must receive an equivalent momentum in the opposite direction. Or, if the system is not free, an equivalent impulse will be felt. The details of the process are not needed for this discussion, but a sketch of the situation may help. In Fig. 2–2 a rocket engine is pictured. In the combustion chamber, fuel is burned to produce vapor at high pressure and temperature, which escapes through the nozzle. One can account for the reaction force by integrating the pressure over all the walls of combustion chamber and nozzle. If the nozzle were not open this integral would be zero, but since the lower end is open, a net force acts upward. The effectiveness of the rocket engine is increased by increasing the ejection velocity of the vapor, so rocket engine designers choose the shape and size of the nozzle and combustion chamber to optimize this. The choice of propellants will also influence the ejection velocity.

Fuels such as alcohol or kerosene oxidized by liquid oxygen, alcohol oxidized by red fuming nitric acid, hydrogen plus fluorine, and many other liquids which can be pumped into the combustion chamber have been used. Some have the advantage of storability, others do not. Solid propellants have also been used. Many are similar to smokeless powder, but are usually slower burning. In this case the fuel and oxidizers are already mixed and in the combustion chamber, which is simply the casing for the fuel. They have obvious storage advantages, but their burning is not so easily controlled as that of pumped liquids.

As the rocket engine ejects vapors at high velocities, a thrust **F** is exerted on the rocket, as we have seen. This is an important property of the engine. It may range from a small value to tremendous values such as 10^6 lb. Engines such as those used in Thor, Atlas, and Titan, have thrusts of the order of 10^5 lb. The impulse imparted by the rocket engine in a time t is then **F**t, assuming **F** remains constant, as it usually does (except for direction). Since the amount of fuel used is usually proportional to t, another quantity of interest is the specific impulse of the fuel, the impulse provided per unit weight burned. (A physicist would prefer to work with impulse per unit mass, but the engineers' influence has determined the practice followed.)

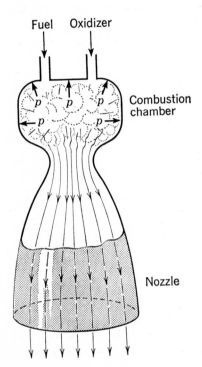

Fig. 2–2. A rocket engine.

We will denote this specific impulse by I. Its value depends on the rate of use of all ingredients of the propellants. Typical values range from 249 sec for kerosene and liquid oxygen to 371 sec for hydrogen plus fluorine. Since I equals impulse furnished (say in pound-seconds) divided by fuel burned (in pounds), its units are commonly seconds. The impulse provided by a weight of propellant $w = mg$ is $G = Iw$ pound-seconds. The size of the thrust is therefore

$$F = \frac{dG}{dt} = -I\frac{dw}{dt}.$$ (2–17)

Evidently a kerosene-liquid oxygen engine with a thrust of 100,000 lb burns (counting both hydrocarbon and oxygen) at the rate of 400 lb sec^{-1}.

2–3. The Motion of a Rocket. Let us now consider a single-stage rocket and see how it may perform. It will have a certain payload (warhead, or more peaceful device) weighing W_p. Then there will be the engine, the fuel tanks, and the structure with a total weight W_s. These weights are unchanging, but the weight of the fuel w will change with time from its original weight w_0 to zero. While the engine is running there is a thrust $\mathbf{F}$ along the axis of the engine; while the rocket is in the atmosphere there is a drag $\mathbf{D}$ opposite to the motion; and finally there is the pull of the earth, the weight of the rocket. Since all of these may act in different directions, calculation of the motion is often quite complicated. We will take the simplest case, assuming that the drag is zero and that the rocket is free from any significant gravitational fields. We will also assume that the direction of the thrust does not change. Under these conditions, the only external force on the rocket is the thrust with magnitude F where

$$F = -I \frac{dw}{dt}. \qquad (2\text{–}18)$$

The weight of the rocket is $W_p + W_s + w$ pounds and its mass is $(W_p + W_s + w)/g$ slugs, so the motion of the rocket is described by

$$F = -I \frac{dw}{dt} = \frac{(W_p + W_s + w)}{g} \frac{d^2s}{dt^2}$$

or

$$\frac{d^2s}{dt^2} = -\frac{Ig}{W_p + W_s + w} \frac{dw}{dt} \qquad (2\text{–}19)$$

We assume that the rocket burns fuel at the steady rate of $dw/dt = -c$ so that $w = w_0 - ct$. This makes it possible to write the equivalent of Eq. 2–19:

$$\frac{dv}{dt} = \frac{Igc}{W_p + W_s + w_0 - ct}. \qquad (2\text{–}20)$$

The integral of this is

$$v = Ig \ln \frac{W_p + W_s + w_0}{W_p + W_s + w_0 - ct}, \qquad (2\text{–}21)$$

since $v = 0$ when $t = 0$. The burn-out speed, that is, the speed attained when the fuel is exhausted, v_b is

$$v_b = Ig \ln \frac{W_p + W_s + w_0}{W_p + W_s}. \qquad (2\text{–}22)$$

The burn-out speed is often a critical quantity; it is necessary for the rocket designer properly to allocate structural weight and fuel to obtain the proper burn-out velocity for the payload.

The second integration gives

$$s = Ig\left(t - \frac{W_p + W_s + w_0}{c}\right)\ln\frac{W_p + W_s + w_0}{W_p + W_s + w_0 - ct} + Igt, \quad (2\text{-}23)$$

and the total distance traveled at burn-out is

$$s_b = Ig\left(\frac{W_p + W_s}{c}\right)\ln\frac{W_p + W_s}{W_p + W_s + w_0} + Ig\frac{w_0}{c}. \quad (2\text{-}24)$$

Of course the rocket then continues at constant speed.

These formulas describe the motion of what is called a single-stage rocket. It is more efficient to use several stages; that is, to construct the rocket so that after part of the fuel has been burned, the tanks and heavy engines can be jettisoned and only lighter tanks and engines used for further acceleration. Another "staging" to still lighter tanks and engines is then possible, and so on. Two, three, four, five, and even more stages are not unusual. In principle one might even jettison structure continuously. In fact, if a fraction f of the material burned away is structure, so that only the fraction $(1 - f)$ of the weight lost contributes to the thrust, one can show that the burn-out speed should be

$$v_0 = Ig(1 - f)\ln\frac{W}{W_p}, \quad (2\text{-}25)$$

where W is the initial total weight including payload, structure, and fuel. This is often referred to as "continuous staging" but is seldom used in practice.

These paragraphs can be considered only an introduction to rocketry. Problems of heating during passage through the atmosphere, problems of steering and guidance, problems of motion in a complicated gravitational field, and others equally vital to a thorough consideration of this subject, are outside the scope of this book.

EXAMPLE 1. A rocket completely loaded for takeoff weighs 42,000 lb. The initial acceleration on vertical takeoff is 6 ft sec^{-2}. (a) What is the thrust of the engine? (b) At what rate is propellant used if its specific impulse is 295 sec?

The last stage of this rocket has a payload of 10 lb, a combined structure and engine weight of 50 lb, and 200 lb of propellants having a specific impulse of 295 sec. Final staging occurs outside the atmosphere and where gravitational forces do not influence the tangential acceleration appreciably. The velocity of the rocket at the moment of staging is 20,000 ft sec^{-1} and the thrust is parallel to the motion increasing the speed. (c) What is the final speed of the payload?

a. Let F represent the thrust. The resultant force on the rocket is

$F - 42{,}000 = (W/g)a$. Thus we compute

$$F = 42{,}000 + \frac{42{,}000}{32}\, 6 = 42{,}000 + 7{,}900 = 49{,}900 \text{ lb}.$$

b. $F = Ic = 295c$.

$$c = \frac{49{,}900}{295} = 169 \text{ lb sec}^{-1}.$$

c. Eq. 2–22 really gives the change in velocity that results from the burning of all the final-stage propellant; so the final speed will be

$$v_f = 20{,}000 + Ig \ln \frac{W_p + W_s + w_0}{W_p + W_s}$$

$$= 20{,}000 + 295\,(32) \ln \frac{260}{60}$$

$$= 20{,}000 + 295\,(32)1.47 = 20{,}000 + 13{,}900$$

$$= 33{,}900 \text{ ft sec}^{-1}.$$

2–4. Collisions. As we mentioned earlier, another case in which the use of the law of conservation of linear momentum can simplify the treatment of an otherwise difficult problem is the case of collisions. When two bodies collide with each other, affect each other, and then separate, their behavior may provide valuable information concerning the nature of the bodies. It is possible that we may have a preconceived idea of the nature of the bodies and predict a behavior during a collision which may or may not actually occur. If it does occur, our early idea is supported; if something else occurs, we use the results to reconstruct our ideas about the bodies. In modern physics, collisions between atoms or nuclei occur when incident particles emerge from radioactive sources, high energy accelerators, or from nuclear reactors and are directed toward a target of the material under study. A measurement of the number and energy of the scattered particles gives information about the target. These experiments are called scattering experiments.

Sometimes the collision is between charged particles; sometimes it is between neutral bodies. In the latter case we can say that there is no interaction or force between them until they actually touch each other. This latter case, further idealized by neglecting forces from other bodies, provides an interesting set of examples for developing collision theory and also is commonly found in nature.

All observations are made from a fixed coordinate system called the "laboratory system" (designated by the abbreviation LS). This is the coordinate system we are familiar with from our daily experience. For example, as we watch two football players collide while we sit on the sidelines, we are in what we have called the LS. A different frame of reference, namely, one moving with the center of mass of the two particles (designated by the abbreviation CMS) is also a convenient and important frame of reference in which to describe the collision.

We shall then classify each collision into a number of categories. When the original and the final motion of both the bodies involved is along a straight line, we have a *head-on* collision; when the paths of the two bodies in the LS, either before or after the collision, are separated by an angle, we have a *glancing collision*. Each of these two types of collisions may be further subdivided on the basis of energy considerations. *Elastic* collisions are collisions in which *dynamical energy* is conserved. The term dynamical energy refers to the sum of the kinetic energy of gross body motion plus potential energy. The use of the term here has the additional advantage in that it avoids the possible confusion that may arise because the energy that has been converted into heat is also kinetic energy but is kinetic energy of random motion of molecules, not the kinetic energy we are talking about here. *Inelastic* collisions are collisions in which dynamical energy is converted to other forms of energy such as heat, sound, or some form of internal energy.

Since it may be quite difficult to determine the details of the variation of forces during the collision, we shall find that the law of conservation of linear momentum is particularly useful. Its validity depends upon the determination to consider only systems in which no external forces are acting. It is equally valid for neutral bodies which interact with very short-range forces and for charged bodies in which electrical forces are acting when the particles are separated by long distances.

2–5. Elastic Head-on Collisions. In a head-on collision all particles move along the same line, so only the speed and sense (whether forward or backward) need to be specified. If one of the particles is at rest, the other must be directed toward the first. If the line of motion should miss the center of the target, the "miss distance," that is, the distance from the center of the target to the line of motion of the projectile, is called the *impact parameter* (see Fig. 2–3). Thus a head-on collision is one for which the impact parameter is zero.

The example of the two masses sliding on the rod discussed in Art. 2–2 is a case of elastic head-on collision. The spring typifies the forces between the two objects. In collisions between billiard balls, the elastic compression of the ivory is the equivalent of the compression of the spring. In the case of repulsive collision between electrically charged particles, the electrostatic repulsion is responsible for the redistribution of momentum. Other types of forces may occur in atomic and nuclear collisions, but the nature of the forces does not change the results obtained.

Eqs. 2–10 through 2–16 all hold for any elastic head-on collision in which $v_2 = 0$. We may also eliminate v_1, giving

$$v'_1 = v'_2 \frac{m_1 - m_2}{2m_1}. \tag{2-26}$$

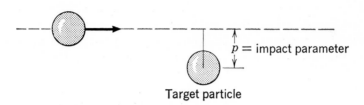

$p = $ impact parameter

Target particle

Fig. 2–3.   An illustration of an impact parameter.

We can also take the value for v'_1 given by Eq. 2–13 to compute the ratio of the kinetic energy retained by particle 1, K_a, to the energy it had before the collision, K_0. The result is

$$\frac{K_a}{K_0} = \frac{\frac{1}{2}m_1 v'^2_1}{\frac{1}{2}m_1 v_1^2} = \left(\frac{m_1 - m_2}{m_1 + m_2}\right)^2. \tag{2-27}$$

In a similar way we find that the energy transferred to particle 2, K_t, to the original energy of particle 1 is

$$\frac{K_t}{K_0} = \frac{\frac{1}{2}m_2 v'^2_2}{\frac{1}{2}m_1 v_1^2} = \frac{4m_1 m_2}{(m_1 + m_2)^2}. \tag{2-28}$$

2–6. Perfectly Inelastic Head-on Collisions.   This is a simple but interesting collision in which we can easily prove that dynamical energy decreases and that the decrease goes into some other form such as heat.

In Fig. 2–4 the two particles are shown stuck together after the col-

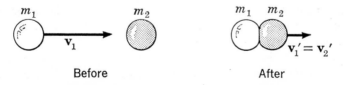

Before   After

Fig. 2–4.   Perfectly inelastic head-on collision.

lision (this is the meaning of perfectly inelastic) and moving with a speed v'_2. Then

$$m_1 v_1 = (m_1 + m_2) v'_2. \tag{2-29}$$

This is the only basic equation available for this case. However, separate sums of the energies are

$$K_0 = \tfrac{1}{2}m_1v_1^2 \quad \text{before collision} \tag{2-30}$$

$$K_a = \tfrac{1}{2}(m_1 + m_2)v'_2{}^2 \quad \text{after collision;} \tag{2-31}$$

therefore

$$\frac{K_a}{K_0} = \frac{m_1 + m_2}{m_1} \cdot \frac{v'_2{}^2}{v_1^2},$$

and using the solution of Eq. 2–29 for the speed ratio gives

$$\frac{K_a}{K_0} = \frac{m_1}{m_1 + m_2}. \tag{2-32}$$

From Eq. 2–32 we see that the energy K_a after the collision is always less than the original energy K_0. If we believe the law of conservation of energy, we must believe that the difference $K_0 - K_a$ has not really been lost, but only converted into some other form or forms such as heat. No known experience contradicts this.

EXAMPLE 2. A neutron (mass = 1.65×10^{-27} kg) collides head-on with a nitrogen nucleus (mass = $14 \times 1.65 \times 10^{-27} = 23.1 \times 10^{-27}$ kg). The initial velocity of the neutron is 1.4×10^7 m sec^{-1}. Find (a) the final velocity of the neutron, (b) the final velocity of the nitrogen nucleus, (c) the kinetic energy of both particles after the collision, and compare with (d) the kinetic energy of the neutron before the collision.

a. The initial velocity of the neutron is v_1, its final velocity is v'_1, and that of the nitrogen nucleus is v'_2.

$$v'_1 = \frac{m_1 - m_2}{m_1 + m_2} v_1 = \frac{(1 - 14)1.65 \times 10^{-27}}{(1 + 14)1.65 \times 10^{-27}} 1.4 \times 10^7$$

$$= -1.21 \times 10^7 \text{ m sec}^{-1}.$$

The negative sign indicates that the neutron rebounds in the negative direction.

b. $$v'_2 = \frac{2m_1}{m_1 + m_2} v_1 = \frac{2}{1 + 14} 1.4 \times 10^7 = 1.87 \times 10^6 \text{ m sec}^{-1}.$$

c. $\tfrac{1}{2}m_1v'_1{}^2 = \tfrac{1}{2} 1.65 \times 10^{-27}(1.21 \times 10^7)^2 = 1.20 \times 10^{-13}$ j
    $\tfrac{1}{2}m_2v'_2{}^2 = \tfrac{1}{2} 23.1 \times 10^{-27}(1.87 \times 10^6)^2 = 0.42 \times 10^{-13}$ j
      Total = 1.62×10^{-13} j.

d. $\tfrac{1}{2}m_1v_1^2 = 1.62 \times 10^{-13}$ j.

This problem might have been given in a form in which the velocity of the nitrogen nucleus after the collision was measured and you were to determine the velocity of the neutron before the collision and also the velocity of the neutron after the collision. The arithmetic would then have looked like:

a. $v_1 = \dfrac{m_1 + m_2}{2m_1} v'_2 = \dfrac{15}{2} 1.87 \times 10^6 = 1.40 \times 10^7 \text{ m sec}^{-1}.$

b. $v'_1 = \dfrac{m_1 - m_2}{2m_1} v'_2 = -\dfrac{13}{2} 1.87 \times 10^6 = -1.21 \times 10^7 \text{ m sec}^{-1}.$

Suppose that instead of having a perfectly elastic collision, the neutron had simply entered the nitrogen nucleus and stayed there. (a) What would be the velocity of the combination? (b) What would be the kinetic energy of the new nucleus, and (c) how much internal energy was added to the combination (not including any work done by binding forces between the nucleus and the neutron)?

a. $v'_1 = v'_2 = \dfrac{m_1}{m_1 + m_2} v_1 = \dfrac{1}{15} 1.40 \times 10^7 = 9.33 \times 10^5 \text{ m sec}^{-1}.$

b. $K_0 = \frac{1}{2} m_1 v_1^2 = 1.62 \times 10^{-13} \text{ j}$

$K_a = \dfrac{m_1}{m_1 + m_2} K_0 = \dfrac{1}{15} K_0 = 1.08 \times 10^{-14} \text{ j};$

or

$K_a = \frac{1}{2}(m_1 + m_2) v'_2{}^2 = \frac{1}{2} 15 \times 1.65 \times 10^{-27} (9.33 \times 10^5)^2$
$= 1.08 \times 10^{-14} \text{ j}.$

c. $\Delta E_{\text{int}} = K_0 - K_a = 16.2 \times 10^{-14} - 1.08 \times 10^{-14}$
$= 15.12 \times 10^{-14} \text{ j}.$

2-7. Glancing Collisions. Glancing collisions occur more frequently than head-on collisions and the situation is at once more complex because of the vector properties of momentum. The vectors must be resolved into components.

Such a glancing collision for the case of a stationary target is shown in Fig. 2–5 as it would be seen in the LS. The law of conservation of momentum requires that the momentum after the collision equal that before the collision; so

$$m_1 \mathbf{v}_1 = m_1 \mathbf{v}'_1 + m_2 \mathbf{v}'_2. \qquad (2\text{–}33)$$

This vector equation may be resolved into component equations to simplify its application. For the x-components we have

$$m_1 v_1 + 0 = m_1 v'_1 \cos \theta_L + m_2 v'_2 \cos \phi_L \qquad (2\text{–}34)$$

and for the y-components

$$0 = m_1 v'_1 \sin \theta_L - m_2 v'_2 \sin \phi_L. \qquad (2\text{–}35)$$

If the collision is an elastic one, we also have for this glancing collision,

$$\tfrac{1}{2} m_1 v_1^2 = \tfrac{1}{2} m_1 v'_1{}^2 + \tfrac{1}{2} m_2 v'_2{}^2. \qquad (2\text{–}36)$$

Eqs. 2–34, 2–35, and 2–36 are three equations from which we can solve for three unknowns. Thus we must know at least two of the five likely variables v_1, v'_1, v'_2, θ_L, and ϕ_L. Very often one of the angles and v_1 are specified. Another common situation is to fix one of the angles, measure either v'_1 or v'_2, and then compute the other variables.

Calculations of the type we have been discussing are also conveniently computed by using the center-of-mass system (CMS) of coordinates.

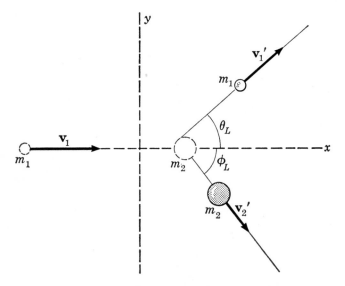

Fig. 2–5. A glancing collision in the LS system.

2–8. The Center-of-Mass Coordinate System. There are a number of advantages in considering the motion of colliding particles as described by their coordinates in a system that has the center of mass of the pair of particles for its origin. In this center-of-mass system (CMS) both particles approach the origin and then recede from it. In each case the motion is along the same straight line, though the line of separation may be rotated from the line of approach. Another simplifying feature of the CMS is that the total linear momentum in this system is zero, as will be shown. The kinetic energy as described in this system also has a particularly fundamental value.

Of course, we shall need to be able to transform from the LS to the CMS and vice versa. These processes are the standard ones of relative motion; any velocity in the CMS is equal to the velocity in the LS minus the velocity of the CMS relative to the LS; and any velocity in the LS is equal to the velocity in the CMS plus the velocity of the CMS relative to the LS. (This is true for high velocities requiring the special theory of relativity, and hence the relativistic summing of velocities, or for lower velocities which require only the familiar form of vector summation.)

Let us now calculate the velocity of the center of mass of a set of n particles in the LS system. We will designate it $\bar{v}$. The x, y, and z coordinates of the center of mass $\bar{x}$, $\bar{y}$, and $\bar{z}$ are given by

$$\bar{x} = \frac{\displaystyle\sum_{i=1}^{n} m_i x_i}{\displaystyle\sum_{i=1}^{n} m_i} ,$$

$$\bar{y} = \frac{\displaystyle\sum_{i=1}^{n} m_i y_i}{\displaystyle\sum_{i=1}^{n} m_i} , \qquad (2\text{–}37)$$

$$\bar{z} = \frac{\displaystyle\sum_{i=1}^{n} m_i z_i}{\displaystyle\sum_{i=1}^{n} m_i} .$$

We obtain the x-, y-, and z-components of the velocity of the center of mass by differentiation with respect to time. This gives

$$\bar{v}_x = \frac{\displaystyle\sum_{i=1}^{n} m_i \frac{dx_i}{dt}}{\displaystyle\sum_{i=1}^{n} m_i} = \frac{\displaystyle\sum_{i=1}^{n} m_i v_{xi}}{\displaystyle\sum_{i=1}^{n} m_i} ,$$

$$\bar{v}_y = \frac{\displaystyle\sum_{i=1}^{n} m_i \frac{dy_i}{dt}}{\displaystyle\sum_{i=1}^{n} m_i} = \frac{\displaystyle\sum_{i=1}^{n} m_i v_{yi}}{\displaystyle\sum_{i=1}^{n} m_i} , \qquad (2\text{–}38)$$

$$\bar{v}_z = \frac{\displaystyle\sum_{i=1}^{n} m_i \frac{dz_i}{dt}}{\displaystyle\sum_{i=1}^{n} m_i} = \frac{\displaystyle\sum_{i=1}^{n} m_i v_{zi}}{\displaystyle\sum_{i=1}^{n} m_i} .$$

Now we are interested primarily in two particles only, one of which is at rest. The above equations are simplified if the line joining the two particles is chosen to be the x-axis. Eqs. 2–37 and 2–38 then become

$$\bar{x} = \frac{m_1 x_1 + m_2 x_2}{m_1 + m_2} \qquad (2\text{–}39)$$

and

$$\bar{v}_x = \bar{v} = \frac{m_1 \dfrac{dx_1}{dt} + m_2 \dfrac{dx_2}{dt}}{m_1 + m_2} = \frac{m_1 v_1 + m_2 v_2}{m_1 + m_2} = \frac{m_1}{m_1 + m_2} v_1. \quad (2\text{-}40)$$

In this equation, since the motion of the center of mass is along the x-axis, the magnitudes are all that is required to determine the velocity vector $\bar{v}$ from the velocity v_1.

The situation as described in the LS system is pictured in Fig. 2–6 in

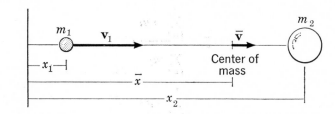

Fig. 2–6.   The center of mass and its velocity in the LS system.

which m_2 is at rest and m_1 is approaching it with a velocity v_1. The velocity of the center of mass $\bar{v} = \bar{v}_x$ is also shown. The same situation as referred to the CMS is pictured in Fig. 2–7. Here the motions of m_1

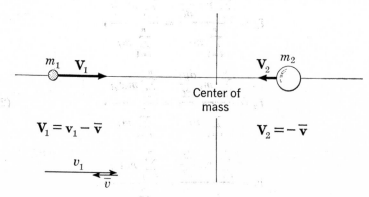

Fig. 2–7.   The velocities of m_1 and m_2 in the CMS system before collision.

and m_2 are indicated by the vectors V_1 and V_2. We shall represent the velocities of particles in the LS with small letters and the velocities of particles in the CMS with capital letters. Before the collision they will not be primed; after the collision they will be primed. The values of V_1

and $\mathbf{V}_2$ are determined by the rule for transforming velocities to the CMS. In the CMS then,

$$\mathbf{V}_1 = \mathbf{v}_1 - \bar{\mathbf{v}} = \frac{m_2}{m_1 + m_2} \mathbf{v}_1 \tag{2-41}$$

and

$$\mathbf{V}_2 = \mathbf{v}_2 - \bar{\mathbf{v}} = -\bar{\mathbf{v}} = -\frac{m_1}{m_1 + m_2} \mathbf{v}_1. \tag{2-42}$$

The momentum of each particle before collision is

$$m_1 \mathbf{V}_1 = \frac{m_1 m_2}{m_1 + m_2} \mathbf{v}_1, \tag{2-43}$$

$$m_2 \mathbf{V}_2 = -\frac{m_2 m_1}{m_1 + m_2} \mathbf{v}_1; \tag{2-44}$$

so we see that the total linear momentum in the CMS is zero. We should also point out that the velocity $\bar{\mathbf{v}}$ of the center of mass does not change since there are no external forces to accelerate the total mass of the system.

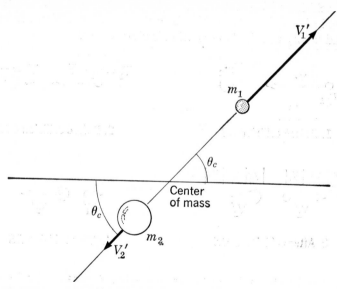

Fig. 2–8. Motion of particles in the CMS system after collision.

The law of conservation of linear momentum requires that the total momentum must not change; so it must also not change in the CMS. Thus we know that after the collision the momentum in the CMS must add to zero. This does not require that the particles recede on the same line upon which they approached. Instead, the line joining them may rotate through an angle θ_c in the CMS; so the two particles are each scattered through the same angle θ_c in the CMS, as shown in Fig. 2–8.

If we now assume that the collision is *elastic*, then once again

$$\tfrac{1}{2}m_1 V_1^2 + \tfrac{1}{2}m_2 V_2^2 = \tfrac{1}{2}m_1 V'_1{}^2 + \tfrac{1}{2}m_2 V'_2{}^2 = \text{constant.}$$

Since this is true and since $m_1 V'_1 = m_2 V'_2$, then the speeds V'_1 and V'_2 must be respectively equal to V_1 and V_2.

Therefore, in summary, an elastic collision as seen in the CMS is always a head-on collision in which the observer sees the particles approach, collide, and rebound with their speeds unchanged; however, the line joining them may be rotated through an angle, θ_c. Of course the velocities as viewed in the LS are changed and the velocities after collision need not be along the same line.

In order to illustrate this, we present the case of the simple head-on collision ($\theta_c = 0$). Note how an observer in the LS can compute the motion in the CMS and then can reconvert to the LS.

EXAMPLE 3. Assume a mass m_1 with velocity v_1 undergoes an elastic head-on collision with a stationary mass m_2 where $m_1 < m_2$. Make vector diagrams in LS and CMS to show how the vectors transform from LS to CMS and finally to LS. The solution is given below.

1. Before collision LS

$$\mathbf{V}_1 = \mathbf{v}_1 - \bar{\mathbf{v}} \qquad \mathbf{V}_2 = -\bar{\mathbf{v}}$$

2. Before collision CMS

$$|\mathbf{V}'_1| = |\mathbf{V}_1| \qquad |\mathbf{V}'_2| = |\mathbf{V}_2|$$

3. After collision CMS

4. After collision LS

2–9. The Relations Between the Scattering Angles in the LS and the CMS.

Now let us consider what may happen if θ_c is not equal to zero. We remember that the rule for transforming from the LS to the CMS and back again requires vector subtraction and addition. The situation is shown in Fig. 2–9. From this figure we see that the relations between θ_c and θ_L and ϕ_L are

$$v'_1 \cos \theta_L = V'_1 \cos \theta_c + \bar{v}, \qquad (2\text{–}45)$$

$$v'_1 \sin \theta_L = V'_1 \sin \theta_c, \qquad (2\text{–}46)$$

and

$$v'_2 \cos \phi_L = \bar{v} - V'_2 \cos \theta_c, \tag{2–47}$$

$$v'_2 \sin \phi_L = V'_2 \sin \theta_c. \tag{2–48}$$

These four equations hold whether the collision is elastic or inelastic. However, again we simplify the problem by assuming that the collisions

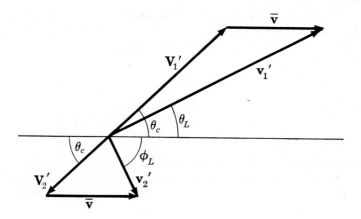

Fig. 2–9. Vector diagram of transformation from CMS to LS after the collision.

are *elastic*. We have seen that for this case in the CMS we have for the speeds before and after the collision,

$$V_1 = V'_1 = \frac{m_2}{m_1 + m_2} v_1 \tag{2–49}$$

and from Eq. 2–40

$$\bar{v} = \frac{m_1}{m_1 + m_2} v_1. \tag{2–50}$$

Therefore Eqs. 2–49 and 2–50 give

$$\frac{\bar{v}}{V'_1} = \frac{m_1}{m_2} = \gamma. \tag{2–51}$$

Now Eqs. 2–45 and 2–46 give for the transformation equation between the LS and the CMS

$$\tan \theta_L = \frac{\sin \theta_c}{\cos \theta_c + \gamma}. \tag{2–52}$$

An alternative expression can also be obtained from Fig. 2–9 with the aid of the law of sines.   It is

$$\frac{\sin \theta_L}{V'_1} = \frac{\sin (\theta_c - \theta_L)}{\bar{v}} \qquad (2\text{--}53)$$

and, using Eqs. 2–49, 2–50, and 2–51, we change this to

$$\sin (\theta_c - \theta_L) = \gamma \sin \theta_L. \qquad (2\text{--}54)$$

We also have the relation

$$\frac{v'_1}{\sin \theta_c} = \frac{\bar{v}}{\sin (\theta_c - \theta_L)} = \frac{V'_1}{\sin \theta_L}. \qquad (2\text{--}55)$$

These equations enable us to examine the dependence of the scattering angles on the masses.   We can use them either to find θ_c when we know θ_L, or to find θ_L if we know θ_c.   (The former is the more likely situation.)

The relation between the recoil angle, ϕ_L in the LS and θ_c in the CMS, can be obtained for the case of a perfectly elastic collision in a similar way. There is the simplifying fact that the speeds of the recoil particles m_2 in the CMS both before and after the collision are equal and are equal to the speed of the center of mass in the LS, thus $V'_2 = V_2 = \bar{v}$.   The portion of Fig. 2–9 that is appropriate to this problem is reproduced in Fig. 2–10.

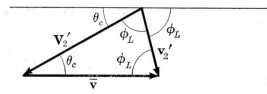

Fig. 2–10.   Recoil vector diagram.

This is for the special case of a perfectly elastic collision.   (In the case of an inelastic collision Fig. 2–9 is still appropriate, but $V'_2 \neq \bar{v}$.)   Since the triangle of Fig. 2–10 is isosceles, the angles have the values shown.   This leads directly to the relation

$$\phi_L = 90° - \frac{\theta_c}{2}. \qquad (2\text{--}56)$$

We can use this relation to find ϕ_L when we know θ_c or vice versa, as before.   We might measure θ_L, use this to calculate θ_c, and then use the result to calculate the recoil angle, ϕ_L.

EXAMPLE 4.   A neutron, mass $m_1 = 1.7 \times 10^{-24}$ kg, collides with a deuteron, mass $m_2 = 3.4 \times 10^{-24}$ kg, which is initially at rest.   The deuteron recoils at an angle of 30° from the direction of the incoming neutron with a speed of 2.2×10^5 m sec^{-1}. (a) In what direction was the neutron deflected, (b) what was the final speed of the neutron, and (c) what was the initial speed of the neutron? (d) Calculate the initial energy of the neutron.

Solution:

a. The recoil of the deuteron as described is sketched for both the LS and CMS. From this and from Eq. 2–56 we see that since $\phi_L = 30°$, we have $\theta_c = 120°$ and we see that $V'_2 = 1.27 \times 10^5$ m sec^{-1}. Thus we also know that $\bar{v} = 1.27 \times 10^5$ m sec^{-1}. We also have $\gamma = \frac{1}{2}$. From Eq. 2–52 we get $\tan \theta_L = 0.866/(-\frac{1}{2} + \frac{1}{2}) = \infty$ or $\theta_L = 90°$.

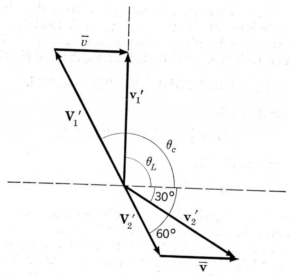

b. Then
$$V'_1 = \bar{v}/\gamma = 2.54 \times 10^5 \text{ m sec}^{-1}$$
and
$$v'_1 = 0.866 \times 2.54 \times 10^5$$
$$= 2.20 \times 10^5 \text{ m sec}^{-1}.$$

c. $v_1 = \dfrac{m_1 + m_2}{m_1} \bar{v} = 3 \times \bar{v} = 3.81 \times 10^5$ m sec^{-1}.

d. $K_0 = \frac{1}{2} 1.27 \times 10^{-24} \times 3.81^2 \times 10^{10} = 12.2 \times 10^{-14}$ j. Compare with $K_a = \frac{1}{2} 1.7 \times 10^{-24} \times 2.2^2 \times 10^{10} + \frac{1}{2} 3.4 \times 10^{-24} \times 2.2^2 \times 10^{10} = 12.2 \times 10^{-14}$ j.

2–10. Energy in the CMS.   In our calculations we have been considering one of the particles at rest in the LS. Of course, this does not need to be the case, though it is often convenient to think of things this way. If we are operating a cyclotron to bombard a target with protons, it is clear that it is most convenient to consider the target as part of the LS. We would hardly want to consider a proton as being at rest in what might be called the LS′ and have the target, cyclotron, etc., all moving toward it. But there are many cases of collisions in which there is no particular reason to pick one system over another.

Consider two cars in a head-on collision; one (car A) has a mass of 1500 kg and before the collision is moving east with a speed of 10 m sec^{-1}; the other (car B) has a mass of 1000 kg and is moving west with a speed of 6 m sec^{-1}. We can recognize four useful coordinate systems. Of course there is the system fixed to the road; then there is a system fixed to car A; there is a system fixed to car B; and finally there is the CMS. The first of these is an LS with two moving particles; and the next two are laboratory systems, each with one moving particle. Let us calculate the kinetic energy in each case. Relative to the road, the total kinetic energy is

$$K_r = \tfrac{1}{2} \, 1500(10)^2 + \tfrac{1}{2} \, 1000(6)^2 = 93{,}000 \text{ j.}$$

Relative to car A as LS,

$$K_A = \tfrac{1}{2} \, 1000(16)^2 = 128{,}000 \text{ j.}$$

Relative to car B as the LS,

$$K_B = \tfrac{1}{2} \, 1500(16)^2 = 192{,}000 \text{ j.}$$

Each of these has an equal validity, though they represent the viewpoint of a bystander, a rider in car A, and a rider in car B. But in the collision that results, the one unchanging thing is the velocity of the center of mass. In the system related to the road, this velocity is east at 3.6 m sec^{-1}; in the system related to A, it is west at 6.4 m sec^{-1}; and in the system related to B, it is east at 9.6 m sec^{-1}. In the CMS A is moving east at 6.4 m sec^{-1} and B is moving west at 9.6 m sec^{-1}; and in all systems A and B are approaching each other at 16 m sec^{-1}. The kinetic energy in the CMS is

$$K_c = \tfrac{1}{2} \, 1500(6.4)^2 + \tfrac{1}{2} \, 1000(9.6)^2 = 30{,}720 + 46{,}080$$
$$= 76{,}800 \text{ j.}$$

Now let us look at this matter more formally. Suppose that in some arbitrary LS system the two masses m_1 and m_2 have velocities v_1 and v_2, respectively (we assume along the same line and hence indicate sense by sign). We have from Eq. 2–40

$$\bar{v} = \frac{m_1 v_1 + m_2 v_2}{m_1 + m_2}. \tag{2–57}$$

We are also interested in the relative velocity between the two, for example, the velocity with which m_1 is approaching m_2. Call this V_r, where

$$V_r = v_1 - v_2.$$ (2–58)

We can solve this equation and Eq. 2–57 to obtain expressions for v_1 and v_2 in terms of V_r and $\bar{v}$. The results are

$$v_1 = \bar{v} + \frac{m_2}{m_1 + m_2} V_r$$ (2–59)

and

$$v_2 = \bar{v} - \frac{m_1}{m_1 + m_2} V_r.$$ (2–60)

If we now calculate K, the kinetic energy of the system in the LS system, we have

$$
\begin{aligned}
K &= \frac{1}{2} m_1 v_1{}^2 + \frac{1}{2} m_2 v_2{}^2 = \frac{1}{2} m_1 \left(\bar{v} + \frac{m_2}{m_1 + m_2} V_r \right)^2 \\
&\quad + \frac{1}{2} m_2 \left(\bar{v} - \frac{m_1}{m_1 + m_2} V_r \right)^2 \\
&= \frac{1}{2} m_1 \bar{v}^2 + \frac{m_1 m_2}{m_1 + m_2} \bar{v} V_r + \frac{1}{2} \frac{m_1{}^2 m_2}{(m_1 + m_2)^2} V_r{}^2 + \frac{1}{2} m_2 \bar{v}^2 \\
&\quad - \frac{m_1 m_2}{m_1 + m_2} \bar{v} V_r + \frac{1}{2} \frac{m_1 m_2{}^2}{(m_1 + m_2)^2} V_r{}^2 \\
&= \frac{1}{2} (m_1 + m_2) \bar{v}^2 + \frac{1}{2} \frac{m_1 m_2 (m_1 + m_2)}{(m_1 + m_2)^2} V_r{}^2 \\
&= \frac{1}{2} (m_1 + m_2) \bar{v}^2 + \frac{1}{2} \frac{m_1 m_2}{m_1 + m_2} V_r{}^2.
\end{aligned}
$$ (2–61)

The two terms of the final expression in Eq. 2–61 are easily identified as follows: The first term is the kinetic energy of motion of the particles treated as a unit with the total mass moving at the speed of the center of mass. The value of this term will depend upon what is considered to be the LS. The second term is a kinetic energy due to the relative motion between the particles; it is independent of the choice of the LS; it is the total kinetic energy measured in the CMS. Because it is independent of the choice of the LS, it has a particularly fundamental importance. You will note that its form is such that the energy can be computed by considering a single mass of magnitude $\dfrac{m_1 m_2}{m_1 + m_2}$ moving at the velocity V_r, the relative velocity between the particles. It is common to represent the value of this mass by the letter μ, and to call it the *reduced mass*. Although we have developed this concept of reduced mass in connection with the problem of collisions, it is equally useful in any situation involving a number of particles moving relative to each other. In the numerical problem we have just previously considered, it is easy to compute K_c the CMS kinetic energy by using the reduced mass and V_r.

2–11. Inelastic Collisions, the Q Value.
We have tended to emphasize perfectly elastic collisions, but there are many examples of inelastic collisions. We shall be especially interested in such collisions between nuclei of atoms. Situations in which the separating particles after the collisions are different from the original particles are also quite common. In all such collisions we can still depend upon the validity of the law of conservation of linear momentum and upon the law of conservation of energy. However, we cannot expect the kinetic energy of the particles to be the same after the collision as before. Instead we must take into account any changes of internal energy when we account for the total energy before and after the collision. If during the collision the internal energy of particle 1 is decreased by W_1 and the internal energy of particle 2 is also decreased by W_2, we can write for the law of conservation of energy

$$K_1 + K_2 = K'_1 + K'_2 - W_1 - W_2. \qquad (2–62)$$

The increase in kinetic energy of the particles is

$$Q = W_1 + W_2 = K'_1 + K'_2 - (K_1 + K_2). \qquad (2–63)$$

If Q is positive, the collision is said to be *exoergic* and if Q is negative, the collision is *endoergic*.

EXAMPLE 5. It is possible to add just 3.37×10^{-19} j to the internal energy of a sodium atom but not anything less. Two sodium atoms, each with a mass of 3.8×10^{-19} kg, collide head-on with each other in a flame. Before the collision one was moving to the right with a speed of 4000 m sec^{-1} and the other was moving to the left with a speed of 3000 m sec^{-1}. Is it possible for the collision to excite one of the atoms to a higher internal energy? What will the motion be afterward? Under what condition will such an inelastic collision be possible or impossible?

Solution: The reduced mass for the combination is $3.8^2/7.6 \times 10^{-26}$ kg and the relative velocity is $V_r = 7000$ m sec^{-1}. In the CMS the kinetic energy is $\frac{1}{2} 1.9 \times 10^{-26} \times 49 \times 10^6 = 4.65 \times 10^{-19}$ j. This is enough to excite one of the atoms and leave 1.28×10^{-19} j over. After the collision the atoms will separate with relative speed $V' = (2 \times 1.28 \times 10^{-19}/1.9 \times 10^{-26})^{1/2} = 3.67 \times 10^3$ m sec^{-1}. Since the center of mass is moving to the right at a speed of $(4000 - 3000)/2 = 500$ m sec^{-1}, one of the atoms will move to the right with a speed of 2335 m sec^{-1} and the other to the left with a speed of 1335 m sec^{-1}. There is no way to tell which will be the excited one.

Such an inelastic collision can occur only if

$$K_c = \tfrac{1}{2}\mu V_r^2 \geq 3.37 \times 10^{-19} \text{ j}.$$

If it is less, the collision will be elastic; and if it is more, the collision may be either elastic or inelastic.

PROBLEMS

2-1. (a) Calculate the momentum of a 10 gm bullet traveling at a speed of 30,000 cm sec^{-1}. (b) What would be the recoil velocity of the gun which fired the bullet if the mass of the gun is 3 kg?

2-2. Calculate the recoil speed of a 3 kg gun following the firing of a 4×10^{-3} kg bullet at a speed of 200 m sec^{-1}. What impulse was given to the gun? What impulse was given to the bullet? In what way was momentum conserved?

2-3. A "bug" in a "jumping bean" has a mass of 3.0×10^{-4} kg and the bean itself has a mass of 2.0×10^{-4} kg. The bug manages to jump upward within the bean with a velocity of 0.6 m sec^{-1}. What impulse did he receive? When he hit the top of the inside of the bean what impulse did he give the bean, assuming he sticks to the bean when he hits its top? To what height will the bean jump?

2-4. The spring-gun in a pinball machine gives an impulse of 360 dyne-sec. With what velocity does a 4 gm ball leave the spring-gun?

2-5. What acceleration can be expected of a 10,000 lb rocket burning fuel at a rate of 250 lb sec^{-1} if the effective specific impulse is 80 sec?

2-6. A satellite in orbit is to have its orbit modified by a rocket engine. The velocity change is to be 3200 ft sec^{-1}. The satellite, including rocket engine (but not propellants), weighs 300 lb. How much propellant with a specific impulse of 250 sec will be required?

2-7. The payload of a rocket is 600 lb, structure and engine amount to 800 more. The propellant load is 8000 lb. What burnout velocity could be produced in free space starting at rest? Let $I = 250$ sec.

2-8. Calculate the final velocity for both particles for a head-on elastic collision in which a mass m with a velocity of 4.2 m sec^{-1} collides with a stationary mass of $6m$.

2-9. In a head-on inelastic collision a mass of 5 kg collides and sticks to a mass of 400 kg originally at rest. The final velocity is 0.12 m sec^{-1}. What was the velocity of the 5 kg mass?

2-10. In a head-on elastic collision the mass M is stationary. The bombarding particle has a mass m and energy K. Calculate the kinetic energy of M and of m after the impact if (a) $m = M$, (b) $m = 4M$, (c) $m = \frac{1}{4}M$, (d) $m = \frac{1}{10}M$, (e) $m = \frac{1}{100}M$.

2-11. In a head-on perfectly inelastic collision the mass M is stationary. The bombarding particle has a mass m and energy K. Calculate the kinetic energy of the combined masses after impact and the energy converted if (a) $m = M$, (b) $m = 4M$, (c) $m = \frac{1}{4}M$, (d) $m = \frac{1}{10}M$, (e) $m = \frac{1}{100}M$.

2-12. A mass of 8×10^{-26} kg is at rest. It is approached by a body with a mass of 3×10^{-27} kg moving at a speed of 4.6×10^5 m sec^{-1}. What is the velocity of the center of mass?

2-13. A mass of 30 gm is moving at a speed of 48×10^4 cm sec^{-1}. Another mass of 15 gm is moving away from the first so that their separating velocity is 64×10^4 cm sec^{-1}. What is the velocity of the center of mass?

2-14. Prove that the relative velocity of approach of two objects is the same in both the LS and CMS.

2-15. Make four diagrams showing schematically for two particles the following: the initial velocities in the LS, the initial velocities in the CMS, the final motion in the CMS, and the final motion in the LS. Assume one particle initially at rest, a head-on elastic collision, and make the four drawings for each of the following three cases: $m_1 < m_2$; $m_1 = m_2$; $m_1 > m_2$. Let the initial velocity be the same in all cases. Compare your results with the example in Art. 2-8.

2-16. Examine Eq. 2-54 for the three special cases of $m_1 \ll m_2$, $m_1 = m_2$, $m_1 \gg m_2$.

2-17. Examine Fig. 2-9. Make diagrams to show the largest scattering angle θ_L in the LS if (a) $m_1 = m_2$, (b) $m_1 > m_2$, (c) $m_1 < m_2$ (elastic collision).

2-18. Show that, for the $m_1 = m_2$ case, the angle between the two particles in the LS after collision is *always* 90° (elastic collision).

2-19. Assume a neutron undergoes a head-on, elastic collision with a graphite moderator. What per cent of the neutron's energy is lost in such a collision?

2-20. A neutron collides elastically with a helium nucleus. The neutron is deflected 30°. What is the recoil angle for the helium atom?

2-21. In an elastic collision between a stationary oxygen nucleus and a proton, the oxygen nucleus recoils at 5° from the original direction of the proton. Through what angle is the proton deflected?

2-22. A perfectly elastic collision occurs when a 0.12 kg ball strikes one with a mass of 0.42 kg. The initial velocity of the ball was 9 m sec^{-1} in the LS. Following recoil the angle $\theta_c = 20°$. Calculate all other quantities in both the CMS and LS.

2-23. A perfectly elastic collision occurs whan a 0.64 kg ball strikes one with a mass of 1.83 kg. The initial velocity of the ball was 3 m sec^{-1} in the LS. Following recoil the angle $\theta_c = 10°$. Calculate all other quantities in both the CMS and LS.

2-24. To excite a mercury atom requires at least 4.9 ev. Two mercury atoms collide. If one is at rest and the other moving, what is the least energy the moving one can have to excite one of them?

2-25. Calculate the minimum energy an object must have to produce an inelastic collision when it strikes an identical atom at rest if the minimum energy transfer is E_0.

2-26. Calculate the reduced mass of an alpha particle—uranium atomic system.

2-27. Calculate the reduced mass of an alpha particle—copper atomic system.

SELECTED REFERENCES

BECKER, R. A. *Introduction to Theoretical Mechanics.* McGraw-Hill Book Co., Inc., New York, 1954. Chap. 8.

HOLTON, G., and D. H. D. ROLLER. *Foundations of Modern Physical Science.* Addison-Wesley Publishing Co., Inc., Reading, Mass., 1958. Chap. 17.

RESNICK, R., and D. HALLIDAY. *Physics for Students of Science and Engineering.* John Wiley & Sons, Inc., New York, 1960. Chap. 9.

ROGERS, E. M. *Physics for the Inquiring Mind.* Princeton Univ. Press, Princeton, N. J., 1960. Chap. 8.

SEARS, F. W., and M. W. ZEMANSKY. *College Physics.* Addison-Wesley Publishing Co., Inc., Reading, Mass., 1960. 3d ed., chap. 8.

SHORTLEY, G., and D. WILLIAMS. *Elements of Physics.* Prentice Hall, Inc., Englewood Cliffs, N. J., 1961. 3d ed., chap. 7.

SYMON, K. R. *Mechanics.* Addison-Wesley Publishing Co., Inc., Reading, Mass., 1960. 2d ed., chap. 4.

3

Angular Momentum and Magnetic Effects

The third important conservation law that we shall treat in these early chapters is the *law of conservation of angular momentum.* We shall first review and perhaps extend the reader's background in the laws governing the motion of extended bodies. In earlier chapters we have confined ourselves to the motion of point particles, a simplification which enables us to disregard all rotations. The consideration of point particles ensures that the vectors, such as force and velocity, associated with the situation all pass through a common point, namely, the particle itself. This is, in fact, merely an alternative way of stating that there will be no rotation.

When we consider an extended (and usually rigid) body we find there are analogies with particle motion; but there are also important differences. We shall discuss two of these differences. First, we shall examine rotations and see under what conditions a rotation can be considered a vector. Second, we shall examine the implications of multiplying vectors that do not have a common origin, although they intersect. Finally, we shall find it useful to carry some of the results of our analysis to the consideratio1 of the electrical and magnetic effects of atoms.

3-1. Rotation as a Vector. Several *linear displacements* can be made in any order and the resultant displacement is independent of the order. We conclude that for these, the addition rule is commutative. However, several *finite angular displacements* lead to different results, depending on the order in which they are performed. Thus we conclude that *finite* angular displacements cannot be represented by vectors, or at least by vectors that obey the commutative law of addition. This statement can be confirmed by taking a closed book, placing it in front of you closed with the front cover up in the normal position to prepare for reading. Now keeping it closed, rotate it through 90° about an axis parallel to the bottom edge, so that it stands with its front cover facing you right side up. Next, rotate it 90° counterclockwise, as viewed from above, about a vertical axis. Its final position is one ready to go on a shelf. Now replace the book to the position from which you started, perform the same 90° rotation about the same axes but in the other order; i.e., first around the vertical axis, and then about the edge. The result is that the book now rests on its bound edge with the front face toward you, an entirely different orientation.

It can be shown that *infinitesimal* angular displacements may be combined in any order and, in fact, can be represented by vectors which add according to the commutative law, provided the direction of the vector points along the axis of the infinitesimal rotation, has a magnitude proportional to the angle turned through, and an appropriate pointing rule is followed. Usually the vector is considered to point in the direction which a right-hand screw would advance if given this angular displacement (the right-hand rule or "screwdriver" rule). We designate this vector by **dθ**. Fig. 3-1 illustrates how the rule is applied and how such quantities can be represented.

That infinitesimal angular displacements can indeed be represented by vectors is not easy to show and we shall not demonstrate it here. Actually, infinitesimal rotations are extremely subtle and, in fact, are transformations of coordinate axes in which the components of a vector are nearly the same in the two sets of axes. This connection with transformation theory leads to very interesting conclusions and shows that **ω**, the angular velocity, is a *pseudovector* or *axialvector*. This means, essentially, that **ω** behaves as a vector in most mathematical operations, but reverses sign under certain transformations. An advanced treatment of this point will be found in Goldstein's *Classical Mechanics*.[1] However, a feeling for the fact that infinitesimal rotations can be represented by vectors may be arrived at by repeating one degree rotations of the book about the axes described above instead of 90° rotations. In this manner, one would see that the order seems to make little difference. In the limit of infinitesimal rotations, it makes no difference.

Dividing **dθ** by the corresponding infinitesimal time interval dt leads to the *angular velocity*

$$\boldsymbol{\omega} = \frac{\mathbf{d\theta}}{dt} \tag{3-1}$$

and a further differentiation with respect to time leads to the *angular acceleration*

$$\boldsymbol{\alpha} = \frac{d\boldsymbol{\omega}}{dt}. \tag{3-2}$$

[1] H. Goldstein, *Classical Mechanics*, Addison-Wesley Publishing Co., Inc., Reading, Mass., 1951, pp. 124-131.

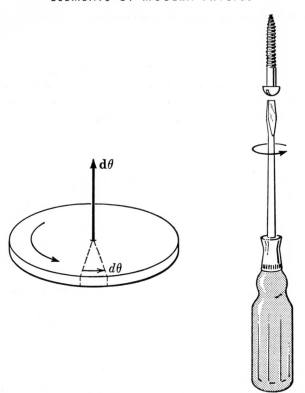

Fig. 3–1. An infinitesimal angular displacement and the right-hand or "screwdriver" rule.

3–2. Vector Product, Torque. Suppose there is a force **F**, as shown in Fig. 3–2, which can produce rotational effects around the axis shown (this may be a real axle and bearings, or simply a particular line in space). The plane perpendicular to the axis and containing **F** is shown in the figure, as is another vector **r** extending from the axis to the point of attachment (and tail of the arrow) of **F**. You will recall from elementary physics that the rotational effects of **F** are given by the torque **L** (*moment of the force about the axis*), which has a magnitude equal to the magnitude of the force times the perpendicular distance from the axis to the line of action of the force. Thus

$$L = Fd = rF \sin \theta. \tag{3–3}$$

You will also note that a rotation produced by such a torque would advance a right-hand screw as shown. The fact that this torque is a directed quantity suggests that it can be represented by a vector. Therefore the torque, designated by the vector **L**, is defined as

$$L = r \times F, \tag{3-4}$$

where the magnitude of **L** is given by Eq. 3–3 and the direction follows the right-hand rule. This relation is often read, "The vector **L** is equal to the vector **r** cross the vector **F**," and hence is often called a *cross product*, though its more formal designation is *vector product.*

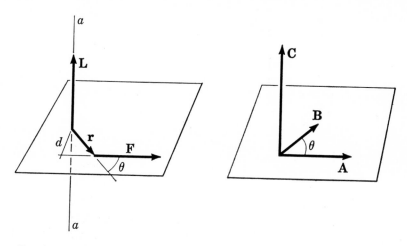

Fig. 3–2. The torque due to **F** about the axis *a-a*. A vector product.

In general, two vectors **A** and **B** have a vector product **C** given by

$$C = A \times B. \tag{3-5}$$

C has a magnitude

$$C = AB \sin \theta, \tag{3-6}$$

while the direction of **C** is perpendicular to the plane containing **A** and **B**. **C** points in the direction a right-hand screw would advance if it were turned in the direction that takes **A** from its position to one parallel to **B**, turning it through less than 180°. The reader, by using this definition, can see that the order in which the vectors are written in the vector product is important. Vectors are non-commutative in the multiplication process called the vector or cross product. In fact,

$$A \times B = -(B \times A). \tag{3-7}$$

3-3. Angular Momentum. Now let us consider the vector $p = mv$, the linear momentum of a mass m moving with velocity **v**, and suppose that the mass is located at the end of **r** extending from the origin. We define the vector

$$\mathbf{J} = \mathbf{r} \times \mathbf{p} \qquad (3\text{--}8)$$

and call it the *angular momentum* of m, about the origin.

Next, consider any rigid body. A rigid body is defined as one for which no *relative* change of position of individual particles is possible. At any instant, the motion of the whole body may be considered to consist of a motion of translation and one of rotation. It is the rotation that we wish to examine, so the pure translation is taken to be zero. That is, we shall assume that there is a line of points *all at rest*—the axis of rotation of the body. All other points in the body move in circles which lie in planes perpendicular to this axis and the centers of the circles lie on the axis. A single element of mass dm in the body moves with a velocity **v** having a speed

$$v = \frac{ds}{dt}.$$

Its motion is in a circle, and since we have $s = r\theta$, then

$$v = \frac{ds}{dt} = r\frac{d\theta}{dt} = r\omega, \qquad (3\text{--}9)$$

and we define the vector **ω** using the screwdriver rule as shown in Fig. 3–3. For all points in the body, **ω** in Eq. 3–9 has the same magnitude.

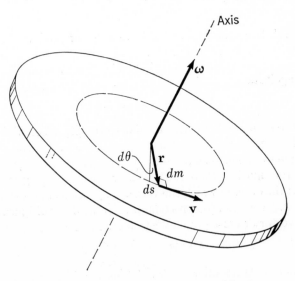

Fig. 3–3.   Angular motion of a rigid body.

We can define the angular momentum of the body about an axis by integrating the differential vector

$$dJ = r \times v \, dm \tag{3-10}$$

over the entire body. Because we have limited our consideration to the special case of a fixed axis, it is possible to make use of Eq. 3-9 to simplify the integral of Eq. 3-10. The result can be written

$$J = \int dJ = \int r \times v \, dm = \omega \int r^2 \, dm = I\omega. \tag{3-11}$$

The quantity I is called the *moment of inertia* about the fixed axis. The process of evaluating it is discussed in most calculus courses. For certain symmetric geometrical shapes, it is easy to evaluate. Some of these results are given in Table 3-1.

TABLE 3-1

Moments of Inertia of Homogeneous Bodies

Body	Axis	I
Thin hoop of radius R and mass M	Perpendicular to plane through center of hoop	MR^2
Disk or cylinder of radius R and mass M	Perpendicular to disk or along axis of cylinder	$\frac{1}{2}MR^2$
Ring or cylindrical shell of internal radius R_1, external radius R_2, and mass M	Perpendicular to disk or along axis of cylinder	$\frac{1}{2}M(R_1^2 + R_2^2)$
Sphere of radius R and mass M	Through center	$\frac{2}{5}MR^2$

It can be shown by integration that, if I_0 is the moment of inertia about an axis through the center of mass, the moment of inertia about another axis parallel to the first but separated by a distance d is given by

$$I = I_0 + md^2. \tag{3-12}$$

This is often referred to as the "parallel axis theorem" or "transfer theorem."

A further concept often useful in discussing moments of inertia is that of the *radius of gyration*. No matter what the shape of a body, it is always possible to find a radial distance from an axis at which the mass of the body could be concentrated without changing the moment of inertia of the body about the axis. This distance is customarily represented by k, so that if m is the mass of a body and I is its moment of inertia,

$$I = mk^2$$

an equation often used to define the radius of gyration.

The relation to be applied to rotating rigid bodies that is analogous to Newton's second law in linear motion is

$$\frac{d\mathbf{J}}{dt} = \mathbf{L}, \qquad (3\text{--}13)$$

that is, the time rate of change of angular momentum $\mathbf{J}$ is equal to $\mathbf{L}$ where $\mathbf{L}$ is the applied external torque. For the special case that $\mathbf{L}$ and $\mathbf{J}$ have the same directions, we can simplify Eq. 3–13 to

$$L = \frac{dJ}{dt} = \frac{d(I\omega)}{dt} = I\frac{d\omega}{dt} = I\alpha. \qquad (3\text{--}14)$$

This last expression is appropriate to describe the speeding up (or slowing down) of flywheels which have torques applied to them.

EXAMPLE 1. Consider a flywheel in the form of a disk of radius R with uniform thickness, except for a hub of negligible mass and radius r, and having a mass M; and suppose a cord which is wrapped around the hub supports a mass m. What sort of motion results? See Fig. 3–4.

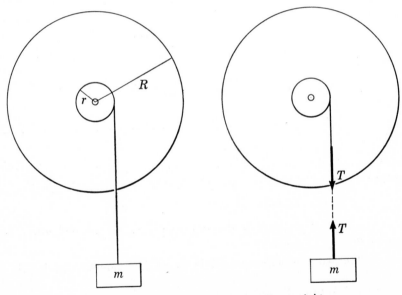

Fig. 3–4. Flywheel with accelerating weight.

The torque produced by the tension in the cord produces an angular acceleration α of the flywheel. The moment of inertia of the wheel is $I = \frac{1}{2}MR^2$, so we have from Eq. 3–14

$$L = I\alpha = \tfrac{1}{2}MR^2\alpha.$$

To evaluate the torque, we must know the tension T in the cord. If the wheel has an angular acceleration α, the mass m has a linear acceleration $a = \alpha r$. The acceleration of a mass requires a force. The forces acting on m are its weight mg and the tension T in the cord. The resultant force is related to a by

$$mg - T = ma;$$

so we see that

$$T = mg - ma = mg - m\alpha r.$$

The torque, of course, is

$$L = Tr = m(g - \alpha r)r,$$

so

$$m(g - \alpha r)r = \tfrac{1}{2}MR^2\alpha,$$

and

$$\alpha = \frac{mgr}{\tfrac{1}{2}MR^2 + mr^2}. \tag{3-15}$$

Before we come directly to the matter of conservation of angular momentum, let us consider the matter of energy associated with rotation. A reference to Fig. 3-3 indicates that we may calculate the kinetic energy of an element of mass dm in the rotating body by

$$dK = \tfrac{1}{2}(dm)v^2 = \tfrac{1}{2}(dm)r^2\omega^2$$

so that

$$K = \int dK = \int \tfrac{1}{2}r^2\omega^2 dm = \tfrac{1}{2}\omega^2 \int r^2 dm = \tfrac{1}{2}I\omega^2. \tag{3-16}$$

Incidentally, in the previous flywheel example, one can perceive that the change in total kinetic energy equals the change in potential energy of m, or

$$\tfrac{1}{2}I(\omega_2{}^2 - \omega_1{}^2) + \tfrac{1}{2}m(v_2{}^2 - v_1{}^2) = mg(z_1 - z_2)$$

where v_1, v_2, z_1, z_2 represent the initial and final velocity and initial and final altitude of m, respectively.

3-4. The Law of Conservation of Angular Momentum. Eq. 3-13 is

$$\frac{d\mathbf{J}}{dt} = \mathbf{L}$$

If $\mathbf{L} = 0$, then

$$\mathbf{J} = \text{constant},$$

that is, the total angular momentum is a constant when the external torques are zero. This is the law of conservation of angular momentum.

We note that the *external* torques must be zero if angular momentum is to be conserved. Systems exist in which the external torques are zero, but internal torques are applied within the system. These internal torques change the angular momentum of parts of the system, but to keep the total angular momentum constant, other parts must receive equal and opposite changes. A familiar example is found in the action of performers such as skaters, dancers, divers, and trapeze artists. By extending arms and legs, they change their moment of inertia with a resulting change in rate of rotation since the product of moment of inertia and angular velocity, *their* angular momentum, must remain unchanged. Another example has been the extension of masses on rods or cables to "de-spin" satellites.

In such cases it can be seen that while the angular momentum remains constant, the kinetic energy will change. If I is reduced so that ω increases, the kinetic energy will increase. For this to happen, work must be done in decreasing I. Conversely, if I increases, ω decreases and so does the kinetic energy; therefore this decrease in energy must go into some other form. For example, in Fig. 3–5, if the masses of the freely spinning frame

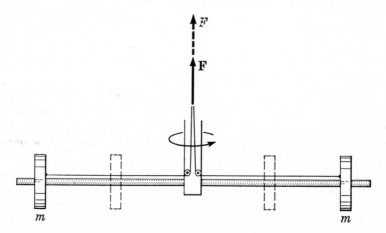

Fig. 3–5. Pull necessary to redistribute mass in a rotating system.

are pulled into the positions shown by the dotted lines, the moment of inertia will be decreased, the angular velocity will increase, and the kinetic energy will increase. The work required to do this is provided by the force F in moving the weights in. If the weights move back, the reverse process takes place.

We have been considering, principally, cases in which $\mathbf{L}$ changes only the magnitude of $\mathbf{J}$. In the next article we shall give a brief consideration to another case, one in which the direction of an applied torque is different from $\mathbf{J}$.

Finally, we examine the time integral of the torque. This function is called the angular impulse **H**, that is,

$$\mathbf{H} = \int \mathbf{L}\, dt. \tag{3–17}$$

It should be clear that the relation analogous to Eq. 2–5 is

$$\mathbf{H} = \mathbf{J}_2 - \mathbf{J}_1. \tag{3–18}$$

3–5. The Gyroscope.   A spinning wheel, a top, or for that matter any spinning object, has a number of interesting characteristics which arise because of the laws of motion.   In order to make the most effective use of these characteristics, the spinning wheel is usually carefully balanced so that it spins smoothly.   It may also be mounted in gimbals so that it can turn into various orientations freely.   Such a system is called a gyroscope. Once it has started spinning in a certain orientation, it will continue to do so if the gimbals permit free movement.   If the gimbals do not permit free rotation, torques can be applied and the angular momentum will not remain constant.   Use can be made of the resulting effects in many ways. We shall look at several applications.   Before we do, there is an important special case that should be examined quantitatively.   It avoids the quite complicated situation of the most general case.

The situation consists of a gyroscope to which a torque of constant magnitude is applied, with its direction perpendicular to the angular momentum of the gyroscope.   There are numerous ways in which this can happen but one simple way is illustrated in Fig. 3–6.   A gyroscope spinning as shown is supported at A by a pivoting support which exerts an upward force F.   A load, such as m, may be attached as shown.   If the mass of the rotor and frame is M and the weight acts through the center of the wheel (as will be the case if the frame and wheel are symmetrical), the force $F = (M + m)g$ and $L = Mga + 2mga$.   The directions of the various vectors are shown in the figure and we note that **L** and **J** are at right angles. In an infinitesimal time dt this torque adds an infinitesimal element of angular impulse **L** dt and thus produces an infinitesimal change in angular momentum **dJ**.

Fig. 3–7 is a diagram showing the relations among the vectors for this case.   The change in **J** is always perpendicular to **J** since **ΔJ** must be in the direction of **L**; thus, there can be no change in the magnitude of **J**. Only the direction can change.   For infinitesimals, in Fig. 3–7

$$d\phi = \frac{dJ}{J}\,. \tag{3–19}$$

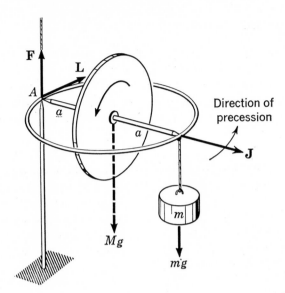

Fig. 3–6. A gyroscope precessing because of its weight.

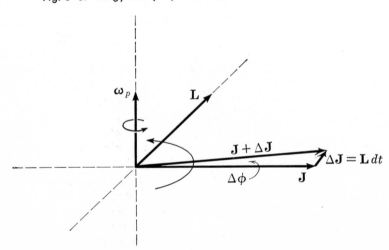

Fig. 3–7. Vector diagram for an angular acceleration due to a torque perpendicular to **J**.

Since

$$L = \frac{dJ}{dt},$$

we have

$$d\phi = \frac{L\,dt}{J}$$

or
$$\frac{d\phi}{dt} = \frac{L}{J}.$$ (3–20)

The motion that is implied by this is a steady turning of the direction of $\mathbf{J}$ about an axis perpendicular both to it and $\mathbf{L}$. This motion is called *precession* and $d\phi/dt$ is the *precessional angular speed*. If I is the moment of inertia of the gyroscope about the spin axis, and if ω is the spin angular speed, then if we write the precessional angular speed as $\omega_p = d\phi/dt$, Eq. 3–20 gives

$$L = I\omega\omega_p$$ (3–21)

which may be a more familiar form. Note that this derivation is somewhat similar to the one commonly used for centripetal relations. They are, in fact, analogous.

If the torque is applied suddenly, the motion is more complicated. The spin axis will bob up and down as it precesses. In time, this part of the motion, called nutation, may be damped by frictional forces. We shall not go into the matter in greater detail.

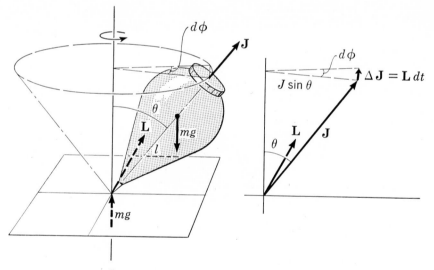

Fig. 3–8.   Precession of a spinning top.

Another simple case is the spinning toy top (see Fig. 3–8). If the point rests on the floor without friction, the torque $mgl \sin \theta = L$ produces a precession of the top so that its axis moves in a cone about the vertical with a half-angle θ. Since there is no torque about the vertical, the vertical component of $\mathbf{J}$ does not change. Actually there is some friction between the point and the floor, which makes the axis of the top slowly rise into a vertical position and "sleep" or spin with no visible precession. The precessional rate for the top can be derived as it was in the previous case, but the vector **J** of Fig. 3–7 should be replaced by the line segment $J \sin \theta$ of Fig. 3–8, so

$$\omega_p = \frac{d\phi}{dt} = \frac{L}{J \sin \theta} = \frac{mgl \sin \theta}{J \sin \theta}$$

$$= \frac{mgl}{J}. \tag{3–22}$$

Note that this is independent of θ.

Now picture a gyroscope supported in gimbals, as shown in Fig. 3–9,

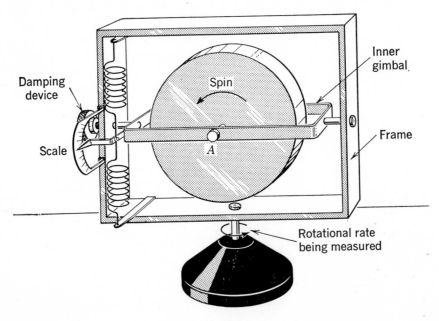

Fig. 3–9. Rate gyro.

and suppose the whole frame is rotated slowly around a vertical axis. The torque exerted by the gimbals starts a precession in which the end A rises. The distortion of the spring produces a torque which leads to a precession in the direction of the rotation being measured. When the torque due to the spring produces a precession rate the same as the rotation of the frame, everything is in adjustment. The amount the spring is stretched then becomes a measure of the rate of rotation of the frame. The system would oscillate about this position except for a damping device. A gyroscope so arranged is called a *rate gyro*.

If the springs had not been attached to the frame, the precession would have tended to bring the angular momentum vector parallel to the axis of rotation of the outer frame. If the outer frame were attached to the earth, the spin axis would have lined up parallel to the earth's axis and thus would have pointed north. Then, if the outer frame were permitted to swing freely, the axis would remain constantly directed parallel to the earth's axis and we would have a compass, a *gyrocompass*.

EXAMPLE 2.   A rate gyro has a wheel in the form of a solid disk 0.08 m in diameter with a mass of 0.6 kg spinning at a rate of 120 rev sec^{-1}. The body in which the gyro is mounted is turning about an axis perpendicular to the spin axis at the rate of 1° sec^{-1}.   (a) What torque must be produced by the springs of the rate gyro?   (b) The spring constant k is 150 newton m^{-1} and the springs are attached 0.06 m from the gimbal axis. What deflection s is produced?

Solution: The moment of inertia of the wheel is $I = \frac{1}{2}Mr^2 = \frac{1}{2} \times 0.6 \times 0.04^2 = 4.8 \times 10^{-4}$ kg-m^2.

The spin angular momentum is

$$J = I\omega_s = 1.2 \times 10^{-4} \times 2\pi \times 120 = 3.62 \times 10^{-1} \text{ kg-m}^2 \text{ sec}^{-1}.$$

a. Since

$$\omega_p = \pi/180 = 1.74 \times 10^{-2} \text{ radian sec}^{-1},$$

$$L = J\omega_p = 0.362 \times 1.74 \times 10^{-2} = 6.30 \times 10^{-3} \text{ newton-m}$$

b. The force due to the spring is ks and the torque is

$$L = 6.30 \times 10^{-3} = 150s \times .06,$$

so

$$s = \frac{6.30 \times 10^{-3}}{0.06 \times 1500} = 7.00 \times 10^{-4} \text{ m} = 0.7 \text{ mm}.$$

3–6. Magnetic Fields.   Since atoms contain electrically charged particles and since these charged particles may move in orbits, the atoms may simultaneously display the effects of the angular momentum due to this motion of mass and magnetic effects due to the motion of electric charge. As we shall see later on, the electrons, protons, and neutrons of which atoms are composed also have an intrinsic angular momentum in addition to their orbital momenta, much as the earth has due to rotation around its own axis as well as its orbital motion about the sun. The intrinsic angular momentum can be considered the result of a spin. In each of these cases magnetic effects also result, producing many interesting and important properties of atoms.

It would be well to recall, first, some of the relations between electric charges in motion (electric currents) and magnetic fields. In so far as is now known, all magnetic effects are associated with the motion of electric charges. No true, pure, free magnetic poles are known to exist. Many people have sought them unsuccessfully, and although there is a group of physicists who believe it is still possible that they may exist, even they are agreed that ordinary effects can be explained with the basic assumption of no free magnetic poles. What appear to be magnetic poles in permanent magnets can be identified with the motion of charges in atoms.

It turns out to be convenient to describe magnetic effects in terms of two vector quantities: **H**, the magnetic field intensity, and **B**, the magnetic flux density. It is not easy to explain the need for two. As a matter of fact, if one could identify in detail all electric currents and the motion of all electric charges in the system, it would not be necessary to use both, but this is usually difficult, if not impossible, to do. The reason for using two vectors rather than one is associated with situations involving magnetic materials whose presence disturbs the magnetic effects as compared to those in free space. The influence of such magnetic materials is due to the motion of charges within the individual atoms. When such materials are present it is then convenient to use both **B** and **H**. In free space either could be used alone. A somewhat oversimplified description identifies **H** with the electric currents flowing in wires because of batteries, generators, or similar devices, and identifies **B** with the result of the motion of *all* charged particles including those within the atom. A little later we shall give the expression for calculating **H** in *free space*. It is convenient to say that

$$\mathbf{B} = \mu\mathbf{H}, \tag{3-23}$$

where μ is the permeability of the matter. This relation is considered to hold even for free space where, in the mks system, $\mu = \mu_0 = 4\pi \times 10^{-7}$ webers per ampere-meter (or henrys per meter) and in the cgs Gaussian system, $\mu = 1$. In the mks system the units of B are webers per square meter and the units of H are amperes per meter; in the cgs Gaussian system the units of B are gauss and of H are oersted.

This description overlooks a special significance of **B** that goes beyond this oversimplified view. There is good reason to attach a special significance to **B** because experiments on the force exerted on charged particles moving in a magnetic field all indicate that the force is best described by using **B**. For this reason, it is best to describe magnetic effects by using **B**.

In order to clarify our position with regard to the vectors **H** and **B**, let us summarize the above statements. **H** is a quantity which can be computed theoretically if the currents are known in a given situation. **B** is a quantity which describes the forces on charges or whose time rate of change determines voltages induced in circuits and hence can be determined experimentally.

3–7. Currents and Magnetic Fields.   In this article **H** will be treated as a quantity to be computed, not measured.   Consider an infinitesimal length of wire **ds** carrying a current i.   At a point P (see Fig. 3–10),

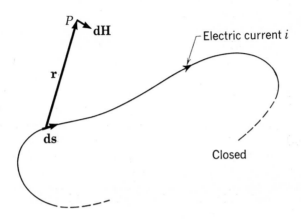

Fig. 3–10.   Magnetic field due to current element.

located at the end of the vector **r** extending from **ds** to P, the element of magnetic field intensity due to i in **ds** is

$$\mathbf{dH} = \frac{i}{4\pi}\, \mathbf{ds} \times \frac{\mathbf{r}}{r^3}\ \text{amp m}^{-1}. \qquad \left[\mathbf{dH} = \frac{i}{c}\, \mathbf{ds} \times \frac{\mathbf{r}}{r^3}\ \text{oersted.}\right] \quad (3\text{–}24)$$

The constant c in the cgs equation is the velocity of light.   This relation is often called *Ampère's law*.   One can now sum (integrate) for all elements carrying current to get **H**.   This can be done for any point in space; so one can, in principle, compute the complete magnetic field due to any known set of currents.   Three examples of the results of such summing of the contributions due to currents are given below for the configurations pictured in Fig. 3–11a, b, and c.

a. At the center of the circular loop we have

$$H = \frac{i}{2R}\ \text{amp m}^{-1}. \qquad \left[H = \frac{2\pi}{R}\frac{i}{c}\ \text{oersted.}\right] \quad (3\text{–}25)$$

The process of integration is particularly easy in this case.   The vector **r** has a constant value R and is always perpendicular to **ds**.   In fact, each element **dH** is perpendicular to the plane of the loop in the direction shown in Fig. 3–11. Thus, the summing of the vectors is simple and the magnitude is

$$H = \int_{\text{loop}} dH = \frac{i}{4\pi}\frac{1}{R^2}\int_{\text{loop}} ds = \frac{i}{4\pi}\frac{1}{R^2}\int_0^{2\pi} R\,d\phi = \frac{i}{2R}.$$

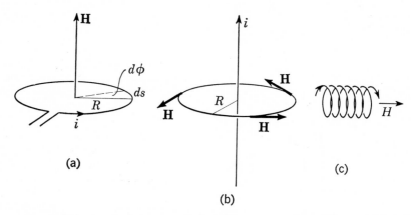

Fig. 3–11. Ampère's law applied to (a) a current loop (b) a straight wi e (c) a solenoid.

b. The magnetic intensity is a circular field around a very long wire and its magnitude at a distance R from the wire is

$$H = \frac{i}{2\pi R}. \qquad \left[H = \frac{2}{R}\frac{i}{c}.\right] \tag{3-26}$$

This is sometimes called the law of Biot and Savart.

c. In the interior of a long solenoid with n turns per meter (n turns per centimeter, cgs), the value of magnetic intensity is

$$H = ni. \qquad \left[H = 4\pi n\frac{i}{c}.\right] \tag{3-27}$$

3–8. Magnetic Forces and Torques. Experimentally it is found that if an infinitesimal element of a conductor carrying a current i is located in a magnetic field (see Fig. 3–12), it experiences an infinitesimal force given by

$$d\mathbf{F} = i\,d\mathbf{s} \times \mathbf{B}. \qquad \left[d\mathbf{F} = \frac{i}{c}\,d\mathbf{s} \times \mathbf{B}.\right] \tag{3-28}$$

One can in fact use such a current bearing wire to measure $\mathbf{B}$ (or, knowing $\mathbf{B}$, to measure i). Since it is also possible to compute $\mathbf{H}$, the ratio $B/H = \mu$, so determined, gives the permeability of the medium. In free space, it turns out to be $\mu_0 = 4\pi \times 10^{-7}$ (in cgs Gaussian units it is 1).

From Eq. 3–28, an expression for the force on a single charged particle moving in a magnetic field can be derived. Suppose there are N particles in a length **ds** of a wire, each bearing a charge q and each moving at a

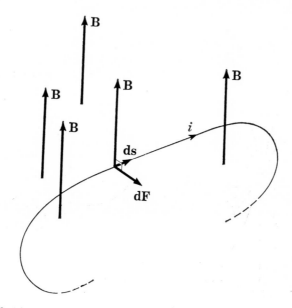

Fig. 3–12.   Force on a current carrying wire in a magnetic field.

speed v. Since a total charge Nq will pass one end of the portion of wire in a time ds/v for the most remote charge to reach the end, we have a current $i = Nq/(ds/v)$. The total force on **ds**, if it is in a magnetic field with a flux density **B**, is from Eq. 3–28

$$\mathbf{F}_N = i\,\mathbf{ds} \times \mathbf{B} = \frac{Nq\,ds}{ds}\mathbf{v} \times \mathbf{B}, \qquad \left[\mathbf{F}_N = N\frac{q}{c}\mathbf{v} \times \mathbf{B},\right]$$

since **ds** and **v** must be parallel. Thus, the force on a single particle is

$$\mathbf{F} = \frac{\mathbf{F}_N}{N} = q\mathbf{v} \times \mathbf{B}. \qquad \left[\mathbf{F} = \frac{q}{c}\mathbf{v} \times \mathbf{B}.\right] \qquad (3\text{–}29)$$

This is called the *Lorentz force*.

Fig. 3–13 shows the magnetic field produced by a small loop of wire carrying current and the field produced by a small bar magnet such as a compass needle. Their similarity should be apparent. The main features of the field are determined by the strength of the poles p (the regions from which the field seems to originate) and their separation d. At distances large compared to d, the field's size and direction are determined only by the product pd and the orientation of the bar, not by the individual values of p and d. It is therefore useful to consider the vector

$$\mathbf{M} = p\mathbf{d}, \tag{3-30}$$

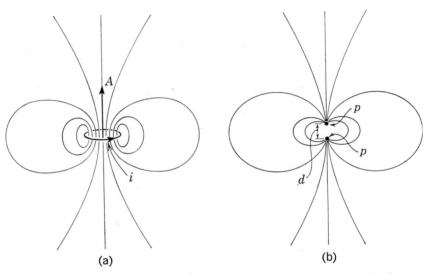

Fig. 3-13.   Fields due (a) to a current loop, (b) to a magnetic dipole.

called the *magnetic moment* of the magnet. The direction of $\mathbf{d}$, and hence of $\mathbf{M}$, is taken to point as a compass needle points, so that it would point north (in the USA) if lined up freely in the earth's magnetic field. We say it points from the south-seeking pole toward the north-seeking pole of the magnet. At a point P (see Fig. 3–14), the magnetic field strength is given by the component equations

$$H_r = \frac{M \cos \theta}{2\pi r^3},$$

$$H_\theta = \frac{M \sin \theta}{4\pi r^3}. \tag{3-31}$$

These equations and Eq. 3–30 can be taken to define the size of the unit magnetic pole in which p is measured.

It can be shown that the component Eqs. 3–31 will also give the value and direction of **H** produced by the current in the loop if we set

$$\mathbf{M} = i\mathbf{A} \qquad \left[\mathbf{M} = \frac{i}{c}\mathbf{A}\right], \qquad (3\text{–}32)$$

where **A** is a vector having a magnitude equal to the area of the loop, is perpendicular to the plane of the loop, and has the sense indicated in Fig. 3–13a.

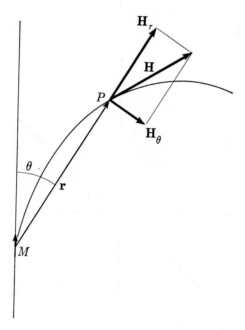

Fig. 3–14.   Field due to a dipole.

Not only can we say that the external fields due to the loop and elementary magnet are equivalent, but if both are placed in an equal external magnetic field with flux density **B**, they will experience the same torque, namely,

$$\mathbf{L} = \mathbf{M} \times \mathbf{B}. \qquad (3\text{–}33)$$

You can check this expression in the case of a rectangular loop lying with its plane parallel to **B** (so that the vector **A** is perpendicular to **B**) using Eq. 3–28.

We can also compute the potential energy of a magnetic moment in a magnetic field with flux density **B**. At an orientation, such as shown in Fig. 3–15, the dipole experiences the torque **L** given by Eq. 3–33. To turn it to this position requires the application of an opposite torque. This applied torque does work on the dipole, increasing the dipole's potential energy. If the initial position was $\theta = 0$ and the final position is $\theta = \theta'$, the external agent did an amount of work given by

$$W = \int_0^{\theta'} L \, d\theta. \tag{3-34}$$

Since $L = BM \sin \theta$, we have

$$W = BM \int_0^{\theta'} \sin \theta \, d\theta = BM \, (1 - \cos \theta'). \tag{3-35}$$

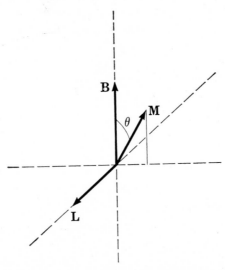

Fig. 3–15.   A magnetic moment **M** in a magnetic field with flux density **B**.

We shall represent the potential energy by $V(\theta)$ and choose to let $V(90°) = 0$. Then we see that

$$V(\theta) = W - BM = -BM \cos \theta. \tag{3-36}$$

Note from this that equivalent units for M are ampere-square meter, unit pole-meter, joule (weber m^{-2})$^{-1}$.

EXAMPLES.   1. A proton is moving in a plane perpendicular to a magnetic field of 0.22 weber m^{-2} after falling through a potential difference of 30,000 v. What will be the radius of curvature of its path? The proton has a kinetic energy of $eV = 30{,}000 \times 1.6 \times 10^{-19} = 4.8 \times 10^{-15}$ j. Its velocity is $\sqrt{2eV/m} = (2 \times 4.8 \times 10^{-15}/1.66 \times 10^{-27})^{1/2} = 2.4 \times 10^6$ m sec^{-1}.

The force on the proton is therefore $F = Bev = 0.22 \times 1.6 \times 10^{-19} \times$ $2.4 \times 10^6 = 8.45 \times 10^{-14}$ newton.

This produces the centripetal force mv^2/R, so

$$R = \frac{1.66 \times 10^{-27} \times 2.4^2 \times 10^{12}}{8.45 \times 10^{-14}} = 0.113 \text{ m.}$$

These calculations could of course have been collapsed into a single formula, but fewer quantities would have been displayed.

2. A hydrogen atom can be considered to be a magnetic dipole with a magnetic moment equal to 9.27×10^{-23} amp-m². How much work must be done to change its orientation from being parallel to a magnetic field with flux density of 1.4 weber m⁻² through 180° until it is antiparallel to the field? What is the torque on the atom when the magnetic moment is perpendicular to the field?

The work done is

$$\begin{aligned} W &= V(180°) - V(0°) \\ &= 9.27 \times 10^{-23} \times 1.4 - (-9.27 \times 10^{-23} \times 1.4) \\ &= 2.60 \times 10^{-22} \text{ j.} \end{aligned}$$

The torque is

$$\begin{aligned} BM \sin 90° &= 1.4 \times 9.27 \times 10^{-23} \times 1.0 \\ &= 1.30 \times 10^{-23} \text{ newton-m.} \end{aligned}$$

3. What current flowing in a loop which encloses an area of 8.8×10^{-21} m² will produce a magnetic moment equal to that used in Example 2?

$$i = \frac{M}{A} = \frac{9.27 \times 10^{-23}}{8.80 \times 10^{-21}} = 1.05 \times 10^{-2} \text{ amp.}$$

3-9. Magnetic Effects of Electrons.   Now let us consider the case of an electron moving in a circular or elliptical orbit. Unless an external torque is acting on it, the angular momentum remains constant. Its magnitude is

$$J = mvr \sin \phi, \tag{3-37}$$

where ϕ is the angle between $\mathbf{r}$ and $\mathbf{v}$ (see Fig. 3-16). The rate of change of area covered by the radius vector is

$$\frac{dA}{dt} = \frac{1}{2} rv \sin \phi,$$

so the angular momentum becomes

$$J = 2m \frac{dA}{dt}. \tag{3-38}$$

Since J is constant, dA/dt is also constant (Kepler's second law). If τ is the period of rotation, the value of dA/dt is therefore $A/\tau = A\omega/2\pi$, and hence

$$J = \frac{2mA\omega}{2\pi} = \frac{2mA}{\tau}. \tag{3-39}$$

The motion of the electron can be considered equivalent to an electric current flowing in the reverse direction (because the charge of the electron

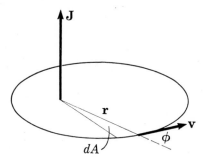

Fig. 3–16.   An electron in an orbit.

is negative). The equivalent current is given by the charge passing a given point on the orbit per second or

$$i_{eq} = \frac{-e}{\tau}. \tag{3-40}$$

Thus we have the important concept that the moving electron acts like an elementary magnet of moment

$$\mathbf{M}_e = i_{eq}\,\mathbf{A} = -\frac{e}{\tau}\mathbf{A} = -\frac{e}{2m}\mathbf{J}.$$

$$\left[\mathbf{M}_e = \frac{i_{eq}}{c}\mathbf{A} = -\frac{e}{c\tau}\mathbf{A} = -\frac{e}{2mc}\mathbf{J}.\right] \tag{3-41}$$

The negative sign which results from the negative sign of the electronic charge also indicates that $\mathbf{M}$ is opposite in direction to $\mathbf{J}$.

As we shall see later, atomic systems have angular momenta that are generally integral multiples of $\hbar = h/2\pi$, where h is Planck's constant. Thus the magnetic moment due to the orbital motion of an electron is generally an integral multiple of

$$\mu_B = \frac{e}{2m}\hbar = \frac{eh}{4\pi m}. \qquad \left[\mu_B = \frac{eh}{4\pi mc}.\right] \tag{3-42}$$

This quantity is regarded as the unit of magnetic moment and is called a *Bohr magneton.* The use of μ_B to stand for the magneton is customary and there should be no confusion with the use of μ and μ_0 for permeabilities. The value of μ_B is

$$\mu_B = 9.273 \times 10^{-24} \text{ amp-m}^2 \text{ (or j-m}^2 \text{ weber}^{-1}).$$

$$[\mu_B = 9.273 \times 10^{-21} \text{ emu (or erg gauss}^{-1}).]$$

Let us now suppose that this system is placed in a magnetic field (see Fig. 3–17). Because the orbiting electron has the characteristics of a

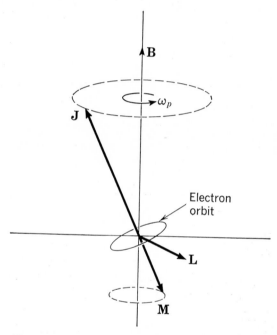

Fig. 3–17.   The precession of an electron in an external magnetic field.

magnet when placed in the field **B**, it will experience a torque, as do all magnets placed in a magnetic field. The value of this torque is

$$\mathbf{L} = \mathbf{M} \times \mathbf{B}.$$

Except when **M** and **B** are aligned, the effect of this torque is to make the angular momentum vector **J** precess about the direction of **B** (again see Fig. 3–17), much as the top of Fig. 3–8 precessed under the torque applied by the weight of the top. The precessional angular velocity ω_p from Eq. 3–21

$$\omega_p = \frac{L}{J \sin \theta} = \frac{BM \sin \theta}{J \sin \theta} = \frac{BM}{J};$$

using Eq. 3–41, this reduces to

$$\omega_p = \frac{e}{2m} B. \qquad \left[\omega_p = \frac{e}{2mc} B. \right] \qquad (3\text{–}43)$$

This precession is called the *Larmor precession* and the frequency the *Larmor precessional frequency*. There are ways of measuring ω_p by applying an alternating field of variable frequency which will reorient the magnetic moment when the frequency $\nu_p = \omega_p / 2\pi$ is reached. It is one of the good ways of measuring the specific charge e/m of electrons. The fact that the value obtained by this method is equal to that determined for cathode rays and other examples of electrons is one of the principal ways of knowing that electrons are important constituents of atoms.

As mentioned earlier, electrons are known to have an intrinsic angular momentum called *spin* (an abbreviation for spin angular momentum). This is in addition to that arising from their orbital motion. Any attempt to measure any component of this intrinsic angular momentum always shows this component to be $\frac{1}{2}\hbar = (1/4\pi)h$ where one might expect it to be $\hbar$. Quantum mechanical laws show that this should be the case. One might expect this to lead to a magnetic moment of $\frac{1}{2}\mu_B$, but in fact it is μ_B (more precise measurements give $1.00115\ \mu_B$).

Protons and neutrons also have a spin angular momentum and both have magnetic moments. Their values are

$$\mu_p = 1.41 \times 10^{-26}\ \text{amp-m}^2,$$

$$\mu_N = -9.66 \times 10^{-27}\ \text{amp-m}^2.$$

$$\left[\begin{aligned} \mu_p &= 1.41 \times 10^{-23}\ \text{erg gauss}^{-1}, \\ \mu_N &= -9.66 \times 10^{-24}\ \text{erg gauss}^{-1}. \end{aligned} \right]$$

3–10. Summary. Before we leave these preliminary chapters to start detailing the facts of modern physics let us review briefly the main point of these three chapters. We have tried to emphasize the role of the three conservation laws that were discussed. In treating the class of phenomena to which classical physics applies one *could* use the classical laws of motion (Newton's laws of motion) directly and in detail. However, their use may be unwieldy and impractical. What we have discovered is that three laws of conservation have such generality and their application is usually so direct and easy that important results can often be obtained from them in spite of the complexities of the problems. The three quantities, energy, linear momentum, and angular momentum, thus have special significance in the field of mechanics.

The special significance is no less important in the fields of relativistic mechanics and of quantum mechanics. It is true that certain modifications and special interpretations are called for, but the three quantities and their conservation laws provide an important bridge between the classical and modern laws.

PROBLEMS

3-1. If a force is applied parallel to the x-axis at a distance r from the origin, in what direction is the torque vector if the force acts in the direction of (a) the positive x-axis, (b) the negative x-axis?

3-2. Calculate the torque about the z-axis due to a force of 3 newtons passing through the point $x = 0.5$ m, $y = 0.12$ m, and $z = 0$ making equal angles with all three coordinate axes.

3-3. A rectangular box has sides 1 m by 1.2 m by 1.5 m. A force of 5 newtons acts along a diagonal that connects any pair of most remote corners. Calculate the torque due to that force about each edge of the box.

3-4. A circular platform with a weight w and radius r is supported by three balls 120° apart at its circumference. What is the least downward force that will bring one of the balls off of the floor? Where must it be applied?

3-5. Show that a force directed toward or away from the hinge of a door will not cause the door to rotate.

3-6. Derive the parallel axis theorem, Eq. 3-12.

3-7. Derive the expression for the moment of inertia of a sphere about a line tangent to the sphere.

3-8. A mass of 4 kg is whirled around in a circle in a horizontal plane 20 times a minute at the end of a light rod 98 cm long. Compute (a) its linear momentum, (b) its angular velocity, (c) moment of inertia, (d) angular momentum, and, (e) the tension in the rod. Show in a diagram any of the above quantities that are vectors.

3-9. A steam turbine has a rotor with a moment of inertia of 7.5 kg-m². What torque will give it an angular speed of 1800 rpm in 1 min? How much work does this require?

3-10. A flywheel with a moment of inertia of 25 kg-m² about its axis is rotating at a speed of 3600 rpm. What frictional force applied through brake shoes at its rim 0.6 m from the axis will bring it to rest in 90 sec? How much energy is converted into heat?

3-11. A thin rod of length 0.5 m and mass 500 gm spins freely with an angular velocity of 10 rpm about an axis perpendicular to its length and passing through its center of gravity. (a) Compute its angular momentum about this axis. (b) Compute its kinetic energy.

3-12. A man of mass m stands at the rim of a turntable (a thin solid disk) of radius r and mass M. The shaft of the turntable is frictionless. Initially both man and table are at rest. The man then walks around the rim at a velocity v_0 relative to the ground. Derive (a) the angular velocity of the turntable, (b) the angle in radians through which the disk will have rotated when the man reaches his initial position on the turntable, and (c) the angle in radians through which the disk will have rotated when he reached his initial position with respect to the earth.

3–13. A satellite may be approximated by a cylindrical shell with a radius of 0.6 m and a mass of 15 kg. When put into orbit it is spinning about its own axis at a rate of $\frac{1}{3}$ rps. A small electric motor of moment of inertia 1.2×10^{-3} kg-m² is located on the axis of the satellite. To what rate must it be spun to just stop the spin of the satellite?

3–14. In Fig. 3–5 suppose the masses are each 1 kg and when fully extended are a distance 0.4 m from the axis. Suppose the frame was turning at a rate of 5 rps. Then the masses are pulled in until they are a distance of 0.3 m from the axis. At what rate does the frame now spin? How much work was done by F?

3–15. A hydrogen molecule has the shape of a dumbbell. Compute the angular momentum of a free molecule if the distance between atoms is 0.75 Å and its rotational velocity is 4×10^{13} radians sec⁻¹. If the separation was suddenly doubled, what would be the new rotational velocity?

3–16. In an experiment using a gyroscope of the type shown in Fig. 3–6, the following information is obtained: moment of inertia of gyroscope about the spin axis = 2×10^4 gm-cm², angular momentum of gyroscope about the spin axis = 4×10^6 (dyne-cm)/(radian/sec), mass of load m attached to frame = 100 gm, length of lever arm for mass m = 5.0 cm (a = 2.5 cm), mass of wheel = 400 gm. (a) Calculate the period of precession for this system. (b) What would be the effect of doubling the mass of the load m?

3–17. In Fig. 3–6, a is 0.07 m, M is 0.150 kg, and m = 0.050 kg. The precessional angular velocity ω_p is 0.05 radian sec⁻¹. What is J?

3–18. Discuss the role of gyroscopic motion in the operation of a bicycle.

3–19. A bicycle wheel has an angular momentum of 30 kg m² sec⁻¹. What torque will cause a precessional rate of 0.16 radian sec⁻¹?

3–20. A gyroscope has $J = 10^7$ gm-cm² sec⁻¹. It is to be balanced so accurately that it will not precess more than 1° per day. How small a weight could be tolerated on a lever arm 5 cm long?

3–21. The engine of an automobile seeking a new land speed record is designed to rotate at 5000 rpm at top speed. If the radius of gyration of the rotating parts of the engine is 1 ft and their weight is 400 lb compute their angular momentum. If a bump in the road applies an upward force which leads to a torque of 100 ft-lb on the bearings of the engine what precessional angular velocity (magnitude and direction) will result?

3–22. The angular velocity of the rotor in the rate gyro of the example in the text is doubled. What does this do to the deflection for the same turn rate?

3–23. Derive Eq. 3–26.

3-24. Calculate the field a distance R above the center of a loop of wire of radius R carrying a current i.

3-25. Calculate the force on an electron moving with a speed of 1.4×10^6 m sec^{-1} in a flux density of 0.3 weber m^{-2}.

3-26. A proton is moving with a velocity of 4.7×10^4 m sec^{-1} in a magnetic field of 0.006 weber m^{-2}. What force does it experience?

3-27. At a certain instant an electron travels parallel to a long straight wire and 10 cm from it with a velocity of 10^6 cm sec^{-1}. The current in the wire is 2 amp. Calculate the force exerted on the electron and the direction of this force for both possible directions of travel of the electron at this instant.

3-28. If an electron were moving in a circular orbit with a radius of 0.5×10^{-10} m, what is its angular velocity if it has a magnetic moment of 1 Bohr magneton?

3-29. It is stated in the text that a current loop can be replaced by an equivalent elementary magnet of moment **M** and that if both are placed in an equal external magnetic field of flux density **B**, they will experience the same torque, namely, **L = M ✕ B**. Verify this for the special case of a rectangular loop lying with its plane parallel to **B**.

3-30. Compute the difference in energy of a dipole aligned with, and against, a field of 1 weber m^{-2} if the dipole has a magnetic moment of 1 Bohr magneton.

3-31. Compute the magnetic moment per unit volume in a solid with 3×10^{28} atoms m^{-3} each with a magnetic moment of 1 Bohr magneton.

3-32. What is the Larmor precession for a magnetic field of 2 weber m^{-2}?

3-33. A proton has a precessional angular velocity of 1.62×10^8 radian sec^{-1} in a magnetic field of 0.6 weber m^{-2}. What is its magnetic moment if its angular momentum is $\hbar/2 = 0.53 \times 10^{-34}$ j-sec?

SELECTED REFERENCES

BECKER, R. A. *Introduction to Theoretical Mechanics.* McGraw-Hill Book Co., Inc., New York, 1954. Chap. 12.

DUCKWORTH, H. E. *Electricity and Magnetism.* Holt, Rinehart, & Winston, Inc., New York, 1960. Chap. 8.

RESNICK, R., and D. HALLIDAY. *Physics for Students of Science and Engineering.* John Wiley & Sons, Inc., New York, 1960. Chaps. 13 and 34.

ROGERS, E. M. *Physics for the Inquiring Mind.* Princeton Univ. Press, Princeton, N. J., 1960. Chaps. 22 and 34.

SEARS, F. W. *Electricity and Magnetism.* Addison-Wesley Publishing Co., Inc., Reading, Mass., 1951. Chap. 11.

SEARS, F. W., and M. W. ZEMANSKY. *College Physics.* Addison-Wesley Publishing Co., Inc., Reading, Mass., 1960. 3d ed., chaps. 8 and 33.

SHORTLEY, G., and D. WILLIAMS. *Elements of Physics.* Prentice Hall, Inc., Englewood Cliffs, N. J., 1961. 3d ed., chaps. 10 and 37.

SYMON, K. R. *Mechanics.* Addison-Wesley Publishing Co., Inc., Reading, Mass., 1960. 2d ed., chap. 4

4

The Special Theory of Relativity

The relativity theory revised some of the fundamental concepts in classical physics. We meet the concepts of motion and of time very early in our study of physics. Their interpretation by Galileo, Newton, and others led to the development of the very beautiful and complete theory which we call *classical mechanics*. However, the concepts of motion and time were found by Einstein[1] to require close and careful examination if certain experimental results were to be believed.

4–1. The Postulates of the Special Theory of Relativity. In order to appreciate the necessity for the revision of these fundamental concepts of motion and time, it is necessary to understand the deadlock between experiment and theory that occurred in the early 1900's. We can present here a portion of the experimental data and some of the logic that led Einstein to two postulates upon which the special theory of relativity is based. Let us first state these postulates and explain them briefly before we examine the evidence that led to them.

The First Relativity Postulate: The laws of physics have the same form for all unaccelerated systems moving at constant velocity relative to each other.

The Second Relativity Postulate: The speed of light relative to an observer who is measuring it is a constant independent of the motion of the light source and is the same for all observers.

By the term *system* is meant a *frame of reference*, i.e., some coordinate system in which measurements are made. This system or frame of reference could be the laboratory desk top in a simple experiment, or the inside of a completely closed satellite moving through space in some complex astronomical observation. It is to be emphasized that the coordinate systems

---

[1] A. Einstein, *Ann. Physik,* **17**, 891 (1905).

we are dealing with must be unaccelerated. Therefore, their relative motion must be one of uniform translation. In such systems Newton's first law of motion (a body will not be accelerated unless a force is acting on it) holds; so such systems are often called "inertial systems."

The first relativity postulate tells us that no matter in which unaccelerated frame of reference we place any given experiment, the results of the experiment will be identical. By *experiment* we mean *any* type of experiment such as optical or electrical as well as mechanical. We may state this another way: *There is no observable effect by which we can determine whether the system in which the effect is being measured is at absolute rest or is in motion or with what velocity it is in motion.*

The consequences of the special theory of relativity and the revised view of motion and time are most noticeable when the relative velocity of systems is close to the velocity of light. Such cases are not uncommon in atomic and nuclear physics. It was also through the special theory of relativity that the equivalence of mass and energy was discovered.

We shall now look at some of the reasons that led to the decision made by Einstein that the two postulates are the correct ones to apply to nature.

4–2. The Ether. Wave motion is a concept encountered early in physics and in fact was very well known before the year 1900. The general idea was that if some medium (such as water, or a string) were properly set into oscillation, a wave was propagated in the medium with a certain velocity, with respect to the medium, which was determined essentially by the properties of the medium. Moreover, the medium can serve as a frame of reference which marks the progress of the wave.

Before 1900 several separate determinations had fixed the velocity of light (universally designated by the symbol c) as $c = 3 \times 10^8$ m sec^{-1}. Since "light" was known in classical electrodynamics to be propagated by wave motion, and since this same electrodynamical theory had predicted that the velocity of propagation should be 3×10^8 m sec^{-1}, everything seemed to be quite tidy. However there remained the question of what was the intangible medium through which light traveled and which could be used to indicate the progress of this wave of very high velocity.

A medium called the *ether* was proposed. The ether was claimed to fill all space between the planets, it was to transmit light at high velocity, and it was to be the frame of reference with respect to which c was measured. Yet it was not to impede the planets in their motion, since astronomical observations indicated an absence of friction.

If there should be such a medium as the ether, it should be capable of experimental confirmation. The most famous of the experiments concerning the ether is the Michelson-Morley[2] experiment which we shall examine soon.

[2] E. W. Morley and A. A. Michelson, *Phil. Mag.*, **24**, 449 (1887).

If the ether exists, then the earth moves through it and consequently we should be able to detect and measure this motion much as we can determine the velocity of a boat in which we are riding on a river. This in fact was the approach of the Michelson-Morley experiment. An alternative possibility, that the earth drags the ether with it and hence would show no relative motion, was eliminated by early astronomical observations. If the earth dragged the ether with it, then other planets and stars are likely to do the same. Somewhere between them, then, the ether must shear and in this shear region light waves from the stars would be deflected, an effect that could be detected by astronomical observations. No such change in star positions has been observed. Since this possibility is eliminated, let us now turn to the important experiment to measure the relative motion of the earth through the ether.

4-3. The Michelson-Morley Experiment. In the previous article we saw the tendency to accept the existence of an ether. Michelson and Morley accepted the ether as a reality, thinking that light moved with a velocity c with *respect to the ether*, and that the earth moved through the ether at velocity v.

Their experiment was an optical experiment based on interference principles. We know that if a beam of light from a single given source is somehow divided into two beams and then recombined, interference can occur. If one beam travels farther than the other, or is delayed en route before it again meets the other, then reinforcement or cancellation can occur, depending on the amount of phase shift caused by the path differences. The arrangement, called an interferometer, used by Michelson is schematically shown in Fig. 4-1. L represents the source, T a telescope, A is a half-silvered mirror while M and M' are identical front-surfaced mirrors.

As one looks into the telescope one can see bands of alternately light and dark, as shown in Fig. 4-2. These occur where the difference in path $LAMAT - LAM'AT$ is either an even or odd number of half wavelengths, thus producing either constructive or destructive interference.

In Fig. 4-3 two situations are shown. In (a) there is no relative motion between the interferometer and the ether, while in (b) the interferometer is moving parallel to LAM through the ether at a speed v. Let us take the distance $\overline{AB} = \overline{AC} = l$, where B and C are the positions of M' and M, respectively. The time for the light to travel from A to M and back to A is $2l/c$, and so is the time for the light to travel from A to M' and back to A. Thus we should expect the two waves of light to interfere constructively at the center of the field of the telescope.

In the case of the moving interferometer shown in Fig. 4-3b, the time to go from A to M is $l/(c-v)$ since the velocity of light relative to the mirror is $(c-v)$. The time for the light to return is $l/(c+v)$ since now

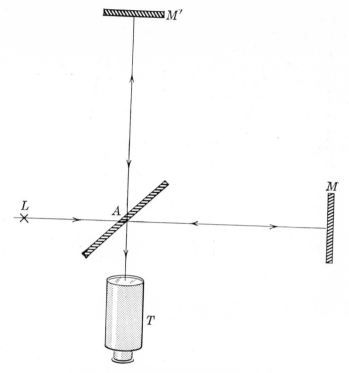

Fig. 4–1.   A Michelson interferometer.

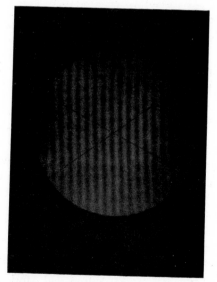

Fig. 4–2.   Michelson interferometer fringes.

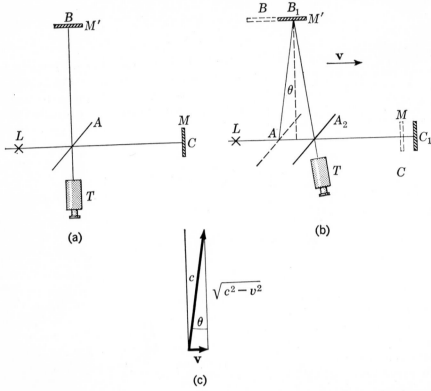

Fig. 4–3. Comparision of an interferometer at rest with one moving through the ether, (a) at rest, (b) moving, (c) velocity vector triangle of apparatus.

the velocity of light relative to the interferometer is $(c + v)$. This makes the time for the light to go from A to M to A_2

$$t = \frac{l}{c - v} + \frac{l}{c + v} = \frac{2lc}{c^2 - v^2}. \tag{4-1}$$

The time t' for the light to travel from A to M' and back to A_2 must be calculated with care. From Fig. 4–3b we see that it must travel a distance

$$d = 2AB_1 = \frac{2l}{\cos \theta}.$$

Since the light is traveling through the ether over this distance, then, according to the assumption of Michelson and Morley, it travels with a speed c. Hence

$$t' = \frac{d}{c} = \frac{2l}{c\,(\cos\theta)}.$$

It remains to compute $\cos\theta$. This can be done by considering the velocity vector triangle associated with the apparatus as shown in Fig. 4-3c. In this diagram the vector velocity of the apparatus with respect to the ether $\mathbf{v}$, plus the vector velocity of the light with respect to the apparatus $\mathbf{v}_{La}$ must add (vectorially) to give the vector velocity of the light with respect to the ether. The angle θ is as shown in the diagram, hence

$$\cos\theta = \sqrt{\frac{c^2 - v^2}{c^2}}$$

and

$$t' = \frac{2l}{c\sqrt{1 - \dfrac{v^2}{c^2}}}. \tag{4-2}$$

These two times t' and t are different, consequently we do not expect exactly constructive interference at the center of the field of the telescope.

In order to find out the phase difference, it is convenient to expand Eq. 4-1 and Eq. 4-2 using the binomial expansion, since the astronomical motions of parts of the earth have speeds which are small compared to c. The expanded forms are

$$t = \frac{2l}{c}\left(1 + \frac{v^2}{c^2} + \frac{v^4}{c^4} + \cdots\right), \tag{4-3}$$

and

$$t' = \frac{2l}{c}\left(1 + \frac{1}{2}\frac{v^2}{c^2} + \frac{3}{8}\frac{v^4}{c^4} + \cdots\right). \tag{4-4}$$

The difference in time is

$$\Delta t = t - t' = \frac{2l}{c}\left(\frac{1}{2}\frac{v^2}{c^2} + \frac{5}{8}\frac{v^4}{c^4} + \cdots\right). \tag{4-5}$$

This corresponds to a fraction

$$\frac{\Delta t}{\tau} = \frac{2l}{\tau c}\frac{1}{2}\frac{v^2}{c^2} \tag{4-6}$$

of a period τ of the light and hence the same fraction of a wavelength. Thus there will be a shift of this fraction of a fringe width in the fringe pattern seen in the telescope (we have neglected the fourth and higher powers of v/c). We cannot get the situation claimed in Fig. 4-3a, but we can interchange the legs of the interferometer by rotating it through 90°. This should produce a fringe shift of equal size in the opposite direction; therefore we should expect a total fringe shift of

$$\Delta f = \frac{2l}{\lambda}\frac{v^2}{c^2}. \tag{4-7}$$

Of course at any given moment we might find that our part of the earth did not happen to have any relative velocity to the ether, but twelve hours later the diurnal motion is reversed, and, much more important, six months later the orbital motion is reversed. In the apparatus used by Michelson, $l \simeq 11$ m, $\lambda = 5.9 \times 10^{-7}$ m, the earth's orbital velocity is $v \simeq 3 \times 10^4$ m sec^{-1}; so one would expect a fringe shift of 0.37 of a fringe at one season and a reverse fringe shift of the same amount six months later. It would have been possible to detect a much smaller fringe shift, and *only a negligible fringe shift was ever observed.* Similar experiments performed later by other experimeters have also given a negative result.

This experimental result tells us that we cannot use this straight-forward experiment to detect any motion relative to a fixed ether. Similar experiments indicated the impossibility of performing any experiment that would demonstrate and measure any absolute constant velocity of the system performing the experiment. These facts led Einstein to propose the two postulates upon which the theory of relativity is based. The second postulate can also be seen to be implied by the results of the Michelson-Morley experiment.

In spite of the fact that the two postulates follow directly from the results we have just quoted, it should be recognized that the acceptance of the postulates is not in accord with our usual "common sense" or common experience, and we must recognize that uncommon insight was required to propose them initially.

We must stress here that these postulates are a result of our experience, that is, our experiments. Our intuition, conditioned by early experiences with wind, thrown objects, sound, and other phenomena, is disturbed by the concept of a constant value for the velocity of light for all observers. We must now accept the fact that closer examination shows it is indeed a constant. The ether, which really is an attempt to set up an *absolute frame of reference*, does *not exist.* There is no absolute frame of reference.

4-4. Some Consequences of the Postulates of Relativity. Newton probably never worried about whether two events were simultaneous in time or not when he was establishing the laws of motion, but simply assumed that simultaneity could be established easily. Einstein realized that the postulates required a re-examination of our concept of time. The finite value for the velocity of light requires us to think carefully about how we define two events as simultaneous. If two events occur at the same place, it is easy to say whether or not they are simultaneous. But it is not so easy if one event occurs at one place and the other at a different place, and if they are associated with systems moving relative to each other.

Let us designate two coordinate systems as S and S' and let us agree to communicate between the two by means of light signals. Let us further suppose that two events occur at two places A and B in system S and that the same two events occur at A' and B' in system S'. If S and S' are at rest with respect to each other, then we can easily establish that the two events were simultaneous as observed in both S and S'. To do this we have two light signals sent out at the moment of occurrence of the two events. If the signals arrive together at the midpoint M of AB, we say the events occurred simultaneously. The midpoint of $A'B'$ is M' at the same place as M; so S' will also judge the two events to be simultaneous. This is illustrated in Fig. 4–4.

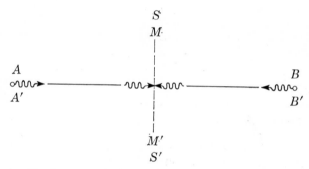

Fig. 4–4.   Simultaneity for systems at rest with respect to each other.

But if S' is moving relative to S, we find that the two systems will not agree on the simultaneity of the events. Let us suppose that the events occur simultaneously in S as pictured in Fig. 4–5. When the light signals reach M, they cannot also both reach M' at the same moment. That from B' will reach M' before the signal for A' will reach M'. Thus the event at B' must have occurred before that at A' as judged in S'. We could have had the occurrence of events such that the light signals reached M' at the same moment. Then the events would have been considered simultaneous in S'. The signals would have passed M at different moments. The one from A would have passed it before the one from B; so S judges that the event at A occurred before that at B. Remember that observers in both S and S' observe the same velocity of propagation of the light signals.

These results show that the intercomparison of position and time between two systems moving relative to each other cannot be made in the simple classical way. This inability to agree on simultaneity manifests itself in a number of ways that we shall examine soon. We will find that both time intervals and distances will be judged differently in the two systems.

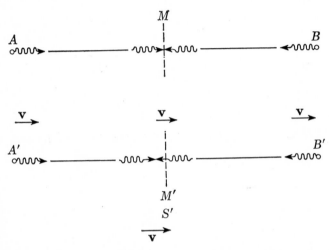

Fig. 4–5. Lack of common simultaneity when one system moves relative to another.

4–5. The Lorentz Transformation. Let us now find what is a suitable transformation between the coordinates in two systems moving relative to each other. The two coordinate systems are designated by S and S' and it is assumed that there is an observer fixed in each system. x and x' lie along the same line, while y is parallel to y', and z is parallel to z'. Let $x'y'z'$ be moving at constant velocity v to the right, along the line $OO'xx'$, as shown in Fig. 4–6. We let $x'y'z'$ first be to the left of x, y, z. As it passes to the right, a flash of light is produced at the origin of both co-ordinate systems just when the origin O coincides with O'. At this instant, the clocks at the origins of the two systems are also set to zero so that $t = t' = 0$. The velocity of light is c. In S the light spreads out over a sphere whose equation is

$$x^2 + y^2 + z^2 = c^2 t^2, \qquad (4\text{–}8)$$

and in S'

$$x'^2 + y'^2 + z'^2 = c^2 t'^2. \qquad (4\text{–}9)$$

The situation is sketched in Fig. 4–7a, which shows the view of the situation as seen by the observer fixed in S, and Fig. 4–7b, which shows the situation as seen by the observer fixed in S'. Only the xy-plane has been drawn

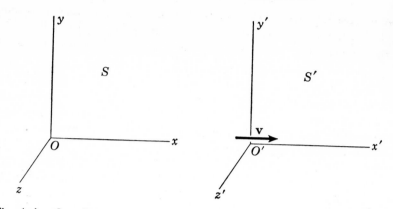

Fig. 4–6.　Coordinate systems used in obtaining the Lorentz transformation.

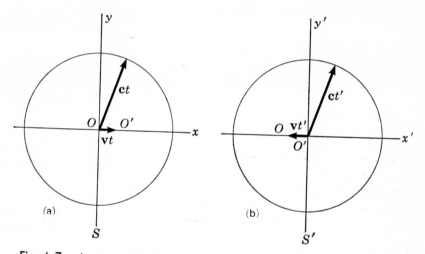

(a)

(b)

Fig. 4–7.　An expanding light wave front in two systems moving relative to each other.

showing the intersection of the expanding wave front of light with that plane. It will be found impossible to use the classical transformation between the coordinates, called the Galilean transformation, and at the same time satisfy both Eq. 4–8 and Eq. 4–9. This transformation is

$$x' = x - vt, \qquad x = x' + vt,$$
$$y' = y, \qquad y = y',$$
$$z' = z, \qquad z = z', \qquad (4\text{--}10)$$
$$t' = t. \qquad t = t'.$$

The direct substitution of these relations into Eq. 4–8 does not lead to Eq. 4–9, nor does the substitution into Eq. 4–9 lead to Eq. 4–8.

The Galilean transformation must therefore be replaced by another if the postulates of the special theory of relativity are to be satisfied. Since there seems to be no trouble arising from the relations $y = y'$ and $z = z'$, they can be taken to be correct and only modifications of the transformation relations for x and t will be needed. The most hopeful relation is a linear one, since a quadratic or higher order transformation would result in multivalued possibilities. Therefore

$$x' = ax + bt,$$
$$t' = ex + ft. \tag{4-11}$$

It is possible to simplify the evaluation of the constants, and the equivalent ones for the inverse transformations, by noting that for low values of v one should expect the equations to tend toward those of the Galilean transformation. Thus it is possible to let

$$x' = \lambda(x - vt), \tag{4-12}$$

where λ may depend on v and c, but not on x and t. Since all systems moving relative to each other at constant velocity are equivalent, the transformation equations must be symmetric except for the reversal of v. Therefore, the same constant λ will appear and

$$x = \lambda(x' + vt'). \tag{4-13}$$

By substituting Eq. 4–12 into Eq. 4–13,

$$t' = \left(\frac{1}{\lambda} - \lambda\right)\frac{x}{v} + \lambda t, \tag{4-14}$$

or

$$t = \left(\lambda - \frac{1}{\lambda}\right)\frac{x'}{v} + \lambda t'. \tag{4-15}$$

Now Eq. 4–8 and Eq. 4–9 are equations describing the development of the same light wave front. It should be possible to start with one of them, transform to the other coordinate system, and obtain the other. If Eq. 4–12 and Eq. 4–14 and the relations $y' = y$ and $z' = z$ are inserted into Eq. 4–9, the result is

$$x^2\left[\lambda^2 - \frac{c^2}{v^2}\left(\frac{1}{\lambda} - \lambda\right)^2\right] - 2xt\left[v\lambda^2 + \frac{c^2}{v}\lambda\left(\frac{1}{\lambda} - \lambda\right)\right]$$
$$+ y^2 + z^2 = c^2 t^2\left(\lambda^2 - \frac{v^2}{c^2}\lambda^2\right). \tag{4-16}$$

A comparison between this expression and Eq. 4–8 shows that

$$\lambda^2 - \frac{c^2}{v^2}\left(\frac{1}{\lambda} - \lambda\right)^2 = 1, \tag{4–17}$$

$$v\lambda^2 + \frac{c^2}{v}\lambda\left(\frac{1}{\lambda} - \lambda\right) = 0, \tag{4–18}$$

and

$$\lambda^2\left(1 - \frac{v^2}{c^2}\right) = 1. \tag{4–19}$$

All three relations are satisfied if

$$\lambda = \frac{1}{\sqrt{1 - \dfrac{v^2}{c^2}}} = \frac{1}{\sqrt{1 - \beta^2}} \tag{4–20}$$

where $\beta = v/c$.

This result then gives us the following transformation, called the *Lorentz transformation*.

$$x' = \frac{x - vt}{\sqrt{1 - \beta^2}},$$

$$y' = y,$$

$$z' = z, \tag{4–21}$$

$$t' = \frac{t - \dfrac{v}{c^2}x}{\sqrt{1 - \beta^2}}.$$

The inverse of this is

$$x = \frac{x' + vt'}{\sqrt{1 - \beta^2}},$$

$$y = y',$$

$$z = z', \tag{4–22}$$

$$t = \frac{t' + \dfrac{v}{c^2}x'}{\sqrt{1 - \beta^2}}.$$

These are the transformation equations that should be used to relate the time and space coordinates of two systems moving relative to each other at a constant velocity if the postulates of the special theory of relativity are to hold. They make it possible to find the space and time coordinates

x', y', z', and t' of a particular event if the unprimed coordinates x, y, z, and t are known, and vice versa.

4–6. The Lorentz-Fitzgerald Contraction. We now consider the problem of comparing the lengths of rods moving with respect to each other. A measurement of length is performed by placing a meter stick along the object to be measured and reading the marks on the stick at a given instant. If the object is moving, it is important to make the two readings *simultaneously*.

Let $l = x_2 - x_1$ be the length of an object stationary in S. Eq. 4–22 gives the following relation for the points x_1 and x_2:

$$x_1 = \frac{x'_1 + vt'_1}{\sqrt{1 - \beta^2}}, \tag{4-23}$$

and

$$x_2 = \frac{x'_2 + vt'_2}{\sqrt{1 - \beta^2}}. \tag{4-24}$$

Now the observer in S' will say that points 1 and 2 which mark the ends of the object are separated by the distance $x'_2 - x'_1$ determined when $t'_2 = t'_1$. Thus

$$l' = x'_2 - x'_1 = \sqrt{1 - \beta^2}\,(x_2 - x_1). \tag{4-25}$$

This shows that the observer in S' watching the object go by measures a length l' shorter than l, the length measured by S at rest with respect to the object. This result is often called the Fitzgerald or Lorentz-Fitzgerald contraction.

It has long been claimed that a consequence of this would be that a body looking like a sphere to an observer moving with it would appear squeezed into an oblate spheroid as viewed from a system past which it is moving. Similarly that a cube would appear less long than wide and high. Recently it has been shown[3] that this is not so. When viewed at a distance, a sphere will look spherical and a cube will look cubical. They will, however, appear to be turned slightly about an axis perpendicular to the plane containing the x-axis and the line of sight. Previously, people had failed to account properly for the extra time required for the light to reach the observer's eye from the more remote portions of the sphere or cube.

4–7. The Einstein Time Dilation. The measurement of time is affected by relative motion, as is the measurement of length. Consider identical clocks belonging to an observer in S and to an observer in S'. The clock in S is placed at some fixed location in S and indicates regular time intervals

[3] J. Terrell, *Phys. Rev.*, **116**, 1041 (1959), and R. Weinstein, *Am. Jour. Phys.*, **28**, 607 (1960).

of length $\Delta t = t_2 - t_1$. The observer in S' will see this clock as a moving clock with intervals as given by Eq. 4–21, that is,

$$\Delta t' = \frac{t_2 - t_1}{\sqrt{1 - \beta^2}} = \frac{\Delta t}{\sqrt{1 - \beta^2}}. \tag{4–26}$$

This equation shows that an observer in S', watching a moving clock, sees the time interval on the S clock to be *lengthened* as compared with what is seen by an observer in S.

Conversely, we could derive an expression by assuming that the clock in S' is fixed at a particular point in S' (say fixed in a space rocket). If an observer on earth (in frame S) watched the clock, he would in effect interchange the prime symbols in Eq. 4–26 and would also see the time interval as lengthened. Thus all moving clocks appear to run slow to an observer seeing them in motion.

Now an interesting point arises. Since the *unit* of time is increased by a factor of $(1 - \beta^2)^{-\frac{1}{2}}$ in Eq. 4–26 for a moving clock (i.e., for observers who see the clock moving) and since these moving clocks run slow, the *elapsed time* actually shown on these moving clocks must be *less* by a factor of $(1 - \beta^2)^{+\frac{1}{2}}$ than on the stationary clock. In the example of the clock in the rocket, a man on earth measures an elapsed time t_e for the rocket to make a particular journey, but the man on earth knows that a shorter time t_r will have been indicated by the clock in the rocket. In fact $t_r = t_e \sqrt{1 - v^2/c^2}$.

An interesting example of this behavior arises in the study of μ-mesons (particles with a mass of 207 electronic masses and a charge of one electronic charge) which are created as the result of the bombardment of the upper atmosphere by primary cosmic rays (see Chapter 20). They can also be created in laboratories and can be observed at low velocities. They are radioactive, producing electrons, with an average life of 2.2×10^{-6} sec. Most of the μ-mesons created in the cosmic ray processes are observed to live for much longer times before they decay. But this is because they are traveling at speeds very close to the speed of light. In fact, if one calculates what the average life of these particles must be as measured with a clock moving with them, the result is close to 2.2×10^{-6} sec.

It is probably desirable to emphasize again that, in spite of the apparent changes in lengths and in time intervals, all physical phenomena are observed the same in either S or S'. The view of an experiment being carried out in one system S' as seen by an observer in another S moving relative to the first at constant velocity is different, but an application of the Lorentz transformation will tell the second observer (in S) that the experimenter (in S') is observing just the same laws he (the one in S) would see if he performed the experiment in his system (S).

The term *clock* used in this article should be understood to stand for any device that can denote the passage of regular intervals of time. It need not be a particular device such as a pendulum clock, but can be an oscillating crystal, a vibrating atom, or a radioactive particle. Each clock does not behave a bit differently because of the motion of the system to which it belongs. It is only that its timekeeping is viewed differently from another system relative to which it is moving.

Many people have been interested in the paradox that if twins A and B boarded systems in motion relative to each other, they would each judge the other to live "more slowly." Thus when A reached an age T_A, he would say that the age of B was $T_B < T_A$. But at the same time B would think that when his age was T'_B, the age of A would be $T'_A < T'_B$. These opinions, which are exactly opposite to each other, disturb some. They ask, "Suppose A and B are brought together again, what would their comparative ages be?" We note that no such test could be performed without accelerating one or the other. Since our theory applies only to inertial systems, it cannot predict the answer. Recently the equivalent of sending one "twin" off and bringing him back has been performed using the Mössbauer effect (see Chapter 18), which has phenomenal accuracy in measuring time intervals. The results show that the clock in the system that moves back and forth, that is, the one that turns around and returns (and hence is accelerated) always loses. These results were pointed out by Sherwin.[4]

4–8. The Transformation Formulas for Velocities.

We will now show that the relativistic velocity transformation is quite different from the classical transformation. Let an object have a velocity with an x-component u_x in S and u'_x in S'. As before, S' moves with velocity v with respect to S with the x- and x'-axes sliding along one another. The definition

$$u'_x = \frac{dx'}{dt'} \qquad \text{and} \qquad u_x = \frac{dx}{dt}$$

along with the appropriate relation from Eq. 4–21, gives

$$u'_x = \frac{dx - v\,dt}{dt - \dfrac{v}{c^2}\,dx} = \frac{u_x - v}{1 - \dfrac{vu_x}{c^2}}, \qquad\qquad (4\text{–}27)$$

which is seen to lead to the classical expression $u'_x = u_x - v$ when $v \ll c$. Note that in order to get the inverse transformation here, one interchanges

[4] C. W. Sherwin, *Phys. Rev.*, **120**, 17 (1960).

primes and reverses the sign of v.   Hence

$$u_x = \frac{u'_x + v}{1 + \frac{vu'_x}{c^2}}. \tag{4–28}$$

From Eq. 4–28 note that even if u' and v are both close to c, the combined velocity is still less than c.

Even the y- and z-components are affected by the transformation, for

$$u'_y = \frac{dy'}{dt'} = \frac{\sqrt{1 - \beta^2}}{1 - u_x \frac{v}{c^2}} u_y, \tag{4–29}$$

and

$$u'_z = \frac{dz'}{dt'} = \frac{\sqrt{1 - \beta^2}}{1 - u_x \frac{v}{c^2}} u_z. \tag{4–30}$$

EXAMPLE 1.   Suppose it is possible to accelerate a rocket to a speed of 10^8 m sec^{-1}.   Further suppose that the rocket contains two detectors placed 12 m apart along the length of the rocket that respond to the passage of a cosmic-ray particle through them by making a signal in the form of a voltage pulse.   The time between passage through these two detectors is then radioed back to the earth.   A cosmic-ray particle passes through the detectors in a direction exactly opposite to that of the rocket.   The information radioed back is that the time between passage through the detectors was 5×10^{-8} sec.   The cosmic ray continues toward the earth. With what velocity does it strike the earth?   Discuss in detail the lengths and time intervals involved.

Solution: We visualize a coordinate system along the rocket moving with it and with its x-axis parallel to the rocket.   We shall use primes on all these coordinates, and call the system R.   A set of coordinates, called system E, are fixed with the earth and are parallel to those of R.   They will be unprimed.   We choose the positive direction of the x-axis to be in the direction of motion of the rocket.   Thus $v = 10^8$ m sec^{-1} and $u'_x = -12/(5 \times 10^{-8}) = -2.4 \times 10^8$ m sec^{-1}.   Eq. 4–28 gives

$$u_x = \frac{(-2.4 + 1) \times 10^8}{1 + \frac{-1 \times 2.4}{9}} = -1.91 \times 10^8 \text{ m sec}^{-1}.$$

The Lorentz-Fitzgerald contraction gives the length between cosmic-ray detectors as measured by an earth observer to be

$$L = L'\sqrt{1 - \beta^2} = 12\sqrt{1 - \tfrac{1}{9}} = 11.31 \text{ m}.$$

The time dilation phenomenon tells the observer on the earth that the equivalent time interval is

$$t_e = \frac{t_r}{\sqrt{1 - \beta^2}} = \frac{5 \times 10^{-8}}{0.943} = 5.31 \times 10^{-8} \text{ sec.}$$

Now note that one cannot take the ratio L/t_e to get u_x, for $L/t_e = 2.13 \times 10^8$ m sec^{-1}. Instead we need to use the Lorentz transformation in detail. Let us call $t = 0$ and $t' = 0$ at the moment the cosmic ray passed through the first detector, and let us say that this happened at $x = 0$ and $x' = 0$. This is just a convenient choice of origins. The experiment on R gave the second event at $x'_2 = -12$ m and at $t'_2 = 5 \times 10^{-8}$ sec. The Lorentz transformation then tells us that $x_1 = 0$, $t_1 = 0$,

$$x_2 = \frac{-12 + (10^8 \times 5 \times 10^{-8})}{0.943} = -7.43 \text{ m,}$$

and

$$t_2 = \frac{5 \times 10^{-8} - \dfrac{10^8 \times 12}{9 \times 10^{16}}}{0.943} = 3.89 \times 10^{-8} \text{ sec.}$$

To compute u_x we should now compute the value of

$$\frac{x_2 - x_1}{t_2 - t_1} = \frac{-7.43}{3.89 \times 10^{-8}} = -1.91 \times 10^8 \text{ m sec}^{-1}.$$

4–9. The Relativistic Variation of Mass. As one looks at the various familiar laws of physics, he finds that not all of them really hold within the meaning of postulate one. It becomes a problem then to find the laws that are in fact true for all inertial frames. It has been found that the law of conservation of momentum is such a law. We shall see that if the law of conservation of momentum is to hold, the measure of the value of the mass of an object must depend upon its velocity relative to the observer. In addition the rule for computing the mass must be the same for all observers. How this works out can be seen as follows:

Consider two observers. One of these is in system S and the other is in system S', which is moving in the x-direction at a speed v. Suppose there are two identical balls A and B, each with a mass m_0 when measured at rest in either system, capable of a perfectly elastic collision. In Fig. 4–8a we see the collision as viewed by S, and in Fig. 4–8b we see it as viewed by S'. We should point out that because of the identical nature of the balls, this is the type of collision in which the speeds after impact are the same as before, and that the figure should be symmetric about the y-direction and the x-direction. That is, the motion is a simple reflection in the point of collision.

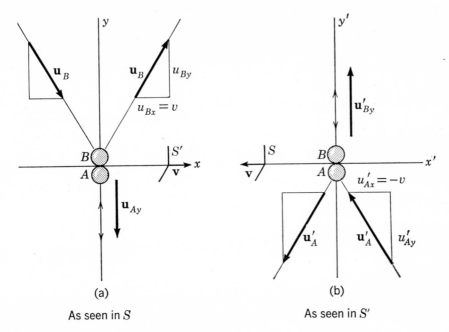

(a)   (b)

As seen in S As seen in S'

Fig. 4–8. A symmetric perfectly elastic collision as seen in S and S'. S sees S' moving to the right at a speed v. S' sees S moving to the left at a speed v.

For our special case in which $u_{Bx} = v$, the rules for the addition of velocities, Eq. 4–27 and Eq. 4–29, give

$$u'_{Ax} = -v, \qquad u'_{Ay} = \sqrt{1 - \beta^2}\, u_{Ay},$$

$$u'_{Bx} = 0, \qquad u'_{By} = \frac{u_{By}}{\sqrt{1 - \beta^2}}, \qquad (4\text{–}31)$$

where $\beta = v/c$.

The ratio between the y-components of the velocities of the balls in S' is thus

$$\frac{u'_{Ay}}{u'_{By}} = \left(1 - \frac{v^2}{c^2}\right) \frac{u_{Ay}}{u_{By}}. \qquad (4\text{–}32)$$

This shows that it is impossible to arrange things so that both u_{Ay}/u_{By} and u'_{Ay}/u'_{By} can equal 1. (There would have been no difficulty if the Galilean transformation was proper.) It would be wrong to expect to have this ratio equal unity in one of the systems and not in the other, so we expect both to differ from unity. What we really want is for the ratio of the y-components of the momentum to be unity in both systems. Since the y-components of momentum are to be equal and the y-components of

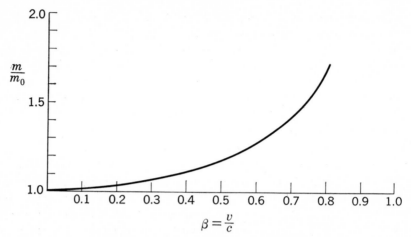

Fig. 4–9.   Variation of mass with velocity.

velocity are not equal, the masses used in computing momentum must be unequal.   The original assumption was that they were the same when at rest, so we expect their value to depend upon the velocity.   We expect the momentum to have the same direction as the velocity.   This means that the quantity m in $\mathbf{p} = m\mathbf{u}$ must be a scalar and be independent of the direction of $\mathbf{u}$.   This leads to the form $m = m_0\alpha(u)$ where m_0 is the mass of each ball as judged by either observer S or S' when the balls are at rest in each respective system.   The problem is to find the correct form for $\alpha(u)$ which will work in all systems, for all kinds of collision problems.

It can be shown that the correct form is

$$\alpha(u) = \frac{1}{\sqrt{1 - \dfrac{u^2}{c^2}}},\tag{4–33}$$

so that

$$m = \frac{m_0}{\sqrt{1 - \dfrac{u^2}{c^2}}}.\tag{4–34}$$

That this preserves the equality of the components of linear momentum after collision for our special case can be easily verified (see Problem 4–30).

Many experiments have been carried out since this was proved, all of which confirm this result.   The most notable of these historically are those of Kaufmann[5] and of Bucherer.[6]   Beta rays emitted by some radio-

[5] W. Kaufmann, *Gottingen Nach.*, **2**, 143 (1901).
[6] A. H. Bucherer, *Ann. d. Phys.*, **28**, 513 (1909).

active materials travel at speeds close enough to c to test this law. By deflecting these beta particles by both a magnetic field and an electric field, it is possible to determine their mass (see Chapter 6). These experiments gave results which are shown in composite in Fig. 4–9. Since different beta particles are emitted at different speeds, it is possible to measure the mass for a wide range of $\beta = v/c$. The measured mass divided by the rest mass, m_0, is then plotted versus β. The curve that is drawn is the representation of Eq. 4–34.

4–10. The Equivalence of Mass and Energy. Changes in the concept of length and time forced on us by the acceptance of the postulates of the special theory of relativity have also changed our concepts of velocity addition and our concept of mass, as we have seen. This latter change forces a revision of our concept of energy. The derivation of the expression for kinetic energy given in Chapter 1 used Newton's second law in the form of $\mathbf{F} = m\, d\mathbf{v}/dt$, implying that the value of m was constant. But the result just arrived at shows that this is not appropriate if the consequences of relativity are to be taken into account. Instead, the second law should be used in the form given in Eq. 2–2, namely, $\mathbf{F} = d\mathbf{p}/dt$. If the force and momentum are in the same direction, we may use only the magnitudes, so we have

$$F = m\frac{dv}{dt} + v\frac{dm}{dt}.$$

(4–35)

We now assume that the applied force does not change the potential energy. Hence any work done on a particle gives it kinetic energy K. Thus

$$dK = F\,dx = m\frac{dv}{dt}dx + v\frac{dm}{dt}dx$$

$$= mv\,dv + v^2\,dm.$$

(4–36)

The differential of Eq. 4–34 is

$$dm = \frac{m_0 v\,dv}{c^2(1 - v^2/c^2)^{3/2}}.$$

(4–37)

Eliminating dm from Eq. 4–36 and setting $\beta = v/c$ gives

$$dK = \frac{m_0 v\,dv}{(1 - \beta^2)^{1/2}} + \frac{m_0 v^3\,dv}{c^2(1 - \beta^2)^{3/2}}$$

$$= \frac{m_0 v\,dv}{(1 - \beta^2)^{3/2}} = \frac{m_0 v\,dv}{(1 - v^2/c^2)^{3/2}}.$$

(4–38)

This can be integrated between the limits $v = 0$ and $v = v$ by letting

$w = 1 - v^2/c^2$ so that $dw = -2v \, dv/c^2$. The result is

$$K = m_0 c^2 \left[\frac{1}{(1 - v^2/c^2)^{1/2}} - 1 \right]$$
$$= mc^2 - m_0 c^2. \tag{4-39}$$

Now if we say that $m_0 c^2$ is the energy of the particle when it is at rest, then $K + m_0 c^2$, the sum of the kinetic energy and the rest energy, can be called the total energy E. Hence

$$E = K + m_0 c^2 = mc^2 \tag{4-40}$$

and m is the total mass of the body. Eq. 4–40 tells us that total mass and total energy are equivalent. This equation underlies all nuclear physics. Its consequences have had a tremendous effect on the world, so the special theory of relativity can no longer be thought of as a curious, abstract, unimportant branch of physical theory.

We next note that if we write,

$$E = \frac{m_0 c^2}{(1 - v^2/c^2)^{1/2}} = m_0 c^2 \left(1 - \frac{v^2}{c^2} \right)^{-1/2}$$

and expand the bracket by means of the binomial theorem,

$$E = m_0 c^2 \left(1 + \frac{v^2}{2c^2} + \frac{3}{8} \frac{v^4}{c^4} + \cdots \right). \tag{4-41}$$

If we assume that $v \ll c$, we can keep only the first and second term of the series, so

$$E = mc^2 = m_0 c^2 + \tfrac{1}{2} m_0 v^2. \tag{4-42}$$

In this relation we see that the classical expression for the kinetic energy $K = \tfrac{1}{2} m_0 v^2$ is valid only when $v \ll c$. At other times the kinetic energy is given by Eq. 4–39.

The non-relativistic expressions for momentum and energy, because of the constancy of mass, give a simple relation between them, namely,

$$p^2 = 2mK. \tag{4-43}$$

A similar relation between momentum and energy can be found in the special theory of relativity. This is found by noting that

$$m^2 c^4 - m_0^2 c^4 = m_0^2 c^4 \left[\frac{1}{1 - \beta^2} - 1 \right] = \frac{m_0^2 c^4 \beta^2}{1 - \beta^2}$$
$$= \frac{m_0^2 c^2 v^2}{1 - \beta^2} = m^2 v^2 c^2 = c^2 p^2.$$

Thus

$$E^2 = c^2 p^2 + m_0^2 c^4 = c^2 p^2 + E_0^2 \tag{4-44}$$

where $E_0 = m_0c^2$ is the rest energy. This can be rewritten as

$$E^2 = (K + E_0)^2 = K^2 + 2KE_0 + E_0{}^2 = c^2p^2 + E_0{}^2,$$

so

$$c^2p^2 = K^2 + 2KE_0. \tag{4-45}$$

EXAMPLE 2. A proton has a mass of 1.67×10^{-27} kg when at rest.
It is traveling at a speed of $0.99c$. Compute (a) its mass, (b) its kinetic
energy, (c) its total energy, and (d) its momentum. Use these figures to
check Eq. 4-44 and Eq. 4-45.

Solution: $\beta = 0.99$, $\beta^2 = 0.9801$, $1 - \beta^2 = 0.0199$; so $\sqrt{1 - \beta^2} = 0.141$.

a. $m = m_0/\sqrt{1 - \beta^2} = 1.67 \times 10^{-27}/0.141 = 11.8 \times 10^{-27}$ kg.
b. $E_0 = m_0c^2 = 1.67 \times 10^{-27} \times 9 \times 10^{16} = 1.50 \times 10^{-10}$ j.
    $K = mc^2 - m_0c^2 = 9.2 \times 10^{-10}$ j.
c. $E = mc^2 = 11.8 \times 10^{-27} \times 9 \times 10^{16} = 1.07 \times 10^{-9}$ j.
d. $p = mv = mc\beta = 0.99 \times 3 \times 10^8 \times 11.8 \times 10^{-27}$
    $= 3.52 \times 10^{-18}$ kg-m sec^{-1}.

To check Eq. 4-44 and Eq. 4-45, we compute

$$E^2 = 113.8 \times 10^{-20} \text{ j}^2$$

$$E_0{}^2 = 2.25 \times 10^{-20} \text{ j}^2$$

$$c^2p^2 = 111.5 \times 10^{-20} \text{ j}^2,$$

so

$$c^2p^2 + E_0{}^2 = (111.5 + 2.3) \times 10^{-20}$$
$$= E^2.$$

$$K^2 = 83.8 \times 10^{-20} \text{ j}^2$$

$$2KE = 27.4 \times 10^{-20} \text{ j}^2$$

$$K^2 + 2KE_0 = 111.2 \times 10^{-20} \text{ j}^2.$$

4-11. Electromagnetism and Relativity. Although the postulates of
relativity arose from an experiment with light, an electromagnetic phenomenon, most of our discussion has been more mechanical and kine-
matical. The laws of electromagnetism are equally preserved in a shift
between systems moving relative to each other at constant speed, that is,
by a Lorentz transformation. As a result of this, the following relations
hold between the primed and unprimed (S' and S) values for the components of the electric and magnetic vectors

$$E'_x = E_x \qquad\qquad B'_x = B_x$$

$$E'_y = \lambda(E_y - \beta cB_z) \qquad B'_y = \lambda\left(B_y + \frac{\beta E_z}{c}\right)$$

$$E'_z = \lambda(E_z + \beta cB_y) \qquad B'_z = \lambda\left(B_z - \frac{\beta E_y}{c}\right) \tag{4-46}$$

where $\lambda = 1/\sqrt{1 - \beta^2}$, and $\beta = v/c$.

$$\begin{bmatrix} E'_x = E_x & H'_x = H_x \\ E'_y = \lambda(E_y - \beta H_z) & H'_y = \lambda(H_y + \beta E_z) \\ E'_z = \lambda(E_z + \beta H_y) & H'_z = \lambda(H_z + \beta E_y) \end{bmatrix}$$

Thus one can see that a field which appears to be a pure electric field in one system will look like an electric and magnetic field in the other system; or a pure magnetic field will appear as a mixed magnetic and electric field. Charges are unaffected by the transformation, but currents are, since they involve the velocities of the charges.

The theory of relativity is an excellent example of the procedure we have pointed out in the preface. It illustrates how classical mechanics furnishes a portion of the picture of nature. It is found to be incomplete, if not erroneous. A combination of groping for a better model and flashing insight leads to a plateau which lays bare completely unforeseen parts of the science.

PROBLEMS

4–1. Prove algebraically that it takes longer to swim upstream and back than it takes to swim the same distance across the stream and back. Let $v =$ velocity of the water and $c =$ the swimmer's velocity in still water.

4–2. The Michelson interferometer is often illustrated using sound waves in air instead of light. A whistle serves as a source, a microphone is the detector and a set of slats is the partially reflecting mirror. If the frequency of the whistle is 5000 cps, the velocity of sound is 350 m sec^{-1}, and each leg of the interferometer is 5 m long, what wind velocity parallel to a leg would change the interference at the microphone from constructive to destructive?

4–3. Using Fig. 4–5, suppose $AB = 5000$ m and the velocity of S' with respect to S is 300 m sec^{-1}. Two events at A and B were judged simultaneous in S. What difference in time will an observer in S' think occurred between the same two events at A' and B'?

4–4. Using Fig. 4–5, suppose $AB = 5$ m and the velocity of S' with respect to S is 14×10^3 m sec^{-1}. Two events at A and B were judged simultaneous in S. What difference in time will an observer in S' think occurred between the same two events at A' and B'?

4–5. Suppose two satellites meet each other traveling in almost identical orbits with velocity relative to the earth of 7×10^3 m sec^{-1} in opposite directions. In one satellite two lights 5 m apart flash and A. Shepard in this satellite thinks the two flashed simultaneously. Y. Gagarin in his disagreed. What time interval did he think separated the flashes?

4-6. Verify Eq. 4-16.

4-7. Check that $\lambda = 1/\sqrt{1 - \beta^2}$ does in fact satisfy Eqs. 4-17, 4-18, and 4-19.

4-8. Using the Lorentz transformation, calculate the value of the primed coordinates for an event for which $x = 2$ m, $y = 17$ m, $z = -1.5$ m at $t = 1.6 \times 10^{-6}$ sec, if $v = 3.6 \times 10^4$ m sec^{-1}.

4-9. In the primed coordinates an event occurred at $x' = -600$ m, $y' = 0$, $z' = 5$ m, and $t' = 3 \times 10^{-5}$ sec. What were x, y, z, and t for the event if $v = \frac{4}{5}c$, where c is the speed of light?

4-10. Reanalyze Problem 4-3 using the Lorentz transformation.

4-11. Reanalyze Problem 4-4 using the Lorentz transformation.

4-12. A runner does the 100 m dash in 9.30×10^{-7} sec at constant speed. How far apart does he judge the start and finish marks to be? What time interval does his own watch show elapsed? Is his estimate of the velocity of the ground relative to him the same as the timer's judgment of his speed?

4-13. Observers A (at the origin) and B at rest in S' are 12×10^{10} m apart and have synchronized their watches. S' moves in the usual manner past S at a velocity $v = \frac{7}{25}c$. Observer C is at the origin in S. If A and C pass one another when their clocks read zero, what is the separation of A and B as seen by C? What is the difference between A's clock and B's clock as seen by C?

4-14. Observers A (at the origin) and B at rest in S' are 15×10^{10} m apart and have synchronized their watches. S' moves in the usual manner past S at a velocity $v = \frac{3}{5}c$. Observer C is at the origin in S. If A and C pass one another when their clocks read zero, what is the separation of A and B as seen by C? What is the difference between A's clock and B's clock as seen by C?

4-15. Rocket A carrying a man has a velocity of 100,000 mps relative to rocket B. Assume they both moved along the x-axis in the same direction. The man in A knows that the length of his rocket is 200 yd. As they pass, each takes a picture of the other. (a) How long is A according to B? (b) If A measures B as 160 yd, what length does B know that his own rocket has?

4-16. Compute the time between the ticks of a clock fixed in S as seen by an observer moving at $\frac{1}{10}$ the speed of light if the ticks are 1 sec apart as heard by an observer at rest.

4-17. A rocket moves at 7 mps. How long a time would it have to move at this constant velocity to have 1 sec difference in time recorded by a clock on board and one on the earth?

4-18. Cosmic rays are nuclear particles from outer space traveling at very high speeds. In the atmosphere they may form particles that are not stable, but break up, on the average, in a time called the "half-life." The half-life for one such particle at rest is 2×10^{-8} sec. What is its half-life when moving at $\frac{9}{10}$ the speed of light?

4-19. A high-speed proton passes through two counters 30 m apart. Its velocity is 0.8c. What time interval was observed? To the proton, what was the separation of the counter and what time interval elapsed? Does its evaluation of the speed of the earth and counters give 0.8c?

4–20. A man standing at the rear end of a railroad car fires a bullet to the front end of the car. The velocity of the bullet, as measured by the gunman, is 0.5c. The length of the car, as measured by the gunman, is 20 m. An observer on the ground observes all this, as the train passes him with velocity 0.7c. What values does this observer measure for the following quantities? (a) Length of the car, (b) velocity of the bullet, (c) length of time the bullet is in the air, (d) distance the bullet travels, and (e) distance the train travels while the bullet is in the air.

4–21. A nucleus has a diameter when measured at rest of 7×10^{-15} m. A neutron in it moves with a velocity of 0.3c. The nucleus is accelerated in a laboratory to a speed of 0.5c. Calculate (a) the diameter of the nucleus as measured in the laboratory system, (b) the velocity of the neutron as measured in the laboratory system, (c) the time taken for the neutron to cross the nucleus as judged by observers in the LS and in the nucleus, (d) the distance the neutron travels while crossing the nucleus as judged by the laboratory observer, (e) the distance the nucleus moves while the neutron crosses the nucleus, and (f) the laboratory measure of neutron velocity using the results of (c) and (d).

4–22. A rocket moves with speed $\frac{3}{5}c$ with respect to the earth in the positive x direction. The x and x' axes are aligned as usual. A second rocket moves such that $y = z = 0$ and $x = \frac{4}{5}ct$. Find its position as seen by an observer in the first rocket.

4–23. An electronic flash lamp is at rest in S at $x = 0$. It emits flashes of light separated by a time T. S' moves at $\frac{4}{5}c$ in the usual manner with O' passing O when $t = 0$. An observer is at rest at the origin of S'. Compute the successive points and times from which the observer in S' sees pulses. Compute the time interval between the flashes as seen by the observer.

4–24. On a level, straight stretch of highway car A travels north at 50 mph and car B travels south at 60 mph. Calculate their relative velocity by (a) Newtonian methods (b) relativistic methods ($c = 186,000$ mps).

4–25. A body A is moving in S' at a velocity $\frac{4}{5}c$ along the x'-axis. If the velocity of S' is also $\frac{4}{5}c$, what does S say the velocity of A is?

4–26. Two protons are each given a velocity of 0.3c in a laboratory. One moves to the right, the other to the left. With what velocity does each think the other is approaching?

4–27. Two electrons are accelerated to such a velocity that each judges the velocity of the other to be approaching at a speed 0.5c. In the laboratory they have equal speeds in opposite directions. What speed does each have?

4–28. Two accelerators are pointed at one another and emit particles with a speed of 1.5×10^8 m sec^{-1} and 2.0×10^8 m sec^{-1} respectively. Compute the speed of one relative to the other.

4-29. A body B is moving in S at a velocity $\frac{2}{3}c$ in the negative x direction. If the velocity of S' is $\frac{2}{3}c$ in the positive x direction, what does S' measure as the velocity of B?

4-30. Verify that Eq. 4-34 leads to equal y-components of linear momentum as discussed in Art. 4-9.

4-31. An electron is accelerated in a machine. It travels in a circular path in the machine and acquires 300 ev of energy each revolution. What fraction of an electron rest mass is acquired each revolution? What fraction is acquired after 100,000 revolutions?

4-32. Compute the percentage increase in mass for an electron which is accelerated to a speed of $0.9c$.

4-33. Using the mass-energy relation, prove that $E = m_0c^2 + \frac{1}{2}m_0v^2$ if the velocity v is small compared to the velocity of light.

4-34. If $\frac{1}{10}$ of 1% of the mass of 1 kg of water could be converted into energy, what would this be in joules and kilowatt-hours?

4-35. If 1 gram mass were completely converted to energy, how much water would it bring to the boiling point from $0°C$?

4-36. A 20 kiloton atom bomb releases 8×10^{13} j. How much mass must have been converted into other energy forms?

4-37. Compute the total energy of (a) an electron, (b) a proton (the nucleus of hydrogen), and (c) an alpha particle (the nucleus of helium), after acceleration through 5×10^6 v.

4-38. Compute the v/c ratio for the particles of Problem 4-37.

SELECTED REFERENCES

EINSTEIN, A. *The Meaning of Relativity.* Princeton Univ. Press, Princeton, N. J., 1950. 3d ed., chaps. 1 and 2.

GAMOW, G. *Mr. Tompkins in Wonderland; or Stories of c, G and h.* The Macmillan Co., New York, 1940.

MICHELSON, A. A., and E. W. MORLEY. "The Michelson-Morley Experiment." In *A Source Book in Physics.* W. F. Magie, ed. McGraw-Hill Book Co., Inc., New York, 1935. P. 369.

LIEBER, L. R. *The Einstein Theory of Relativity.* Holt, Rinehart & Winston, Inc. New York, 1945. Part I.

RICHTMYER, F. K., E. H. KENNARD, and T. LAURITSEN. *Introduction to Modern Physics.* McGraw-Hill Book Co., Inc., New York, 1955. 5th ed., chap. 2, pp. 49–76.

SHAMOS, M. H., ed. *Great Experiments in Physics.* Holt, Rinehart & Winston, Inc., New York, 1959. Appendix 3, p. 315.

5

Molecular Theory of Gases

Up to this point, we have not been concerned with the detailed structure of matter. Instead, we have been trying to build a background and have been presenting laws and principles having general application. The state of matter called the gaseous, or vapor, state is a good place to begin a more detailed look. In time we shall consider some of the special circumstances that arise in the case of the liquid and solid states of matter but not until after we have looked with increasingly finer detail at the molecules and atoms of which matter is composed. The reason for starting with gases is that they appear to be simple. But even with them, it is convenient to make a number of simplifying assumptions regarding their nature.

We will assume that gases are composed of individual particles which are of submicroscopic size and for any pure substance are all alike. These are the objects called molecules. We will assume these are in motion within the container holding the gas and are constantly colliding with the walls. Because the number of molecules is very large, the collisions are so frequent and so uniformly spread that the effect is one of a steady pressure against the wall. The effects of these collisions are comparatively independent of the exact structure of the molecules, so the simplifying assumptions can neglect such structural details reasonably safely and still provide results in good agreement with the actual behavior of nature.

5–1. The Assumptions for an Ideal Gas. By considering an enclosure containing a quantity of molecules of an ideal gas, idealized by making the following additional assumptions concerning the nature of gas molecules, we can arrive at Boyle's law. The required assumptions are:

1. All molecules have the same mass m.
2. Each molecule has a velocity $\mathbf{v}$ with components v_x, v_y, and v_z.
3. The molecules are so small that no collisions occur between molecules.
4. Collisions of molecules with the walls are perfectly elastic.
5. There are no forces between the molecules.

Assumption 3 is not very important because we have seen in Chapter 2 that two identical bodies will simply exchange their motion if the collision is perfectly elastic, as is the case with gas molecules. The actual path of the molecules, between collisions, is somewhat shorter than that based upon this assumption because of the finite size of the molecules. This turns out to be equivalent to considering the volume to be less than the measured value, as we will point out again in Art. 5–6. Thus, it is possible to proceed as if there were no collisions and then correct for the impropriety of this assumption later.

5–2. Boyle's Law. In the discussion that follows, the shape of the container is not taken into account since only the volume appears in the final result. Assuming that the container is a rectangular parallelepiped with smooth walls, let us follow one molecule as it moves about in this box (Fig. 5–1). It will hit various walls in succession. On each collision

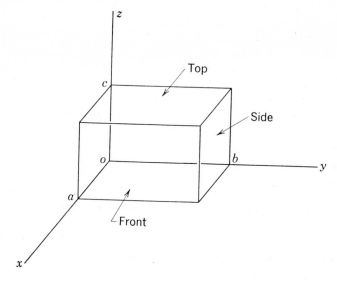

Fig. 5–1.   Box containing molecules.

with a wall, its motion perpendicular to the wall is changed, but its motion parallel to it is not changed. Thus, if we watch only its x-motion, it bounces back and forth between the front and back with an unchanged speed v_x. In its y-motion it bounces back and forth between the sides at a speed v_y. Its z-motion takes it up and down between the top and bottom at a speed v_z. While this molecule is doing this, all the others are behaving in a similar manner.

When the first molecule hits the front wall, its x-momentum is changed from mv_{1x} to $-mv_{1x}$, a change of momentum of $2mv_{1x}$. The second molecule has a change in momentum, in the x-direction, of $2mv_{2x}$ and the ith molecule, of $2mv_{ix}$. The first molecule crosses over and back $v_{1x}/2a$ times a second (one round trip is $2a$ meters and it goes v_{1x} meters per second in that direction). It therefore collides with the front wall (and also the back wall) $v_{1x}/2a$ times per second, so the change in its momentum at the front wall is $2mv_{1x}^2/2a = mv_{1x}^2/a$ per second. Meanwhile the second molecule has a change of momentum, in the x-direction, of $2mv_{2x}$ and makes $v_{2x}/2a$ trips, so its change in momentum at the front wall is mv_{2x}^2/a per second. In fact, any molecule (such as the ith molecule) has a momentum change of mv_{ix}^2/a per second at the front wall. The total change in momentum per second, at the front wall, is therefore the sum of all these, namely,

$$\frac{mv_{1x}^2}{a} + \frac{mv_{2x}^2}{a} + \cdots + \frac{mv_{nx}^2}{a} = \frac{m}{a} \sum_{i=1}^{n} v_{ix}^2 \tag{5-1}$$

where it has been assumed that there are n molecules.

Remember that the number of molecules n is very large, say 3×10^{22} molecules in a liter under ordinary conditions, so the summation above has very many terms (as many terms as there are molecules). The force producing this change in momentum is exerted by the front wall on the molecules. Newton's third law of motion then tells us that the molecules exert an equal force on the wall. This force, divided by the area of the wall, we interpret as a pressure exerted by the gas. The force on the front wall is

$$f_f = \frac{m}{a} \sum_{i=1}^{n} v_{ix}^2 \tag{5-2}$$

and the pressure is obtained by dividing this force by the area of the wall bc, giving

$$p = \frac{f_f}{bc} = \frac{m}{abc} \sum_{i=1}^{n} v_{ix}^2 = \frac{m}{V} \sum_{i=1}^{n} v_{ix}^2, \tag{5-3}$$

where $V = abc$ is the volume of the box.

In the meantime there has been side-to-side motion with the ith molecule making $v_{iy}/2b$ trips per second and experiencing a momentum change $2mv_{iy}$ so that the force on one side f_s is

$$f_s = \frac{m}{b} \sum_{i=1}^{n} v_{iy}^2. \tag{5-4}$$

The pressure on the side is

$$p = \frac{f_s}{ac} = \frac{m}{abc} \sum_{i=1}^{n} v_{iy}^2 = \frac{m}{V} \sum_{i=1}^{n} v_{iy}^2. \tag{5-5}$$

In a similar way we can show that the pressure against the top or bottom is

$$p = \frac{f_t}{ab} = \frac{m}{abc} \sum_{i=1}^{n} v_{iz}^2 = \frac{m}{V} \sum_{i=1}^{n} v_{iz}^2. \tag{5-6}$$

There is no reason to prefer one direction over another and experience confirms the resulting conclusion that

$$p = \frac{m}{V} \sum_{i=1}^{n} v_{ix}^2 = \frac{m}{V} \sum_{i=1}^{n} v_{iy}^2 = \frac{m}{V} \sum_{i=1}^{n} v_{iz}^2. \tag{5-7}$$

It is now time to get rid of the summation symbols. Suppose we want the average (mean) value of all the v_{ix}^2's. The way to get this is to add all the n different v_{ix}^2's and then divide by n. We will call this C_x^2, so

$$C_x^2 = \frac{1}{n} \sum_{i=1}^{n} v_{ix}^2. \tag{5-8}$$

Similarly,

$$C_y^2 = \frac{1}{n} \sum_{i=1}^{n} v_{iy}^2, \tag{5-9}$$

and

$$C_z^2 = \frac{1}{n} \sum_{i=1}^{n} v_{iz}^2. \tag{5-10}$$

In this notation we can rewrite Eq. 5-7 as

$$p = \frac{mn}{V} C_x^2 = \frac{mn}{V} C_y^2 = \frac{mn}{V} C_z^2. \tag{5-11}$$

If we calculate the average of the squares of the velocities,

$$C^2 = \frac{1}{n} \sum_{i=1}^{n} v_i^2 = \frac{1}{n} \sum_{i=1}^{n} (v_{ix}^2 + v_{iy}^2 + v_{iz}^2)$$
$$= \frac{3}{n} \sum_{i=1}^{n} v_{ix}^2 = 3C_x^2. \tag{5-12}$$

Finally then,

$$p = \frac{nm}{V} C_x^2 = \frac{1}{3} \frac{nm}{V} C^2. \tag{5-13}$$

In this expression, nm is the total mass of the gas, so

$$p = \frac{1}{3} \frac{M}{V} C^2 = \frac{1}{3} \rho C^2, \tag{5-14}$$

where ρ is the density of the gas. This can be written in the more familiar form of Boyle's law

$$pV = \tfrac{1}{3} M C^2. \tag{5-15}$$

The quantity C which is $(\overline{C^2})^{\frac{1}{2}}$ is not the average velocity (which is zero) or even the average speed. It is the square root of the average of of the square of the velocities. It is therefore usually called the "root-mean-square speed" (abbreviated rms speed). In Art. 5–9, we shall relate the root-mean-square speed to the average speed.

5–3. The Ideal Gas Law. Boyle's law holds for a fixed temperature. Experiment has shown that when the temperature is changed, most gases behave according to the relation

$$pV = p_0 V_0 (1 + at), \qquad (5\text{–}16)$$

where p_0 is the pressure at the ice point (the temperature of water in equilibrium with ice at standard pressure, 0°C), V_0 is the volume at the ice point for the pressure p_0, t is temperature above the ice point, and a is a constant which is practically the same for all gases. Its value is 0.00366 per °C.

We can rewrite Eq. 5–16 as

$$pV = p_0 V_0 a \left(\frac{1}{a} + t \right). \qquad (5\text{–}17)$$

Now we define a new temperature scale having the same size degrees but a different zero, namely, $1/a$ below the ice point. Thus we have

$$T = t + \frac{1}{a},$$

$$T_0 = 0 + \frac{1}{a}. \qquad (5\text{–}18)$$

The measured value of $1/a$ is very nearly 273 (273.16) centigrade degrees.

$$T = t + 273°\text{K},$$

$$T_0 = 273°\text{K}.$$

The letters °K stand for "degrees Kelvin," the common designation for the centigrade absolute scale. This temperature is called the ideal gas, or absolute, temperature. Eq. 5–17 then becomes

$$pV = \frac{p_0 V_0}{T_0} T = QT, \qquad (5\text{–}19)$$

where Q is a constant that depends upon the amount of gas used. It has been found that a mole (one gram–molecular weight) of two different gases will occupy the same volume provided they are at the same pressure and temperature. This fact of nature is usually called Avogadro's hypothesis. At standard atmospheric pressure (76 cm of mercury), and at the ice point, this volume is 22.4 liters. Consequently, if V refers to the volume of a mole, Q is the same for all gases. It is customary to use the letter R for this constant, so

$$pV_{\text{mole}} = RT. \qquad (5\text{--}20)$$

The value of R is 8.32 j mole^{-1} °K^{-1} or 1.99 cal mole^{-1} °K^{-1}.

5-4. The Law of Equipartition of Energy. Let us now combine Eq. 5-13 and Eq. 5-20. The assumption that Avogadro's hypothesis is true implies that the number of molecules in a mole is the same for all materials. If this were not true, the combining laws of chemistry would not make sense. The number of molecules in a mole is called Avogadro's number and is usually designated by the letter N. We have then

$$pV = \tfrac{1}{3}NmC^2 = RT. \qquad (5\text{--}21)$$

If we divide this by $\tfrac{2}{3}N$, we get

$$\frac{1}{2}\,mC^2 = \frac{3}{2}\,\frac{R}{N}\,T. \qquad (5\text{--}22)$$

The left side of Eq. 5-22 is the average kinetic energy of the molecules. R/N may be thought of as "the gas constant for a single molecule." It is called the Boltzmann constant and is designated by the letter k, so we have as the average kinetic energy of a molecule

$$K_{\text{av}} = \tfrac{1}{2}mC^2 = \tfrac{3}{2}kT. \qquad (5\text{--}23)$$

The experimentally determined value of N is

$$N = 6.03 \times 10^{23} \text{ molecules mole}^{-1},$$

so

$$k = 1.38 \times 10^{-23} \text{ j °K}^{-1}.$$

Remember, we have been paying no attention to any structure or special shape of the molecules. Consequently, the location and configuration of each molecule is completely described (aside from its motion) if *three* coordinates, such as the x, y, and z of the molecule, are given. This fact is described by saying that each molecule has three *degrees of freedom*. Note then that *the average kinetic energy for each molecule is $\tfrac{1}{2}kT$ for each degree of freedom*. This is called the *law of equipartition of energy*. Classical statistical mechanics shows that this relation should hold in all cases. Experiment bears this out for sufficiently high temperatures. It does not seem to hold generally and the explanation appears only when classical laws are replaced by quantum laws.

5-5. Specific Heats of Gases. The specific heat of a material is often defined as the *energy required to raise the temperature of unit mass of a* *substance* 1 *degree.* If there is no change in volume, this is called the specific heat at constant volume and is designated by c_v; if there is no change in pressure, it is c_p, etc. It is often more convenient to work with molar heats, *the energy required to raise the temperature of* 1 *mole of the substance* 1 *degree.* We will use capital letters C_v, C_p, etc., to designate molar heats.

If u is the internal energy (the total kinetic energy of all molecules plus any potential energy due to forces between or within molecules) of a unit mass of a material,

$$c_v = \left(\frac{\partial u}{\partial T}\right)_v. \tag{5-24}$$

Likewise, if U is the internal energy of a mole of a material,

$$C_v = \left(\frac{\partial U}{\partial T}\right)_v. \tag{5-25}$$

Both c_v and C_v should be constants independent of temperature, since for an ideal gas, all the internal energy is in the kinetic energy of the molecules. We have then

$$U = N\left(\frac{1}{2}mC^2\right) = N\left(\frac{3}{2}\frac{R}{N}T\right) = \frac{3}{2}RT.$$

Consequently, the molar heat should be

$$C_v = \left(\frac{\partial U}{\partial T}\right)_v = \frac{d}{dT}\left(\frac{3}{2}RT\right) = \frac{3}{2}R \tag{5-26}$$

$$= 12.5 \text{ j mole}^{-1} \, {}^\circ\text{K}^{-1}$$

$$= 2.98 \text{ cal mole}^{-1} \, {}^\circ\text{K}^{-1}.$$

If the volume of a gas does not remain constant as it is warmed, external work is done by the gas as it expands (or on the gas, if it is compressed). This requires additional energy. Since gases expand when heated at constant pressure, the molar heat at constant pressure C_p is always larger than the molar heat at constant volume C_v, that is, $C_p > C_v$. In fact, since $pV = RT$, the work done during an infinitesimal expansion of an ideal gas is

$$p \, dV = R \, dT. \tag{5-27}$$

Thus

$$C_p = C_v + p\frac{dV}{dT} = C_v + R, \tag{5-28}$$

or

$$C_p - C_v = R.$$

C_v represents the energy increase of the molecules, R represents the external work done.

A constant of some importance for gases is the ratio between C_p and C_v,

$$\gamma = \frac{C_p}{C_v}. \tag{5-29}$$

For example, the velocity of sound in a gas can be shown to be

$$v_s = \sqrt{\gamma \frac{p}{\rho}}. \tag{5-30}$$

For an ideal gas, $C_v = \frac{3}{2}R$ and $C_p = \frac{5}{2}R$, so

$$\gamma = \frac{\frac{5}{2}R}{\frac{3}{2}R} = \frac{5}{3} = 1.667.$$

Thus, the velocity of sound in an ideal gas should be

$$v_s = \sqrt{\gamma \tfrac{1}{3} C^2} = \sqrt{(\tfrac{5}{3})(\tfrac{1}{3}) C^2}$$

$$= \frac{\sqrt{5}}{3} C. \tag{5-31}$$

The values we have given for an ideal gas are quite close to those for the noble gases—helium, neon, etc. Diatomic gases have a structure, so more than three coordinates must be specified. At ordinary temperatures, gases like O_2 and N_2 have $\gamma = \frac{7}{5} = 1.40$, corresponding to $C_v = \frac{5}{2}R$ and $C_p = \frac{7}{2}R$. Evidently they have five degrees of freedom, the number for a rigid "dumbbell" molecule. Actually one would expect that such a molecule should not be rigid but should be capable of vibrating. The energy of vibration should require an additional kT ($\frac{1}{2}kT$ for the average kinetic energy and another $\frac{1}{2}kT$ for the average potential energy), since the average kinetic energy and average potential energy of a harmonic oscillator are equal. At high enough temperatures these gases tend to have the larger molar heats that are indicated by this theory, namely, $C_v = \frac{7}{2}R$, $C_p = \frac{9}{2}R$, and $\gamma = \frac{9}{7}$. The reason they do not, at ordinary temperature, is a consequence of quantum laws.

5-6. Real Gases. Real gases match the laws we have derived fairly well, unless the pressure becomes quite high or the temperature quite low. The deviations then become considerable. Two reasons for this are the fact that the molecules have a finite size and that there are small attractive forces between the molecules. One attempt to take these into account is given below.

The finite size of the molecules results effectively in their not having to travel quite as far because their path is shortened at each collision. Thus, the equivalent volume is less than that measured, as we pointed out in Art. 5-1. We call this equivalent volume $(V - b)$. The attractive forces reduce the impacts of each molecule against the walls. The measured pressure is thus smaller than that predicted by the simpler theory. It is not so clear how to correct this effect, but it does seem likely that whatever modification is required should increase with the density. Van der Waals proposed to treat the correction as proportional to the square of the density. Thus, p is replaced by $(p + a/V^2)$. The resulting equation

$$\left(p + \frac{a}{V^2}\right)(V - b) = RT \tag{5-32}$$

is called van der Waals' equation. A plot of p versus V is shown for three values of T in Fig. 5-2. The shape is similar to that shown for T_1 for all values of T below T_2. It can be shown that the part of the curve $abcde$

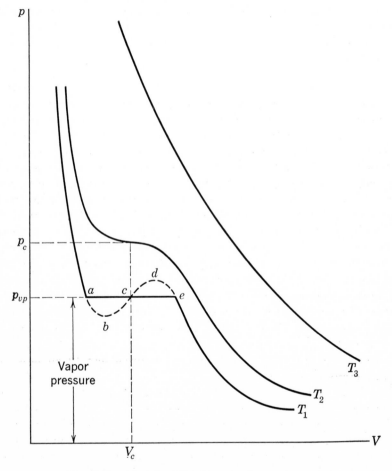

Fig. 5-2. Van der Waals' curve for real gases.

represents an unstable condition. If V is decreased and T maintained constant, when the condition of point e is reached, some of the material changes to the state represented by the point a. As V continues to decrease, this process continues so that the experimental plot appears as if it were just the straight line ace. This corresponds to liquefaction or condensation. The pressure p_{vp} is the vapor pressure at temperature T_1. The line ace is drawn so that the area $abca$ equals the area $cdec$. The curve for T_2 has no alternations in slope, as does the curve for T_1, but has a horizontal slope at p_c, V_c. T_2 is called the critical temperature; p_c is the critical pressure; and V_c is the critical volume. For any temperature such as T_3 above $T_2 = T_c$ the curve has no horizontal slope, and it is impossible to liquefy the gas.

Actual gases behave in just such a manner. However, a detailed study of the theory and a comparison with the actual behavior of real gases or vapors show that this theory is too simple. For example, a, b, v_c, p_c, and T_c are all interrelated in a very special way according to this theory. The results of experiment do not confirm these predictions exactly.

5–7. Distribution Functions. In our discussion of gases we have been dealing with very large numbers of molecules. In dealing with such "assemblies" of particles, we are unable to predict the exact behavior of each particular particle. This is no great handicap, for the quantities which can be measured, like pressure or energy content, are *average* values. However, there are some circumstances where knowing the average is not enough; for example, a case in which all particles have the same value of some quantity might not be equivalent to a case of mixed large, medium, and small values even though the averages were the same. Such differences in distributions of values are the subject of these next few articles.

The study of such distributions and their averages can be done best through the use of the techniques of *statistical mechanics* mentioned in Art. 5–4. This consists of applying the principles of the theory of probabilities to assemblies of a very large number of particles. If the particles obey classical laws of mechanics, the results are those of classical statistical mechanics; but if the particles obey quantum laws, the results are those of quantum statistical mechanics.

The application of classical statistical mechanics to an ideal gas is appropriate to any assembly of neutral particles in which the particles are far enough apart so that any interactions can be neglected. Early treatment of this problem was given by Maxwell and certain improvements were made by Boltzmann. As a result, their names often are attached to the distribution of speeds or velocities for molecules of an ideal gas.

Before we look at the Maxwell distribution, let us examine the mathematics of describing such distributions. The problem is to observe a very large assembly of molecules which are in continual motion. If, somehow, at a particular instant of time, we could attach to each molecule a small arrow representing the velocity of the molecule, and instantaneously photograph this imaginary collection, we could then sit back and at our leisure count the number of molecules that have vectors of a certain length (or if we wished, length and direction, or certain x-components of velocity, etc.). We might then, by our imaginary technique, repeat the process a very large number of times. In this tedious (and impossible) manner, we would get an over-all picture of the behavior of the assembly.

An imperfect example of such a technique is taking the census every ten years by our government. The results of these census counts are often reported pictorially in a type of graph called a "histogram." A hypothetical histogram is shown in Fig. 5–3. It pictures a fictitious distribution in ages of the males of New York State.

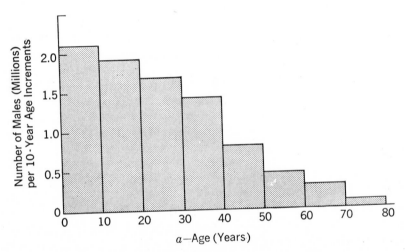

Fig. 5–3.   Histogram for age distribution by ten-year groups.

Note that the ordinate axis plots the number of males *per unit interval of age*. This really is a fractional quantity, the total number in the range divided by the range. The term "density" is often used for such quantities. The use of the ten-year range is probably not very good for most purposes, so let us take the intervals to be one year instead. The histogram of Fig. 5–3 might then look like that of Fig. 5–4. No population distribution can be plotted properly in the continuous form shown in Fig. 5–5, but it is convenient to do so anyway.

The use of Figs. 5–3 and 5–4 is fairly obvious. Fig. 5–3 tells us that there are 1.7 million males in the age range of 20 to 30. Fig. 5–4 gives more detailed information, such as 185,000 of age 20, 181,000 of age 21, 170,000 of age 26, 169,000 of age 29, with a total of 1,700,000 of age 20 to 30.

The continuous curve of Fig. 5–5 provides more detailed information. Suppose we ask how many have ages between 22.00548 (22 yr and 2 days)

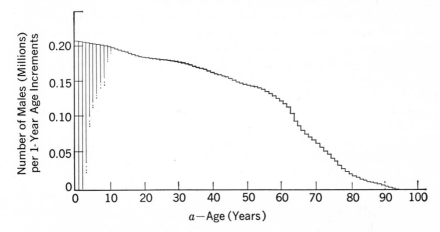

Fig. 5–4.   Histogram for age distribution by one-year groups.

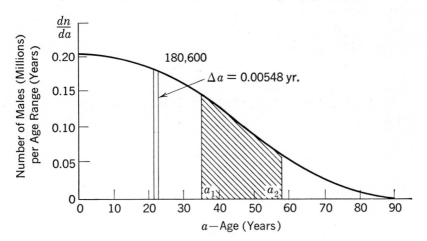

Fig. 5–5.   Continuous representation of age distribution.

and 22.01096 (22 yr and 4 days).   The curve gives the value for dn/da for 22 yr as 180,600 per yr.   The value does not change appreciably over the range of interest, therefore the number in the age group range of interest is

$$\Delta n = 180,600(22.01096 - 22.00548)$$
$$= 180,600(0.00548) = 989.688.$$

This example shows how such a *continuous* distribution function can be used and also shows where it can go wrong. Clearly we can't have 0.688 of a person as part of the answer; only integral values are proper. But this only stretches the example. There will be no problem of fractional molecules in the examples to be considered.

It should now be clear that the plot of the distribution function (or density dn/da) can be used to give Δn, the number in an infinitesimal range Δa by

$$\Delta n = \frac{dn}{da} \Delta a. \qquad (5\text{--}33)$$

In the case of an extended range a_1 to a_2, the number N is

$$N = \int dn = \int_{a_1}^{a_2} \frac{dn}{da} \, da. \qquad (5\text{--}34)$$

This is the area under the curve between a_1 and a_2 as shown in Fig. 5–5.

5–8. The Calculation of Averages with the Aid of Distribution Functions. The calculation of averages when a distribution function is known involves the normal process of computing averages. The sum of the quantities is taken and this is divided by the total number. Suppose the distribution function $dn/da = f(a)$ is known, within the range of a_1 to a_2. Suppose a quantity $y(a)$ depends on a. The accumulation of y corresponding to the range a to $a + da$ is

$$y \, dn = y \frac{dn}{da} \, da. \qquad (5\text{--}35)$$

The total accumulation of y for the range is the sum of all these, namely, the integral

$$I = \int_{a_1}^{a_2} y \frac{dn}{da} \, da. \qquad (5\text{--}36)$$

The total sample is

$$N = \int_{a_1}^{a_2} \frac{dn}{da} \, da, \qquad (5\text{--}37)$$

so the average is

$$\bar{y} = \frac{I}{N} = \frac{\displaystyle\int_{a_1}^{a_2} y \frac{dn}{da} \, da}{\displaystyle\int_{a_1}^{a_2} \frac{dn}{da} \, da}. \qquad (5\text{--}38)$$

The bar is used to indicate the average.

The following concrete example may help. Suppose we have a distribution of population such that dn/da is $3000 - 300a$ per year from

$a = 0$ to $a = 10$ years and $dn/da = 0$ for $a \geq 10$ yr. This is plotted in Fig. 5–6.

We first calculate the average age from 0 to 10. Here $y = a$, so we have

$$\bar{a} = \frac{\displaystyle\int_0^{10} a(3000 - 300a)\,da}{\displaystyle\int_0^{10} (3000 - 300a)\,da} = \frac{\left. \dfrac{3000a^2}{2} - \dfrac{300a^3}{3} \right|_0^{10}}{\left. 3000a - \dfrac{300a^2}{2} \right|_0^{10}}$$

$$= \frac{50{,}000}{15{,}000} = 3\tfrac{1}{3} \text{ yr.}$$

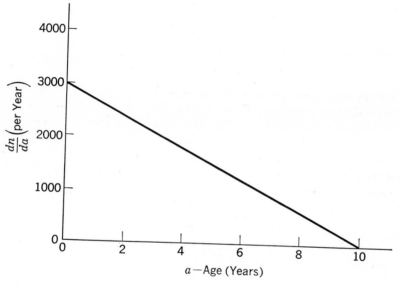

Fig. 5–6.   Distribution function (example).

Suppose that by some peculiarity of nature each creature having an age a weighed $4a^2$ lb. Let us now calculate the average weight. Here $y = w = 4a^2$, so

$$\bar{w} = \frac{\displaystyle\int_0^{10} 4a^2(3000 - 300a)\,da}{\displaystyle\int_0^{10} (3000 - 300a)\,da} = \frac{\left. 12{,}000\,\dfrac{a^3}{3} - 1200\,\dfrac{a^4}{4} \right|_0^{10}}{15{,}000}$$

$$= \frac{4{,}000{,}000 - 3{,}000{,}000}{15{,}000}$$

$$= 66\tfrac{2}{3} \text{ lb.}$$

5–9. The Maxwell Distributions. Let us now reconsider the box of molecules each with its vector showing its instantaneous velocity. It is, as has been indicated earlier, completely impossible to make a count of the 3×10^{22} molecules and their velocities. However, Maxwell, using the methods of statistical mechanics, was able to find a suitable expression for the distribution functions for the components of the velocity and for their speed. These distribution functions are of importance in dealing with the motion of molecules and also serve as a good example of the use of such distribution functions, so we quote them without proof.

First, we give the distribution function for a component of the velocity. For a box of gas with no bulk motion, no direction is preferred over any other, so the choice of the x-component is arbitrary and the formula applies equally well to any other component. We have then,

$$\frac{dn}{dv_x} = N \left(\frac{m}{2\pi kT}\right)^{\frac{1}{2}} \exp -\frac{mv_x^2}{2kT}. \qquad (5\text{–}39)$$

Here dn = the number of molecules per unit volume with an x-component of velocity in the range of v_x to $v_x + dv_x$, N = the total number of molecules per unit volume, m = molecular mass, k = Boltzmann's constant, T = the absolute temperature, and "exp" designates the exponential function of the quantity following it, often written e (the base of the natural logarithms) raised to the power $-mv_x^2/2kT$.

To show the essential features of this distribution function we might rewrite it as

$$\frac{dn}{dv_x} = A \exp -bv_x^2 \qquad (5\text{–}40)$$

where the constants A and b can be identified from the previous equation. The Maxwell distribution function of Eq. 5–39 is plotted in Fig. 5–7.

Several features of the curve can immediately be seen with the aid of Eq. 5–39.

1. The maximum value of $dn/dv_x = N(m/2\pi kT)^{\frac{1}{2}}$ and occurs when $v_x = 0$.
2. Many molecules have a v_x which is near zero. (This does *not* mean their velocity is zero, since they can have any value of v_y and v_z.)
3. dn/dv_x has fallen to a very low value (less than 0.13 times the value for $v_x = 0$) by the time v_x has become greater than $2(2kT/m)^{\frac{1}{2}}$.
4. The average v_x is zero. (Just as many traveling left as right.)
5. When the temperature is increased, the curve broadens and flattens out. More molecules have a larger value of v_x.

Another distribution function of interest is the one which gives the distribution of speeds. The analytic expression is

$$\frac{dn}{dv} = \frac{4N}{\sqrt{\pi}} \left(\frac{m}{2kT}\right)^{\frac{3}{2}} v^2 \exp -\frac{mv^2}{2kT}. \qquad (5\text{–}41)$$

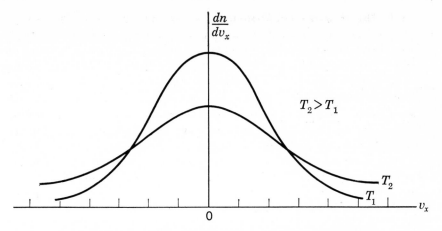

Fig. 5–7.   Maxwell's distribution of velocity components.

Here dn = the number of molecules per unit volume with *speeds* between v and $v + dv$.   Again, the essential features of this relation perhaps can be better shown by simplifying it.   Hence, we write

$$\frac{dn}{dv} = Bv^2 \exp -bv^2, \qquad (5\text{–}42)$$

and again the constants can be deduced from the previous expression. This expression is plotted in Fig. 5–8.

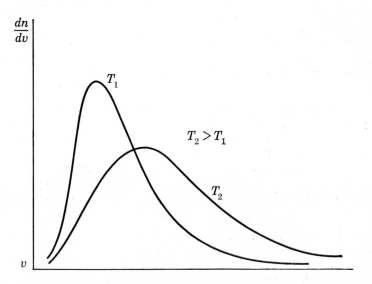

Fig. 5–8.   Maxwell's distribution of molecular speeds.

This form of representing the behavior of molecules also has several important features that should be pointed out.

1. dn/dv goes to zero as v goes to zero. This indicates that it is unlikely that any molecule will be even nearly at rest.
2. The curve has a maximum at $v_m \neq 0$. This is called *"the most probable speed."*
3. The probability of a molecule having a high speed $(v \gg v_m)$ is small.
4. When the temperature is increased, this curve also broadens and flattens and v_m increases.

These distribution functions have been directly verified by experiments using "molecular beams." Beams of neutral molecules are produced by allowing molecules to escape from a slit in the walls of an oven which is held in a very low pressure container. A series of slits limits the molecules to a beam, as shown in Fig. 5–9 where we schematically show

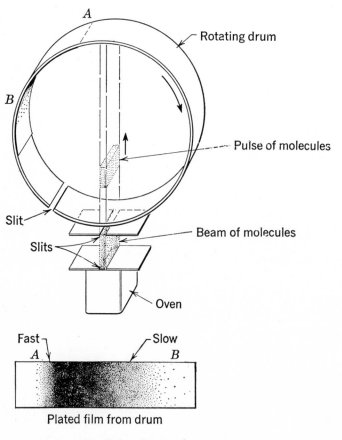

Fig. 5–9. Zartman's experiment.

the apparatus used by Zartman.[1]   Molecules evaporated from the heated
oven pass through the slits.   The slits effectively select only molecules
with x-components of velocity.   A pulse of molecules enters the drum each
time its slit passes through the beam from the oven.   This cloud travels
across the drum, the faster ones arriving first.   They are all plated out
across the cold plate AB according to their time of arrival.   The fraction
of the molecules which arrive at a particular position on AB is determined
by optically studying the blackening of the plate.   A few hours exposure
to the oven permits a study of the speed of the molecules.   Excellent
agreement with the Maxwell distribution is found.

Now let us make use of the technique of computing averages discussed
in Art. 5–8 to determine the average speed and the average of the square
of the speed.

First, we have

$$\bar{v} = \frac{\displaystyle\int_0^\infty v \frac{dn}{dv} \, dv}{\displaystyle\int_0^\infty \frac{dn}{dv} \, dv} = \frac{\displaystyle\int_0^\infty v \frac{4N}{\sqrt{\pi}} \left(\frac{m}{2kT}\right)^{3/2} v^2 e^{-\frac{mv^2}{2kT}} \, dv}{\displaystyle\int_0^\infty \frac{4N}{\sqrt{\pi}} \left(\frac{m}{2kT}\right)^{3/2} v^2 e^{-\frac{mv^2}{2kT}} \, dv}$$

$$= \frac{\displaystyle\int_0^\infty v^3 e^{-\frac{mv^2}{2kT}} \, dv}{\displaystyle\int_0^\infty v^2 e^{-\frac{mv^2}{2kT}} \, dv} = \sqrt{\frac{8kT}{\pi m}}. \tag{5–43}$$

For the average of the square of the speed, we have

$$\overline{v^2} = \frac{\displaystyle\int_0^\infty v^2 \frac{dn}{dv} \, dv}{\displaystyle\int_0^\infty \frac{dn}{dv} \, dv} = \frac{\displaystyle\int_0^\infty v^2 \frac{dn}{dv} \, dv}{N}$$

$$= \int_0^\infty \frac{4}{\sqrt{\pi}} \left(\frac{m}{2kT}\right)^{3/2} v^4 e^{-\frac{mv^2}{2kT}} \, dv = \frac{3kT}{m}. \tag{5–44}$$

The square root of the latter expression is called the *root-mean-square speed*,
and we will designate it here by v_{rms}.   It is identical with the quantity C
used in Eqs. 5–13, 5–14, and 5–15.   We can now relate $C = v_{\mathrm{rms}}$ to $\bar{v}$.   We
have, in fact,

$$v_{\mathrm{rms}} = \sqrt{\frac{3kT}{m}} = \sqrt{\frac{3\pi}{8}} \, \bar{v} = 1.085\bar{v}. \tag{5–45}$$

One can also find the value of v for which dn/dv is a maximum.   This
is done the usual way of setting the derivative of dn/dv with respect to v

[1] I. F. Zartman, *Phys. Rev.*, **37**, 383 (1931).

equal to zero. This leads to the result

$$v_m = \sqrt{\frac{2kT}{m}}.$$ (5–46)

We summarize all these results by the relation

$$v_m : \bar{v} : v_{\text{rms}} = 1 : 1.128 : 1.24.$$ (5–47)

EXAMPLE. In case the reader still is unsure of the averaging scheme, we add the following example. The reader should plot the distribution function and check his understanding of the following equations.

If, under unusual circumstances, the molecular speeds were given by the distribution function

$$\frac{dn}{dv} = kNv, \qquad (0 \le v \le v_m)$$

compute the rms speed of the molecules under this distribution if v_m is the maximum speed, so that $dn/dv = 0$ for $v > v_m$.

Solution: Using Eq. 5–38 gives the average of the squared speeds,

$$\overline{v^2} = \frac{\displaystyle\int_0^{v_m} v^2 \frac{dn}{dv}\, dv}{\displaystyle\int_0^{v_m} \frac{dn}{dv}\, dv} = \frac{\displaystyle\int_0^{n} v^2\, dn}{\displaystyle\int_0^{n} dn}$$

$$= \frac{\displaystyle\int_0^{v_m} v^2(kNv)\, dv}{\displaystyle\int_0^{v_m} kNv\, dv} = \frac{kN\displaystyle\int_0^{v_m} v^3\, dv}{kN\displaystyle\int_0^{v_m} v\, dv}$$

$$= \frac{\dfrac{v_m{}^4}{4}}{\dfrac{v_m{}^2}{2}} = \frac{v_m{}^2}{2}.$$

Then the rms value is $\sqrt{\overline{v^2}} = v_m/\sqrt{2}$.

5–10. The Maxwell-Boltzmann Energy Distribution. The Maxwell distributions of velocities and speeds are applicable only to the cases of systems of non-interacting (ideal gaslike) particles. They are related to a more general distribution of *energies* which has quite general application within the range of validity of classical laws. This distribution, called the Maxwell-Boltzmann distribution of energies, is derivable from classical mechanics using the methods of statistical mechanics.

For the case in which the total energy E is independent of position we can write the distribution with respect to energy in the forms

$$\frac{dn}{dE} = \frac{2N}{\sqrt{\pi}} \left(\frac{1}{kT}\right)^{3/2} E^{1/2} \exp -\frac{E}{kT}. \qquad (5\text{--}48)$$

This energy distribution function, which is based on classical mechanics and statistics, has proved to be useful for a broad range of phenomena. However, in the next article in this chapter, other distributions whose derivations employ concepts from the quantum theory will be examined.

5–11. Quantum Distributions. The derivation of Eq. 5–48 is based on the assumption that the particles do not interact (or at least interact only weakly), are identical, and yet are distinguishable from each other. Two other important distributions can be derived by assuming that the particles are *indistinguishable*. These turn out to be useful in describing aggregates of large numbers of particles which obey the laws of quantum mechanics. Which distribution is applicable depends on whether the particles have an intrinsic angular momentum of $(1/2)(h/2\pi)$, $(3/2)(h/2\pi)$, $(5/2)(h/2\pi)$ (or in general, half-integral spin) or have an intrinsic angular momentum of 0, $h/2\pi$, $2h/2\pi$ etc. (integral spin). In the case of particles with half-integral spin, *Pauli's exclusion principle* must be satisfied, i.e., two particles cannot be in the same energy state (see Chapter 11), and the resultant distribution law is called a *Fermi* or *Fermi-Dirac* distribution. In the case of particles with integral spin there is no such restriction and the resultant distribution is called a *Bose* or *Einstein-Bose* distribution. Electrons, protons, and neutrons obey *Fermi-Dirac* statistics; most nuclei and whole atoms obey *Einstein-Bose* statistics. In this discussion we shall restrict ourselves to the discussion of energy distributions since these are of prime interest in modern physics.

It is useful in discussing the quantum distributions to express them in a form that eliminates the detailed properties of the system. This simplification is brought about by the *occupation index*, defined as the *probability* of a particle being in a particular state of energy E. The occupation index used in discussing Fermi-Dirac distributions we call the *Fermi factor* $f_{\mathrm{FD}}(E)$. The Fermi factor is

$$f_{\mathrm{FD}}(E) = \frac{1}{\exp\left(\dfrac{E - E_f}{kT}\right) + 1} \qquad (5\text{--}49)$$

and the *Einstein-Bose factor* is

$$f_{\mathrm{EB}}(E) = \frac{1}{\exp\left(\dfrac{E - E_B}{kT}\right) - 1}, \qquad (5\text{--}50)$$

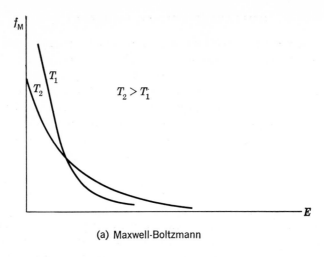

(a) Maxwell-Boltzmann

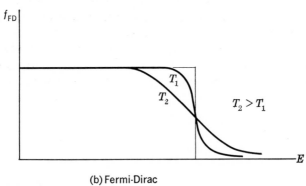

(b) Fermi-Dirac

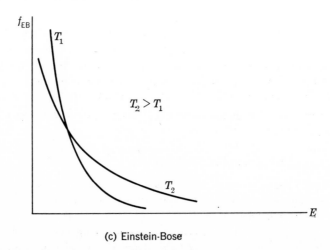

(c) Einstein-Bose

Fig. 5–10. Occupation index functions: (a) Maxwell-Boltzmann, (b) Fermi-Dirac, (c) Einstein-Bose.

where k is Boltzmann's constant, T is the absolute temperature, E_f is a constant called the *Fermi* energy of the system, and E_B is a quantity dependent on the system under discussion.

Since the Fermi and Einstein-Bose factors are occupation indices giving the probability of a particular energy state being occupied, the distribution functions can be obtained if the details of the possible energy levels are known. This knowledge of the energy levels is contained in a function $S(E)$ called the density of states. Thus the distribution function can be written as

$$\frac{dn}{dE} = S(E)f(E). \tag{5-51}$$

Three occupation index functions are plotted in Fig. 5–10 for comparison.

Although some of the problems at the end of this chapter will consider these functions, we shall not elaborate on or make use of them at this point. Let us only point out that the behavior of electrons in metals is governed principally by the Fermi-Dirac law. Many of the electrical characteristics of metals can be accounted for by the peculiarities of this distribution. The Einstein-Bose statistics are useful for describing photons (particles of light) and certain other unusual situations such as the anomalous behavior of liquid helium at very low temperatures (liquid helium II).

PROBLEMS

5–1. Use the standard value for the volume of a mole at standard conditions to compute R.

5–2. (a) Find the volume of a mole of a gas at a pressure of 10 cm of mercury and at 375°C. (b) What is the pressure for this problem in absolute units?

5–3. An ideal gas having a mass of 2.52 gm occupies 3600 cm^3 at a pressure of 64 cm of Hg and at a temperature of 20°C. (a) What volume would it occupy under standard conditions? (b) What is its molecular weight?

5–4. What mass of nitrogen gas would be present at 27°C in a vacuum flask 2 liters in volume if the pressure is 10 microns?

5–5. How many molecules would be present at 27°C in a vacuum system 3 liters in volume if the pressure is 10 microns?

5–6. Outer space contains approximately 1 proton per cm^3. Assuming that this is 1 hydrogen atom per cm^3, what pressure is found in outer space at a point where the temperature is 10°K?

5–7. A very good vacuum system will provide a pressure of 10^{-12} cm of mercury. If the temperature is 27°C, compute the density of oxygen gas at this pressure.

5–8. The density of oxygen at standard temperature and pressure is 0.00143 gm cm^{-3}. (a) Calculate its molecular weight. (Use the given data—do not get it elsewhere.) (b) Find the root-mean-square speed at this temperature.

5–9. Compare the root-mean-square speed of an oxygen molecule at 20°C with the speed of sound at that temperature.

5–10. Calculate the rms speed for carbon dioxide molecules at 200°C and for water vapor at the same temperature.

5–11. Calculate the average translational energy of a molecule at -263°C, at 0°C, at 500°C, at 1500°C, at 6000°C, and at 10^6°C. Express in electron volts as well as joules.

5–12. Find the average kinetic energy of translation of a molecule at 10°K, 300°K, 1000°K, 5000°K, and 1.5×10^{7}°K. Express in electron volts as well as in joules.

5–13. The law of Dulong and Petit says that the atomic heat of a solid element at constant volume should be $3R$. Derive this.

5–14. (a) What is the total internal kinetic energy of a mole of helium at 0°C? (b) What is the root-mean-square speed of a helium molecule at this temperature?

5–15. Using your estimates of the heights of the various bars in Fig. 5–3, calculate the average age of males for that distribution.

5–16. Use your best estimate of the height of each bar in Fig. 5–3 and from this calculate the average of the squares of the ages of males for that distribution.

5–17. Using the Maxwell distribution function for the x-component of velocity, find the value of v_x at which $dn/dv_x = 1/e$ of its maximum value.

5–18. Prove analytically that $\bar{v}_x = 0$ for a Maxwell distribution.

5–19. Comment on the fact that Eq. 5–23 at its conclusion does not contain the *mass* of the molecule.

5–20. Calculate the average of the squares of the x-components of velocities for the distribution of Eq. 5–39.

5–21. Calculate the average of the cubes of the speed for the distribution of the example on page 120.

5–22. Prove that Eq. 5–39 gives $\frac{1}{2}kT$ for the average kinetic energy $\frac{1}{2}mv_x^2$ associated with the motion in the x direction.

5–23. Let K be the kinetic energy of a molecule traveling with a speed v. Using this, convert Eq. 5–41 to a kinetic energy distribution function. What is the most probable energy?

5–24. Derive the expression for the most probable speed of a molecule (Eq. 5–46).

5–25. If under unusual circumstances the distribution function for molecular speeds were given by $dn/dv = kN/v^4$, $v_1 \leq v \leq \infty$, compute the rms speed of the molecules under this distribution, where k = a constant and N = the total number of molecules.

5–26. If under unusual circumstances the distribution function for molecular speeds were given by $dn/dv = kNv^2$, $0 \leq v \leq v_m$, compute the rms speed of the molecules under this distribution, where k = a constant and N = the total number of molecules.

5–27. Plot the Fermi factor $f_{FD}(E)$ as a function of E for a temperature $T = 0°\text{K}$. (Hint: to do this quickly consider first $E \ll E_f$, then $E \gg E_f$.) What physical significance does the value obtained for $f_{FD}(E)$ have in this plot? What is the physical significance of E_f in this plot?

5–28. Plot the Einstein-Bose factor $f_{EB}(E)$ as a function of E at a temperature $T = 1000°\text{K}$ if $E_B = 0$. (Hint: express kT in electron volts and plot E in electron volts.)

5–29. What is the form of the Fermi factor if $E \gg E_f$ and $T > 0°\text{K}$? Is this a familiar form?

5–30. Silver requires the use of Fermi-Dirac statistics for the analysis of its electron behavior and has a Fermi energy $E_f = 5.5$ ev. If $T = 300°\text{K}$ find the value of the Fermi factor for this material at energies 0.1 ev above and below the Fermi energy level. What physical conclusion can you draw from this result and Problem 5–29 concerning the electrons near the Fermi level?

5–31. Prove that for $T = 0°\text{K}$ the average kinetic energy of electrons in a metal is $\frac{3}{5}E_f$ if the density of states is $S(E) = AE^{1/2}$ where A is a constant. Discuss the physical significance of this result in terms of the average energy of the molecules in a gas and the exclusion principle.

5–32. Consider two pennies. (a) Apply classical statistics to find how many different ways they can be set out on the table, i.e., consider them as identical but distinguishable. (b) Apply the Einstein-Bose statistics to see how many ways they can now be set out, i.e., considering them as identical but not distinguishable. (c) Apply Fermi-Dirac statistics to the same problem.

SELECTED REFERENCES

The general physics texts reference for Chapters 1, 2, and 3.

BORN, M. *Atomic Physics.* Hafner Publishing Co., Inc., New York, 1957. Chap. 1.

KENNARD, E. H. *Kinetic Theory of Gases.* McGraw-Hill Book Co., Inc., New York, 1938. Chaps. 1, 2, and 10.

SEARS, F. W. *Thermodynamics, The Kinetic Theory of Gases, and Statistical Mechanics.* Addison-Wesley Publishing Co., Inc., Reading, Mass., 1955. 2d ed., chaps. 11 and 12.

6

Electrons

The idea that electric charge might exist only as integral multiples of a certain fundamental amount of charge probably goes back to the recognition of the atomic nature of matter. The historical details are of little concern to us, but it may be of some interest to note that the concept of a fundamental charge was clearly recognized by Faraday.

However, the whole picture of the nature and the role of different charged particles is still developing and by now we recognize that there are quite a few "fundamental particles" which have the same amount of electric charge. Some of these are negatively charged, others are positively charged. There are also fundamental particles which are neutral. We can thus apply a label to any fundamental particle of $-$, $+$, or 0 to indicate its charge. We are now finding that the various charged particles occur in both kinds. Among these we list:

$$+ \text{ and } - \text{ electrons}$$
$$+ \text{ and } - \text{ protons}$$
$$+ \text{ and } - \text{ } \pi\text{-mesons}$$
$$+ \text{ and } - \text{ } \mu\text{-mesons}$$

and an extensive set of other particles (see Chapter 20), all with the same size charge of either sign.

Of all the above, two particles are most familiar. They are the *negative electron* (or simply electron), and the *positive proton* (or simply proton).

Since the size of the fundamental unit of charge possessed by these particles is so basic to all modern physics, in this chapter we shall examine some of the ways in which the charge and related quantities were measured.

6–1. Faraday's Laws of Electrolysis. The investigations of Michael Faraday[1] into the problems of electrochemical processes led to the dis-

---

[1] These may be found in their original wording in *Experimental Researches in Electricity* by Michael Faraday (these are reprints from Philosophical Transactions of 1831–1838), Vol. I. See paragraphs 377, 505, 821, and 836. The reader should find that any of the writing of Faraday makes fascinating reading and is well worth looking up.

covery and statement of two laws. We summarize them here in the form generally called *Faraday's laws of electrolysis* as follows:

1. *In a given electrolytic reaction, the amount of material deposited (or released) is proportional to the electric charge which has passed through the electrolyte.*
2. *When several materials are deposited (or released) by electrolytic action by the same amount of charge, the amount of each material is proportional to W, its equivalent weight (the atomic weight A divided by v the valence).*

These laws when cast into the form of equations become:

$$\text{I.}\quad M_j = \mathcal{E}_j \int i\, dt = \mathcal{E}_j q, \tag{6-1}$$

and

$$\text{II.}\quad \frac{M_j}{M_k} = \frac{W_j}{W_k} = \frac{A_j/v_j}{A_k/v_k}, \tag{6-2}$$

where the M's are masses deposited, i is the instantaneous value of the current through the cell, and the total charge is q. The proportionality constant $\mathcal{E}_j$, the mass deposited by a unit charge, is often called the *electrochemical equivalent* of the material. Both of the laws may be combined and written formally as

$$M_j = \frac{1}{F} \frac{A_j}{v_j} q. \tag{6-3}$$

The proportionality constant F in the denominator of Eq. 6-3 is the charge required to deposit 1 gram-equivalent of any material. This universal constant is called the faraday and is known to considerable precision. An accepted value is[2]

$$F = 96,520.1 \pm 2.5 \text{ coulomb (gm-equiv)}^{-1}.$$

The results just discussed have a very great significance in the light of the atomic theory. One seems to be forced to the almost inescapable conclusion that each ion involved in an electrolytic transformation carries v_j (a small integer) elementary units of charge all of the same size. Let us call the size of this charge the electronic charge[3] and designate it by e. It then follows from Eq. 6-3

$$n\mathfrak{M} = \frac{1}{F}\left(\frac{N\mathfrak{M}}{v}\right) nve, \tag{6-4}$$

---

[2] J. W. M. Dumond and E. R. Cohen, *Rev. of Mod. Phys.*, **25**, 691 (1953).

[3] G. Johnstone Stoney is responsible for the term *electron*. The ideas discussed here were presented by him in an address before the British Association in 1874 [published in *Phil. Mag.*, Vol. XI (1881), 5th series, 384]. The term itself was used in a paper published in 1891, *Sci. Trans. of Royal Dublin Society*, Vol. IV (1891; 11th series), p. 563. Since the word electron has now come to refer to the particle, the modification used here is now common.

where there are n particles of mass $\mathfrak{M}$ deposited and where N is Avogadro's number (the number of molecules in a mole). The consequence of this is the simple, but important relation

$$F = Ne. \tag{6-5}$$

Eq. 6–5 is of great importance because of the precision to which F is known. It makes it possible to determine either N or e to the relative precision of the other. That is, if one can be determined to an accuracy given by a relative error of a, then the relative error of the other will also be a.

It is interesting to note that Faraday was aware of this basic idea, but of course could not measure either N or e.[4]

There has been an interesting alternation in the improvement of the accuracy with which N and e have been measured. We will pay particular attention to only two of these, and will summarize the experiments in Table 6–1.

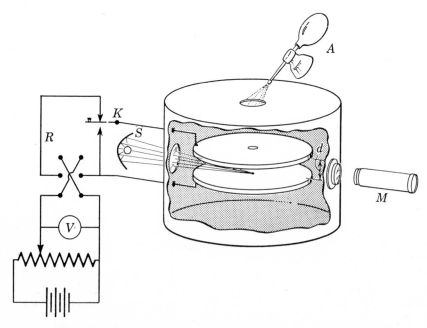

Fig. 6–1.   Schematic representation of Millikan's oil-drop apparatus.

6–2. The Millikan Oil-Drop Experiment. The determination of e by Millikan is of such basic importance that an article will be devoted to it. It was the first precise determination of e and, in addition, served as a direct verification that no fractional charges less than e exist.

[4] M. Faraday, *op. cit.*, Vol. I, Sec. 13, titled, "On the Absolute Quantity of Electricity Associated with the Particles or Atoms of Matter."

TABLE 6-1

Landmarks in the History of the Measurement of e

1874   Stoney[a] determined N from kinetic theory data

$N \sim 10^{25}$ molecules mole^{-1}

$e \sim 1 \times 10^{-20}$ coulomb

1897-1903   Townsend, Thomson, and Wilson[b] determined e by the condensation of water on ions

$e \sim 1.0 \times 10^{-19}$ coulomb

$N \sim 9.6 \times 10^{23}$ molecules mole^{-1}

1908   Perrin[c] determined N by a study of colloidal suspensions

$N = 6.8 \times 10^{23}$ molecules mole^{-1}

$e = 1.4 \times 10^{-19}$ coulomb

1910-1917   Millikan determined e with his famous Oil Drop Experiment[d]

$e = 1.59 \times 10^{-19}$ coulomb

$N = 6.06 \times 10^{23}$ molecules mole^{-1}

1931   Bearden[e] used x-ray diffraction to determine N

$N = (6.0221 \pm .0005) \times 10^{23}$ molecules mole^{-1}

$e = (1.6012 \pm .0002) \times 10^{-19}$ coulomb

N and e are interrelated with other quantities.   Using all relations, Dumond and Cohen[f] obtain

$e = (1.60207 \pm .00007) \times 10^{-19}$ coulomb

$e = (4.80288 \pm .00021) \times 10^{-10}$ statcoulomb

$N = (6.02472 \pm .00036) \times 10^{23}$ molecules mole^{-1}

---

[a] G. J. Stoney, *Phil. Mag.*, Vol. XI (1881), 5th series, p. 384.

[b] J. S. E. Townsend, *Proc. Camb. Phil. Soc.*, **9**, 244 (1897), J. J. Thomson, *Phil. Mag.*, **46**, 528 (1898), and H. A. Wilson, *Phil. Mag.*, **5**, 429 (1903).

[c] *Compt. rend.*, **147**, 475, 530, 594 (1908); **152**, 1380, 1569 (1917).   Jean Perrin, *Brownian Movement and Molecular Reality*, translated from *Annales de Chimie et Physique*, Sept., 1909.

[d] *Electrons (+ and −), Protons, Photons, Neutrons, and Cosmic Rays.*   Univ. of Chicago Press, Chicago, 1947.   The original papers are by R. A. Millikan in *Phil. Mag.*, **19**, 209 (1910); *Phys. Rev.*, **32**, 349 (1911); *Phys. Rev.*, **2**, 109 (1913); and *Phil. Mag.*, **34** (1917).

[e] J. A. Bearden, *Phys. Rev.*, **37**, 1210 (1931) and *Phys. Rev.*, **38**, 2089 (1931).

[f] J. W. M. Dumond and E. R. Cohen, *Rev. of Mod. Phys.*, **25**, 691 (1953).

The apparatus is indicated schematically in Fig. 6-1.   Two conducting plates, plane and parallel, have a uniform electric field in the central region between them.   The direction of the field can be reversed by changing the position of the commutator R, or the field can be made zero by pressing key K.   The field strength is

$$E = V/d, \qquad (6-6)$$

where V is the potential difference, which may be read from the volt-meter, and d is the separation between the plates. The plate separation may be measured with great precision with a cathetometer. The two plates are surrounded by a tank to exclude dust particles, to maintain a constant temperature, to avoid convection currents, and in general to isolate the system from unwanted external influences. However, oil droplets from an atomizer A can be let into the region above the plates and then fall into the region of the field between the plates by falling through a small hole in the top plate. The position of such a drop can be observed by a microscope M which has a calibrated scale in the eyepiece, if the drop is illuminated by a light S. Thus, one can measure the velocity of fall or rise of the drop.

The sizes of the drops are so small (radii ranging from 1.0×10^{-4} cm to 5.8×10^{-4} cm were used by Millikan) that they reach their terminal velocity almost immediately. This terminal velocity occurs when the size of the retarding force of viscous friction equals the applied force. The viscous force is given by Stokes' law of fall for spheres through a viscous medium, namely,

$$F_{\text{vis}} = 6\pi a \eta v = Cv, \tag{6-7}$$

where a is the radius of the drop, v is its velocity, and η is the coefficient of viscosity of the medium. This law is not accurate for spheres as small as those used. Millikan discovered that his observations fitted a law which is only a slight modification of Eq. 6–7. It is

$$F_{\text{vis}} = \frac{6\pi a \eta v}{\left(1 + \dfrac{b}{pa}\right)} = C'v, \tag{6-8}$$

where b is a constant that can be determined experimentally and p is the pressure of the gas. The correction term $b/(pa)$ is not large, so it is possible to use the value of a, determined from Eq. 6–7, in the denominator though not in the numerator. Thus, we see that any applied force can be measured by determining the velocity of the oil drop.

The applied force can be the weight mg of the drop, or it can include the force on a charge due to an electric field. Let the drop first fall freely except for the viscous force. Its weight mg determines its terminal velocity v_0 by the relation

$$F_{\text{vis}} = 6\pi a \eta v_0 = \tfrac{4}{3}\pi a^3 \rho g,$$

so

$$a^2 = \frac{9}{2} \frac{\eta v_0}{\rho g}, \tag{6-9}$$

where ρ is the density of the oil. The constant C of Eq. 6–7 can thus be determined from

$$C = 6\pi a\eta = 6\pi\eta^{3/2} \left(\frac{9}{2}\frac{1}{\rho g}\right)^{1/2} v_0^{1/2}, \tag{6-10}$$

or the more exact value C' for Eq. 6–8 is

$$C' = \frac{6\pi a\eta}{\left(1 + \dfrac{b}{pa}\right)} = 6\pi\eta^{3/2} \left(\frac{9}{2}\frac{1}{\rho g}\right)^{1/2} \frac{v_0^{1/2}}{\left(1 + \dfrac{b}{pa}\right)^{3/2}}. \tag{6-11}$$

The a multiplying p in the correction term can be the approximate value obtained from Eq. 6–9.

If the drop bears a charge q_n which we presume to be an integral number n of elementary charges e and the electric field is turned on in the proper direction, there will be a resultant upward force on the drop

$$Eq_n - mg = C'v_n \tag{6-12}$$

where v_n is the upward terminal velocity. Thus we have

$$Eq_n = C'v_n + mg = C'v_n + C'v_0. \tag{6-13}$$

In this equation we have chosen the signs in such a way that the v's are to be given their absolute values.

The measurement of upward velocity can be made for the same drop for a number of different values of the charge q_n. The charge is changed by exposing the drop to radiation such as x-rays or radiation from a radioactive substance. Sometimes q_n will change spontaneously. Thus, one can prepare a table of the values for

$$q_n = \frac{C'}{E}(v_n + v_0) = ne \tag{6-14}$$

and seek the greatest common factor e. Usually the n's are large enough that the experimental errors may introduce an ambiguity in each n.

One therefore looks at the differences or changes in charges, noting that

$$\Delta q = (n' - n)e = e\Delta n = \frac{C'}{E}(v_{n'} - v_n). \tag{6-15}$$

In most cases Δn will be a small integer such as 1, 2, 3, etc., so there is little chance for ambiguity. Thus, a reasonably good preliminary estimate of e can be determined from the experiment and this value used to decide the n's in Eq. 6–14. Finally, one can obtain an average for e from all the data.

Many such determinations should be made using different drops. In Millikan's experiment these ran into the hundreds. Not once was a charge less than e observed. In addition, experimental verification of the correction to Stokes' law was obtained from the variation of the results with both a and p. This gave the value for b which was introduced in Eq. 6–8.

The final value obtained by Millikan[5] was

$$e = (1.591 \pm 0.002) \times 10^{-19} \text{ coulomb.}$$

$$[e = (4.774 \pm 0.005) \times 10^{-10} \text{ statcoulomb.}]$$

This value is the result of using the value of 1.825×10^{-5} newton-sec m^{-2} [1.825×10^{-4} poises] for the viscosity of air. Now it will be seen that later determinations of N have indicated that the value for e obtained by Millikan was about 0.6% low. It was suggested by Shiba[6] that this was caused by the use of a low value of η. Subsequently, seven different determinations of η were made which have an average of 1.8324×10^{-5} newton-sec m^{-2}. If this value for η is put into Millikan's data, one obtains the value

$$e = 1.604 \times 10^{-19} \text{ coulomb,} \qquad [e = 4.811 \times 10^{-10} \text{ statcoulomb,}]$$

which is now slightly high as compared to the value indicated by the best determination of N.

A recent determination, using a modification of the oil-drop experiment, was performed by Laby and Hopper.[7] In this experiment the electric field was horizontal so that the drops fell along slanting trajectories. These were photographed by flashes of light $\frac{1}{25}$ sec apart. Thus a permanent record for each drop was made. The vertical and horizontal components of velocity make it possible to compute $q = ne$. Laby and Hopper chose the value 1.830×10^{-5} newton-sec m^{-2} for η and obtained

$$e = (1.6018 \pm 0.0004) \times 10^{-19} \text{ coulomb.}$$

$$[e = (4.8020 \pm 0.0013) \times 10^{-10} \text{ statcoulomb.}]$$

6–3. The X-Ray Determination of Avogadro's Number. The other approach to the determination of the electronic charge, of course, is through the determination of Avogadro's number N. Early attempts at this are listed in Table 6–1, but the most accurate determination depends upon the use of x-rays to measure the interatomic spacing in crystals such as the experiments of Bearden.[8] Crystals consist of collections of atoms in a very regular arrangement of a three-dimensional lattice structure. Some of these are slightly complicated, but in all cases one can find certain sets of parallel planes within the crystal, each containing frequently placed atoms.

[5] R. A. Millikan, *Phil. Mag.*, **34**, 1 (1917).
[6] K. Shiba, *Sci. Papers, Inst. Phys. and Chem. Research (Tokyo)*, **19**, 97 (1932).
[7] T. H. Laby and V. D. Hopper, *Nature*, **143**, 157 (1939); **145**, 1932 (1940).
[8] J. A. Bearden, *Phys. Rev.*, **37**, 1210 (1931) and *Phys. Rev.*, **38**, 2089 (1931).

The simplest type of crystal is one in which the atoms are corners of cubes, as illustrated in Fig. 6–2. Besides the planes parallel to the coordinate planes, there are many others some of which have been indicated. For each set of planes there is a separation distance d and the various d's are determined by a, the size of the side of an elementary cube.

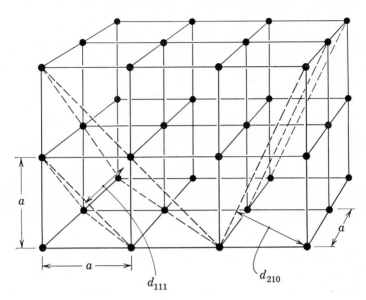

Fig. 6–2. A cubic crystal. Besides the coordinate planes two other planes are shown, a (111) plane, and a (210) plane. Their separation distances are also shown.

For such a simple cubic crystal there is one atom per elementary cube of volume a^3, since each atom at the corners is shared with 8 elementary cubes. In one gram atom, there are A (the atomic weight) grams of material. The volume occupied by the gram atom is A/ρ, where ρ is the density of the crystal. There will be Avogadro's number of atoms (and therefore little elementary cubes) in this volume, so

$$N = \frac{A}{\rho a^3}. \tag{6–16}$$

For more complicated crystals this expression must be modified, but this does not change the ability to determine N if one can determine the lengths of the sides of the elementary crystal cell. This measurement can be made using the diffraction of x-rays.

In Chapter 13 we shall discuss the nature and properties of x-rays in some detail. For the moment, it is necessary only to know that it is possible to produce electromagnetic radiation of very short wavelength (of the order of 10^{-10} m), and that it is possible to obtain x-rays that are monochromatic (that is, they have only one wavelength present). If a beam of such x-rays falls on a ruled grating, the beam will be diffracted much as visible light waves are diffracted by ruled gratings and it is possible to determine the wavelength with great precision. The kind of grating used is one in which many lines or grooves are ruled into a polished surface. A section of such a ruled surface is shown in Fig. 6–3. The gratings used

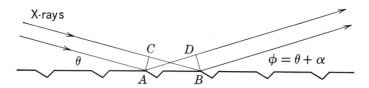

Fig. 6–3.   Diffraction of x-rays by a ruled grating.

by Bearden[9] had 50 lines/mm, 143 lines/mm, 287 lines/mm, and 600 lines/mm ruled on glass. X-rays will be deflected and diffracted only if they strike the grating at grazing incidence. The action of the grating is almost identical with its action for light, so that x-rays will be observed only if

$$\overline{CB} - \overline{AD} = s \cos \theta - s \cos \phi = n\lambda. \tag{6-17}$$

This is the formula showing that x-rays scattered by adjacent rulings reach the detector by paths differing by an integral number of wavelengths, and hence are in phase. The grating line separation is s. The incident beam makes an angle θ with the plane of the grating. The diffracted beam makes an angle ϕ with the grating. If we set $\phi = \theta + \alpha$ (see Fig. 6–3),

$$n\lambda = 2s \sin \frac{\alpha}{2} \sin \left(\frac{2\theta + \alpha}{2} \right). \tag{6-18}$$

Since s, θ, and α can be determined with high precision, the wavelength can also be precisely determined. Bearden obtained a wavelength of 1.54172 Å (1 Å $= 10^{-10}$ m) for the x-ray line he was using. His arrangement is shown in Fig. 6–4.

By making two exposures, one with the photographic plate at P_1, and the other with the plate at P_2, it is possible to measure θ and α with a precision which yields the value of λ indicated above.

The next thing we need to know is the fact that x-rays will also be diffracted by the lattice arrangement of atoms in a crystal. We can think

[9] J. A. Bearden, op. cit.

of each layer of atoms as a reflecting plane; so x-rays will be reflected with
a reflection angle equal to the angle of incidence. Since x-rays penetrate

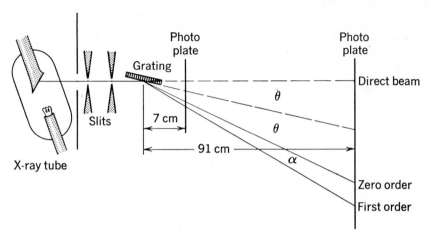

Fig. 6–4.   Schematic of Bearden's measurement of x-ray wavelengths.

the crystal and are reflected by each successive layer, then the path length
for each successive layer is $2d \sin \theta$ greater than for each preceding layer

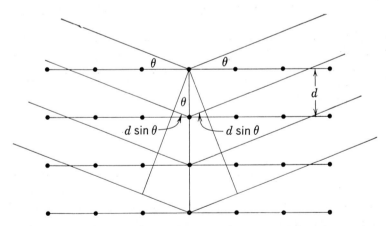

Fig. 6–5.   Bragg's law.   Constructive interference occurs when each scattering path introduces a path difference of an integral number of wavelengths.

where d is the layer separation (see Fig. 6–5). If this path difference is
just an integral number of wavelengths, the waves from each layer all
add with constructive interference, giving a comparatively intense x-ray

beam.   Thus, this happens for

$$n\lambda = 2d \sin \theta, \qquad (6\text{–}19)$$

where n is an integer.   This is called the *Bragg law*.

Since the grating experiments described previously have given λ with precision, it is now possible to determine d with equivalent precision. Fig. 6–6 shows a sketch of the experiment.

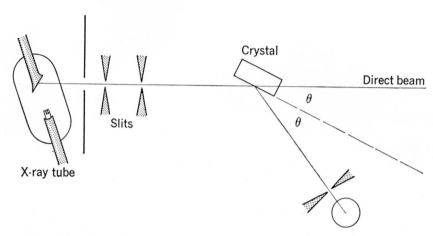

Fig. 6–6.   Crystal spectrometer to determine crystal plane separations.

From the values of the various d's one can compute a and the use of Eq. 6–16 then gives N.

The results obtained gave $N = (6.0221 \pm 0.0005) \times 10^{23}$ molecules mole^{-1} and hence

$$e = (1.6026 \pm 0.0002) \times 10^{-19} \text{ coulomb.}$$

$$[e = (4.8036 \pm 0.0005) \times 10^{-10} \text{ statcoulomb.}]$$

These results were higher than Millikan's by more than the probable error.   Bearden didn't think Millikan was wrong at first and felt that the theory of diffraction was in error.   However, others began questioning Millikan's results and it was found, as was mentioned earlier, that the value for the viscosity of air, given at that time, was incorrect.   A revision of the value of viscosity of air brings Millikan's results into agreement with Bearden's.

The work of Dumond and Cohen uses many other sources of information to fix the values at those quoted in Table 6–1.

6–4. The Specific Charge of the Electron.   During the last part of the nineteenth century, it was discovered that an electric discharge could occur between electrodes in a gas at low pressure. When the pressure is reduced sufficiently (to about 10^{-3} mm of mercury), the discharge acts as if it consists of some sort of rays from the cathode. These were called *cathode rays*. Sir J. J. Thomson showed that these rays behaved like streams of negatively charged particles. They transfer both momentum and energy to any object they strike and, as we shall see, are deflected by electric and magnetic fields in accordance with the laws of electrodynamics and particle mechanics. These particles are now called *electrons*. Heated filaments of metal or metallic oxides may also emit electrons and this convenient method is used to produce electrons in x-ray tubes and vacuum tubes. We expect these particles to have a charge just equal to e. There are no results indicating that the charge is $2e$ or greater.

A whole series of experiments have been performed to measure the mass of these particles. Actually, it is impossible to measure the mass directly. Instead, the quantity that is measured is e/m, the charge per unit mass of the cathode rays. The ratio is called the *specific charge* of the cathode rays.

There are many other places in which similarly charged particles are found. For instance, light drives negatively charged particles out of photosensitive surfaces; negatively charged particles are the parts of atoms which radiate light; negatively charged rays come from certain radioactive materials; and negatively charged particles are the carriers of electric currents in metals. Experiments show that those particles all have the same value of specific charge. Whenever negatively charged particles are found that have this same specific charge, it is natural to assume that they are all alike and are the same fundamental particle which we call electrons.

Let us now look at two experiments for measuring the specific charge of electrons. Very similar experiments can be used to measure the specific charge of other ions.

6–5. The Measurement of Specific Charge by Magnetic Deflection. Electrons evaporated from a hot filament will be attracted by a conducting cylinder, "the plate," around the filament if the plate is at a positive potential relative to the filament. The kinetic energy of the electrons when they reach the plate is

$$\tfrac{1}{2}mv^2 = eV, \tag{6–20}$$

where V is the potential difference between the filament and plate. Now if there is a slit in the wall of the cylindrical anode, a thin "ribbon" of electrons will emerge from it, all having nearly the same energy, eV. The arrangement of electrodes just described is often known as an *electron gun*.

If these electrons now move through a magnetic field of flux density (magnetic induction) **B**, they will experience a force due to the field. In

Art. 3–8, we derived the expression for this force.   It is Eq. 3–29

$$\mathbf{F} = q(\mathbf{v} \times \mathbf{B}). \qquad \left[\mathbf{F} = \frac{q}{c} (\mathbf{v} \times \mathbf{B}). \right] \tag{6–21}$$

Since these particles are electrons, the charge q of each is e and the magnitude of the force becomes

$$F = evB \sin \theta, \qquad \left[F = \frac{evB \sin \theta}{c}, \right] \tag{6–22}$$

where θ is the angle between $\mathbf{v}$ and $\mathbf{B}$.   If $\mathbf{v}$ is perpendicular to $\mathbf{B}$, $\sin \theta = 1$ and we find that the force is

$$F = Bev. \qquad \left[F = \frac{Bev}{c}. \right] \tag{6–23}$$

This force is a centripetal force which makes the path of the electron a circle lying in a plane perpendicular to $\mathbf{B}$.   The usual laws of mechanics give

$$F = Bev = \frac{mv^2}{R}, \qquad \left[F = \frac{Bev}{c} = \frac{mv^2}{R}, \right] \tag{6–24}$$

where R is the radius of the path.   This can be rewritten as

$$mv = BeR. \qquad \left[mv = \frac{BeR}{c}. \right] \tag{6–25}$$

Note that this shows that the product of the radius of the circular path of a charged particle in a magnetic field and the magnetic flux density is a measure of the momentum of the particle.

We can solve Eq. 6–25 for v and substitute it into Eq. 6–20.   The result is

$$\frac{1}{2} m \left(\frac{BeR}{m} \right)^2 = eV, \qquad \left[\frac{1}{2} m \left(\frac{BeR}{mc} \right)^2 = eV, \right] \tag{6–26}$$

or

$$\frac{e}{m} = \frac{2V}{B^2 R^2}. \qquad \left[\frac{e}{m} = \frac{2V c^2}{B^2 R^2}. \right] \tag{6–27}$$

The experiment can be performed in a number of ways.   One way involves a direct application of the above.   The electron gun is placed in an evacuated tube in which there is some mercury vapor.   The purpose of the mercury vapor is to make the ribbon-like beam of electrons visible. As the electrons pass through the mercury vapor, a small fraction hit mercury atoms and give them enough energy to enable them to emit light. The experimental arrangement is indicated in Fig. 6–7.   If two circular coils of wire of radius a each with n turns are placed parallel to each other

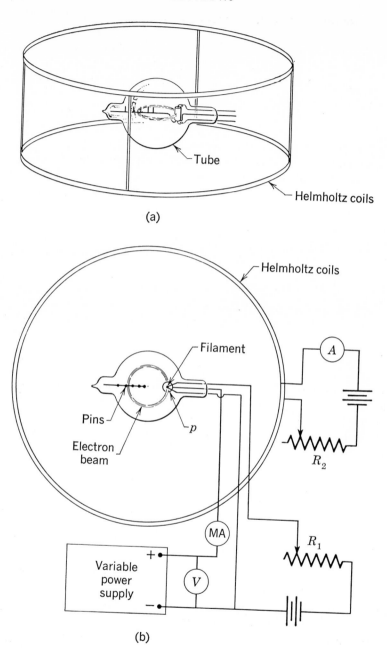

Tube

Helmholtz coils

(a)

Helmholtz coils

Filament

A

Pins

R_2

p

Electron
beam

MA

R_1

Variable
power
supply

V

+

−

(b)

Fig. 6–7.   Apparatus for measuring the specific charge of electrons.   (a) Side
view.   (b) View from above showing circuits.

and are spaced so that their planes are separated by a distance a the magnetic field produced by a current i flowing through the coils is nearly uniform over a rather large volume and the value of the flux density is

$$B = \frac{8ni\mu_0}{a\sqrt{125}}. \qquad \left[B = \frac{32\pi ni}{a\sqrt{125}\,c}. \right] \qquad (6\text{–}28)$$

Such coils, called Helmholtz coils, are used to produce the magnetic field in the region of the tube. Electrons emitted from the heated filament f are accelerated by the electric field between f and the plate p. Some pass through the slit and are bent into a circular path (as shown by the dotted line) by the magnetic field produced by the Helmholtz coils around the tube. In a darkened room, it is possible to see the beam of electrons easily because of the light emitted by the mercury atoms. The radius R of the path may be determined by certain marker pins within the tube. Their distance from the filament was carefully determined when the tube was built. The rheostat R_1 controls the current through the filament. This, in turn, determines the magnitude of the electron beam current which is shown by the milliammeter MA. The accelerating potential through which the electrons fall can be measured by the voltmeter V and is adjusted by controls in the power supply. The magnetic field can be controlled by rheostat R_2 and its value measured by ammeter A. Thus all the quantities, V, B, and R, needed for Eq. 6–27 are determined.

At present, the accepted value for the specific charge of the electron is

$$e/m = (1.75888 \pm 0.00005) \times 10^{11} \text{ coulomb kg}^{-1}.$$

$$[e/m = (5.27299 \pm 0.00016) \times 10^{17} \text{ statcoulomb gm}^{-1}.]$$

From this we can infer that

$$m = (9.1085 \pm 0.0006) \times 10^{-31} \text{ kg}.$$

6–6. Other Determinations of the Specific Charge of the Electron.

The method described above is only one of many used to determine e/m. The fact that single lines in the spectra of atoms split into multiple lines, when the source is placed in a strong magnetic field, is called the Zeeman effect (see Chapter 12). The amount of wavelength shift depends upon the specific charge of the radiating object as well as upon the magnetic field strength. It is very significant that the specific charge measured by the Zeeman effect is identical with that measured for cathode rays. The inference that both cathode rays and the radiating part of atoms are the same, namely, electrons, is certainly clear.

There is an inertial effect when current starts to flow or ceases flowing in wires. This effect should not be confused with self induction. We shall not describe the experiment, but it too yields the same value for the specific charge of the current carriers in the wire as that for electrons.

Deflection experiments similar to the one described in the preceding article have been performed with the particles ejected by light falling on a metal surface. The same value of e/m is found, so we know they are also electrons—*photoelectrons*. Similar deflection experiments show that beta rays from radioactive materials are electrons.

The very first of the deflection experiments was one done by Sir J. J. Thomson.[10] Cathode rays, produced by a high voltage discharge through a moderate vacuum, then pass through a region in which either an electric or magnetic field alone can be produced, or both fields can function at the same time as shown in Fig. 6–8. In this figure, the electric field **E** is

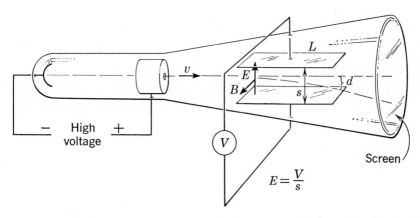

Fig. 6–8. Thomson's apparatus for determining the specific charge of cathode rays.

vertical and the magnetic field **B** is horizontal either into the page, or out of it. With one of the fields on, a deflection is produced. If it is the magnetic field, the path is circular with a radius R. Thus,

$$R = \frac{mv}{Be} \cdot \qquad \left[R = \frac{mvc}{Be} \cdot\right] \qquad (6\text{–}29)$$

If the electric field is on alone, the path is parabolic and the "drop" d is

$$d = \frac{1}{2}\frac{eE}{m}\frac{L^2}{v^2} \cdot \qquad (6\text{–}30)$$

In any case, this can be related to the observed deflection at the screen S.

[10] J. J. Thomson, *Phil. Trans. Roy. Soc. London*, **170**, 135, 641 (1879).

It is possible to make the effect of the electric field just balance that of the magnetic field. This will happen when

$$B'ev = eE'. \qquad \left[\frac{B'ev}{c} = eE'. \right] \qquad (6\text{--}31)$$

Thus, we know that the velocity is given by

$$v = \frac{E'}{B'}, \qquad \left[v = \frac{E'}{B'} c, \right] \qquad (6\text{--}32)$$

where E' and B' are a pair of values that give no deflection. Eq. 6–32 furnishes a value for v which can be inserted into either Eq. 6–29 or Eq. 6–30 to obtain the value of e/m.

Still another form of measuring specific charge is based upon the fact that Eq. 6–20 shows that

$$\frac{e}{m} = \frac{v^2}{2V}, \qquad (6\text{--}33)$$

so any scheme for measuring the velocity of a particle that has fallen through a potential difference of V will make it possible to determine the specific charge of the particle. This can be done by measuring the time required for the particle to travel a known distance. It is possible to do this, since the time for reasonable distances is in the range of the period of radio frequencies. One such scheme was used by Dunnington.[11] In brief, he accelerated electrons with an alternating field, picked a fixed momentum by using a magnetic field and slits to define a circle of radius R, and observed the time it took to go around the circle by making it just one period of the alternating field.

A similar scheme has been used to determine the specific charge of atomic sized particles. The determination of the specific charge of particles can be thought of as a scheme for determining their mass. This is done with atomic and molecular size particles (usually with a positive charge) in various *mass spectrographs*. Some of these have great precision and have furnished useful information for understanding nuclei of atoms, others provide a useful analytic instrument.

PROBLEMS

6–1. The electrochemical equivalent for silver is 0.001118 gm coulomb^{-1}. Compute the faraday from this.

6–2. Compute the electrochemical equivalent for divalent copper.

[11] F. G. Dunnington, *Phys. Rev.*, **43**, 404 (1933).

6–3. Write out the derivation that leads to the expression $F = Ne$.

6–4. Compute the force on an electron which is found between parallel metallic plates 0.30 cm apart if the potential difference between the plates is 500 v. How long would it take for the electron, starting at rest, to pass from one plate to the other in a vacuum? What would this time be for a singly charged oil drop of mass 3.8×10^{-12} gm also in a vacuum? What would the time be for this drop moving in standard air if its radius is 10^{-4} cm?

6–5. An oil drop falls at a constant speed of 0.018 cm sec^{-1} in air which has a viscosity of 1.82×10^{-4} dyne-sec cm^{-2}. It has 18 electrons on it. What potential difference is required to balance it? What potential difference will make it rise at the same rate it falls? The density of the oil is 0.90 gm cm^{-3} and the plate separation is 0.45 cm.

6–6. If the oil drop of Problem 6–5 loses 2 electrons, what velocity of rise will it have in the same field?

6–7. An oil drop bearing 26 electronic charges is just balanced by a potential difference of 260 v applied to two plates 4.6 mm apart. What is the radius of the drop for oil with a specific gravity of 0.90?

6–8. An oil drop is just supported by the electric field between two plates 8.2 mm apart when the potential difference is 500 v. Suddenly, it requires 520 v to balance it. Still later it requires 540 v to balance. What is a plausible estimate of the weight of the drop?

6–9. Calculate the terminal velocity of a freely falling golf ball, radius $r = 2.13$ cm, mass 45 gm.

6–10. An oil drop falls at a constant speed of 0.093 mm sec^{-1} and rises at a speed of 0.031 mm sec^{-1}. How many electronic charges does it bear if the upward motion is produced by a field due to 280 v between plates 3.2 mm apart?

6–11. A Millikan oil-drop experiment has a drop that falls 2 mm in 12 sec. When a potential difference of 420 v is applied across the plates 6 mm apart it rises 2 mm in 18 sec. What is its approximate charge in electronic units?

6–12. The density of NaCl is 2.16 gm cm^{-3}. Find the distance between Na and Cl atoms in the crystal. The crystal is simple cubic.

6–13. X-rays which have a wavelength of 1.62×10^{-8} cm will be diffracted by a set of crystal planes 2.78×10^{-8} cm apart. What will be the angle through which these x-rays will be diffracted?

6–14. If the crystal in Problem 6–13 had a simple cubic structure with single atoms of one element at the corners of the elementary cube 2.78×10^{-8} cm on a side, and if the density of the crystal is 6.78 gm cm^{-3}, what should be the atomic weight of the material?

6–15. A simple cubic crystal of atomic weight 26 has a density of 8 gm cm^{-3}. What is the size of the edge of an elementary lattice cube? Calculate the d for planes parallel to the x-axis and intersecting the y- and z-axes at 45°. What Bragg diffraction angle is appropriate to x-rays with a wavelength of 0.36 Å?

6–16. X-rays with a wavelength of 1.38 Å are diffracted through 22° ($\theta = 11°$) by a set of atomic planes in a crystal. What is the separation of the planes? If this is the size of the elementary cube and if the density of the material is 6.3 gm cm^{-3}, what is the atomic weight of the material?

6–17. An electron moves at 10^7 m sec^{-1} initially along the x-axis. A magnetic field of 10^{-3} webers m^{-2} is in the direction of the positive y-axis. (a) What is the direction of the magnetic force on the electron; (b) what is the magnitude of this force; (c) what is the radius of the path traced by the electron?

6–18. A particle with one electronic charge moves in a circular path with a radius of 1.7 m in a field of 0.60 weber m^{-2}. What is the momentum of the particle?

6–19. What is the momentum of an electron that moves in a circular path with a radius of 8 cm when the magnetic flux density is 1.20×10^{-3} weber m^{-2}?

6–20. Electrons are bent into a circle with a radius of 8 cm by a magnetic field of 6 gauss. (a) What is their momentum? (b) What potential difference did they fall through to obtain this momentum? (c) What is their energy?

6–21. A beam of electrons emerges from an electron gun after it has fallen through a potential difference of 150 v. What value of B is required to bend the beam into a circular path which has a radius of 0.15 m?

6–22. Electrons fall through a potential difference of 120 v and then are bent by a magnetic field in a circular path of 4 cm radius. What is the magnetic field strength (flux density)?

6–23. Electrons have fallen through a potential difference of 70 v. What is the radius of the circular path they move in if they pass into a region where the magnetic flux density is 5×10^{-4} weber m^{-2}?

6–24. Electric field lines are produced between two parallel plates 8 mm apart by a potential difference of 450 v. A uniform magnetic field of 640 gauss is placed with its lines at right angles to the electric field but across the same region. Compute the speed of the ions which travel undeflected in a straight line at right angles to the fields.

6–25. Electrons with a velocity of 2.6×10^6 m sec^{-1} pass between plates 2 cm apart with a potential difference of 1200 v. What magnetic flux density will keep the path of the electron straight? Protons with the same velocity are then passed through the region. What must be changed to keep their paths straight?

6–26. Design a velocity selector to pass particles having a speed of 1.8×10^6 m sec^{-1}.

6–27. A common mass spectrograph for determining the mass of ions employs semicircular deflection of the particles. If an accelerating voltage of 1000 v and a magnetic field of 0.1 webers m^{-2} is available, what mass of singly charged ions will be measured in an apparatus of radius 7 cm? How can the apparatus be modified to measure a succession of higher masses?

SELECTED REFERENCES

BRAGG, SIR W. H., and W. L. BRAGG. *X-Rays and Crystal Structure.* Harcourt Brace & Co., New York, 1924. Chap. 8.

COMPTON, A. H., and S. K. ALLISON. *X-Rays in Theory and Experiment.* D. Van Nostrand Co., Inc., Princeton, N. J., 1935. Chap. 1.

GLASSTONE, S. *Source Book on Atomic Energy.* D. Van Nostrand Co., Inc., Princeton, N. J., 1958. 2d ed., chap. 20.

HARNWELL, G. P., and J. J. LIVINGOOD. *Experimental Atomic Physics.* McGraw-Hill Book Co., Inc., New York, 1933. Chap. 3 contains an especially good account of the details of a Millikan oil-drop experiment.

MILLIKAN, R. A. *Electrons (+ and −), Protons, Photons, Mesotrons, and Cosmic Rays.* Univ. of Chicago Press, Chicago, 1947. Chap. 3.

SHAMOS, M. H., ed. *Great Experiments in Physics.* Holt, Rinehart & Winston, Inc., New York, 1959. Chap. 16.

STRANATHAN, J. D. *The "Particles" of Modern Physics.* Blakiston Div., McGraw-Hill Book Co., Inc., New York, 1942. Chap. 2. Besides containing excellent descriptions of the experiments, it has a very good set of references to original papers.

THOMSON, J. J. "The Electron." In *A Source Book in Physics,* W. F. Magie, ed. McGraw-Hill Book Co., Inc., New York, 1935. P. 583.

7

The Scattering of Alpha Particles

The identification of the electron by Sir J. J. Thomson showed that its mass must be very much less than that of the lightest atom. The specific charge of the electron was found to be 1.76×10^{11} coulomb kg^{-1} while it requires only 9.58×10^7 coulomb to release 1 kg of hydrogen by electrolysis. Since we believe that one electronic charge is associated with each hydrogen atom released electrolytically, it appears that the mass of the electron is only about 1/1840 of that of a hydrogen atom. The Zeeman effect, mentioned in Chapter 6, shows that electrons are one of the constituents of atoms, and since atoms are neutral there must be another constituent with a positive electrical charge. The mass ratio above suggests that the positive portion of any atom must make up most of the mass of the atom. The fact that atoms are generally electrically neutral shows that the charge of the positive constituent must be integral multiples of the electronic charge. The commonest and simplest unit of positively charged matter is this positive part of a hydrogen atom. It is called a *proton*. Now if the proton and the electron are the main constituents of all atoms, then it is clearly important to know how these two particles are put together to form neutral atoms. Two principal models were suggested.

7–1. Models of the Atom. The first model, proposed by Thomson early in the twentieth century, pictured an atom as spherical in shape with the positive charge distributed uniformly throughout the sphere and with the electrons embedded among these positive charges. Vibrations of the electrons about their positions of equilibrium would account for the radiation of light by the atoms.

The other model was proposed by Lord Rutherford[1] to explain the results of experiments performed in Rutherford's laboratory by Geiger.[2] He proposed that the positive charge of an atom, and most of its mass,

---

[1] E. Rutherford, *Phil. Mag.*, **21**, 669 (1911).
[2] H. Geiger, *Proc. Roy. Soc.* (London), series A, **83**, 492 (1910).

was concentrated in a small dense core, called the *nucleus* of the atom. The electrons were pictured as surrounding this nucleus in some sort of cloud, probably moving in regular orbits about the nucleus.

7–2. The Experiment on the Scattering of Alpha Particles by Atoms.

The experiment by Geiger and a series of experiments carried out later at the Cavendish Laboratory furnished the evidence that settled which of the two models was the more satisfactory. Energetic charged particles

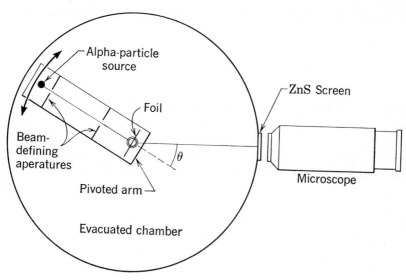

Fig. 7–1. An alpha particle scattering experiment. The alpha particles are deflected by the foil through various angles. Those falling on the ZnS screen have been deflected by angle θ.

(in this case alpha particles from a radioactive source) were directed at a thin metallic foil target and particles (here, the same alpha particles) were observed to be scattered in all directions. The distribution of particles with scattering angle was experimentally measured.

The arrangement of equipment is shown in Fig. 7–1. The alpha particles were collimated into a narrow beam and then directed at a gold foil approximately 5×10^{-6} m thick. After passing through the foil, the alpha particles then struck a zinc sulphide screen which was viewed through a low-power microscope. Each time an alpha particle hit the zinc sulphide, a scintillation or flash of light could be observed in the microscope. Thus, the number of alpha particles striking a unit area of the screen per unit time could be determined. The apparatus was constructed so that scattering angles, ranging from a few degrees to 180°, could be studied.

If the *Thomson* model of the atom is correct, one atom could never deflect a high speed alpha particle through any angle but a very small one. The positive and negative charge is so uniformly spread out over the atom in this model that at no time will the alpha particle experience forces due to more than a few electronic charges and these will be separated from the alpha particle by an appreciable fraction of the radius of the atom (of the order of 10^{-10} m). The alpha particle is traveling so fast (about 1.5×10^7 m sec^{-1}) that these forces can act for only a very short time. However, since the foil used is several hundred atomic layers thick, it might be possible for a succession of deflections, all in the same direction, to produce a larger resultant deflection. Unfortunately, the probability of such a cumulative deflection is extremely small. The experiment showed an appreciable number deflected through almost 180°, very many more cases of large deflections than could possibly be explained by the Thomson model.

These results showed that another model was required, and that this model must provide an atom that will apply a much greater impulse to the alpha particle. The Rutherford model does this because it permits the alpha particle to come very much closer to a large positive charge in the scattering atom.

7-3. The Theory for the Experiment. In the Rutherford model the situation is quite different from that of the Thomson model. It is still true that there is practically no deflection as the alpha particle passes through most of the atom. A significant deflection occurs only if the alpha comes close to a nucleus. In the thin films used in the experiment there is little chance that an alpha particle will be deflected by more than one atom. Therefore, it is possible to consider the deflection process entirely as a collision between the alpha particle and a single nucleus. The very light electrons do not disturb the trajectory appreciably. The force between the two particles is due entirely to electrostatic forces. The alpha particle has a charge of $+2e$ and the nucleus is assumed to have a charge of $+Ze$, where Z is an integer; so the force between the particles when they are a distance r apart is

$$ F = \frac{2Ze^2}{4\pi\epsilon_0 r^2} \cdot \qquad \left[F = \frac{2Ze^2}{r^2} \cdot \right] \qquad (7\text{-}1) $$

Although the forces are too small to produce a significant deflection except when the alpha particle is close to the nucleus, such electrostatic forces are often called *long-range forces* since their effect falls off no more rapidly than the inverse of the square of the separation (except for the "screening" or cancellation of the force by the presence of the electrons at distances of the order of 10^{-9} m). There are other kinds of forces that arise between nuclei, but their effects do not extend much beyond 10^{-15} m and the forces fall off exponentially, or even faster. It is possible to perform an alpha scattering experiment in which such *short-range forces* play a role, but these become practically the equivalent of a nuclear reaction such as we will discuss in Chapter 17. Of course, these facts were not established before the experiment was performed, and it was the results of the experiment that made it clear that only electrostatic forces were acting in the experiment.

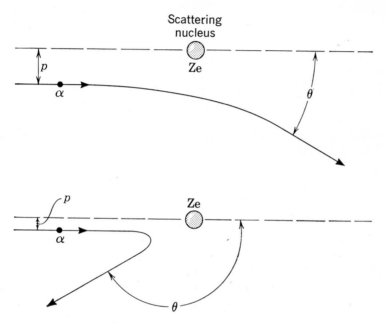

Fig. 7–2.   A demonstration of the effect of impact parameter p on scattering angle.

The collision is a glancing, perfectly elastic, collision and the angle of deflection, or scattering angle θ, is dependent upon the impact parameter p, the distance by which the alpha particle would miss the atom if no repulsion were acting. In Fig. 7–2 two examples in which p is different are shown and the point is made that as p gets smaller, θ gets larger until for the head-on case, $p = 0$, the deflection is 180°. The experiments were performed with such massive scattering nuclei that the center of mass is close to the scattering nucleus and the velocity of the center of mass is small. It is possible, therefore, to take the results based on a fixed scattering nucleus and use it directly without transforming to the CMS and back to the LS (in other words, the LS and CMS are equivalent if the center of mass is taken to be fixed at the scattering nucleus).

Whenever an object is attracted to or repelled by a force center and the force varies as the inverse square of the distance from the center, the trajectory of the object will be one of the conic sections (a circle, ellipse, parabola, or hyperbola) with the force center at one of the foci. Which type of curve it is depends upon the total energy of the system. As is

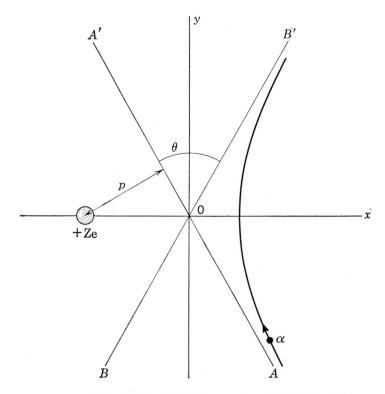

Fig. 7–3.   The hyperbolic path of a scattered alpha particle.

customary, the potential energy is considered to be zero when the object is located at a very great distance from the force center. Then, if the total energy is positive, the trajectory is a hyperbola; if the energy is zero, the trajectory is a parabola; and if the energy is negative, the trajectory is an ellipse or circle. Actually the energy is determined by the force and in the case of a repulsive force, such as the one being considered, the energy is always positive, so the path followed is a hyperbola. This is shown in Fig. 7–3 with the nucleus fixed at rest at the focus f of the hyperbola. The impact parameter p is also shown. The asymptote AA' is the original direction of the particle. The asymptote BB' is the path after scattering, when the alpha particle is approaching the detector. Thus, θ is the deflection or scattering angle.

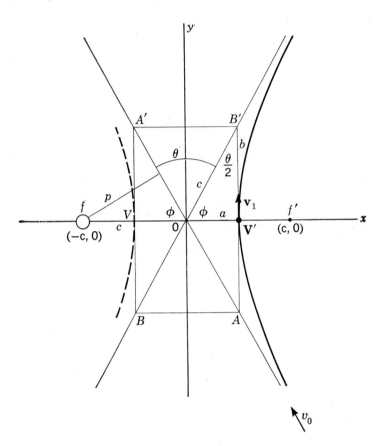

Fig. 7–4. The geometry of the hyperbolic trajectory.

Just three parameters determine the deflection angle. They are the impact parameter p, the initial kinetic energy of the alpha particle K_0, and the product of the charges on the alpha particle and the scattering center $2Ze^2$. The relation among all these quantities follows from the laws of mechanics, and can be arrived at by using the law of conservation of energy, the law of conservation of angular momentum, and certain geometrical properties of hyperbolas. In Fig. 7–4, some of the geometry of the hyperbolic path is indicated. The usual location of the origin and axes lead to its representation by the equation

$$\frac{x^2}{a^2} - \frac{y^2}{b^2} = 1. \tag{7-2}$$

Here a is half the width of the rectangle placed between the two vertices V and V' for which the asymptotes are the diagonals, and b is half the height. The distance $2a$ is sometimes called the transverse or "major" axis and $2b$ is the "minor" axis. There is no requirement that $a > b$, but

$$b^2 = c^2 - a^2 \tag{7-3}$$

where c is half the length of a diagonal of the rectangle and is also half the distance between the two foci f and f'. The eccentricity ϵ is defined as

$$\epsilon = \frac{c}{a} = \frac{\sqrt{a^2 + b^2}}{a} > 1. \tag{7-4}$$

The distance of closest approach s for the alpha particle is

$$\overline{fV'} = s = c + a. \tag{7-5}$$

In addition Fig. 7–4 shows that

$$p = c \sin \phi = b. \tag{7-6}$$

The next step is to find the relation between s and the other parameters. This is done by using the two conservation laws appropriate. The kinetic energy of the alpha particle, as it is emitted by the radioactive atom, is K_0. The mass of the alpha particle is m and its initial velocity is v_0. The velocity at the vertex V' is v_1. The law of conservation of energy thus gives,

$$K_0 = \frac{1}{2} m v_0{}^2 = \frac{1}{2} m v_1{}^2 + \frac{2Ze^2}{4\pi\epsilon_0 s}. \qquad \left[K_0 = \frac{1}{2} m v_1{}^2 + \frac{2Ze^2}{s}. \right] \tag{7-7}$$

It is convenient to set

$$K_0 = \frac{2Ze^2}{4\pi\epsilon_0 D}, \qquad \left[K_0 = \frac{2Ze^2}{D}, \right] \tag{7-8}$$

so D, a quantity known as the *collision diameter*, is the distance of closest approach for a head-on collision, or the distance for which the potential energy is just equal to the original kinetic energy. By dividing Eq. 7–7 by K_0, one obtains

$$1 = \frac{v_1{}^2}{v_0{}^2} + \frac{D}{s}. \tag{7-9}$$

The angular momentum of the alpha particle about the scattering nucleus initially is $m v_0 p$, and as the alpha particle passes through V', the point of closest approach, it is mv_1s. There is only the mutual repulsion between the particles and, consequently, no torques acting on the system; so the angular momentum must be conserved. Thus,

$$mv_0p = mv_1s \tag{7–10}$$

or

$$\frac{v_1}{v_0} = \frac{p}{s}. \tag{7–11}$$

If Eq. 7–11 is combined with Eq. 7–9, the result is

$$\frac{v_1{}^2}{v_0{}^2} = 1 - \frac{D}{s} = \frac{p^2}{s^2}. \tag{7–12}$$

Since $s = a + c$ and $p = b$, Eq. 7–12 can be written

$$(c + a)^2 - (c + a)D = b^2, \tag{7–13}$$

and since $b^2 = c^2 - a^2$, this becomes $2a(c + a) = (c + a)D$ or

$$D = 2a. \tag{7–14}$$

Fig. 7–4 shows that

$$\cot \frac{\theta}{2} = \frac{b}{a}. \tag{7–15}$$

Combining this with Eq. 7–14 and Eq. 7–6 gives the result

$$p = \frac{1}{2} D \cot \frac{\theta}{2}. \tag{7–16}$$

This, then, is the relation connecting θ with p and D (that is, with p, K_0, and $2Ze^2$). The next step is to see how this affects the experiment.

Eq. 7–16 tells us what will happen to a *particular* alpha particle and atom. However, we cannot check this relation directly in the laboratory for we cannot choose a particular p and measure the corresponding θ. In the actual experiment, a *beam* of alpha particles collides with a large number of atoms in the foil and all that can be measured is the *fraction* of the alphas scattered through a certain angle. The impact parameter p for each alpha that is deflected by a nucleus may have any value ranging from zero to so large that the deflection is negligible. If p' represents a particular value for p, Eq. 7–16 shows that for any $p < p'$ the alpha particle will be deflected more than the θ' appropriate to p'. Thus, as is shown in Fig. 7–5, one can think of a circle of radius p' drawn around any atom, and this circle has the property that any alpha headed for any point within the circle will be deflected by θ' or more. This circle has an area $\sigma = \pi p'^2$ which is called the *cross-section for scattering through more than* θ'. One can also increase p' by the differential dp' and any alpha headed for the ring of area $d\sigma = 2\pi p'\,dp'$ will be deflected through an angle lying between θ' and $\theta' - d\theta'$, where $d\theta'$ is calculated by differentiating Eq. 7–16. The area $d\sigma$ is the *differential cross-section for scattering into the angle between θ' and $\theta' - d\theta'$*. It should be clear from Fig. 7–5 that alpha particles so scattered may go in any direction within the two cones formed by θ' and $\theta' - d\theta'$.

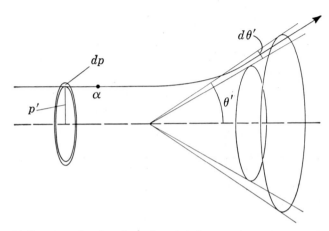

Fig. 7–5. A circle of radius p' and deflection through an angle θ'.

If n is the number of alpha particles incident during the experiment and N is the number of target nuclei per square meter, then these n alpha particles will "see" N targets per square meter as they approach (perhaps as shown in Fig. 7–6 where circular strips of radius p and area $2\pi p\,dp$ have been drawn around each target nucleus). If any of the incoming alpha particles has an impact parameter lying between p and $p + dp$ for one of these nuclei, it will be scattered through an angle lying between θ and $\theta - d\theta$. The fraction dn/n scattered into this region will be determined by the fraction of the total area covered by the circles. This fraction is the *probability of scattering*. It is

$$\frac{dn}{n} = N(2\pi p)\,dp = N\,d\sigma. \qquad (7\text{–}17)$$

From Eq. 7–16

$$dp = -\frac{D}{4}\csc^2\frac{\theta}{2}\,d\theta, \qquad (7\text{–}18)$$

so that the fraction scattered (or the probability of scattering) is

$$\frac{dn}{n} = N\,d\sigma = -\pi N\frac{D^2}{4}\cot\frac{\theta}{2}\csc^2\frac{\theta}{2}\,d\theta. \qquad (7\text{–}19)$$

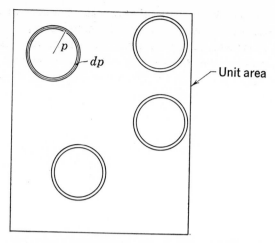

Fig. 7–6. The cross-section for scattering into $d\theta$ at θ. An alpha must be aimed at one of the strips of width dp and radius p. If one considers this a unit area, N is 4 targets per unit area.

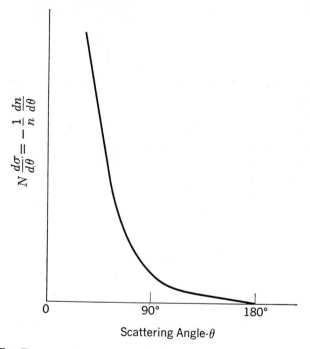

Scattering Angle-θ

Fig. 7–7. The variation of scattering cross-section with angle: the plot of
$$N\frac{d\sigma}{d\theta} = -\frac{1}{n}\frac{dn}{d\theta}.$$

The negative sign simply indicates that p must decrease as θ increases. We will not be concerned about this and will only use the absolute value. The plot of $(-1/n)\, dn/d\theta = N d\sigma/d\theta$ is shown in Fig. 7–7.

Only a small fraction of the dn alphas that are scattered fall on the scintillating screen of the detector. This fraction can be computed with the help of Fig. 7–8. One can picture a band of area, perpendicular to

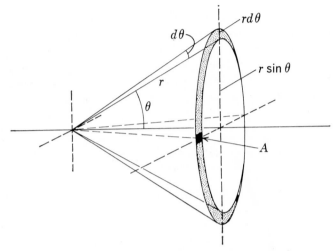

Fig. 7–8. A portion A of the band at θ is intersected by the zinc sulphide screen whose area is A.

the radius extending out from the foil, covering that portion of the solid angle lying between the cones determined by θ and $\theta + d\theta$. Its area is $2\pi r \sin\theta\, rd\theta$, where r is the distance from the foil to the detector; so if the area of the detector is A, the fraction of those scattered reaching the detector is

$$f = \frac{A}{2\pi r^2 \sin\theta\, d\theta}. \tag{7-20}$$

Combining Eq. 7–19 and Eq. 7–20, we get the fraction of all the alpha particles that reach the detector. This is

$$\frac{\Delta n}{n} = f \frac{dn}{n} = \frac{\pi N D^2 A}{8\pi r^2 \sin\theta} \cot\frac{\theta}{2} \csc^2\frac{\theta}{2},$$

which, after applying trigonometric identities for cot and csc, becomes

$$\frac{\Delta n}{n} = \frac{N D^2 A}{16 r^2 \sin^4 \dfrac{\theta}{2}}. \tag{7-21}$$

It is interesting to multiply Eq. 7–21 by $4\pi r^2/NA$. This gives a quantity having the dimensions of an area which we will call the Rutherford scattering cross-section, $\sigma(\theta)$. We have

$$\sigma(\theta) = \frac{4\pi r^2 \, \Delta n}{NAn} = \frac{\pi D^2}{4 \sin^4 \dfrac{\theta}{2}} = \frac{\pi D^2}{4} \csc^4 \frac{\theta}{2}. \tag{7–22}$$

This "fourth power of the cosecant" law can be interpreted in the following manner which is sometimes useful for describing scattering processes and scattering cross-sections: If $\sigma(\theta)$ is multiplied by the number of nuclei per unit area of scattering foil, the fraction of incident alpha particles that would have been scattered isotropically (equally in all directions) to give a uniform intensity of alpha particles equal to that *actually* observed at θ, is obtained. However, the equation easiest to relate to the experimental results is Eq. 7–21. Since

$$4\pi\epsilon_0 D = \frac{2Ze^2}{\frac{1}{2}mv_0^2} = \frac{2Ze^2}{K_0},$$

where K_0 = the kinetic energy of the particle, we see that Eq. 7–21 shows us that the number of alpha particles reaching the screen depends on (1) the reciprocal of the fourth power of the sine of half the scattering angle, (2) N the number of target particles per unit area, (3) Z^2, and (4) the inverse of the square of the initial kinetic energy.

This concludes the theoretical analysis of the problem. Let us briefly examine the experimental confirmation.

7–4. Experimental Results and Their Interpretation. Geiger and Marsden's experimental work confirmed the theoretical analysis of Rutherford. They found for both silver and gold foils that the factor $(\Delta n)(\sin^4 \theta/2)$ was a constant for scattering angles θ between $5°$ and $150°$, thus verifying the angular dependence.

Secondly, they varied the speed and hence the kinetic energy of the alpha particles by using different radioactive sources. They found that the product $(\Delta n)K_0^2$ was a constant as predicted by the Rutherford theory.

Thirdly, they investigated the dependence of the scattering on the thickness of the foil. In Eq. 7–21, N is the number of target nuclei per unit area and we can write this as $N_v t = N$, where N_v is the number of nuclei per unit volume, and t is the thickness of the foil. Geiger and Marsden used foils of various thickness and materials (Au, Ag, Cu, Al) and found that Δn depended directly on t as predicted.

The quantity Δn also has a dependence on the nuclear charge Z. In 1920, Chadwick[3] measured the nuclear charge of Cu, Ag, and Pt, using an

[3] E. J. Chadwick, *Phil. Mag.*, **40**, 734 (1920).

improved scattering technique.   He obtained

$$\text{Cu:} \quad Z = 29.3$$
$$\text{Ag:} \quad Z = 46.3$$
$$\text{Pt:} \quad Z = 77.4$$

agreeing well with the now known values for these elements.   This additional and separate experiment served to strengthen confidence in the nuclear atom.

EXAMPLE 1.   In planning a laboratory experiment on the scattering of alpha particles it is decided to use gold in a film with a thickness of 5×10^{-7} m.   The source is to be polonium which emits alpha particles with an energy of 5.30 Mev.   After the beam has been made narrow by the collimating apertures, 1.4×10^5 alpha particles emerge per sec.   The scattered alpha particles fall on a scintillation screen with an area of 10^{-4} m² at a distance of 4×10^{-2} m from the foil.   This is viewed by a photomultiplier whose output is counted by an electronic counter.   What counting rate can be expected when θ is 45° and when it is 135°?

Solution:

$$K_0 = 5.3 \times 1.6 \times 10^{-13} = 8.5 \times 10^{-13} \text{ j.}$$

$$D = \frac{2Ze^2}{4\pi\epsilon_0 K_0} = \frac{2 \times 79 \times 1.6^2 \times 10^{-38}}{1.11 \times 10^{-10} \times 8.5 \times 10^{-13}}$$

$$= 4.3 \times 10^{-14} \text{ m.}$$

Since the density of gold is 19.3 gm cm⁻³, there are

$$\frac{19.3}{197} \times 6.03 \times 10^{23} = 5.91 \times 10^{22} \text{ atoms cm}^{-3},$$

or

$$N = 5.91 \times 10^{28} \times 5 \times 10^{-7} = 2.96 \times 10^{22} \text{ atoms m}^{-2}.$$

$$A = 10^{-4} \text{ m}^2 \text{ and } r = 4 \times 10^{-2} \text{ m.}$$

$$\text{Sin}^4 \, 22.5° = 0.0213 \text{ and sin}^4 \, 67.5° = 0.730.$$

Thus the fractions for 45° and 135°, respectively, are

$$\left(\frac{\Delta n}{n}\right)_{45°} = \frac{2.96 \times 10^{22} \times 18.4 \times 10^{-28} \times 10^{-4}}{16 \times 16 \times 10^{-4} \times 0.0213}$$

$$= \frac{2.14 \times 10^{-5}}{0.0213} = 1.00 \times 10^{-3},$$

and

$$\left(\frac{\Delta n}{n}\right)_{135°} = \frac{2.14 \times 10^{-5}}{0.730} = 2.94 \times 10^{-5}.$$

Therefore we expect the following counting rates:

For 45°: $1.00 \times 10^{-3} \times 1.4 \times 10^5 = 140$ counts sec^{-1}.

For 135°: $2.94 \times 10^{-5} \times 1.4 \times 10^5 = 8.8$ counts sec^{-1}.

PROBLEMS

7-1. Compute the force on an alpha particle and the acceleration of the alpha when its distance from a gold nucleus is 10^{-14} m, 10^{-13} m, and 10^{-12} m.

7-2. Compute the force on an alpha particle and the acceleration of the alpha when its distance from a bismuth nucleus is 10^{-14} m, 10^{-13} m, and 10^{-12} m.

7-3. Suppose an alpha particle collides with a free electron. Assume that although the impact parameter is not zero it is very close to zero so that to a first approximation the electron and alpha approach each other and then recede in the CMS each along its original path. Assume initially that in the LS the velocity of the electron was zero and that of the alpha was that appropriate to 4 Mev. Find the final velocity of the electron and alpha and how much energy was transferred to the electron.

7-4. Suppose an alpha particle collides with a free electron in such a way that in the CMS the electron and alpha retreat on lines 90° from the original direction of motion of the alpha. If in the LS the electron was at rest and the alpha had an energy of 3 Mev, what was the final velocity of the electron and the alpha and how much energy was transferred from alpha to electron in the LS?

7-5. A gold nucleus ($Z = 79$) has a radius of 7×10^{-15} m. How much energy would an incident (a) proton (b) alpha particle need to strike a gold nucleus? Neglect the radii of the incident particles.

7-6. A silver nucleus ($Z = 47$) has a radius of 5.8×10^{-15} m. What would the initial speed of a proton have to be in order to collide head-on with a silver nucleus?

7-7. An 8.0 Mev alpha particle approaches a gold nucleus ($Z = 79$) head-on. At what distance from the gold nucleus is the kinetic energy reduced to one-half its original value?

7-8. This problem is intended to review the analytic geometry of hyperboli. (a) Choose rectangular coordinates and two points at $(-c,0)$ and $(+c,0)$. Show that the locus of a point that moves such that the difference of its un-directed distances from the two fixed points is constant is given by Eq. 7-2. Denote the constant by $\pm 2a$. (b) What is a rectangular hyperbola? What is the equation of its asymptotes? What is the angle between them? (c) For the following hyperbola, find the coordinates of the vertices and the foci, the ec-centricity, and the equation of the asymptotes: $x^2 - 4y^2 = 16$.

7-9. In a collision between an alpha and a nucleus $p = 1.5 \times 10^{-14}$ m and $\theta = 90°$. Write the expression for the hyperbolic path of the alpha (Eq. 7-2) with proper numerical values for a and b.

7-10. Draw to a scale of 1 in. = 10^{-14} m the path of an alpha such that $p = 2.2 \times 10^{-14}$ m and $a = 2b$. What is θ for this case?

7-11. Calculate the original kinetic energy for the alpha of Problem 7-9 if $Z = 47$ (silver).

7-12. Calculate the original kinetic energy for the alpha of Problem 7-10 if $Z = 82$ (lead).

7-13. Calculate the angular momentum for the alpha of Problems 7-9 and 7-11.

7-14. Calculate the angular momentum for the alpha of Problems 7-10 and 7-12.

7-15. The distance of closest approach of an alpha particle to a gold nucleus is 2×10^{-13} m. If its impact parameter is 1×10^{-13} m, through what angle will it be scattered?

7-16. Compute the angular momentum of an alpha particle about a nucleus if it follows a hyperbolic path and has a velocity of 1.41×10^6 m sec^{-1} at the distance of closest approach, 1.0×10^{-14} m. Is the angular momentum a constant? Why?

7-17. A 7.68 Mev alpha particle approaches a gold nucleus with an impact parameter of 2.5×10^{-13} m. What is the distance of closest approach?

7-18. A 5 Mev alpha particle moves along the right-hand branch of a hyperbola of the same shape as found in Problem 7-8c. A nucleus of a gold atom ($Z = 79$) is located at the left-hand focus. (a) Find the kinetic energy of the alpha particle when it is at the distance of closest approach. (b) Compute its initial angular momentum. (c) Compute the impact parameter.

7-19. Alpha particles from radium (4.78 Mev) bombard a gold foil 10^{-5} cm in thickness. The density of gold is 19.3 gm cm^{-3}. Calculate the fraction of the incident alphas scattered through angles greater than 90°.

7-20. The density of gold is 19.32 gm cm^{-3} and its atomic weight is 197. (a) Calculate the number of nuclei per unit area for a foil with a thickness of 10^{-3} mm. (b) What fraction of incident alphas with an energy of 4.5 Mev will be deflected greater than 60°?

7-21. The density of silver is 10.5 gm cm^{-3} and its atomic weight is 109.7. (a) Calculate the number of nuclei per unit area for a foil with a thickness of 2×10^{-3} mm. (b) What fraction of incident alphas with an energy of 5.1 Mev will be deflected greater than 135°?

7-22. Consider a sphere with a radius of 0.04 m. Picture parallels of latitude on the surface of this sphere. Compute the area enclosed by the parallels of 0° and 1°; of 45° and 46°; of 89° and 90°.

7-23. If a body scatters particles isotropically what will be the ratio of the numbers of particles captured by two detectors each capturing all particles scattered through a 2° range when detector A is centered for scattering through 30° and detector B is centered for scattering through 75°?

7–24. A lead foil, density 10.7 gm cm^{-3} is 1×10^{-7} m thick. (a) Compute the number of nuclei per unit area in the foil surface. (b) What total area do these nuclei cover on the foil surface? (c) If the radius of the lead nucleus is 6×10^{-15} m, what is the probability of a single incoming particle of zero electrical charge being deflected by this foil?

7–25. Tantalum is a metal useful in neutron experiments. Tantalum, $A = 181$, density $= 16.6$ gm cm^{-3}, is used as a foil 0.01 cm thick. (a) Compute the number of nuclei per unit area in the foil. (b) What is the probability of a single neutral particle being deflected when incident normally on the foil? (c) If 10^{12} particles cm^{-2} sec^{-1} are incident normally on the foil, what is the probable rate of collision? Use a cross-section of 22×10^{-24} cm^2.

7–26. If the alpha particle cross-section for scattering through more than an angle θ_D is $\sigma_D = \pi D^2$, where D is defined as in Eq. 7–8, what is θ_D?

7–27. Find the cross-section (in terms of D) for a deflection of 90° or greater.

7–28. Alpha particles with an energy of 6.3 Mev are used in a Rutherford scattering experiment on iron. A detector with an area of 5×10^{-6} m^2 is located at a distance of 3×10^{-2} m from the iron foil which has a thickness of 3×10^{-7} m. If n alphas are striking the foil each second, how many will reach the detector per second if the deflection angle is 40°?

7–29. A film of tin with a thickness of 4×10^{-7} m is bombarded by S alphas per second with an energy of 4.1 Mev. How many will reach the screen of a detector at a deflection angle of 55° if the area of the screen is 10^{-5} m^2 and it is located 0.05 m from the scattering foil?

7–30. Alpha particles from thorium ($Z = 90$, $A = 230$) have an energy of 4.0 Mev. A thorium alpha source producing a beam of 10,000 particles per sec strikes a gold foil (density 19.3 gm cm^{-3}) 1.5×10^{-7} m thick. An alpha particle counter with a screen 1 cm^2 in area is located 10 cm from the foil at an angle of 60° in an evacuated chamber. How many counts are made per minute?

7–31. Alpha particles from polonium (5.30 Mev) are scattered by gold nuclei. Calculate the distance of closest possible approach.

7–32. Using the distance found in Problem 7–31 as the radius of the gold nucleus, find an approximate value for the density of nuclear matter.

SELECTED REFERENCES

BECKER, R. A. *Introduction to Theoretical Mechanics*. McGraw-Hill Book Co., Inc., New York, 1954. Chap. 10.

KAPLAN, I. *Nuclear Physics*. Addison-Wesley Publishing Co., Inc., Reading, Mass., 1954. Chap. 3.

RUTHERFORD, E., J. CHADWICK, and C. D. ELLIS. *Radiation from Radioactive Substances*. Cambridge Univ. Press, London, 1930. Chap. 8.

SEMAT, H. *Introduction to Atomic and Nuclear Physics*. Holt, Rinehart & Winston, Inc., New York, 1954. Chap. 3.

SYMON, K. R. *Mechanics*. Addison-Wesley Publishing Co., Inc., Reading, Mass., 1960. 2d ed., chaps. 3 and 4.

8

Quantum Effects

Around the beginning of the twentieth century physicists began to realize that the classical laws of physics, based upon the mechanics of Newton, and the electrodynamics of Ampère, Faraday, and Maxwell, were not adequate to describe many experimentally observed phenomena. Numerous examples occurred within a brief period of time. We list some of these phenomena here. In all cases, the behavior observed differed significantly from the behavior to be expected on the basis of classical theory.

1. Optical spectra emitted by atomic sources of light
2. Infrared and visible radiation from heated solids
3. The photoelectric effect
4. The Zeeman effect (the splitting of spectral lines by applying a strong magnetic field to a light source)
5. The specific heats of solids
6. X-ray spectra
7. The Compton effect (the change of wavelength of radiation when scattered by free electrons)
8. Diffraction of electrons

Concentrated study of all of these facts during the twentieth century and the growing understanding of them, has led to the development of *quantum mechanics*. This set of laws *replaces* the "classical" laws when dealing with particles of atomic size, and reduces to the classical laws when considering macroscopic systems. The theory is well developed, but it would be presumptuous to suggest that it is the "last word" for the history of most theories has included its replacement by a better one.

Many of the results of quantum mechanics can be described at the level of this book and even many of the techniques used in the theory can be illustrated. We shall devote Chapter 11 and parts of other chapters to this theory. In this present chapter, we shall investigate some of the eight effects listed above. We shall see how classical laws were modified, how the quantum theory developed, and how these ideas led to the quantum mechanics. We begin with item 2 because historically this was the first problem treated by the quantum theory.

8–1. Thermal Radiation—Experimental. If a body is warmer than its surroundings, it will lose heat faster than it will gain heat. Conduction and convection may play an important role in this process, but we neglect them and concentrate on radiation. Radiation is the transmission of energy by an electromagnetic wave. Electromagnetic waves require no "medium" or matter for their transmission as do water waves or sound waves. Electromagnetic energy is transferred through a vacuum without difficulty. It is in this way that our earth receives most of its energy from the sun.

All solid bodies emit and absorb thermal radiation at all temperatures. If the temperature of a heated solid is approximately 550°C, we can see some of the radiation that it emits and we say it is "glowing." As the temperature is increased, the solid turns from red to orange, then to yellow, and finally to "white-hot." Tungsten light bulbs operate at approximately 3000°C, while the temperature at the visible surface of the sun is estimated to be 6000°C.

Experimentalists in the latter half of the nineteenth century measured the spectral distribution of thermal radiation. That is, they measured at various wavelengths the amount of radiation emitted in a narrow wavelength range per unit area per second by a heated solid. This is called the monochromatic emittance and is designated by W_λ. The results are shown in Fig. 8–1 for three temperatures. The three temperatures 550°C, 3000°C, and 6000°C cover too wide a range of temperatures to plot easily on a single graph. If the radiation comes from the interior of a cavity, the shape of each curve is independent of the materials used to make the cavity and depends only upon the temperature of the cavity.

The important features of the curves to be noted are, (a) there is a continuous distribution of energy, that is, energy is radiated at all wavelengths, (b) the total energy radiated (the area under the curve) increases rapidly as the temperature is increased, (c) there is a shift of the peak of the curve to shorter wavelengths (exemplified by the change from red to white hot) as the temperature is increased.

Since the energy radiated lies only partly in the visible range, the measurement of W_λ requires spectrometers using prisms made of materials other than glass since glass is opaque to radiation whose wavelength is larger than 2 microns. Rock salt, fluorite, and quartz are commonly used in conjunction with mirrors and gratings to produce the required separation of wavelengths. For detection of the radiation, thermocouples, thermopiles, platinum resistance thermometers coated black, or specially designed pressure cells are used.

Gases emit an entirely different kind of spectra. In a gas, the atoms are relatively far apart and they interact very little with one another. The radiation they emit is characteristic of the individual atoms emitting

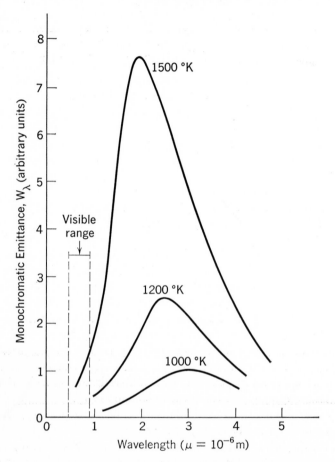

Fig. 8–1. Spectral distribution of radiation from a heated solid.

it and *line* spectra result. If we increase the pressure of the gas, the atoms crowd closer together and more and more spectral lines appear. The continuous spectrum of the heated solid is a result of the tight binding of the atoms in the solid.

8–2. Thermal Radiation and Kirchhoff's Law. Let the *emittance*, the amount of energy (including all wavelengths) emitted per unit area per second be designated W. The mks units, watts per square meter, are often replaced by mixed units, watts per square centimeter (for example, for tungsten at 1000°K, $W = 0.65$ watts cm^{-2}). The part of this total energy that is emitted in the range of wavelengths between λ and $\lambda + d\lambda$ we write as

$$dW = W_\lambda \, d\lambda, \tag{8–1}$$

so that the monochromatic emittance $W_\lambda = dW/d\lambda$. Again, mixed units such as watts per square centimeter micron^{-1} (1 micron $= 10^{-6}$ m $=$ 10,000 Å, since 1 angstrom unit $= 10^{-10}$ m) are often used.

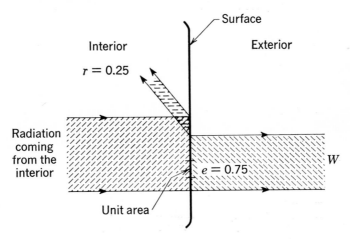

Fig. 8–2. Schematic diagram of imperfect emission.

The processes occurring at the surface during the emission of energy by a body can be approximately and symbolically illustrated as in Fig. 8–2. Some of the radiation incident on the surface from the interior is reflected. The *fraction* reflected is called r, the *reflectivity*. In our example $r = 0.25$. The other 75% of the radiation is emitted. The fraction emitted is called e, the *emissivity*. In our example $e = 0.75$.

The surface in Fig. 8–2 can also receive energy. The situation is shown in Fig. 8–3. H is the *irradiance*, the amount of energy falling on the surface per unit area per unit time.

Since it is the same surface, $r = 0.25$ but now 75% of the radiation is absorbed. Thus the *absorptivity* $a = 0.75$ is the fraction of the incident radiation absorbed. From the diagram, $a + r = 1$. The *monochromatic absorptivity* a_λ, *monochromatic reflectivity* r_λ, and *monochromatic emissivity* e_λ can similarly be defined.

The above suggests that we should expect a good absorbing surface to be a good emitting surface. A classic experiment by Ritchie demonstrates

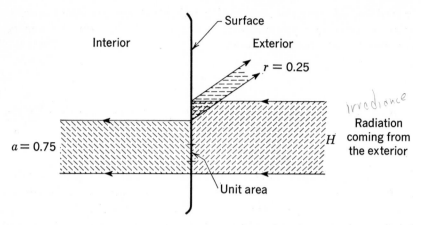

Fig. 8–3.   Schematic diagram of imperfect absorption.

that good absorbers are good emitters.   The apparatus is shown in Fig. 8–4.
Three hollow cylinders numbered 1, 2, and 3 are free to turn (pivots not
shown in figure) about a vertical axis.   Each cylinder is highly polished
over end A and coated with lampblack over end B.   Cylinders 1 and 3 are
connected by a capillary tube containing an indicating liquid.

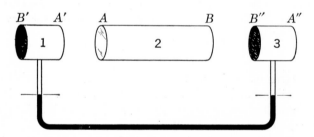

Fig. 8–4.   Ritchie's apparatus.

Hot water is introduced into cylinder 2.   If now B faces B'' and A'
faces A as shown, the liquid level drops on the right and rises on the left,
indicating an expansion of the air in 3 due to heat transferred from 2 to 3
through the black surfaces B and B''. B and B'' are emitting well *and*
absorbing well as compared with A and A'.   If we turn number 2 so that
A' faces B and A faces B'', there is no change in the equilibrium level of
the liquid when the hot water is added to 2.   From this experiment, we
can conclude that a good absorber of radiation becomes, when it is internally
heated, a good emitter of radiation.

The formal representation of the fact demonstrated above is called *Kirchhoff's law of radiation,* after its discoverer. For the total energy absorbed or emitted it states that

$$\frac{W_1}{a_1} = \frac{W_2}{a_2} = \frac{W_i}{a_i}, \qquad (8\text{--}2)$$

for surfaces $1, 2 \ldots i \ldots$. For the wavelength range $d\lambda$, it is also true that

$$\frac{(W_\lambda)_1}{(a_\lambda)_1} = \frac{(W_\lambda)_2}{(a_\lambda)_2} = \cdots \qquad (8\text{--}3)$$

Kirchhoff's law is a direct consequence of the second law of thermodynamics. Consider two bodies initially at the same temperature and located in an enclosure having perfectly reflecting walls. There will be a steady exchange of energy between the two bodies because of the emission and absorption of radiation by both. Suppose that Kirchhoff's law did not hold and that $W_1/a_1 > W_2/a_2$, either because $W_1 > W_2$, or $a_1 < a_2$, or both. Then body 1 would be giving off energy faster than it would be absorbing energy from body 2, and body 2 would be absorbing energy faster from body 1 than it would be emitting energy. Thus, body 1 would cool and body 2 would warm, and there would be a free net flow of energy from a body to a warmer body without the action of an external agency, contrary to the second law of thermodynamics. The similar proof for the monochromatic emittance and monochromatic absorptivity only requires the use of radiation filters to limit the exchange of energy through radiation in a narrow band of wavelengths.

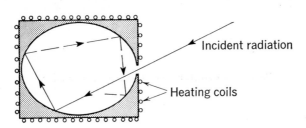

Fig. 8–5.   A black body.

This places us in a position to define a hypothetical body which is a perfect absorber. For a perfect absorber, $a = 1$ and $a_\lambda = 1$. We call this perfect absorber a *black body.* Such a black body is also a perfect emitter ($e = 1$, $e_\lambda = 1$).

A black body can be approximated in the laboratory. Fig. 8–5 is a diagram of an apparatus which produces such an ideal body. It consists of a closed container with a small hole in one end. The *hole* acts as a black body since very nearly all radiation falling on the hole is trapped inside and absorbed. We are able, therefore, to experimentally observe the radiation from the ideal black body when it is heated by an external heat source, such as the heating coils shown. The curves observed have the form and behavior shown in Fig. 8–1.

8–3. Thermal Radiation and the Quantum Theory. By the year 1900 it was apparent that "classical" physics, the electromagnetic theory of Maxwell, and the established principles of mechanics and thermodynamics could *not* explain the shape of these curves. The proper procedure had seemed clear to the theorists. It seemed (a) that the radiation in the interior of the black body would behave like an assembly of oscillators because of the existence of standing waves in the interior, (b) that the distribution function of the fraction of the oscillators vibrating at a particular wavelength could be calculated, and (c) that each oscillator possessed an average energy of kT where k is the Boltzmann constant. The resultant law based on these ideas, called the Rayleigh-Jeans law (see Eq. 8–11), does not fit the curves of Fig. 8–1 except for long wavelengths.

The German physicist, M. Planck, presented the quantum theory of black body radiation in 1900. Without knowing why at first and with serious doubts in his own mind, he was able to fit the experimental curves by discarding the idea that the oscillators in the black body possessed a continuous range of energies with an average of kT.

He assumed, instead, that the oscillators could have *only discrete energies*, differing in amount by integral multiples of $h\nu$, where the constant h now called Planck's constant, is equal to 6.63×10^{-34} j-sec, and ν is the frequency of the oscillator. The result of his calculation is *Planck's radiation law* and is

$$W_\lambda = \frac{2\pi c^2 h}{\lambda^5} \frac{1}{\exp{(hc/k\lambda T)} - 1}.$$ (8–4)

We can rewrite this law in terms of the frequency ν if we remember that

$$c = \nu\lambda,$$

so that,

$$d\lambda = \frac{-c d\nu}{\nu^2} = \frac{-\lambda d\nu}{\nu}.$$ (8–5)

Therefore, since only magnitudes need to be considered and

$$dW = W_\lambda \, d\lambda = W_\nu \, d\nu,$$

$$W_\nu = W_\lambda \frac{d\lambda}{d\nu}$$

$$= \frac{c}{\nu^2} W_\lambda.$$

Eq. 8–4 then becomes

$$W_\nu = \frac{2\pi h}{c^2} \nu^3 \frac{1}{\exp{(h\nu/kT)} - 1}. \qquad (8\text{–}6)$$

In these relations, c is the speed of electromagnetic waves in free space, and k is Boltzmann's constant. Under Planck's assumption, if the atomic oscillators on the walls of the enclosure were to absorb or emit radiation, they could only do so in amounts $h\nu$. These amounts are now known as *quanta* and we write for their energy

$$E = h\nu. \qquad (8\text{–}7)$$

Because of these quanta, the radiation seems to possess a particle nature. These particles are usually called *photons*. Planck's success with this problem marked the beginning of the *quantum theory*.

8–4. Planck's Radiation Law and Earlier Theories. Let us now use the radiation law to investigate the earlier classical attempts to solve this problem. Since

$$dW = W_\lambda \, d\lambda,$$

the total energy radiated is

$$W = \int_0^\infty W_\lambda \, d\lambda. \qquad (8\text{–}8)$$

Setting $\nu = c/\lambda$ in Eq. 8–4 and performing the required integration gives

$$W = \frac{2\pi^5 k^4}{15 c^2 h^3} T^4, \qquad (8\text{–}9)$$

or

$$W = \sigma T^4. \qquad (8\text{–}10)$$

This is the *Stefan-Boltzmann law*. This fundamental law also can be derived from classical thermodynamics and has been experimentally confirmed. The constant

$$\sigma = 5.67 \times 10^{-8} \text{ j sec}^{-1} \text{ m}^{-2} \, {}^\circ\text{K}^{-4}.$$

$$[\sigma = 5.67 \times 10^{-5} \text{ erg sec}^{-1} \text{ cm}^{-2} \, {}^\circ\text{K}^{-4}.]$$

At long wavelengths, and hence low frequencies, expanding the exponential of Eq. 8–6 as a series gives

$$\exp\left(\frac{h\nu}{kT}\right) - 1 = 1 + \frac{h\nu}{kT} + \frac{1}{2}\left(\frac{h\nu}{kT}\right)^2 + \cdots - 1$$

$$= \frac{h\nu}{kT},$$

if terms of higher order than the first are neglected. Using this approximation in Eq. 8–6,

$$W_\nu = \frac{2\pi\nu^2}{c^2}\, kT, \qquad\qquad (8\text{–}11)$$

which is the *Rayleigh-Jeans law*. This relation, which was obtained by Rayleigh and Jeans from the classical argument that the average energy of the oscillators should be kT, obviously fails at high frequencies. It is easy to see that in Eq. 8–11, W_ν approaches infinity as ν becomes very large. This is often referred to as "the ultraviolet catastrophe."

In the short wavelength region (high frequency region) the exponential term in the denominator of Eq. 8–6 dominates, so that the -1 in the denominator can be neglected. This approximation was first suggested by Wien and is called *Wien's radiation law*. Finally, we obtain *Wien's displacement law* by noting that the form of Planck's law is such that

$$W_\lambda = \frac{C_1}{\lambda^5} f(\lambda T),$$

where

$$f(\lambda T) = \frac{1}{\exp{(hc/k\lambda T)} - 1} \qquad\qquad (8\text{–}12)$$

or

$$W_\lambda = C_2 T^5 F(\lambda T),$$

where

$$F(\lambda T) = \frac{\lambda^{-5} T^{-5}}{\exp{(hc/k\lambda T)} - 1}. \qquad\qquad (8\text{–}13)$$

Wien had been able to predict that the radiation law should be capable of being written in this form by using only the laws of thermodynamics and Doppler's principle. But the form of f (or F) could not be obtained. Experiments which gave the curves of Fig. 8–1 showed that F has a maximum. Wien's displacement law then shows that, if λ_m is the wavelength at which W_λ is a maximum, then

$$\lambda_m T = \text{a universal constant.} \qquad\qquad (8\text{–}14)$$

The value of this constant can be obtained from the Planck result by differentiating Eq. 8–4 with respect to λ and setting $dW_\lambda/d\lambda = 0$, giving

$$\frac{hc}{k\lambda_m T} = 5\left[1 - \exp\left(-\frac{hc}{k\lambda_m T}\right)\right].$$

This equation for $\lambda_m T$ can be solved to give

$$\lambda_m T = \frac{hc}{4.96k},$$

or

$$\lambda_m T = 2.898 \times 10^{-3} \text{ m-°K.} \qquad [\lambda_m T = 0.2898 \text{ cm-°K.}] \quad (8\text{–}15)$$

This constant agrees with experimental values.

The reader should note that the Stefan-Boltzmann law, Wien's displacement law, Wien's radiation law, and the Rayleigh-Jeans law were originally obtained from other considerations before Planck proposed his law and were actually instrumental in directing his thoughts toward the law which includes them all.

The conclusions to be drawn from the success of the work of Planck are the following:

1. Energy can be absorbed from an electromagnetic wave or emitted to it, in amounts
$$E = h\nu,$$
where ν is the frequency of the electromagnetic wave.
2. Electromechanical systems can have only certain definite amounts of energy (energy levels).

EXAMPLE 1. A solid metal sphere is a grey body, that is, it has an emissivity that is constant for all wavelengths. In this case, its emissivity is 0.85. The sphere has a radius of 0.03 m and it is heated to a temperature of 927°C. (a) At what wavelength is the radiation a maximum? (b) At what rate is the sphere losing heat by radiation? (c) If the temperature cools 200°C, what will be the new wavelength for maximum radiation and what will be the ratio of emittance at that wavelength to the maximum emittance at the higher temperature?

Solution:

a. The temperature is $927 + 273 = 1200°K$.

The value of $\lambda_m = 2.898 \times 10^{-3}/1200$
$$= 2.42 \times 10^{-6} \text{ m} = 2.42 \text{ microns.}$$

b. The rate of heat loss is

$$G = aAW = aA\sigma T^4 = 0.85 \times 4\pi(0.03)^2 \times 5.67 \times 10^{-8} \times (1200)^4$$
$$= 1130 \text{ w.}$$

c. Wien's displacement law states that $\lambda_{m1}/\lambda_{m2} = T_2/T_1$; so at 1000°K the wavelength of maximum emissivity is $2.42 \times 1.2 = 2.90$ microns. At such corresponding wavelengths the ratios of the emissivities is $W_{\lambda 2}/W_{\lambda 1} = (T_2/T_1)^5$; so at 1000°K $W_{\lambda m2}/W_{\lambda m1} = (1/1.2)^5 = 0.40$.

8–5. The Photoelectric Effect. In 1887, Heinrich Hertz discovered that light falling on the metal of a spark gap made it easier for a spark to jump across the gap. This is because the light ejects electrons from the metal. This discovery was then investigated in great detail by many different people. It was found that the effect was most easily studied in a vacuum where electrons from an illuminated cathode could be collected at an anode. The current was found to be proportional to the intensity of illumination. It was also found that the wavelength of the light affected the current. About 1900, Lenard showed that the charged particles have the same specific charge as that of regular cathode rays. This proved that the current was made up of electrons.

This effect has had wide application in several fields such as photometry, photo-recording of sound, and control circuitry. We shall not enlarge on these applications, but instead shall examine what can be learned about the laws of nature from this effect.

One of the natural things to study is whether the energy of the photo-electrons depends upon the intensity of the incident light. This can be done in the following way. The photoelectric emitter can be placed inside a collector electrode as shown in Fig. 8–6. The collector is made negative

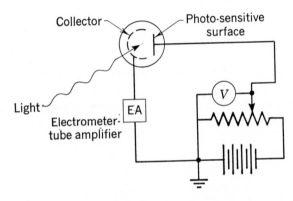

Fig. 8–6. Photoelectric experiment.

relative to the emitter. Only electrons with enough energy to overcome this negative potential barrier will form the photocurrent. This current is measured by a very sensitive electrometer-tube amplifier EA. Such an amplifier can be made to show currents as small as 10^{-16} a, though such sensitivity is not required for this experiment. As V, the potential between the two electrodes, is made more and more negative, there comes a value for which no electrons can reach the collector. This is called the *stopping potential* and it is clearly a measure of the maximum kinetic energy of an ejected electron. Typical curves of the photocurrent versus applied potential for monochromatic light of *different* wavelengths are shown in Fig. 8–7. The currents are made equal at $V = 0$ by adjusting the intensity of the light in each case. V_1, V_2, and V_3 are the three stopping potentials for three different wavelengths. The wavelength for curve 1 is shorter than that for curve 2. The wavelength for curve 3 is the longest of the

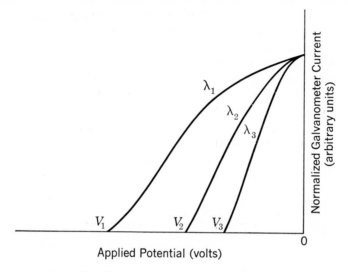

Fig. 8–7.   Photocurrent versus retarding potential.

three. The experiments show that the stopping potential is independent of the intensity of the light, but is dependent upon the frequency of the light.

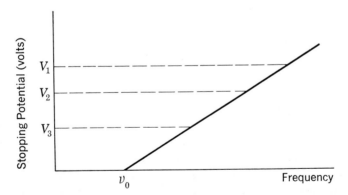

Fig. 8–8.   Relation of stopping potential to frequency of incident light.

If we now plot the stopping potential versus frequency of the light, we get a straight line as shown in Fig. 8–8. It is also found that no electrons can be released if the frequency of the incident light is lower than the intercept ν_0. Corresponding to this *threshold frequency*, there is a *threshold wavelength* $\lambda_0 = c/\nu_0$. Wavelengths longer than λ_0 do not eject electrons. The threshold values ν_0 and λ_0 are different for different materials, but the slope of the line in Fig. 8–8 is independent of the material.

These results lead to contradictions if classical electromagnetic theory is applied to the problem. Classically, the energy carried by an electromagnetic wave is described by the *intensity* of the wave, that is, the square of the amplitude of the wave. The photoelectrons ejected from the metal should then have energies which are dependent on the intensity, but the above experimental results show that this is not so. In addition, the electrons should be released by light of any frequency, under classical concepts, as long as the intensity and the time of exposure is great enough. The experimentally determined threshold frequency shows that this is not true.

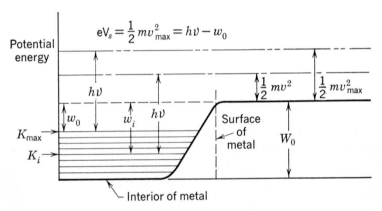

Fig. 8–9. Energy transformation in the photoelectric effect.

The more satisfactory explanation was given by Einstein[1] as follows. Within a metal at least one electron per atom is free to move about, unattached to any particular atom. At the surface of the metal there is a rapid rise in the potential energy of the electron because of the attractive fields of all the atoms on the surface. This has been plotted schematically in Fig. 8–9, in which the heavy line represents the potential energy of an electron. There are actually fluctuations of the potential energy of the electron within the metal that are not shown, but this makes no difference in the theory. Although these free electrons can be thought of as behaving like a gas in a box, their kinetic energies are not distributed according to the Maxwell-Boltzmann distribution, but in accordance with a Fermi-Dirac distribution (see Art. 5–11 and Chapter 14). At ordinary temperatures,

[1] A. Einstein, *Ann. Physik*, **17**, 132 (1905).

this distribution is shaped much like that of Fig. 8–10 with a rather sudden decrease occurring at K_{max}. Although K_{max} is perhaps imperfectly defined, the range of energy in which the decrease occurs is narrow and it occurs very close to the Fermi level E_f of Eq. 5–49. Einstein proposed that Planck's theory should apply to this model. Accordingly, energy of light

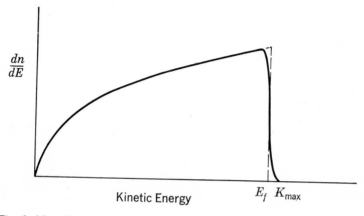

Fig. 8–10.   The distribution of kinetic energy of electrons in a metal.

with frequency ν can only be absorbed in amounts of size $h\nu$; so an electron within the metal will suddenly have its energy increased by that amount. Now it requires a certain amount w_i of the energy to get each electron out of the metal. The amount left over is the kinetic energy of the electron after it escapes, thus

$$\tfrac{1}{2}mv^2 = h\nu - w_i. \tag{8–16}$$

Fig. 8–9 can be interpreted by this relation. W_0 is the height of the potential wall at the surface of the metal. The kinetic energy K_i of the different electrons is represented by the horizontal lines within the metal. The maximum kinetic energy is shown by K_{max}. Thus it can be seen that the amount of energy required to get the electron out of the metal is

$$w_i = W_0 - K_i, \tag{8–17}$$

or, in the case of the most energetic electrons,

$$w_0 = W_0 - K_{max}. \tag{8–18}$$

Since the stopping potential V_s is related to the maximum kinetic energy, we should expect

$$eV_s = \tfrac{1}{2}mv_{max}{}^2 = h\nu - w_0. \tag{8–19}$$

It is also convenient to write

$$w_0 = e\Phi_0, \tag{8-20}$$

and

$$w_0 = h\nu_0.$$

The quantity Φ_0 is called the photoelectric work function. If we divide Eq. 8–19 by e, we get

$$V_s = \frac{h}{e}\nu - \Phi_0 = \frac{h}{e}(\nu - \nu_0). \tag{8-21}$$

This equation plots as shown in Fig. 8–8. The slope of the straight line should be h/e. This is in complete agreement with experiment and the value of h/e as determined by experiment is in good agreement with values determined in other ways.

There is a very convenient way to work with these quantities. The values of V and Φ_0 are measured in volts; the energies eV and $e\Phi_0$ are measured in electron volts; and the wavelength of the light is measured in angstrom units Å. Since

$$\nu = \frac{c}{\lambda} = \frac{3 \times 10^{18}}{\lambda(\text{Å})}\ \text{sec}^{-1},$$

$$h = 6.63 \times 10^{-34}\ \text{j-sec},$$

and

$$e = 1.6 \times 10^{-19}\ \text{coulomb},$$

we can write,

$$V_s = \frac{6.62 \times 10^{-34}}{1.60 \times 10^{-19}} \frac{3 \times 10^{18}}{\lambda(\text{Å})} - \Phi_0 \tag{8-22}$$

or

$$V_s = 12{,}400 \left(\frac{1}{\lambda(\text{Å})} - \frac{1}{\lambda_0(\text{Å})}\right). \tag{8-23}$$

The results of such photoelectric studies confirm the view that electromagnetic radiation is always absorbed in quanta of size $\Delta E = h\nu$. The value of the energy of the quanta, expressed in electron volts, is

$$\Delta E = \frac{12{,}400}{\lambda(\text{Å})}\ \text{ev}, \tag{8-24}$$

when the light has a wavelength λ.

Photons can also eject electrons which are bound to an atom. If the binding energy (the work required to just remove the electron from the atom) is E_b, then the kinetic energy of such a photoelectron after being ejected from the atom is

$$\tfrac{1}{2}mv^2 = h\nu - E_b. \tag{8-25}$$

For such a bound electron to be ejected, the energy of the photon, of course, must exceed E_b; so the threshold frequency is $\nu_0 = E_b/h$, or the threshold wavelength is $\lambda_0 = 12{,}400/E_b$ (for λ_0 in angstrom units and E_b in electron volts).

EXAMPLE 2. The photoelectric work function for gold is 4.82 v. (a) What is the threshold frequency? (b) What is the threshold wavelength? (c) Light with a wavelength of 2220 Å ejects photoelectrons from the gold. What is the kinetic energy of the most energetic electrons as they leave the gold? What is the stopping potential (neglect contact potentials)?

Solution. a. 4.82 ev = 7.7×10^{-19} j; therefore $\nu_0 = 7.7 \times 10^{-19}/6.63 \times 10^{-34} = 1.16 \times 10^{15}$ sec^{-1}.

b. $\lambda_0 = c/\nu_0 = 3 \times 10^8/1.16 \times 10^{15} = 2.59 \times 10^{-7}$ m = 2590 Å, or $\lambda_0 = 12{,}400/4.82 = 2590$ Å.

c. A photon with a wavelength of 2220 Å has an energy of $12{,}400/2220 = 5.59$ ev = 8.95×10^{-19} j. The energy left to the electron after it escapes is $5.59 - 4.82 = 0.77$ ev = 1.23×10^{-19} j. The stopping potential thus is 0.77 volts. This could have been worked by computing ν and using $h\nu$, but this is longer and less convenient. The short cut should be used, though only if well understood.

8–6. The Franck-Hertz Experiment. The quantum theory was further strengthened by an experiment performed by J. Franck and G. Hertz[2] in 1914. The experimental arrangement is shown in Fig. 8–11. Electrons

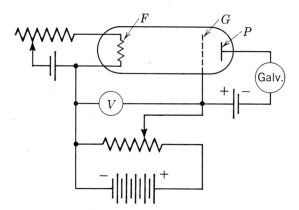

Fig. 8–11. Apparatus and connections for the Franck-Hertz experiment.

are emitted by the hot cathode filament, and are accelerated by the potential difference between the filament and a grid G. Beyond the grid is another electrode P which is maintained at a potential slightly negative

[2] J. Franck, and G. Hertz, *Verhandl deut. Physik. Ges.*, **16**, 512 (1914).

with respect to G. Any electrons reaching P make up the current through the galvanometer, Galv. Inside the tube, an excess of mercury provides a mercury vapor at the temperature of the experiment. The experiment consists of observing the current through the galvanometer as the accelerating potential is changed. A plot, showing how this galvanometer current changes with the accelerating potential, is shown in Fig. 8–12.

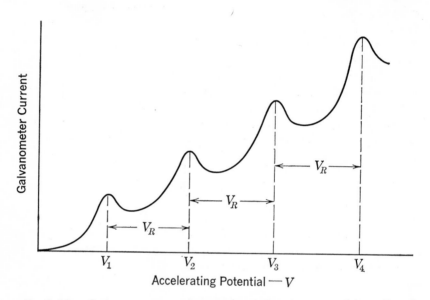

Fig. 8–12. Galvanometer current versus accelerating potential in a Franck-Hertz experiment.

If we assume that the quantum theory applies to this problem, then the succession of peaks in Fig. 8–12 can be explained in the following way. The electrons move through the vapor atoms accelerated by the electric field between F and G in Fig. 8–11 acquiring energy as they drop through the difference of potential. Eventually, they pass through the grid G to the plate P. If the potential difference is increased, the number of electrons moving is increased, hence the current i_{galv} increases.

These electrons moving down the tube are repeatedly in collision with the mercury vapor atoms, but if the accelerating potential is less than V_1 shown in Fig. 8–12, the collisions are elastic collisions. At V_1, electrons near to and approaching G have enough energy to cause an internal energy change in the mercury vapor atoms with which they collide. The electrons deliver a requisite amount of energy to the vapor atoms, are slowed down as a result, and do not have enough energy to overcome the small negative potential barrier between G and P. Since they do not reach P, the current i_{galv} decreases. When the potential is large enough to permit two successive energy transfers during the trip between F and G, the second drop in current appears on the graph.

The significance of this experiment is that it shows that a mercury atom will only change its energy by definite amounts—by a quantum of energy. On the basis of this experiment we can assign *energy levels* to the atom. The difference in the potentials of the peaks in Fig. 8–12 corresponds to the energy difference between two such energy levels for the mercury atom. Fig. 8–13 is a plot of several of the energy levels of mercury atoms in which each horizontal line represents one energy state in which the atom can exist. No atom can exist with an energy lying between the lines.

The lowest possible energy level is called the *ground state*. The process of raising the energy of the atoms is called *excitation* while the potential difference needed to change the energy of an atom to a higher state is called the excitation or *resonance* potential. The first peak in Fig. 8–12 does not necessarily occur when V exactly equals the resonance potential V_R because the field between the filament and grid is often slightly different from V. Contact potentials that result from junctions of different metals are responsible for this difference.

It is possible for an electron to have enough energy to remove an electron from an atom with which it collides. When this happens, the ions produced (the electron and the positive remnant) may contribute to the current between the filament and the grid. The sudden increase in current indicates the potential required for this. This potential is called the *ionization potential*. Whether successive excitations or ionization will occur depends upon the electron current and the vapor density.

Typical values of resonance potentials and ionization potentials are given in Table 8–1.

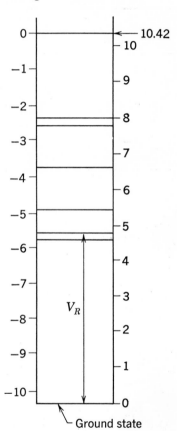

Energies in Electron Volts

Fig. 8–13. Some energy levels of mercury.

The Franck-Hertz experiment demonstrates one way in which atoms may be put into excited states. Other methods may also be used to excite atoms. Among these are thermal excitation, electrical discharges, and optical excitation.

TABLE 8–1

Resonance and Ionization Potentials

Element	Resonance Potential (volts)	Ionization Potential (volts)	Wavelength of Resonance Line (Å)
H	10.15	13.595	1215.67
Li	1.84	5.390	6707.85
Be	3.57	8.296	3470.60
Ne	16.62	21.559	743.71
Na	2.10	5.138	5889.95
Mg	2.71	7.644	4571.10
K	1.61	4.339	7664.91
Ca	1.88	6.111	6572.78
Hg	4.67	10.434	2536.52

The atom is unstable when it is in an excited state. It will return to the ground state, in a characteristic time, by giving up its excess energy. This energy release is usually in the form of the *photon* mentioned in Art. 8–3. Spectral lines in optical radiation, for example, have a frequency which should be given by

$$h\nu = eV, \qquad (8\text{–}26)$$

where V is the potential difference corresponding to the difference in energy between two energy states.

8–7. The Compton Effect. The results that have been described in the last several articles suggest that electromagnetic radiation has a particle nature. In fact, we have already called these particles photons. This particle nature may manifest itself in other respects than those discussed so far. For example, it may be possible that typical collision phenomena may occur. The test of this was made by Compton.[3] The results confirmed the theory very well.

A photon has an energy $h\nu$. If this is set equal to $m_p c^2$ in accordance with the special theory of relativity, we obtain a mass m_p for the photon and

$$m_p = \frac{h\nu}{c^2}. \qquad (8\text{–}27)$$

---

[3] A. H. Compton, *Phys. Rev.*, **21**, 715; **22**, 409 (1923).

The momentum of the photon will be

$$m_p c = \frac{h\nu}{c} = \frac{h}{\lambda}. \tag{8–28}$$

If a photon with an initial energy $E_1 = h\nu_1$ and momentum $p_1 = h\nu_1/c$ collides with a free electron of mass m at rest, the collision might be pictured as in Fig. 8–14. Following the collision, the photon has a final

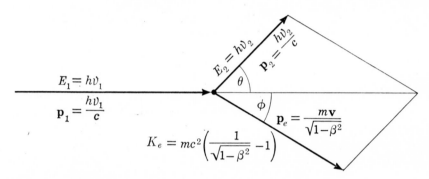

Fig. 8–14.   The Compton effect—a collision of a photon with a free electron.

energy $E_2 = h\nu_2$ and momentum $p_2 = h\nu_2/c$, while the electron has a kinetic energy $K_e = mc^2(1/\sqrt{1-\beta^2} - 1)$ and a momentum $p_e = mv/\sqrt{1-\beta^2}$, where v is the recoil speed of the electron and $\beta = v/c$. The laws of conservation of energy and linear momentum then give

$$h\nu_1 = h\nu_2 + mc^2\left(\frac{1}{\sqrt{1-\beta^2}} - 1\right) \tag{8–29}$$

$$\frac{h\nu_1}{c} = \frac{h\nu_2}{c}\cos\theta + \frac{m\beta c}{\sqrt{1-\beta^2}}\cos\phi \tag{8–30}$$

$$0 = \frac{h\nu_2}{c}\sin\theta - \frac{m\beta c}{\sqrt{1-\beta^2}}\sin\phi. \tag{8–31}$$

These three equations can be thought of as a set of simultaneous equations that can be solved for three unknowns, $h\nu_2$, K_e, and ϕ. We are taking θ to be a parameter determined by the experimental arrangement. All values of θ of course can and do occur, but if we pick a particular angle, then the other three quantities will be determined by the three equations. The wavelength of the scattered photon will be longer than that of the incident one and it is convenient to convert ν to λ. The change in wavelength can be shown, with algebraic manipulation, to be

$$\lambda_2 - \lambda_1 = \frac{h}{mc} (1 - \cos \theta). \tag{8-32}$$

The constant h/mc is called the *Compton wavelength* λ_c. Its value is $\lambda_c = 0.0243$ Å. The electron's kinetic energy is then

$$K_e = mc^2 \left[\frac{1}{\sqrt{1 - \beta^2}} - 1 \right] \tag{8-33}$$

and the electron's recoil angle ϕ is given by

$$\cot \phi = \left(1 + \frac{h\nu_1}{mc^2} \right) \tan \frac{\theta}{2}. \tag{8-34}$$

Compton isolated x-rays of a single wavelength and used them to irradiate a block of carbon, and then measured the wavelength of the scattered x-rays for a number of different scattering angles. The results are sketched in Fig. 8–15. The wavelength of the so-called modified line is shifted an amount predicted by Eq. 8–32. The unmodified, or unshifted, line represents x-rays that have been scattered by electrons which are bound to the carbon atoms. Experiments by Shankland[4] also confirmed Eq. 8–34. Recoil electrons and scattered photons were observed in coincidence only for angles satisfying this relation.

8–8. Conclusions. Other effects have been mentioned such as the Zeeman effect and the specific heats of solids. They too confirm the basic points that we are trying to stress, namely, that:

1. Energy is absorbed or emitted in quanta of size $h\nu$.
2. Atomic systems can exist in only certain energy levels or states.

At one time, there were many who were concerned with whether or not the energy emitted, or absorbed, stays in a limited region as it travels from source to absorber. If the quantum does have such a particle nature, it seems to contradict the experiments with electromagnetic radiation of the interference or diffraction type. Now we know there is no need to worry about this. Experiments that show the particle nature prevent the observation of the wave nature. Similarly, an interference experiment prevents the checking of the particle nature of the quantum.

It is now clear that the full description of light (electromagnetic waves) requires both a particle (quantum) description and a wave description. This duality carries on even to the description of matter. It is referred to as the *complementarity principle* and was formulated by Bohr. The name arises from the fact that both wave and particle descriptions complement

[4] R. S. Shankland, *Phys. Rev.*, **49**, 8 (1936).

each other in the full description of light and matter. In the realm of large things and large amounts of energy, the quantum laws reduce to the classical laws, as they should, according to Bohr's *correspondence principle*. As a result, the problems which we have suggested did not arise in the

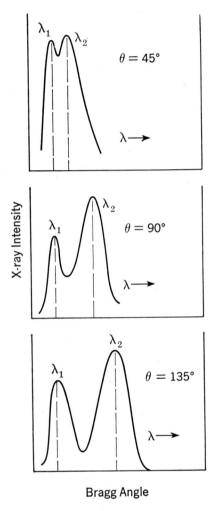

Fig. 8-15.　The modified and unmodified line of the Compton effect.

thinking of people until the discovery of many of the effects associated with the detailed study of atoms.

One of the main features of the complementarity principle is the interpretation of the intensity of an electromagnetic wave as a measure of the likelihood of finding photons in the region. The intensity is proportional to both E^2 and H^2, the squares of the amplitude of both the electric and magnetic field intensities. It is also proportional to the rate at which energy is transmitted through unit area. If one accepts that the electromagnetic wave propagates energy in photons (quanta), the number of photons passing through a unit area per second is proportional to the intensity or to E^2 or H^2. Thus we can interpret E (or H) as a quantity which when squared and multiplied by a volume differential dv gives a value proportional to the number of photons in dv; or better, which gives a value proportional to the probability of finding a photon in dv. This means of reconciling particle and wave characteristics of light seems to avoid all of the difficulties that might arise from such a dual theory. No known experiments can separate particle and wave nature and contradict this interpretation. A similar interpretation will be used for electrons and other forms of matter.

PROBLEMS

8–1. A small sphere with a radius of 0.008 m has an average emissivity of 0.8. At what rate does it radiate energy if its temperature is 1400°C?

8–2. The emissivity of a certain metal surface is 0.73. Calculate the rate at which energy must be fed into a small sphere made of this metal to keep it at a temperature of 800°C when it is surrounded by an enclosure at a temperature of 27°C. The sphere has a radius of 3 cm.

8–3. A metal wire filament with a radius of 5×10^{-4} m and a length of 0.12 m has an emissivity of 0.30 and a resistance of 0.11 ohms. What current must flow through it to maintain its temperature at 2000°K if it only loses heat by radiation? (This temperature is the approximate operating temperature of a filament in a vacuum tube.)

8–4. Let a be the maximum monochromatic emittance of a black body at 300°K. Find the wavelength at which this maximum occurs. Do the same for 600°K, 1000°K, 3000°K, and 6000°K. Also compute the *maximum* monochromatic emittance in terms of a at these temperatures.

8–5. An object reflects 0.36 of the energy that falls on it. What is the total emittance of the material at a temperature of 600°K?

8–6. Calculate the reflectivity of a surface that has a total emittance of 1.5×10^3 w m^{-2} at a temperature of 500°K.

8–7. Two furnaces have peepholes in them. The radiation from one has a maximum monochromatic emittance at 3×10^{-6} m and the other at 4.5×10^{-6} m. (a) What can you immediately tell about the temperature of the two furnaces (that is, without reference to any table of constants)? (b) What are the actual temperatures?

8–8. A tungsten-filament lamp operates at a temperature of approximately 3000°K. At what wavelength does the maximum in the spectral distribution curve of Fig. 8–1 occur for this temperature? Would increasing the temperature create better viewing conditions for the human eye? (The human eye is most sensitive to approximately 5500 Å.)

8–9. Examine the implications of Planck's quantum hypothesis by considering what it implies about the nature of the processes of radiation and what it implies about the nature of the atom.

8–10. The maximum sensitivity of the human eye is approximately 5 quanta $sec^{-1} cm^{-2}$ at 5500 Å. Compute the energy equivalent of this sensitivity.

8–11. Compute the surface temperature of the sun if its most intense radiation is at approximately 5500 Å.

8–12. Calculate the energy in joules and electron volts of a photon with a wavelength of 1850 Å.

8–13. What is the energy of a photon of light with a wavelength of 2536 Å? Of 5500 Å? Express in joules and in electron volts.

8–14. A radio transmitter with a frequency of 1200 kc has a radiated power of 100 w. A high intensity light source gives off light with a wavelength of 5000 Å at a power of 10 w. An x-ray tube puts out 0.2 w of x-rays with an average wavelength of 0.07 Å. Find the number of quanta emitted per second by each device. For comparison purposes, compute the number per second per watt for each device.

8–15. Eq. 8–4 and 8–6 are the equations giving the spectral distribution of Fig. 8–1. In Eq. 8–6 the last factor is a relation of some significance. Write this last factor as a function of energy E and plot the relation as a function of E for a fixed T. Does it agree with an expression met in Chapter 5?

8–16. A certain metal has a photoelectric threshold of 3850 Å. (a) What is its photoelectric work function? Give your answer both in ergs per electron and in volts. (b) What retarding potential is required to stop the photocurrent when the illuminating light is monochromatic with a wavelength of 2536 Å? (Neglect contact potentials.)

8–17. Photoelectrons released by light with a wavelength of 2690 Å have a stopping potential of 2.6 v. What will be their stopping potential for light with a wavelength of 2340 Å?

8–18. Photoelectrons emitted when light with a wavelength of 4820 Å strikes a photosurface have a stopping potential of 0.73 v. When the same phototube is illuminated with monochromatic light of a different wavelength, the stopping potential is 1.47 v. What is the wavelength of this light?

8–19. What is the photoelectric work function of the metal in Problem 8–17?

8–20. What is the photoelectric work function of the metal in Problem 8–18?

8–21. The photoelectric threshold for zinc is 3500 Å. What is the result of using radiation of 3000 Å? What is the result of using radiation of 4000 Å?

8-22. In a Franck-Hertz experiment there are collector current maxima for accelerating potentials of 1.33, 4.04, 6.77, 9.47, and 12.17 v. What is the resonance potential? From Table 8-1 identify the element.

8-23. If a tube containing sodium for a Franck-Hertz experiment showed a maximum collector current for a potential of 1.73 v, what five other potentials should show maximum current?

8-24. A certain x-ray tube has a potential difference of 48,000 v across it. No x-rays with a wavelength shorter than a certain value can be produced by this tube with this potential difference. Calculate the value and explain why.

8-25. What is the difference in energy (in electron volts) of the energy levels of sodium involved in the process of x-ray creation if the wavelength produced is 12.4 Å? What is the difference in energy (in electron volts) of energy levels of sodium involved in the production of the sodium *D*-line at 5890 Å?

8-26. X-rays with a wavelength of 0.612 Å are scattered by free electrons in a Compton effect. (a) If the photon is scattered through 75°, what is its new wavelength? What energy does the scattered electron have? (b) If the photon is scattered through 40° what is its new wavelength? What energy does the electron have?

8-27. Gamma rays with a wavelength of 0.031 Å suffer a Compton scattering by free electrons. What is the wavelength of the photons scattered through 120°? What energy does the electron get?

8-28. Derive the relation for the Compton shift in wavelength by considering the case of 90° scattering of the x-ray photon. Write out the momentum components and use the conservation of energy law neglecting relativistic effects.

8-29. Derive the relation giving the numerical value in Eq. 8-15.

8-30. Perform the integration that leads to the Stefan-Boltzmann law from Planck's law.

SELECTED REFERENCES

BORN, M. *Atomic Physics.* Hafner Publishing Co., Inc., New York, 1957. Chap. 7.
COMPTON, A. H., and S. K. ALLISON. *X-Rays in Theory and Experiment.* D. Van Nostrand Co., Inc., Princeton, N. J., 1935. Pp. 48, 200.
PLANCK, M. *Theory of Heat.* Macmillan & Co., Ltd., London, 1929. Parts 2 and 3.
RICHTMYER, F. K., E. H. KENNARD, and T. LAURITSEN. *Introduction to Modern Physics.* McGraw-Hill Book Co., Inc., New York, 1955. 5th ed., chap. 4.

9

Bohr's Model of the Hydrogen Atom

The Rutherford scattering experiment firmly established the concept of the nuclear atom. The arrangement of the electrons around the nucleus was not vigorously studied by Rutherford, but he and others recognized that this arrangement raised serious questions regarding the origin of the light emitted by atoms, and the resulting optical spectra. In this chapter, Bohr's proposals as to the origin of the radiation emitted by hydrogen will be investigated.

9–1. Atomic Spectra. The optical spectrum produced by an element is studied in the following way. The atoms of the element are made to emit light by passing an electric current through the vapor of the material (this may be in the form of an arc, a high voltage spark, or some other form of gaseous discharge) or by burning a salt of the element in a flame. In an electric discharge, energy is transferred from moving charged particles to the atoms, which then radiate it in the form of light. In a flame, violent inelastic collisions at the high temperature of the flame can similarly increase the internal energy of the atoms so that they can radiate.

The light produced by these methods is then analyzed by passing it through a prism or grating spectrometer. Such a device spreads the light out so that different wavelengths appear at different places on a photographic plate or in an eyepiece. This spectrum makes it possible to discover how the intensity of the light varies with wavelength.

The spectra for such gaseous or vapor sources (especially of the elements) are quite different from the spectra of incandescent solids which were discussed in Chapter 6. Spectra of solids are continuous, that is, some radiation is present at all wavelengths. Atomic spectra consist of bright, individual lines. Each line is an image of the entrance slit formed

187

with light of a certain wavelength. Thus we know there is radiation at only particular or *discrete* wavelengths. Fig. 9–1 represents the visible spectrum of hydrogen, a set of lines called the *Balmer series*. Spectra of this type are called *line spectra*. When such lines are produced by light emitted from vapor or gas, they are also often called *emission spectra*. It is also possible to send a continuous spectrum of light through a vapor

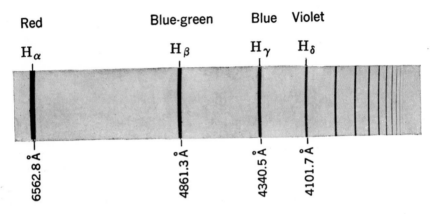

Fig. 9–1. The Balmer series of hydrogen. (By permission from G. Herzberg, *Atomic Spectra and Atomic Structure*. Prentice-Hall, Inc., New York, 1937.)

and then study what comes through. Often light is absorbed by the vapor at certain wavelengths, thus forming a *line absorption spectrum*. Absorption lines coincide in wavelength with some of the emission lines, but many emission lines are not to be found in absorption spectra.

The spectra produced by molecules also have a line structure, but usually there are so many lines so close together that they give the impression of bands of color, and hence are called *band spectra*.

Light elements, such as hydrogen, usually have simple spectra, while heavier elements, such as iron, have complex spectra consisting of a large number of lines (though not so many as molecular spectra). In most cases, certain patterns show up. An example is the Balmer series shown in Fig. 9–1. Notice the regularity in the spectrum—the lines come closer and closer as the wavelength decreases, and there is a shortest wavelength, or *series limit*. Many similar series are to be found in the spectra of elements.

In the late 1800's, much experimental work was done cataloguing the spectra of the elements. One outstanding advance came when Rydberg showed that the wavelengths of the lines of the Balmer series of hydrogen could be predicted by the relation

$$\frac{1}{\lambda} = R_\mathrm{H} \left(\frac{1}{2^2} - \frac{1}{n^2} \right),$$
(9-1)

where $R_\mathrm{H} = 1.097 \times 10^7 \ \mathrm{m}^{-1}$, an experimentally determined constant, and $n = 3, 4, 5, \ldots$. It is common to substitute the wave number, which we represent by $\bar{\nu}$, for the quantity $1/\lambda$. The wave number is thus the number of waves in one meter. Spectroscopists commonly use reciprocal centimeters and we may shift to this unit when dealing with spectra. The value of R_H in such units, of course, is 109,700 cm^{-1}. The Rydberg formula then becomes

$$\bar{\nu} = R_\mathrm{H} \left(\frac{1}{2^2} - \frac{1}{n^2} \right).$$
(9-2)

Since the wavelengths predicted by Eq. 9-2 agree to better than 0.1% with the experimental values, any theory of atomic structure should surely lead us to this equation.

Niels Bohr, a young Danish physicist, visited Rutherford's laboratory during the climax of the scattering experiments. At the time, he was working on the problem of accounting for the form of atomic spectra. The crucial results of Rutherford showed that any explanation must be based upon a nuclear type of atom. No one had yet been able to find a scheme that would accomplish this. As we shall see, Bohr was able to make a tremendous start toward the correct explanation.

9-2. Atomic Spectra and Classical Theory. Before we examine Bohr's theory, let us look at the difficulties that arise with the classical theory of radiation.

An electric charge has an electric field surrounding it. If the charge moves, it generates a magnetic field as well as an electric field. If the charge oscillates back and forth through a position of equilibrium, the electric and magnetic field at any given point also varies periodically. Electromagnetic theory shows that this is equivalent to saying that the charge is radiating an electromagnetic wave. Such a wave carries energy away from the charge. It turns out that a basic result of electromagnetic theory is that *an accelerated electric charge radiates energy.*

Consider the nuclear model of an atom of hydrogen. It consists of a single electron revolving in an orbit about the nucleus. For simplicity, assume the orbit is circular with a radius r. This electron is attracted to the nucleus by the Coulomb attraction

$$F = \frac{e^2}{4\pi\epsilon_0 r^2}. \qquad \left[F = \frac{e^2}{r^2}. \right]$$
(9-3)

For such a circular orbit the centripetal force is

$$F = \frac{mv^2}{r},$$
(9–4)

consequently, the number of revolutions per second about the nucleus is

$$\nu = \frac{v}{2\pi r} = \frac{1}{2\pi}\sqrt{\frac{e^2}{4\pi\epsilon_0 mr^3}}.$$
$$\left[\nu = \frac{v}{2\pi r} = \frac{1}{2\pi}\sqrt{\frac{e^2}{mr^3}}.\right]$$
(9–5)

This electron is being accelerated (the central acceleration) as it rotates. Thus, according to classical ideas, it will lose energy. Let us compute the amount of this energy and see how its decrease will affect the atom.

The total energy E of the electron is made up of kinetic and potential energy, so

$$E = \frac{1}{2}mv^2 + \frac{-e^2}{4\pi\epsilon_0 r}.$$
$$\left[E = \frac{1}{2}mv^2 + \left(\frac{-e^2}{r}\right).\right]$$
(9–6)

The expression for v^2 used to obtain Eq. 9–5, when put into Eq. 9–6, gives

$$E = -\frac{1}{2}\frac{e^2}{4\pi\epsilon_0 r}.$$
$$\left[E = -\frac{1}{2}\frac{e^2}{r}.\right]$$
(9–7)

We see from this that as E continuously decreases (becomes more negative), r must steadily decrease.

This picture which arises from the classical theory disagrees with the facts in two ways. First, a steadily decreasing r means that the electron would collapse into the nucleus. Second, the energy would be radiated continuously and the frequency, according to Eq. 9–5, would change smoothly, contrary to the indications of the line spectrum experimentally found.

Bohr was able to surmount these difficulties by introducing the quantum concept of Planck.

9–3. The Simple Bohr Model of the Hydrogen Atom.
Bohr assumed that a hydrogen atom consisted of a positive nucleus (a proton) and a negative electron revolving in a circular orbit around this nucleus. He then proposed three rules for predicting the behavior of the electron. These rules are a mixture of classical and quantum concepts. The theory was remarkably successful in explaining atomic spectra and in this success lies the justification of the Bohr rules.

These rules are:

Rule 1. *The electron (and hence the entire atom) can exist in stationary states. A stationary state* is a state in which the electron is moving, and is accelerated. However, while the electron is in the stationary state, no

electromagnetic energy is emitted or absorbed. A stationary state, therefore, has a definite energy, E, associated with it.

Rule 2. *The possible stationary states are determined by quantizing the
angular momentum, giving it only integral multiples of* $h/2\pi$. The angular
momentum of an electron of mass m and velocity v moving in a circle of
radius r is of course $\mathbf{r} \times \mathbf{mv}$. Quantizing the angular momentum is equivalent to saying that the only stationary states permissible are those for which

$$mvr = \frac{nh}{2\pi}. \tag{9–8}$$

The positive integer n we call the *principal quantum number*. (For non-
circular orbits the notation is different.)

Rule 3. *A transition from one possible stationary state to another requires
the emission (or absorption) of a quantum of energy.* This rule indicates
that photons, or quanta, of energy $h\nu$ are emitted (or absorbed) when an
electron changes from state to state. The change in energy is given by

$$h\nu = E_1 - E_2 \tag{9–9}$$

where E_1 and E_2 are the respective energies of the two states, and ν is the
frequency of the radiation emitted in the form of a photon.

With Bohr's rules we can calculate the values of the energy of a stationary state. Since for the electron's circular orbit, the electrostatic attraction provides the centripetal force, we have seen that

$$\frac{mv^2}{r} = \frac{Ze^2}{4\pi\epsilon_0 r^2}, \qquad \left[\frac{mv^2}{r} = \frac{Ze^2}{r^2},\right] \tag{9–10}$$

where Z is the number of positive electronic charges (the atomic number)
found on the nucleus. Note that Eq. 9–10 assumes that the nucleus is
fixed. Then we can treat Eq. 9–10 and Eq. 9–8 from Rule 2 as two equations
with two unknowns, r and v, so that

$$r = \frac{n^2 h^2 \epsilon_0}{\pi m e^2 Z}, \qquad \left[r = \frac{n^2 h^2}{4\pi^2 m e^2 Z},\right] \tag{9–11}$$

and

$$v = \frac{Ze^2}{2nh\epsilon_0}. \qquad \left[v = \frac{2\pi Ze^2}{nh}.\right] \tag{9–12}$$

Eq. 9–11 tells us that the radii of the allowed electronic orbits *increase* as
the *square* of n. (See Fig. 9–2.) For hydrogen ($Z = 1$), the value of the
radius of the nth orbit is approximately

$$r_n = 0.53n^2 \text{ angstroms.} \tag{9–13}$$

Therefore, for a hydrogen atom with an electron in its innermost orbit, the radius of the atom is

$$r_1 = 5.3 \times 10^{-11} \text{ m,} \tag{9-14}$$

a value in good agreement with experimentally determined atomic radii.

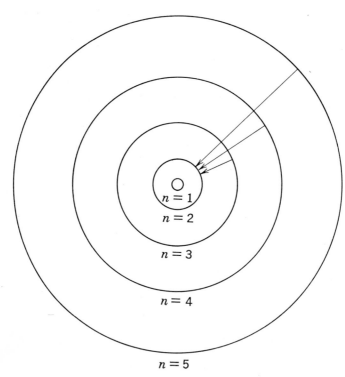

$$n = 1$$
$$n = 2$$
$$n = 3$$
$$n = 4$$
$$n = 5$$

Fig. 9–2.   The first five Bohr circular orbits.   The arrows indicate transitions for three lines of the Balmer series.

The total energy of the electron is the sum of its kinetic energy K and potential energy V. This was computed in Eq. 9–7. If the value of r obtained from Eq. 9–11 is put into this, the result is

$$E_n = -\frac{me^4 Z^2}{8\epsilon_0{}^2 n^2 h^2} \cdot \qquad \left[E_n = -\frac{2\pi^2 me^4 Z^2}{n^2 h^2} \cdot \right] \tag{9-15}$$

The subscript n on E_n indicates that E_n stands for the energy of the nth stationary state. We note that the energy varies *inversely* as the square of the quantum number n. When the values for e and m given in Chapter 6 are inserted in Eq. 9–15 we find that for hydrogen ($Z = 1$),

$$E_n = -\frac{13.6}{n^2} \text{ electron volts.} \tag{9-16}$$

Fig. 9–3 is a plot of these allowed energies, the *energy level diagram* for hydrogen.

The lowest energy level (the level with the largest negative value) is called the *ground state* or the *normal state*. It is the state in which $n = 1$ and therefore that state for which the electron is in the innermost orbit. All the other states are called *excited states* since we must add energy to the electron in order to move it to these states.

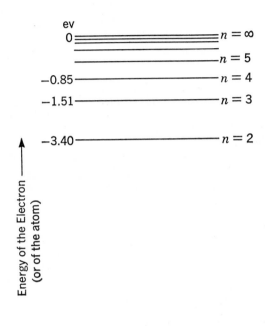

Fig. 9–3. Energy level diagram for hydrogen.

From Eq. 9–15 we can derive an expression for the frequency of the radiation emitted when an electron changes from a high stationary state, n_1, to a lower state, n_2. Rule 3 gives us

$$\nu = \frac{E_1 - E_2}{h}.$$

(9–17)

From Eq. 9–15 we have

$$\nu = \frac{me^4 Z^2}{8\epsilon_0{}^2 h^3} \left(\frac{1}{n_2{}^2} - \frac{1}{n_1{}^2} \right). \qquad \left[\nu = \frac{2\pi^2 me^4 Z^2}{h^3} \left(\frac{1}{n_2{}^2} - \frac{1}{n_1{}^2} \right). \right] \qquad (9\text{–}18)$$

In terms of the wave numbers, $\tilde{\nu} = 1/\lambda = \nu/c$,

$$\tilde{\nu} = \frac{me^4 Z^2}{8\epsilon_0{}^2 h^3 c} \left(\frac{1}{n_2{}^2} - \frac{1}{n_1{}^2} \right). \qquad \left[\tilde{\nu} = \frac{2\pi^2 me^4 Z^2}{h^3 c} \left(\frac{1}{n_2{}^2} - \frac{1}{n_1{}^2} \right). \right] \qquad (9\text{–}19)$$

If we set

$$R = \frac{me^4}{8\epsilon_0{}^2 h^3 c}, \qquad \left[R = \frac{2\pi^2 me^4}{h^3 c}, \right] \qquad (9\text{–}20)$$

then

$$\tilde{\nu} = R Z^2 \left(\frac{1}{n_2{}^2} - \frac{1}{n_1{}^2} \right). \qquad (9\text{–}21)$$

R is called the Rydberg constant. Since $R = 1.097 \times 10^7 \text{ m}^{-1}$ and $Z = 1$ for hydrogen there is excellent agreement between theory and experiment.

The agreement becomes even better when the motion of the nucleus is also taken into account. This can be done by making use of the results of Art. 2–10. The assumption that the nucleus did not move requires that the mass of the electron m must be replaced by the reduced mass μ, where $\mu = mM/(m + M)$, if M is the mass of the nucleus. Inspection of Eq. 9–20 then shows that the more precise form for R should be

$$R = \left(1 + \frac{m}{M} \right)^{-1} R_\infty \qquad (9\text{–}22)$$

in which

$$R_\infty = \frac{me^4}{8\epsilon_0{}^2 h^3 c}. \qquad \left[R_\infty = \frac{2\pi^2 me^4}{h^3 c}. \right]$$

Thus we get three different values for the Rydberg constant for the three isotopes of hydrogen. The slightly different wavelengths that result have made it possible to identify the two heavier isotopes, deuterium and tritium, in which the mass of the nucleus is nearly twice or three times the mass of the nucleus of ordinary hydrogen.

In a similar way the value of R in Eq. 9–21 for atoms such as singly ionized helium and doubly ionized lithium will be different.

Spectral lines can be measured with great precision. As a result, various values of R are well known. For example,

$$R_\infty = 1.09737309 \times 10^7 \text{ m}^{-1},$$
$$R_\text{H} = 1.09677576 \times 10^7 \text{ m}^{-1},$$
$$R_\text{He} = 1.09722267 \times 10^7 \text{ m}^{-1}.$$

We have now shown how Bohr predicted the frequencies and wave numbers of the spectral lines of hydrogen, and that his result is

$$\bar{\nu} = R_H \left(\frac{1}{n_2{}^2} - \frac{1}{n_1{}^2} \right), \tag{9-23}$$

for emitted radiation.

If we set $n_2 = 2$, i.e., make the final state of the electron the second orbit, and let $n_1 = 3, 4, 5$ in turn, we get

$$\bar{\nu} = R_H \left(\frac{1}{2^2} - \frac{1}{n_1{}^2} \right), \tag{9-24}$$

which is exactly Eq. 9-2, the equation for the Balmer series. The lines in the Balmer series are formed when electrons change from the outer orbits to the second orbit. In 1913, when Bohr began this work, a second series called the *Paschen series*, with wavelengths in the infrared region, was also known for hydrogen. The Bohr theory confirmed this series with $n_2 = 3$ and $n_1 = 4, 5, 6, \ldots$, in Eq. 9-23.

The theory also predicts series with $n_2 = 1$, $n_1 = 2, 3, 4, \ldots$, and still others with $n_2 = 4$, and with $n_2 = 5$, etc. Diligent search in the laboratories (1916–1924) verified the presence of these series. They have been called the *Lyman* series ($n_2 = 1$, in the ultraviolet region), the *Brackett* series ($n_2 = 4$, in the far infrared region), and the *Pfund* series ($n_2 = 5$, in the far infrared region), after their discoverers. The transitions leading to the principal lines of these series are shown in Fig. 9-4 on an energy level diagram.

When a hydrogen atom *absorbs* energy, an electron moves into orbits with larger radii and into energy levels with higher (less negative) energy. The *ionization energy* or the *ionization potential* is the energy required to move an electron from the ground state to infinity, that is, to ionize the atom. For hydrogen, 13.6 ev are needed.

Bohr's rules and theory work amazingly well for hydrogen, for the spectra of singly ionized helium, for doubly ionized lithium, etc.—that is, for atoms with a single electron. When more than one electron appears in an atom, Eq. 9-15, which gives the allowed energies of the electron, must be modified. The electrons repel one another and this repulsion changes the energy of the allowed states. Further discussion on this point must await the more general theory of the atom using quantum mechanics.

9-4. Elliptic Orbits and Relativity Effects. Bohr's assumption of circular electron orbits is an obvious oversimplification in the theory. It was pointed out in Chapter 7 that the path of a particle under the influence of an inverse-square force could be an ellipse, parabola, or hyperbola, depending upon the total energy of the particle. Eq. 9-7 shows that the total energy of the electron in a hydrogen atom is negative, so the path is an ellipse. The circular path is just the simplest ellipse.

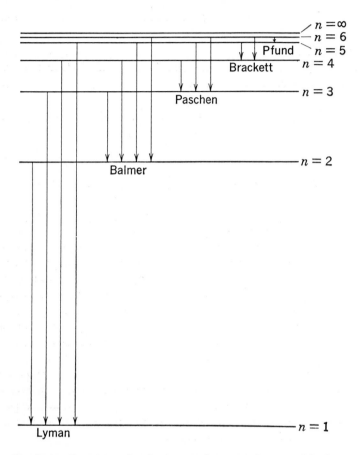

Fig. 9–4.   Transitions for the important spectral series of hydrogen.

Bohr and Sommerfeld investigated the elliptical orbits for the electrons. An electron in an elliptical orbit can be located by the two polar coordinates r and ϕ. There will be momentum associated with both of these coordinates. Rule 2 must be modified to call for the quantization of both momenta. This requires the introduction of two quantum numbers k and n_r. These two quantum numbers determine the shape of the ellipse. The angular momentum J_ϕ must satisfy the requirement that

$$\oint J_\phi \, d\phi = kh, \tag{9–25}$$

and the radial momentum must satisfy

$$\oint p_r \, dr = n_r h. \tag{9-26}$$

The integrals are both to be evaluated over one period of the orbital motion. The quantum number k, the *azimuthal quantum number*, is to be an integer, 1, 2, 3, etc., and the *radial quantum number* n_r also must be an integer, but can take on the value $n_r = 0$. This last case, $n_r = 0$, corresponds to the circular orbits. As n_r increases, the eccentricity also increases. The complete analysis shows that the energy depends only on the sum of k and n_r, the *principal quantum number*,

$$n = n_r + k. \tag{9-27}$$

In fact, the energy of each state is given by Eq. 9-15 in which n should be the n of Eq. 9-27.

The consideration of elliptic orbits thus does not give new energy levels; therefore, new spectral lines should not appear. These elliptic orbits and energy levels are an example of a *degenerate* atomic system, that is, an atomic system described by two quantum numbers, but the two quantum numbers give just one energy value. This result might be expected since classical theory shows that the energy of a particle in an elliptic orbit is determined by the size of the semimajor axis and not by the shape of the orbit. The principal quantum number n determines the size of the semimajor axis. Eq. 9-11 gives the value for the semimajor axis. Of course, in the case of a circle it is also the radius.

The degeneracy is removed, however, by the effects of relativity. Sommerfeld showed that when all the relativistic effects were included the orbits became rosettes (the elliptical orbits precess). The amount of this effect depends upon k, thus removing the degeneracy. Each level of the simple theory is changed by the amount

$$\Delta E_{nk} = - \frac{\mu e^4 Z^4}{8 \epsilon_0{}^2 n^3 h^2} \alpha^2 \left(\frac{1}{k} - \frac{3}{4n} \right), \tag{9-28}$$

$$\left[\Delta E_{nk} = - \frac{2\pi^2 \mu e^4 Z^4}{n^3 h^2} \alpha^2 \left(\frac{1}{k} - \frac{3}{4n} \right), \right]$$

where

$$\alpha = \frac{2\pi e^2}{hc} = \frac{e^2}{\hbar c} = 7.297 \times 10^{-3} \simeq \frac{1}{137}. \tag{9-29}$$

α is called the *fine structure constant*. Note that it forms a dimensionless combination of three particularly important constants of nature.

Since for each value of n, k can take on n values, 1, 2, up to n, each original level will split into n levels very close together as shown in Fig. 9-5.

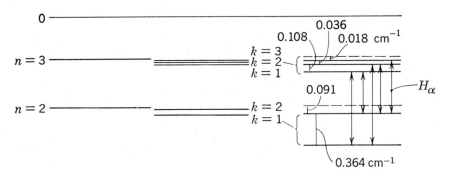

Fig. 9–5. The fine structure of the energy levels of hydrogen (separations are exaggerated).

The separations have been magnified and then magnified again to show the details. Not all transitions are possible. Certain selection rules limit the possibilities. For example, only five transitions are possible for the red Balmer line called the H_α line. It has not been possible to resolve all five, for they are so close together, but two lines such as would be expected from the merging of the two main groups have been resolved. This type of phenomenon is called *fine structure*, which accounts for the name of α.

It is not possible to extend the Bohr theory of the hydrogen atom to more complicated atoms without making quite arbitrary modifications. It is now clear that the success of the Bohr theory was somewhat accidental, but this should not detract from the fact that it was a very big step forward in the understanding of the nature of atoms. More than that, it is still helpful in visualizing some of the features of the structure of more complicated atoms.

The Bohr theory is one more example of the step-by-step development of our understanding of nature.

PROBLEMS

9–1. Make a diagram of a hydrogen atom with a circular electron orbit. (a) Compute the magnitude, in dynes, of the force holding the electron in its innermost orbit, and indicate it on the diagram. (b) From (a), compute the velocity of the electron. Is it relativistic? (c) Compute the frequency of rotation.

9–2. Compute the angular momentum for the electron of Problem 9–1.

9–3. Solve the problem of a satellite rotating about the earth in the same manner as we have treated the hydrogen atom. Recent satellites have had a period of 90 min.

9–4. Compute the potential energy and the kinetic energy of an electron in the first Bohr orbit. What is the relation between them? This problem is an example of the application of the *virial theorem* (see R. B. Lindsay, *Physical Mechanics*, D. Van Nostrand Company, Inc., Princeton, N. J., 1950, p. 159).

9–5. The innermost Bohr orbit has a radius of 0.53 Å. Compute the radius of the 4th orbit.

9–6. The energy of an electron in the innermost Bohr orbit is -13.6 ev. Compute the energy in the $n = 3$ orbit.

9–7. (a) Compute the energy difference in ev between the ground state and the first excited state for hydrogen (the resonance potential). (b) Compute the same energy difference for singly ionized helium.

9–8. Calculate the wave number and wavelengths for the first seven lines of the Balmer series.

9–9. Calculate the wave numbers and wavelengths for the first seven lines of the Lyman series.

9–10. Compute the magnitude of (a) the shortest wavelength possible in the Balmer series, (b) the largest wavelength in the Lyman series. Show from these wavelengths that the ionization potential for hydrogen is 13.6 ev.

9–11. Compute the series limit for the Lyman series of hydrogen.

9–12. Verify that Bohr's theory predicts the value 1.097×10^{-3} Å^{-1} for the Rydberg constant.

9–13. What is the wave number difference between the H_α lines for ordinary hydrogen and for deuterium?

9–14. What is the difference in wavelengths between the H_α lines for ordinary hydrogen and for deuterium?

9–15. What is the highest state to which a hydrogen atom, initially in its lowest state, can be excited by a photon of 12.2 ev energy?

9–16. Determine the total number of spectral lines that can be produced by hydrogen gas if the atoms in the gas are excited to the $n = 4$ state.

9–17. An electron in a hydrogen atom drops from an excited energy level to the one below it and subsequently to the one below that. Show that the sum of the separate frequencies emitted in the two jumps is equal to the frequency emitted in one jump from the high to the lowest.

9–18. Calculate the frequency of the light emitted when $n_i = 4$ and $n_f = 3$, when $n_i = 10$ and $n_f = 9$, and when $n_i = 51$ and $n_f = 50$. Calculate the rotational frequency for the electron for $n = 4$, $n = 10$, and $n = 51$. Do you note any trend?

9–19. Calculate the expression for the frequency of the light emitted when $n_i = n$ and $n_f = n - 1$. Calculate the rotational frequency for the electrons for the nth orbit. What happens as the value of n increases?

9–20. What would be the principal quantum number for which the radius of a hydrogen atom is 1 micron (10^{-6} m)?

9–21. What would be the principal quantum number for a hydrogen atom for which the radius is 1/100 mm?

9–22. Find the energy level difference due to relativity between the two states for $n = 2$. Also find the wave number difference.

9–23. Find the energy level difference and the wave number difference due to relativity between the bottom two states for $n = 3$.

9–24. What is the actual angular momentum according to Sommerfeld-Bohr theory if $n = 4$, and $n_r = 3$?

9–25. An atom of hydrogen has $n = 7$ and $n_r = 2$. What is its angular momentum according to the Sommerfeld-Bohr theory?

9–26. Assume that a particle with a mass of 207 electronic masses and with 1 electronic charge moves around a proton. Calculate the first four energy levels for this "atom."

9–27. An ordinary electron revolving around a positive electron (or vice-versa) is called a "positronium atom." Calculate the first four energy levels for this "atom."

9–28. The π^--meson is a "strange" nuclear particle whose negative charge $= e$ and whose mass is 275 times the electron mass. π^- combines with a proton by rotating in a hydrogen-like orbit around it to form what is known as a "mesic atom." Assuming the proton to be fixed, find the radius of the $n = 1$ orbit of a mesic atom.

9–29. Germanium is an important material in semiconductor technology. Since it has a valence 4 a Ge atom bonds with four other Ge atoms. Sometimes one Ge^{+4} atom core is replaced by arsenic, i.e., by an As^{5+} atom core. When this occurs, four of the five valence electrons of As are bonded to four neighboring Ge atoms thus leaving one electron to be attracted to As^+. Calculate the orbit radius for low temperatures in such a situation, considering that the dielectric constant of Ge is 16.1.

9–30. Compute the energy of the electron in Problem 9–29 and compare it with the binding energy of the hydrogen atom. What wavelength of light would be required to free this electron? Would it be free at room temperature?

SELECTED REFERENCES

BALMER, J. J. "The Hydrogen Spectral Series." In *A Source Book in Physics*. W. F. Magie, ed. McGraw-Hill Book Co., Inc., New York, 1935. P. 360.

BOHR, N. *The Theory of Spectra and Atomic Constitution*. Cambridge Univ. Press, London, 1924. 2d ed., essay I.

WHITE, H. E. *Introduction to Atomic Spectra*. McGraw-Hill Book Co., Inc., New York, 1934. Chap. 1.

10

Simple Harmonic Motion
and Waves

At this point it is desirable to digress again from the regular flow of discussion of modern physics. We are about to begin a discussion of the foundations and the technique of quantum mechanics, but we cannot do this without a background of the mathematics of certain types of differential equations. This background can be developed by a study of simple harmonic motion and it is principally for this reason that we devote this chapter to it. Although the material in this chapter will be somewhat mathematically formal, its applications amply justify its consideration, and perhaps it will arouse an interest in what is basically an exciting portion of mathematics.

Vibratory, harmonic, or periodic motions are very commonplace. Vibrating springs, reeds, strings, forks, structures, machine parts, atoms in crystals, all are examples of this type of motion. Alternating currents and electromagnetic vibrations are other examples of periodic behavior. Often the periodic motion is really quite complicated. But, as we have seen in the past, the use of a simplified or idealized model may shed a great deal of light on the essential features of the process. The model we will use is a mechanical system, but an electrical, acoustical, or other system could serve equally well if it were given an equivalently idealized formulation.

The propagation of energy or of disturbances by waves, the subject of the second half of this chapter, also provides good examples of principles and techniques for use in Chapter 11. In addition, we shall see that there is a close interrelation between the subject of harmonic motions and waves.

10–1. Simple Harmonic Motion and its Differential Equation. The idealized model we shall consider is illustrated in Fig. 10–1. S is a massless spring which exactly obeys Hooke's law. Because of this law, if the spring is stretched an amount x from its undeformed length, it pulls back with a force kx. There are no frictional forces at all. When a mass m is attached and allowed to come to rest, its weight stretches the spring a distance $x_0 = mg/k$ below the unstretched condition. We call this position of rest the *equilibrium position*, designate it $x = 0$, and let upward displacements, velocities, accelerations, and forces be positive. For any general position x of the bob, the set of forces is shown in Fig. 10–2. Since some springs can-

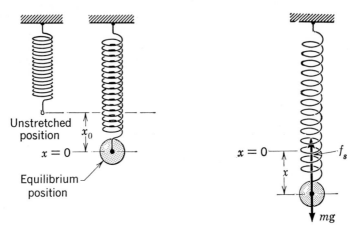

Fig. 10–1.   Spring and mass.   Fig. 10–2.   The forces on
                                        a spring oscillator.

not support a compression, we assume that the mass never rises higher than x_0. The force f_s provided by the spring is

$$f_s = k(x_0 - x). \qquad (10\text{–}1)$$

Remember that $x_0 = mg/k$ and that f_s is positive because it is directed upward. The earth is still pulling downward on the mass. This force (the weight of m) is mg. We find the resultant force by combining these, so that

$$f = f_s - mg = k(x_0 - x) - mg$$
$$= kx_0 - kx - kx_0 = -kx. \qquad (10\text{–}2)$$

Note from Eq. 10–2 that since $f_s - mg = -kx$, if x is positive, the pull of the spring is less than the weight of the bob and the force is down (negative). If x is negative, the pull of the spring is greater than the weight and the resultant force is up (positive).

Before we proceed to discuss this case any further let us reconsider the extent of our approximations or deviations from nature. First, we have assumed the spring obeys Hooke's law; second, we have assumed there are no frictional forces; third, we have neglected the mass of the material in the spring; and fourth, we have directed our attention only to the vertical motion of the bob and have tacitly rejected either the possibility of a pendulum-like motion or any rotational motion about the lengthwise axis of the spring. None of these assumptions hold—no ordinary spring obeys Hooke's law exactly, there are always frictional forces both internal ones and the drag due to air, and the mass of the spring actually participates in the motion. However, such a complete idealization is necessary to make the formulation of the problem easy. The results obtained from this idealization are very helpful in solving problems which do not have such a simple nature.

Newton's second law of motion is next used to obtain what is called the *differential equation of motion* for the system. We have

$$f = ma = -kx,$$

so that

$$a = -\frac{k}{m} x,$$

or

$$\frac{d^2x}{dt^2} = -\frac{k}{m} x. \tag{10–3}$$

It is likely that you will recognize this familiar situation and know that the motion will be *simple harmonic motion*. Eq. 10–3 shows that the acceleration is proportional to the displacement and is oppositely directed (a common definition of simple harmonic motion). It is also likely that you can relate the motion to the projection of uniform circular motion (see almost any text in elementary physics). You may further recall that the motion can be described by the equation

$$x = A \cos\left(\sqrt{\frac{k}{m}}\, t + \Phi\right). \tag{10–4}$$

A is the maximum displacement or *amplitude*, t is the time, and Φ is a constant called the *initial phase*. The motion is repetitive (or periodic) with a period

$$T = 2\pi \sqrt{\frac{m}{k}}. \tag{10–5}$$

Consequently, the frequency or number of full vibrations per second is

$$\nu = \frac{1}{T} = \frac{1}{2\pi} \sqrt{\frac{k}{m}}. \tag{10–6}$$

It is convenient to introduce another quantity ω (sometimes called the angular frequency),

$$\omega = 2\pi\nu = \sqrt{\frac{k}{m}}. \tag{10–7}$$

The properties of trigonometric functions permit Eq. 10–4 to be written

$$x = A \sin\left(\sqrt{\frac{k}{m}}\, t + \Phi'\right), \tag{10–4a}$$

or even as

$$x = a \sin\sqrt{\frac{k}{m}}\, t + b \cos\sqrt{\frac{k}{m}}\, t. \tag{10–4b}$$

In these forms

$$\Phi' = \Phi + \frac{\pi}{2}, \tag{10–8}$$

and

$$A = \sqrt{a^2 + b^2}. \tag{10–9}$$

The plot of x as a function of t is shown in Fig. 10–3.

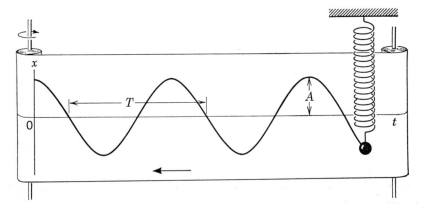

Fig. 10–3.   The trace of position of a bob executing simple harmonic motion versus time, obtained by using a moving tape.

Let us now consider Eq. 10–3 as a formal problem in differential equations in order to introduce some important procedures and ideas concerning differential equations.   Eq. 10–3 can be rewritten as

$$\frac{d^2x}{dt^2} + \frac{k}{m}x = 0. \tag{10–10}$$

We want to determine x as a function of t.

There is no single procedure to be followed in solving such differential equations since many different techniques have been discovered over the years. Much of the "art" of solving differential equations lies in recognizing the easiest approach. Eq. 10–10 will be used to illustrate several methods.

10–2. Solving by Inspection and Test.   One way of solving a problem in mathematics is to make a carefully considered guess and then to test whether the guess is correct. This will be our first method of solving Eq. 10–10.

Note that $x(t)$ and d^2x/dt^2 must be proportional. There are several functions that have this property. Among these are $\cos \omega t$, $\sin \omega t$, and $\exp (rt)$. The second derivatives of the first two of these are $-\omega^2 \cos \omega t$ and $-\omega^2 \sin \omega t$. The second derivative of the third is $r^2 \exp (rt)$. All three derivatives are proportional to the original function, so we shall try them in turn. The first gives, when substituted in Eq. 10–10,

$$-\omega^2 \cos \omega t + \frac{k}{m} \cos \omega t = 0.$$

The second gives

$$-\omega^2 \sin \omega t + \frac{k}{m} \sin \omega t = 0.$$

Both of these will be satisfied if

$$\omega = \pm \sqrt{\frac{k}{m}}. \qquad (10\text{–}11)$$

The third gives

$$r^2 \exp (rt) + \omega^2 \exp (rt) = 0,$$

which can be satisfied only if

$$r = \pm i\omega, \qquad (10\text{–}12)$$

where $i = \sqrt{-1}$ (see Appendix B). Now that we have shown that it is possible to find some solutions that satisfy Eq. 10–10, we look for the most general one.

Since we must integrate twice, essentially, in order to solve a differential equation of the second order (i.e., an equation containing second derivatives), we must expect to see two arbitrary integration constants appear in our complete solution. When the solution contains two undetermined constants such as A and Φ in Eq. 10–4, the solution is called the *general solution*. These two constants in the general solution have their values finally fixed by the manner in which the motion started, or by some other restriction on the motion. These conditions are called *initial conditions* or *boundary conditions* and, since there is a very large number of ways in which the motion can be started or restricted, there are many possible values for the arbitrary constants, and hence many possible solutions. If the arbitrary constants are determined or are prescribed in some given problem, the solution is called the *specialized* solution. At the moment we want only the general not the specialized solution.

It is left to a problem in this chapter to verify that the general solutions

$$x = A \cos (\omega t + \Phi), \qquad (10\text{--}13)$$

$$x = A \sin (\omega t + \Phi'), \qquad (10\text{--}13a)$$

$$x = a \sin \omega t + b \cos \omega t, \qquad (10\text{--}13b)$$

$$x = c \exp (i\omega t) + d \exp (-i\omega t) \qquad (10\text{--}13c)$$

also satisfy the equation. Another problem asks you to verify that all three are equivalent and to find how A, a, b, c, d, Φ, and Φ' are interrelated.

The solution Eq. 10–13c can be seen to be equivalent to the others since

$$\exp (i\omega t) = \cos \omega t + i \sin \omega t, \qquad (10\text{--}14)$$

and since c and d, and even x itself, can be complex quantities (see Appendix B).

10–3. Solving by Direct Integration. The method of the previous article may be hard to apply in cases that are not so easy to guess. Some of the differential equations that cannot be guessed easily can be rearranged and treated by the methods taught in calculus courses in integration. After all, evaluating an integral is nothing but solving a differential equation. The equations

$$F(x) = \int f(x) \, dx + C,$$

and

$$f(x) = \frac{dF}{dx}$$

are practically the same.

The equation of motion for simple harmonic motion can be put into standard form for integration, as we shall now see. Eq. 10–10 can be rewritten

$$\frac{d^2x}{dt^2} = \frac{dv}{dt} = -\omega^2 x$$

where $a = dv/dt$, and we have abbreviated $k/m = \omega^2$. This can be rewritten again in the form

$$\frac{dv}{dx} \frac{dx}{dt} = -\omega^2 x$$

or

$$v \, dv = -\omega^2 x \, dx. \qquad (10\text{--}15)$$

We now integrate both sides of Eq. 10–15,

$$\int v \, dv = -\omega^2 \int x \, dx$$

or

$$\frac{v^2}{2} = -\frac{\omega^2}{2} x^2 + C_1. \tag{10–16}$$

At this point it should be noted that the first integration constant has appeared. To put this in a more convenient form we note that there will be some position, call it $x = A$, for which $v = 0$. This determines the value of C_1, for

$$0 = -\frac{\omega^2}{2} A^2 + C_1$$

or

$$C_1 = \frac{\omega^2}{2} A^2. \tag{10–17}$$

Eq. 10–16 then becomes

$$\frac{v^2}{2} = \frac{\omega^2}{2} (A^2 - x^2) = \frac{1}{2}\left(\frac{dx}{dt}\right)^2, \tag{10–18}$$

which can be written

$$\frac{dx}{dt} = \pm\omega\sqrt{A^2 - x^2},$$

or

$$\frac{dx}{\sqrt{A^2 - x^2}} = \pm\omega \, dt. \tag{10–19}$$

The integral of Eq. 10–19 is

$$\sin^{-1}\frac{x}{A} = \pm\omega t + \Phi', \tag{10–20}$$

or

$$x = A \sin(\pm\omega t + \Phi'). \tag{10–21}$$

Note the appearance of the second integration constant Φ'. The double sign $\pm$ plays no basic role because a change of choice of sign only changes the sign of A and Φ'. So we are back at our previous solution, Eq. 10–13a.

The two methods we have discussed are by no means the only ones that can be used to solve this equation.

EXAMPLE. Discuss the motion of a simple harmonic oscillator in which $m = 0.064$ kg and $k = 4.9$ newtons m^{-1}.

With such a spring the weight of the mass will stretch the spring an amount

$$x_0 = \frac{0.064 \times 9.8}{4.9} = 0.128 \text{ m.}$$

The values of m and k determine the period, frequency, and angular frequency.

$$T = 2\pi \sqrt{\frac{m}{k}} = 2\pi \sqrt{\frac{0.064}{4.9}} = 2\pi \frac{8}{70} = 0.717 \text{ sec,}$$

$$\nu = \frac{1}{2\pi} \sqrt{\frac{k}{m}} = \frac{1}{T} = 1.39 \text{ vibrations/sec,} \qquad (10\text{--}22)$$

$$\omega = \sqrt{\frac{k}{m}} = \frac{70}{8} = 8.75 \text{ radians/sec.}$$

The motion will thus be described by

$$x = A \cos (8.75t + \Phi), \qquad (10\text{--}23)$$

$$x = A \sin (8.75t + \Phi'), \qquad (10\text{--}23\text{a})$$

$$x = a \sin 8.75t + b \cos 8.75t. \qquad (10\text{--}23\text{b})$$

The constants of these equations depend upon the way the motion starts. As an illustration of the determination of these constants, consider what would happen if the bob were pulled down 0.03 m and then let go. The initial conditions would be

$$x = -0.03,$$
$$v = \frac{dx}{dt} = 0, \qquad (10\text{--}24)$$

all at $t = 0$.

Let us start with Eq. 10–23,

$$x = A \cos (8.75t + \Phi),$$

$$v = \frac{dx}{dt} = -8.75 A \sin (8.75t + \Phi).$$

The initial conditions give

$$-0.03 = A \cos (0 + \Phi), \qquad (10\text{--}25)$$

$$0 = -8.75 A \sin (0 + \Phi). \qquad (10\text{--}26)$$

Eq. 10–26 requires that Φ be 0 or π. If we chose $\Phi = 0$, then Eq. 10–25 requires that $A = -0.03$. Thus the final description of the motion is,

$$x = -0.03 \cos 8.75t \text{ m.} \qquad (10\text{--}27)$$

If we had started with Eq. 10–23a we would have had, using the same initial conditions,

$$-0.03 = A \sin (0 + \Phi'), \tag{10–28}$$

$$0 = 8.75 \, A \cos (0 + \Phi'). \tag{10–29}$$

In Eq. 10–29 the cosine will be zero if $\Phi' = \pi/2$ (or $-\pi/2$) and using this with Eq. 10–28 gives $A = -0.03$, so

$$x = -0.03 \sin \left(8.75t + \frac{\pi}{2}\right). \tag{10–30}$$

This is really the same as Eq. 10–27. Finally, if we had started with Eq. 10–23b, we would have had

$$-0.03 = a \sin 0 + b \cos 0 \tag{10–31}$$

$$0 = 8.75 \, a \cos 0 - 8.75b \sin 0. \tag{10–32}$$

In order that Eq. 10–32 can hold, we must set $a = 0$. Then Eq. 10–31 determines that $b = -0.03$ and again we have

$$x = -0.03 \cos 8.75t. \tag{10–33}$$

Other types of initial conditions are treated in a similar way. The problems will give you some experience determining the arbitrary constants once you know the initial conditions, a very important technique.

10–4. Energy Relations in Simple Harmonic Motion. The first integration of Art. 10–3 shows some interesting relations about the various distributions of energy in a system undergoing simple harmonic motion. In fact, it is sometimes called the *energy integral*. Eq. 10–16 becomes

$$\frac{v^2}{2} = -\frac{k}{2m} x^2 + C_1, \tag{10–34}$$

since $\omega^2 = k/m$. This can be written

$$\tfrac{1}{2}mv^2 + \tfrac{1}{2}kx^2 = mC_1 = E. \tag{10–35}$$

The first term is the kinetic energy of the mass. The second term is the potential energy stored in the spring. Note that the sum is a constant, as you would expect. When $v = 0$, $x = A$, so

$$E = \tfrac{1}{2}kA^2. \tag{10–36}$$

When $x = 0$, $v = A\omega = A\sqrt{k/m}$, so

$$E = \frac{1}{2} mA^2\omega^2 = \frac{1}{2} mA^2 \frac{k}{m} = \frac{1}{2} kA^2. \tag{10–36a}$$

For any value of t,

$$E = \tfrac{1}{2}mA^2\omega^2 \sin^2(\omega t + \Phi) + \tfrac{1}{2}kA^2 \cos^2(\omega t + \Phi)$$
$$= \tfrac{1}{2}kA^2 [\sin^2(\omega t + \Phi) + \cos^2(\omega t + \Phi)]$$
$$= \tfrac{1}{2}kA^2. \tag{10-36b}$$

In the example of Art. 10–3, the maximum potential energy is

$$E = \tfrac{1}{2} \times 4.9 \times (0.03)^2 = 2.205 \times 10^{-3}\ \text{j}.$$

The maximum kinetic energy is

$$E = \tfrac{1}{2} \times 64 \times (0.03 \times \tfrac{7.0}{8})^2 = 2.205 \times 10^{-3}\ \text{j},$$

since the maximum velocity is ωA, in this case $0.03 \times \tfrac{7.0}{8}$ m sec^{-1}. We really should say simply that at all times the total energy is $E = 2.205 \times 10^{-3}$ j. There is a continuous redistribution of the energy between the kinetic energy of the bob and the potential energy of the spring.

10–5. Angular Harmonic Motion. The results we have found for linear motion can be used equally well for angular motion. Examples are torsion pendulums, ballistic galvanometers, balance wheels of clocks, etc. The equations are entirely analogous to those with which we have just worked.

For a system rotating about an axis and having a moment of inertia, I, about that axis, Newton's second law gives

$$L = I\alpha \qquad \text{or} \qquad \frac{d^2\Theta}{dt^2} = \frac{L}{I} \tag{10-37}$$

where Θ is the angular displacement and α is the angular acceleration. If there is a restoring torque that obeys Hooke's law,

$$L = -K\Theta. \tag{10-38}$$

The equation of motion is

$$\frac{d^2\Theta}{dt^2} = -\frac{K}{I}\Theta. \tag{10-39}$$

The solution of this is

$$\Theta = A \cos\left(\sqrt{\frac{K}{I}}\,t + \Phi\right) = A \cos(\omega t + \Phi)$$
$$= A \sin\left(\sqrt{\frac{K}{I}}\,t + \Phi'\right)$$
$$= a \sin\sqrt{\frac{K}{I}}\,t + b \cos\sqrt{\frac{K}{I}}\,t. \tag{10-40}$$

The period of the motion is

$$T = 2\pi \sqrt{\frac{I}{K}} ;\tag{10-41}$$

the frequency is

$$\nu = \frac{1}{T} = \frac{1}{2\pi} \sqrt{\frac{K}{I}} ;\tag{10-42}$$

and the angular frequency is

$$\omega = \sqrt{\frac{K}{I}} .\tag{10-43}$$

This ω is not to be confused with $\Omega = d\Theta/dt$. The total energy is

$$E = \frac{1}{2} KA^2 = \frac{1}{2} I\Omega_{\text{max}}^2$$

$$= \frac{1}{2} IA^2\omega^2 = \frac{1}{2} IA^2 \frac{K}{I}\tag{10-44}$$

since $\Omega = d\Theta/dt = -A\omega \sin(\omega t + \Phi)$.

10–6. Damped Harmonic Motion. If all the approximations that lead to the equations of simple harmonic motion are not made, the results, of course, are changed. The distributed mass of the spring can be accommodated by using an effective mass greater than the mass of the bob; but to include the possible pendulum-like motion and torsion of a linear spring leads to a rather complicated motion. The effect of frictional forces, however, can be handled fairly easily if one assumes that these forces have a simple viscous nature in which the force is always oppositely directed to the velocity and proportional to the speed. When the additional force of friction

$$f_f = -nv = -n\frac{dx}{dt}\tag{10-45}$$

is added to the other forces, the equation of motion becomes

$$m\frac{d^2x}{dt^2} = -kx - n\frac{dx}{dt},$$

or

$$\frac{d^2x}{dt^2} + \frac{n}{m}\frac{dx}{dt} + \frac{k}{m}x = 0.\tag{10-46}$$

The constant n introduced here describes the magnitude of the frictional force. Eq. 10–46 is somewhat more difficult to solve than Eq. 10–10. Three types of solutions occur depending upon the relative size of $n/2m$ and $\sqrt{k/m}$. If $n/2m > \sqrt{k/m}$, there will be no free oscillation and the bob will simply return to the equilibrium position after it has been displaced. If $n/2m = \sqrt{k/m}$, there will still be no oscillation, but the return to equilibrium is more rapid. If $n/2m < \sqrt{k/m}$, the system will oscillate following the form

$$x = A \exp\left(\frac{-n}{2m} t\right) \cos (\omega' t + \Phi) \qquad (10\text{--}47)$$

where

$$\omega' = \sqrt{\frac{k}{m} - \frac{n^2}{4m^2}}.$$

Such a motion is illustrated in Fig. 10–4. The last case is called *damped*

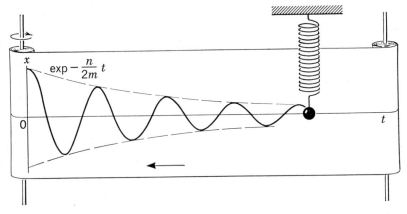

Fig. 10–4. Trace of a damped harmonic vibration.

harmonic motion; the second case is called *critically damped motion*; and the first case is called *overdamped motion*.

10–7. Introduction to Waves. We have just studied some aspects of periodic motion and now we shall examine wave motion as an extension of that discussion. Although wave motion is a topic of *classical* physics, it is an important feature of many branches of physics and is particularly helpful in modern physics. Waves on the surface of water are familiar to all of us. Pressure waves in air and displacement waves on strings, diaphragms, plates, rods, and similar objects are other examples of wave motion, and the study of such waves is known as acoustics. Variations in electric and magnetic fields are propagated as electromagnetic waves. Electromagnetic waves take us into the field of communications (radio, television, radar), optics, or x-rays, depending upon the frequency of these waves. Many other examples of the wave concept in the field of physics

and of engineering can be found.   Much of the development of the theory
of waves and the experimental studies were made in the middle of the
nineteenth century by such men as Helmholtz (1821–1894), Lord Rayleigh
(1842–1919), Maxwell (1831–1879) and Hertz (1857–1894).   Although
many of their results had little application at the time, recent developments
in physics and engineering have often leaned heavily upon this early work.

The fundamental characteristic of a wave is that a change in something
produces a similar effect at a remote place later and at still more remote
places still later.   What is changed may be the displacement of a piece of
a string, the position of a drop of water, the pressure of air, the electric
and magnetic fields, or many other things.   As different as these examples
are, it turns out that the important features are all described by equations
which are very similar for all cases.   In fact, the equations are so similar
that there is a tendency to speak of *the wave equation*.   Perhaps the simplest
case is that of a wave traveling along a very long string.   We will use it
as the example to introduce the characteristics of wave motion and to
illustrate some of the techniques for treating wave propagation.

10–8. The Wave Equation for a Stretched String.   We will now derive
the wave equation for waves traveling in a long, perfectly flexible, stretched
string.   The string must be long (in fact, infinitely long to avoid the complications of reflections), perfectly flexible to eliminate considerations of
friction, and stretched so that a tension $\mathcal{T}$ exists in the string.   The string
can be thought of as being set into motion by the transverse vibration of
a rod as suggested in Fig. 10–5 in which three complete vibrations have

Vibrator

Fig 10–5.   Wave propagation on a string.

occurred since the first disturbance started along the string.   Let us
examine a short element of the string of length Δs and having mass $\mu \Delta s$,
where μ is the mass of a unit length of the string.   This element is pictured
in Fig. 10–6, at a position x along the string and at a small displacement y
above the equilibrium axis.

The tension at each end of the piece of string can be resolved into x
and y components to determine the resultant force on the mass of that
portion of the string.   Newton's second law then gives the acceleration of
this differential portion of string.   The x-component of the resultant forces
and the y-component are respectively,

$$F_x = -\mathcal{T} \cos \theta_1 + \mathcal{T} \cos \theta_2 \qquad (10\text{–}48)$$

and

$$F_y = -\mathcal{T} \sin \theta_1 + \mathcal{T} \sin \theta_2. \qquad (10\text{--}49)$$

Since $\cos \theta = 1 - \theta^2/2 + \theta^4/4! \cdots$, and since the angles are small, the x-components add to zero, thus

$$
\begin{aligned}
F_x &= -\mathcal{T} \, (\cos \theta_1 - \cos \theta_2) \\
&= -\mathcal{T} \, (1 - 1) = 0.
\end{aligned} \qquad (10\text{--}50)
$$

The result is not surprising for one does not expect, or find, any appreciable motion of the string along its length. The motion is all transverse. The

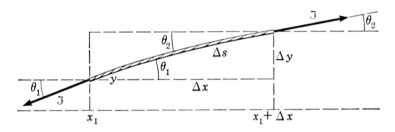

Fig. 10–6.   A differential element of string showing forces.

determination of the y-components can also be seen from Fig. 10–6. At the left end of the elementary length of string, the geometry of Fig. 10–6 gives

$$\sin \theta_1 = \left. \lim_{\Delta x \to 0} \frac{\Delta y}{\sqrt{\Delta x^2 + \Delta y^2}} \right]_{\substack{\text{evaluated} \\ \text{at } x_1}} = \left. \frac{\dfrac{dy}{dx}}{\sqrt{1 + \left(\dfrac{dy}{dx}\right)^2}} \right|_{\substack{\text{evaluated} \\ \text{at } x_1}} ,$$

and at the right end

$$\sin \theta_2 = \left. \lim_{\Delta x \to 0} \frac{\Delta y}{\sqrt{\Delta x^2 + \Delta y^2}} \right]_{\substack{\text{evaluated} \\ \text{at } x_2}} = \left. \frac{\dfrac{dy}{dx}}{\sqrt{1 + \left(\dfrac{dy}{dx}\right)^2}} \right|_{\substack{\text{evaluated} \\ \text{at } x_2 = \\ x_1 + \Delta x}} .$$

In the examples of interest to us the string is bent so little by the wave that the slope is much smaller than 1; so the denominator in each of these expressions may be taken to be 1. When this is done, Eq. 10–49 becomes

$$F_y = \mathcal{T} \left[\left(\frac{dy}{dx}\right)_{x_1 + \Delta x} - \left(\frac{dy}{dx}\right)_{x_1} \right]. \qquad (10\text{--}51)$$

The forces described by Eq. 10–50 and Eq. 10–51 can be put into Newton's second law of motion. The trivial result of Eq. 10–50 needs no further development, it simply says that there is no acceleration along the length of the string. On the other hand, Eq. 10–51 requires more attention. The mass accelerated by the forces described by that equation is the mass of the differential piece of string between x and $x + \Delta x$. Its mass is $\mu \Delta S = \mu \, \Delta x / \cos \theta = \mu \Delta x$, so

$$ma_y = \mu_\Delta x \frac{\partial^2 y}{\partial t^2} = \mathcal{T} \left[\left(\frac{dy}{dx} \right)_{x_1 + \Delta x} - \left(\frac{dy}{dx} \right)_{x_1} \right]. \tag{10-52}$$

If this is divided by Δx and taken to the limit as $\Delta x \to 0$, the result is

$$\mu \frac{\partial^2 y}{\partial t^2} = \mathcal{T} \lim_{\Delta x \to 0} \frac{\Delta \left(\frac{dy}{dx} \right)}{\Delta x} = \mathcal{T} \frac{\partial^2 y}{\partial x^2}. \tag{10-53}$$

The "round" d's (∂) represent *partial derivatives*. The displacement y of an element of string is a function of both x, its location along the string, and t, the time; thus $y = y(x,t)$. The symbol $\partial y / \partial t$ indicates differentiation of y with respect to t keeping x a constant. In doing this, we discover partly how y changes, and hence the name "partial derivative." $\partial^2 y / \partial t^2$ indicates differentiation a second time with respect to t, still keeping x constant. In a similar way, $\partial y / \partial x$ and $\partial^2 y / \partial x^2$ are the first and second derivatives of y with respect to x, with t kept constant, and again they are called partial derivatives. We rewrite this equation

$$\frac{\mathcal{T}}{\mu} \frac{\partial^2 y}{\partial x^2} = \frac{\partial^2 y}{\partial t^2}, \tag{10-54}$$

since it is the result we have been seeking, namely, *the wave equation*. What is shown in essence by Eq. 10–54 is that the accelerating force on an element of string is proportional to the curvature of this string $\partial^2 y / \partial x^2$ at that particular moment.

The treatment of other mechanical examples such as those mentioned in Art. 10–7 lead to equivalent conclusions. Electromagnetic waves are non-mechanical but the nature of the relations between electrical and magnetic effects again leads to a similar equation containing second derivatives. Waves on the surface of a liquid would be described by a two dimensional wave equation while sound waves in a gas would require a three dimensional wave equation (as would light waves in space). The typical three dimensional wave equation for a scalar quantity ϕ is

$$U^2 \left[\frac{\partial^2 \phi}{\partial x^2} + \frac{\partial^2 \phi}{\partial y^2} + \frac{\partial^2 \phi}{\partial z^2} \right] = \frac{\partial^2 \phi}{\partial t^2}. \tag{10-55}$$

This is often written in the abbreviated form

$$U^2\nabla^2\phi = \frac{\partial^2\phi}{\partial t^2}\ .$$

The symbol $\nabla^2\phi$, which is simply a shorthand notation for the bracketed quantity in Eq. 10–55, is read "the Laplacian of ϕ" or sometimes "del squared ϕ."

10–9. The General Form of the Solution. The wave equation, Eq. 10–54, contains a tremendous amount of information and successfully describes a wide variety of situations. If we continue to let y denote the displacement of a stretched string from its equilibrium position, this equation contains nearly all that is needed to predict the behavior of such a string. We need, in addition, only the initial condition of the string and any boundary conditions such as what points are clamped.

We will look at the significance of the wave equation from a number of different approaches in order to abstract as much as we can from it. One of the most important things to realize is that any displacement is felt either to the right or left (or both) at a later time and that all effects are propagated along the string at a velocity, $V = \sqrt{\mathcal{T}/\mu}$. It is just this propagation property that leads to the name "wave."

First, it will be shown that any function which contains the independent variables x and t in either the combination $x - Vt$ or $x + Vt$, is a solution of the wave equation, Eq. 10–54. That is, either

$$y = f(x - Vt) \tag{10–56}$$

or

$$y = f(x + Vt) \tag{10–57}$$

is a solution of the wave equation (where f means any function of $(x \pm Vt)$ that can be differentiated twice). In fact, any linear combination of both forms such as

$$y = f(x - Vt) + g(x + Vt), \tag{10–58}$$

is a solution.

To show that y in Eq. 10–56 is a solution, let $u = x - Vt$ so that we have $y = f(u)$. That is, y is any function of the variable u. The quantity u is called the *phase* of y. Then

$$\frac{\partial y}{\partial x} = \frac{dy}{du}\frac{\partial u}{\partial x} = \frac{dy}{du},$$

since

$$\frac{\partial u}{\partial x} = \frac{d(x - Vt)}{dx}\bigg|_{t\,=\,\text{constant}} = 1.$$

A second differentiation gives

$$\frac{\partial^2 y}{\partial x^2} = \frac{\partial}{\partial x}\left(\frac{dy}{du}\right) = \frac{d^2 y}{du^2}.$$ (10–59)

In a similar way

$$\frac{\partial y}{\partial t} = \frac{dy}{du}\frac{\partial u}{\partial t} = -V\frac{dy}{du},$$

since

$$\frac{\partial u}{\partial t} = \frac{\partial}{\partial t}(x - Vt) = -V,$$

and

$$\frac{\partial^2 y}{\partial t^2} = V^2\frac{d^2 y}{du^2}.$$ (10–60)

If these results are put into Eq. 10–54 we see that it is satisfied if $V = \sqrt{\mathcal{T}/\mu}$, since we have

$$V^2\frac{d^2 y}{du^2} = \frac{\mathcal{T}}{\mu}\frac{d^2 y}{du^2},$$ (10–61)

confirming the original statement that $f(x - Vt)$ is a solution of Eq. 10–54. Note that $V = \sqrt{\mathcal{T}/\mu}$ is a constant, independent of the state of vibration of the string.

It is left to the reader to prove that $y = f(x + Vt)$ is also a suitable solution to Eq. 10–54.

Now the meaning of such a relation as $y = f(u) = f(x - Vt)$ will be demonstrated. The function $f(u)$ can be determined and plotted as shown in Fig. 10–7. At the instant $t = 0$, $u = x$, so the plot of Fig. 10–7a is the plot of y versus x at $t = 0$. At a time $t_1 > 0$, a particular value of the phase u, and hence a given displacement y, will be found at a larger value of x, since $u = x - Vt$. That is, in order to keep the value of u constant, since t is increasing, x must also increase. In fact, the point at which that value of u will be found moves in the positive x direction at the speed V so V is called the *phase velocity*. Thus it will be seen that the pattern of displacement y as given by $f(u)$, will move in the positive x direction without change in shape at the speed V. Fig. 10–7b and Fig. 10–7c show the way the function of Fig. 10–7a has been transformed for two later times t_1 and t_2.

The conclusion that $y = f(x - Vt)$ represents a disturbance moving in the positive x direction with speed V can be arrived at more formally by simply computing dx/dt for $u =$ a constant.

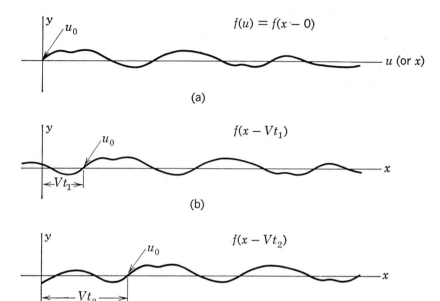

Fig. 10–7.   Wave propagation.

Since $u = x - Vt$ a constant, the differentiation with respect to t gives

$$\frac{dx}{dt} - V = 0$$

or

$$\left(\frac{dx}{dt}\right)_{u=\text{constant}} = +V \qquad (10\text{–}62)$$

We leave it to the reader to go through a similar reasoning process to see what is indicated by $y = f(x + Vt)$.   Either of these solutions is called a *traveling wave*.

10–10. The Separation of Variables.   The differential wave equation can be solved by trying a function $y(x,t)$ that is a product of functions of each of the independent variables x and t.   To do this we write

$$y(x,t) = X(x)\,T(t) \qquad (10\text{–}63)$$

where $X(x)$ and $T(t)$ are unknown functions, but depend only on one variable each.   Substitution in Eq. 10–54 gives

$$V^2 T \frac{d^2 X}{dx^2} = X \frac{d^2 T}{dt^2}, \qquad (10\text{–}64)$$

where V^2 has been written for $\mathfrak{T}/\mu$. The use of ordinary derivatives is proper since X is only a function of x, and since T is only a function of t. Dividing by the product XT, gives

$$V^2 \frac{1}{X} \frac{d^2X}{dx^2} = \frac{1}{T} \frac{d^2T}{dt^2}. \tag{10–65}$$

It can be seen that the wave equation has been separated into two expressions, each containing only one variable. This equation can only be true if both sides are equal to some constant. For convenience, let the constant be $-\omega^2$. Then

$$\frac{d^2T}{dt^2} = -\omega^2 T \tag{10–66}$$

and

$$\frac{d^2X}{dx^2} = -\frac{\omega^2}{V^2} X. \tag{10–67}$$

These are the equations of simple harmonic motion; so their solutions are

$$T = a \sin \omega t \qquad \text{or} \qquad b \cos \omega t,$$

$$X = c \sin \frac{\omega}{V} x \qquad \text{or} \qquad d \cos \frac{\omega}{V} x. \tag{10–68}$$

Then

$$y = TX = e \sin \omega t \sin \frac{\omega}{V} x,$$

or

$$= f \sin \omega t \cos \frac{\omega}{V} x,$$

or

$$= g \cos \omega t \sin \frac{\omega}{V} x, \tag{10–69}$$

or

$$= h \cos \omega t \cos \frac{\omega}{V} x$$

will satisfy the wave equation. Of course, any linear combination of these forms will also work and the general solution is

$$y = A \sin \omega t \sin \frac{\omega}{V} x + B \sin \omega t \cos \frac{\omega}{V} x$$

$$+ C \cos \omega t \sin \frac{\omega}{V} x + D \cos \omega t \cos \frac{\omega}{V} x. \tag{10–70}$$

As a special case let $A = D = 0$ and let $B = -C$ giving

$$y = C \cos \omega t \sin \frac{\omega}{V} x - C \sin \omega t \cos \frac{\omega}{V} x$$

$$= C \sin \left(\frac{\omega x}{V} - \omega t \right) = C \sin \frac{\omega}{V} (x - Vt). \qquad (10\text{--}71)$$

This has the same form as Eq. 10–56 in which $f(x - Vt)$ is a sinusoidal function. A plot of it is given in Fig. 10–8 for both $t = 0$ and for a slightly

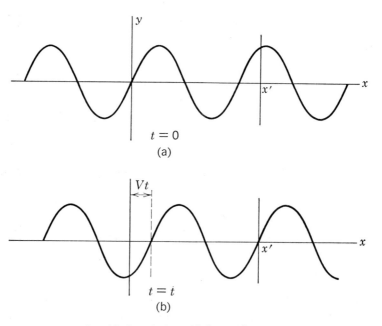

Fig. 10–8.   A sinusoidal traveling wave.

later time. Note that for any one point such as at x' the motion is only up and down.

Since the *pattern* moves to the right, this is called a traveling wave as mentioned in the previous article. Again, we ask the reader to note what happens if $A = D = 0$, and if $B = +C$. Two other interesting cases are those for which $B = C = 0$ and $D = A$, and for which $B = C = 0$ and $A = -D$.

Because of the representation of the time-function by the letter T, we will now represent the period by the letter τ. Thus we can write $\omega = 2\pi/\tau$

so that for a wave traveling in the $+x$ direction

$$y = A \sin \omega \left(t - \frac{x}{V} \right)$$

$$= A \sin 2\pi \left(\frac{t}{\tau} - \frac{x}{V\tau} \right).$$

Now $V\tau$ is just the distance the wave travels in one period. It is the distance from crest to neighboring crest, or trough to neighboring trough. We call this quantity the wavelength, and designate it by λ. Therefore,

$$y = A \sin 2\pi \left(\frac{t}{\tau} - \frac{x}{\lambda} \right). \qquad (10\text{–}72)$$

The relation between τ, λ, and V is

$$\lambda = V\tau \qquad (10\text{–}73)$$

and since the period τ is the reciprocal of the frequency ν then

$$\lambda\nu = V. \qquad (10\text{–}74)$$

EXAMPLE 1.   A string which has a mass of 0.02 kg for 4 m ($\mu = 0.02/4 = 0.005$ kg m^{-1}) is stretched by a mass of 3 kg hanging on the end ($\mathcal{T} = 3 \times 9.80 = 29.4$ newtons). It will propagate a wave at a speed $V = \sqrt{29.4/.005} = 76.5$ m sec^{-1}. If the period of the sinusoidal motion is $1/200$ sec ($\nu = 200$ sec^{-1}), the wavelength is $(1/200) \times 76.5 = 0.3825$ m.

A wave described by Eq. 10–72 may be said to be *monochromatic, plane-polarized*; monochromatic because it has a single, well-defined wavelength λ, and plane-polarized because the particles of the string vibrate on a plane.

It should be noted that the wave form is propagated down the string because each small portion dx of the string is directly fastened to the next one. The force between the elements is supplied by the tension. Some similar mechanism is required for all wave propagation. If we have a three-dimensional medium, transverse waves can only be transmitted if the medium can resist a shear. The shear modulus n then becomes important in the study of waves in a solid. In fact, the velocity of such a transverse wave V is given by

$$V = \sqrt{\frac{n}{\rho}} \qquad (10\text{–}75)$$

where ρ is the density of the solid. (Note how n fills an analogous role to $\mathcal{T}$.) It is also possible to have waves involving pressure changes. In such a case, the oscillatory motion of the particles in the medium is parallel to the direction of propagation (hence these are called *longitudinal waves*). Liquids and gases can transmit such waves. The elastic constant of importance for these waves is the bulk modulus β and

$$V = \sqrt{\frac{\beta}{\rho}} \cdot \qquad (10\text{--}76)$$

In the case of electromagnetic waves the relation between electric and magnetic effects replace the mechanical relations and lead to

$$V = c = \frac{1}{\sqrt{\mu_0 \epsilon_0}} \cdot \qquad (10\text{--}77)$$

10–11. Standing Waves—The Principle of Superposition—Interference. Consider a string which has been shortened to some finite length L. The string can be terminated in various ways. For example, it can be terminated by attaching it to a device that oscillates and feeds energy into the string, a somewhat complicated situation; it can be terminated by fastening it to a wall with a spring (yielding support that will absorb energy from

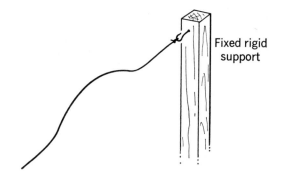

Fixed rigid support

Fig. 10–9.   A string with fixed termination at one end.

the string), also a rather complicated case; it can be terminated by leaving the end of the string entirely free (by hanging the string vertically); or it can be terminated by rigidly fastening one end of the string. The last of these cases will be considered now.

When the end of the string is rigidly fixed, one can write $y = 0$ at $x = L$ for all times t. Such a restriction as this is known as a *boundary condition*.

If an upward pulse is traveling along the string (see Fig. 10–9), the string will exert a force upward on the support when the pulse reaches it. The equal and opposite reaction by the support on the string is equivalent to the injection of an equal pulse of opposite sign traveling in the opposite direction. Thus a reflected pulse travels back along the string with the same amplitude, but with a reversed deflection (see Fig. 10–10).

If a sinusoidal wave such as we discussed in Art. 10–10 approaches the wall, its succession of positive and negative pulses will be reflected with reversed deflection. In such a case, we have waves of the same amplitude, frequency, and wavelength traveling in opposite directions along the string, and we should investigate how they combine. The principle which determines this is the *principle of superposition* (stated first by Young, 1802). This principle says that *the actual displacement of any point of the string is the algebraic sum of the displacements of the individual waves.* Further, when two waves travel out of a region of "interference," *the waves behave as if they had not interfered with one another.* An important example of the validity of this principle is the observation that two beams of light passing at right angles through one another are unaffected, yet they can combine to form fringes such as those formed by a Michelson interferometer.

We now select a cosine solution for a wave traveling toward the right on the string and write it as

$$y_1 = C_1 \cos 2\pi \left(\frac{t}{\tau} - \frac{x}{\lambda} \right), \tag{10–78}$$

and similarly for one traveling toward the left

$$y_2 = -C_1 \cos 2\pi \left(\frac{t}{\tau} + \frac{x}{\lambda} \right). \tag{10–79}$$

The principle of superposition gives for the resultant,

$$y = y_1 + y_2 = C_1 \left[\cos 2\pi \left(\frac{t}{\tau} - \frac{x}{\lambda} \right) - \cos 2\pi \left(\frac{t}{\tau} + \frac{x}{\lambda} \right) \right],$$

and since

$$\cos (a - b) - \cos (a + b) = 2 \sin a \sin b,$$

the resultant is

$$y = 2C_1 \sin \frac{2\pi t}{\tau} \sin \frac{2\pi x}{\lambda}. \tag{10–80}$$

This equation can also be obtained from Eq. 10–70 by letting $B = C = D = 0$. This equation shows us that at any fixed value of x we select, the displacement y of the string is varying periodically at a frequency $1/\tau = \nu$ except where $\sin (2\pi x/\lambda) = 0$, i.e., where $2\pi x/\lambda = n\pi$, or where $x = \lambda/2$, λ, $3\lambda/2 \cdots$. At these values of x, $y = 0$ *for all times*. These points are the nodes familiar in the Melde's experiment of a taut string attached to a vibrator usually performed in the elementary physics laboratory. We note that the nodes are spaced one-half wavelength apart, and that midway

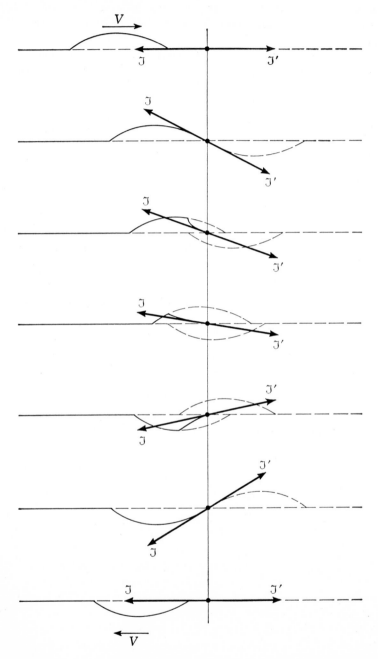

Fig. 10–10.   The reflections of a pulse on a string at a clamped end.

between them ($x = \lambda/4$, etc.) are the antinodes or *loops* where the displacement reaches a maximum $y = 2C_1$ but varies from $+2C_1$ to $-2C_1$ at a frequency $\nu = 1/\tau$.

These waves are standing waves, that is, the wave form does not move along the string but appears to remain stationary so that, as we watch the string, it might appear as in Fig. 10–11. Also note that all points between

Fig. 10–11. Standing waves on a string clamped at one end (Melde's experiment).

each pair of nodes vibrate *in phase* with one another while those in an adjacent loop will have a phase differing by 180°.

10–12. A Uniform String Fastened at Both Ends. This is the most usual case of a vibrating string as, for example, in a violin, piano, or other stringed instrument. A wave placed on the string travels to one end, is reflected, travels to the other, is re-reflected and so on. Standing waves again occur, but now both ends must be nodes. Two boundary conditions now apply to the solutions of the wave equation. They are,

$$y = 0, \quad \text{if } x = 0$$
$$\text{for all } t. \qquad (10\text{–}81)$$
$$y = 0, \quad \text{if } x = L$$

The first condition requires that the x part of Eq. 10–69 be $\sin(\omega x/V) = \sin(2\pi x/\lambda)$. The second boundary condition requires that

$$\sin \frac{2\pi L}{\lambda} = 0, \qquad (10\text{–}82)$$

or

$$\frac{2\pi L}{\lambda} = n\pi, \qquad (10\text{–}83)$$

where $n = 0, 1, 2, 3, \ldots$, or

$$\lambda = \frac{2L}{n}. \qquad (10\text{–}84)$$

Eq. 10–84 shows the important conclusion that only certain wavelengths, those given by Eq. 10–84, are allowed on the string. Since $V = \nu\lambda$, we write

$$\nu = \frac{V}{\lambda} = V\left(\frac{n}{2L}\right) \qquad (10\text{–}85)$$

or

$$\nu = \frac{n}{2L}\sqrt{\frac{\mathcal{T}}{\mu}}, \qquad (10\text{--}86)$$

an expression showing the allowed *frequencies* for the string. The solutions themselves are

$$y_n = 2C \sin\left(n\,\frac{\pi\sqrt{\mathcal{T}/\mu}}{L}\,t\right)\sin\left(n\,\frac{\pi x}{L}\right). \qquad (10\text{--}87)$$

Of course, any linear combination of such solutions is also a solution.

This idea of only certain discrete frequencies is an exceedingly useful one in modern physics. The lowest frequency given when $n = 1$, is called the *fundamental frequency*. The other allowed frequencies are integral multiples of this one and are called *overtones* in acoustics. A more general term has come into use. All the allowed integral frequencies, including the fundamental, are known as *harmonics*. Therefore, $n = 1$ indicates the frequency of the first harmonic (i.e., the fundamental), $n = 2$ the second harmonic (or first overtone), and so on. Most vibrating systems have harmonics. The presence of these harmonics forms the basis of most musical instruments and acoustical harmonic overtones seem musical to the ear.

The problem that we have just been considering can be summarized by noting that we have a partial differential equation, Eq. 10–54, for which we found certain general solutions such as Eq. 10–58 or Eq. 10–70; and that certain boundary conditions, such as Eq. 10–81 limited these to certain particular solutions. This type of problem is often called a *characteristic value problem*. The German name is *eigenwerte* and it is common to use the "mixed" term *eigenvalue problem*. The frequencies, $\nu_1 = V/2L$, $\nu_2 = 2V/2L, \ldots, \nu_n = nV/2L$ of Eq. 10–85 are the *characteristic values* (*eigenvalues*); the solutions y_n, Eq. 10–87, are the *characteristic functions* (*eigenfunctions*). The integers n are often called *quantum numbers*.

The choice of a sinusoidal wave for our examples was not accidental. More complicated periodic wave forms can be described as a sum of sinusoidal ones. Thus a function with a period τ, so that $f(t + \tau) = f(t)$, can be written

$$f(t) = \frac{1}{2}a_0 + \sum_{n=0}^{\infty}\left(a_n \cos\frac{2\pi n}{\tau}t + b_n \sin\frac{2\pi n}{\tau}t\right). \qquad (10\text{--}88)$$

Such a series is called a *Fourier series*. Aperiodic functions can also be represented by an extension of this method called a Fourier integral (see Appendix C).

10–13. Energy Transmission. Even the most elementary consideration will suggest that energy is transmitted by most waves. For example, in the case of a string, since the motion pattern moves along the string, one can think of the kinetic energy associated with the actual motion of the parts of the string as also moving along the string even though the matter itself is not propagated. Similarly, in a water wave the kinetic energy of elements of water may be considered to move with the wave. Some of this energy can be absorbed if the string (or water) is properly fastened to some energy-using device. Of course, the presence of this absorber effects the wave, so the motion beyond it will not be the same as it would have been without the absorber.

If the wave is sinusoidal, each piece of matter has a vibratory energy proportional to the square of the amplitude (see Eq. 10–36b). This is the case for all elastic waves. The rate of transmission of energy is thus proportional to the square of the amplitude. The general term for the rate of transmission of energy is *intensity*, often represented by I.

The intensity in absolute units is the energy transmitted across unit area per unit time, i.e., joules m^{-2} sec^{-1} (watts m^{-2}) or erg cm^{-2} sec^{-1}. Other special units are sometimes used. For example, the unit of intensity in the case of light is the lux or lumen per square meter (1 lumen per square meter $= 0.00161$ watts m^{-2} for monochromatic light with a wavelength of 5560 Å).

In the case of a localized source sending out energy at a rate P, the intensity at a distance r from the source will be

$$I = \frac{P}{4\pi r^2},$$ (10–89)

since the energy is spread over the area of a sphere at radius r. This expression contains the well-known inverse square law.

At any moment, one can think of the energy being transmitted as if it were localized in the medium. Then one can calculate the energy density (the energy per unit volume) at each point in space. If we call this w it is perhaps not surprising that

$$I = wV$$ (10–90)

where V is the wave velocity.

Although electromagnetic waves are different from other waves in many respects, such as not requiring any material medium, they still can be described with the same formalism we have just presented. We will not make any attempt to develop the theory of electromagnetic waves, but instead we will simply point out that electromagnetic waves consist of changing electric fields **E**, and magnetic fields **H**. Static fields play no role in the transmission of energy, only the changing fields do. It can be shown that the electric and magnetic fields are perpendicular to each other and both are perpendicular to the direction in which the wave is traveling.

E and **H** are proportional; so either **E** or **H** can be used to describe the wave. Usually **E**(t) is used. A vector, called the *Poynting vector*,

$$\mathbf{S} = (\mathbf{E} \times \mathbf{H}) \qquad \left[\mathbf{S} = \frac{c}{4\pi}\,(\mathbf{E} \times \mathbf{H})\right] \qquad (10\text{–}91)$$

points in the direction of propagation and its magnitude is the intensity. The corresponding expressions for the energy density are

$$w = \frac{1}{2}\,(\epsilon_0 E^2 + \mu_0 H^2). \qquad \left[w = \frac{1}{8\pi}\,(E^2 + H^2).\right] \qquad (10\text{–}92)$$

PROBLEMS

10–1. Find the period, frequency, and angular frequency of a system consisting of a mass of 20 gm hanging on a spring which is stretched 8 cm, when the bob is hung on the spring.

10–2. The diatomic molecule HCl can be considered crudely as consisting of a mass of 1.6×10^{-24} gm attached to a spring held firmly in place. A frequency of 9×10^{13} vibrations sec^{-1} is observed. What is "k" for the "spring"?

10–3. Oversimplify the conditions of an automobile. Think of it as weighing 2400 lb and assume the springs are such that when 400 lb are added, the springs sink 1 in. Assume the shock absorbers are disconnected and other friction is eliminated. At what frequency would the car "bounce"?

10–4. The motion of a vibrating spring is described by the expression $x = 0.0053 \cos 37.7t$. Find (a) the amplitude, (b) the frequency, (c) the period, (d) the initial phase. Take distance in cms, and time in sec.

10–5. A shadow moves with simple harmonic motion so that the distance between the two extreme positions is 0.30 m. It makes one complete vibration in 0.17 sec. When $t = 0$, $x = 0$. Write an expression relating x and t.

10–6. Substitute each of Eqs. 10–13, 10–13a, 10–13b, and 10–13c into Eq. 10–10 and show that each satisfies that relation. Determine the value of ω.

10–7. Show that Eqs. 10–13, 10–13a, 10–13b, and 10–13c are all equivalent. Find the value of A in terms of a and b. Find a and b in terms of A and Φ. Find c and d in terms of a and b. Give any further interrelations that seem of interest to you.

10–8. A weight hung on the end of a spring is drawn 3 in. below its equilibrium point and released. It then oscillates about the equilibrium position with acceleration, $a = -64x$. Determine the displacement x and velocity v of the weight at any time, the period of the motion, and its greatest speed.

10–9. In Problem 10–1 suppose the bob was lifted 2 cm above the equilibrium point and then suddenly released at time $t = 0$. (a) Find A, Φ, and Φ'.

(b) Find the maximum velocity of the bob. (c) Find the maximum acceleration of the bob. (d) Find the position of the bob at $t = 6.00$ sec.

10–10. Write three forms similar to Eqs. 10–13, 10–13a, and 10–13b describing the motion of a 6×10^{-5} kg mass attached to a spring with a constant $k = 0.42$ newton m^{-1}. When $t = 0$, $x = +1.3 \times 10^{-4}$ m and the speed is away from the center and half the maximum speed.

10–11. A mass of 0.63 kg is mounted on a spring having a constant of 1.8 newton m^{-1}. At $t = 0$, $x = 0$, and $v = 0.7$ m sec^{-1}. Give the expression that describes the motion of the mass. (Give the three forms similar to Eqs. 10–13, 10–13a, and 10–13b.)

10–12. Calculate the energy of the vibrator described in Problem 10–10.

10–13. Calculate the energy of the vibrator described in Problem 10–11.

10–14. The balance wheel of a watch beats five times each second. The moment of inertia of the wheel is 3.6×10^{-13} kg m^2. The amplitude is 2.8π radians. (a) What is the torsion constant of the hair spring? (b) What is the maximum angular velocity? (c) What is the energy of the combined balance wheel and hairspring?

10–15. A torsion pendulum has a torsion constant of 6.3 newton-m radian^{-1} and a period of 1.7 sec. What is the moment of inertia of the pendulum? What energy does it have if the amplitude is 0.16 radian? What is the maximum angular velocity?

10–16. A galvanometer has a coil with a moment of inertia $I = 30$ gm-cm^2. The period of the galvanometer is 7.0 sec. What torque produces a deflection of 0.010 radian?

10–17. Verify that Eq. 10–47 is a solution of Eq. 10–46.

10–18. A wave is described by $y = 2 \exp -\frac{1}{4}(x - 16t)^2$. Plot it for $t = 0$, $t = 0.10$, $t = 0.25$, and $t = 0.5$ sec. What is the velocity of the wave if x is in centimeters? Write the expression for a wave of the same shape moving to the left.

10–19. At $t = 0$ a plot of y versus x is a smooth curve passing through the points $x = -2$, $y = 0$; $x = -1$, $y = 0.5$; $x = 0$, $y = 1.5$; $x = +1$, $y = 0.5$; $x = +2$, $y = 0$; and $y = 0$ for $x < -2$ and for $x > 2$. This pulse is propagated to the right at a speed of 5 units sec^{-1}. Plot the wave for $t = 0$, $t = 0.5$ sec, $t = 1$ sec and $t = 3$ sec.

10–20. A simple periodic wave is given by the relation (distances in centimeters, times in seconds) $y = 2 \sin 2\pi (t/6 - x/4)$. What is the (a) amplitude, (b) period, (c) frequency, (d) wavelength, (e) phase velocity, and (f) phase of this wave?

10–21. A simple periodic wave is given by the relation (distances in centimeters, times in seconds), $y = 4 \sin \frac{1}{4}\pi (t - x/192)$. What is the (a) amplitude, (b) period, (c) frequency, (d) wavelength, (e) phase velocity, and (f) phase of this wave?

10–22. A wave traveling in a stretched string is given by (all lengths in centimeters, t in seconds) $y = 5 \cos 2\pi (t/0.01 + x/600)$. (a) In which direction is this wave traveling? (b) What is the amplitude of the wave? (c) What is the frequency of the vibration? (d) What is the wavelength? (e) What is the propagation velocity? (f) Find the expression giving the position of a peak as a function of the time and sketch a rough graph of the expression.

10–23. In Problem 10–22, find the displacement velocity for the point on the string 300 cm from the origin at a time $t = 0.02$ sec.

10–24. Compute the phase difference between points $x_1 = 1.0$ and $x_2 = 2.5$ cm for the wave of Problem 10–22. What is the phase difference for points $x_1 = 1.0$ and $x_2 = 10.5$ cm?

10–25. Compute the phase difference between points $x_1 = 0$ and $x_2 = 12$ cm for the wave of Problem 10–20. What is the phase difference $x_1 = 0$ and $x_2 = 3.5$ cm?

10–26. Plot two full wavelengths for $t = 0, 1, 2, 3, 4, 5, 6$ sec of the wave $y = 2 \sin (2\pi/6)t \sin (2\pi/5)x$. What is the velocity of the wave if x is in inches?

10–27. Plot two full wavelengths for $t = 0, 0.2, 0.4, 0.6, 0.8, 1.0$, and 1.2 of the wave $y = 0.5 \cos (\pi/0.6)t \cos (\pi/2)x$. What are the frequency, wavelength, and velocity of the wave?

10–28. Plot several wavelengths of the wave $y_1 = 0.3 \sin 2\pi (t/8 - x/6)$ for each quarter period through one full period. Do the same for $y_2 = 0.3 \sin 2\pi (t/8 + x/6)$. Make a third set of plots of every quarter period for $y = y_1 + y_2$.

10–29. Plot several wavelengths of the wave $y_1 = 0.2 \cos 2\pi (t/100 - x/5000)$ for each quarter period through one full period. Do the same for $y_2 = 0.2 \cos 2\pi (t/100 + x/5000)$. Make a third set of plots of every quarter period for $y = y_1 + y_2$.

10–30. A string with a mass per unit length of 0.05 kg m^{-1} is stretched with a tension of 150 newtons and clamped at both ends. Its length is 0.8 m. With what frequencies can it vibrate? If it is held in the exact center with a finger, what frequencies are then possible?

10–31. A string 0.42 m long clamped at both ends has a mass of 0.005 kg. Its fundamental frequency is 400 cps. What is the tension in the string? If it is vibrating so that a number of harmonics are present, what will be the effect of touching the middle of the string?

10–32. What are the eigenvalues for the frequency of the first part of Problem 10–30? Write the eigenfunctions.

10–33. What are the eigenvalues for the frequency of the first part of Problem 10–31? Write the eigenfunctions.

10–34. What is the bulk modulus for air if $V = 300$ m sec^{-1} and $\rho = 1.3$ kg m^{-3}?

10–35. The velocity of propagation of a compression wave in water is 1460 m sec^{-1}. What is the bulk modulus of water?

10–36. On a certain day at 5.30 p.m. the depth at high water over a sand bar at the entrance to a port is 34 ft; at low water 6 hr and 12 min later the depth is 18 ft. If the rise and fall of the tide is simple harmonic motion, what is the latest time that a ship drawing 30 ft of water can enter the port that day?

SELECTED REFERENCES

BECKER, R. A. *Introduction to Theoretical Mechanics.* McGraw-Hill Book Co., Inc., New York, 1954. Chaps. 7 and 15.

CHRISTIE, D. E. *Intermediate College Mechanics.* McGraw-Hill Book Co., Inc., New York, 1952. Chap. 16.

SEARS, F. W. *Mechanics Wave Motion and Heat.* Addison-Wesley Publishing Co., Inc., Reading, Mass., 1958. Chap. 16.

11

Basic Concepts
of Quantum Mechanics

The inability of classical laws to describe the behavior of atomic systems left a serious gap in the framework of physical theories. Something was required to supplement or to replace Newton's laws of motion and the laws of electrodynamics. The development of a replacement has not been simple and has involved a succession of attempts to arrive at an increasingly better understanding of such matters. It is perhaps not surprising that the first steps, such as Planck's work and that of Bohr, were largely arbitrary, often inconsistent, and certainly did not provide a coherent set of laws with the generality of the ones they had to replace. By the middle of the 1930's new laws had been formulated in a consistent fashion. This was particularly true of *quantum mechanics*, the new set of mechanical laws which replace Newton's laws of motion. It has been somewhat more difficult to replace the classical laws of electrodynamics by an appropriate quantum electrodynamics, but the last decade has seen significant developments in this area.

It is unfortunate that the various formulations of quantum mechanics require somewhat abstruse mathematics for their full development; but many of the important features can at least be illustrated in terms that should be easily understood.

Quantum mechanics can be formulated in several different ways which are entirely equivalent. We shall use the formulation called *wave mechanics* because it is the easiest to understand.

11–1. The Work of L. de Broglie. In 1924, Louis de Broglie in his doctoral thesis and in subsequent papers presented a view which started the work in the field of *wave mechanics*. The nature of this theory, which relates such apparently contradictory ideas as wave propagation and particle motion, is so unfamiliar that one may well wonder how it was ever discovered. However, the development came about in a perfectly natural, though imaginative, manner. The general purpose of de Broglie's papers was to consider the use of *Hamilton's analogy* in the solution of the mechanics of atoms. Hamilton's analogy is a straightforward procedure in classical mechanics in which one solves for the trajectory of a particle by considering the trajectory as a path taken by a ray of light. Other than making use of the direction of a wave no further consideration of the waves is ordinarily used to determine the trajectory. De Broglie made the particularly imaginative contribution that one seriously consider other features, including phase and amplitude, of the waves used in the analogy. Before describing de Broglie's contribution let us look briefly at the technique we have called Hamilton's analogy.

The British mathematician and physicist Hamilton had shown that one could solve problems in classical mechanics by using the methods of optics (or do the converse, solve optical problems by using the methods of mechanics). The reason that this is possible is that the mathematics of ray tracing and of trajectory computation are identical in form. In optics the laws of reflection and refraction are equivalent to the requirement that the path of light be such that the time of travel along the path be a minimum (or maximum). This time is

$$t = \int dt = \int \frac{ds}{v} = \frac{1}{c} \int n \, ds, \tag{11–1}$$

where n is the index of refraction. This fact is also known as Fermat's principle. In mechanics one finds that the laws for determining the trajectory of a particle are equivalent to the requirement that the trajectory be one for which the total action

$$S = \int 2K \, dt = \int mv^2 \frac{ds}{v} = \int p \, ds \tag{11–2}$$

is a minimum (or maximum). This fact is also known as the principle of least action. Note how the two integrals look much alike. To solve a mechanical problem by optical methods it is only necessary to find the path of a ray of light through a medium in which the index of refraction varies in the same way the momentum of the particle would. Conversely, the solution of optical problems is accomplished by using a variation of momentum in which

$$p \simeq n. \tag{11–3}$$

The somewhat intricate problem of determining the paths for which these integrals are extremal involves the use of the *calculus of variations*.

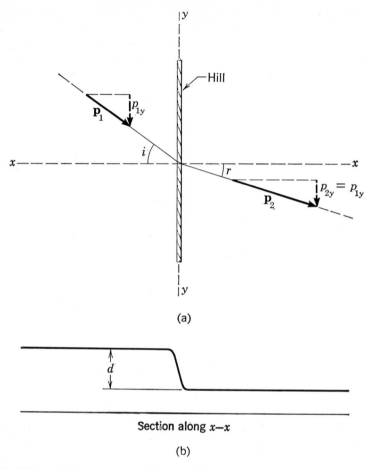

(a)

Section along x–x

(b)

Fig. 11–1.   Ball rolling across upper plateau and downhill to a lower plateau.
(a) Path of ball showing "refraction."   (b) Side view of the hill.

A very simple illustration of these principles is shown in Fig. 11–1 and Fig. 11–2.   In the first figure a hill is shown running parallel to the y direction.   The section along the line xx shows that the difference in level of the two surfaces is d.   A ball rolling on the upper level surface has a momentum p_1.   After it rolls down the hill it has a momentum p_2.   The hill slopes only in the x direction and hence cannot change the y-component of the momentum.   The result (see Problem 11–1) is that

$$\frac{\sin i}{\sin r} = \frac{p_2}{p_1} = \sqrt{1 + \frac{V_1 - V_2}{\frac{1}{2}mv_1{}^2}} = \sqrt{1 + \frac{mgd}{\frac{1}{2}mv_1{}^2}}. \qquad (11\text{–}4)$$

V_1 and V_2 are the potential energies at the top and bottom of the hill. Fig. 11–2 shows the bending of a ray of light as it passes from a medium with index of refraction n_1 across a plane surface into a medium with index of refraction n_2. Snell's law, which can be derived from Fermat's principle, gives

$$\frac{\sin i}{\sin r} = \frac{n_2}{n_1} = n_{21}. \tag{11-5}$$

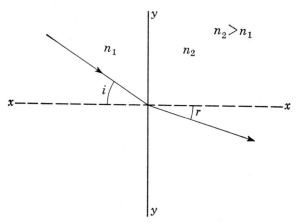

Fig. 11–2. Refraction of a light ray.

where n_{21} is often called the index of refraction of the second medium with respect to the first. The similar appearance of the two figures and the similarity of the two equations are indicative of the application of Hamilton's analogy.

Another example is the motion of a particle subject to a central, inverse square, force field. If we take the particle to be an electron and the center of attraction to be a proton, we have a hydrogen atom and we find that the optical analogy consists of a medium for which the index of refraction is very great near the center of the force field and decreases with distance from the center. The variation of index with r is given by

$$n \simeq p = \sqrt{\frac{e^2 m}{4\pi\epsilon_0 r}}. \qquad \left[n \simeq p = \sqrt{\frac{e^2 m}{r}}. \right] \tag{11-6}$$

It is not easy to show that a ray of light will travel in an elliptical path for such a case, but perhaps it can be understood by thinking of the wave fronts associated with the ray. These surfaces will move more slowly where the index of refraction is large; so they will "wheel" around the nucleus and the corresponding ray will follow in one of the proper classical orbits as shown in Fig. 11–3.

With the exception of the last example there has still been little use made of the wave nature of light. In fact geometrical optics does not demand that light be a wave; but we know that light has a wave nature that produces interference and diffraction effects. The contribution of de Broglie that opened up the field of wave mechanics was to ask whether the optical equivalent for the motion of *material* particles does not have a

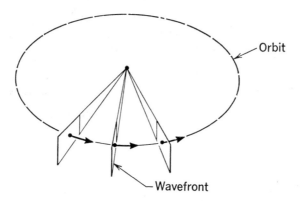

Fig. 11–3. Portions of wave fronts moving near an inverse square force field.

true wave nature capable of producing interference and diffraction effects. This is the converse of the fact that light is known to have a particle nature as well as a wave nature. Of course, one immediately needs some specification of wavelength and frequency for the waves of matter. To talk of the frequency of a particle or of its wavelength does not seem entirely proper, but we have already done just this in Chapter 8. There it was found that the energy of a photon is $E = h\nu$, and also that its momentum is $p = h/\lambda$. These relations were taken over by de Broglie and used with matter waves so that we have for their frequency and wavelength the expressions

$$\nu = \frac{E}{h},$$
(11–7)

and

$$\lambda = \frac{h}{p}.$$
(11–8)

The use of these relations leads to some startling "coincidences." One result is that the Bohr orbits turn out to be those orbits for which there are just an integral number of wavelengths. In fact, the principal quantum

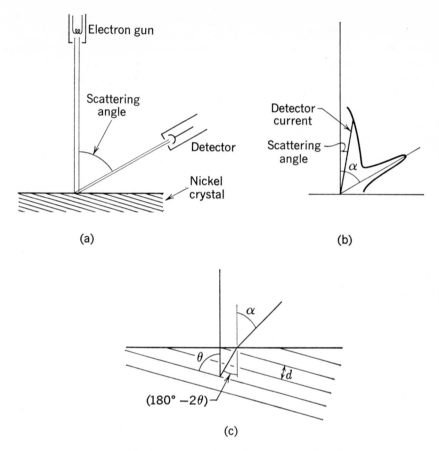

Fig. 11–4.   The Davisson-Germer experiment.

number n is the number of wavelengths in the orbit.   The proof of this makes a nice problem and it is left for that purpose.

One might be inclined to treat this "coincidence" lightly but fortunately it was not ignored.   Davisson and Germer performed an experiment to test if effects due to the wave nature of electrons might be observed and E. Schroedinger got interested in de Broglie's work and developed it in much greater detail.

11–2. Particle Diffraction Experiments.   Two experiments of historical importance showed that a beam of electrons behaves like a wave and will be diffracted by a crystal lattice.   Davisson and Germer[1] at the Bell Telephone Laboratories in 1927 shot a beam of electrons at the face of a single crystal of nickel.   Some bounced back and were caught by a detector. See Fig. 11–4 for a schematic diagram of the experiment.   In Fig. 11–4b

[1] C. J. Davisson and L. H. Germer, *Phys. Rev.*, **30**, 705 (1927).

the collector current is plotted on a polar diagram for various scattering angles. The preferential scattering at the angle α occurred only for a particular accelerating voltage in the electron gun. For some other accelerating voltages and other orientations of the crystal, the preferential scattering angles were different. However, in each case it could be shown that by choosing the right value of wavelength λ' within the crystal, these angles were appropriate to the Bragg law (Art. 6–3),

$$n\lambda' = 2d \sin \theta. \tag{11–9}$$

The wavelength λ' can be obtained from the wavelength outside the crystal λ, by $\lambda' = \lambda(n_2/n_1)$. In addition, $\sin \alpha = (n_2/n_1) \sin 2\theta$. (See Fig. 11–4c.) Thus the relative index n_2/n_1 and the wavelength λ can be measured. The wavelength outside the crystal was found to agree with the form predicted by de Broglie, namely,

$$\lambda = \frac{h}{p} = \frac{h}{\sqrt{2mK}} = \frac{h}{\sqrt{2meV}} \tag{11–10}$$

where K is the kinetic energy of the electrons and V is the accelerating potential difference in the electron gun. The value for the relative index of refraction obtained from such an experiment gives $(V_1 - V_2)$ of Eq. 11–4. This difference should be the same as W_0 in Fig. 8–9 or $w_0 + K_{max}$ of Eq. 8–18. The agreement is good.

The second type of experiment was first performed by G. P. Thomson.[2] This is of particular interest since his father, Sir J. J. Thomson, is noted for his experimental proof of the particle nature of electrons. The experiment consists in sending a beam of electrons through a thin film of metal and then letting them fall on a photographic plate. Since the film consists of microscopic crystals with random orientation the experiment is similar to the Debye-Scherrer method for x-ray diffraction. Fig. 11–5 shows the experimental arrangement for both x-ray diffraction and electron diffraction. There will be crystals with an orientation suitable to satisfy the Bragg law for the particular wavelength and crystal spacings. Thus a series of rings is produced, one ring for each value of crystal spacing d. Fig. 11–6 shows the diffraction rings for TlCl taken with both x-rays and electrons. A comparison of the two leaves little doubt as to the wave nature of the electrons used to make the diffraction picture.

Putting the correct values for h, m, and e, into Eq. 11–10 and giving V in volts leads to the result

$$\lambda = \frac{12.27}{\sqrt{V}} \text{ Å.} \tag{11–10a}$$

[2] G. P. Thomson, *Nature*, **122**, 279 (1928); *Proc. Roy. Soc.*, **117**, 600 (1928).

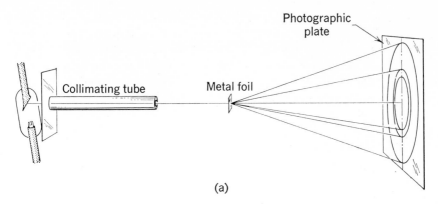

(a)

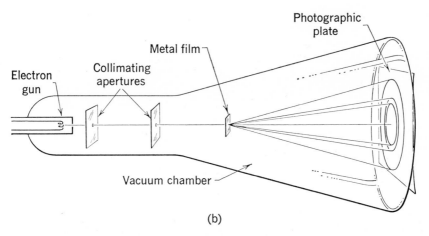

(b)

Fig. 11–5. Experimental arrangement for (a) x-ray diffraction (Debye-Scherrer type), (b) electron diffraction (G. P. Thomson type).

The wave nature of atoms[3] and of neutrons[4] has also been observed.

11–3. The Schroedinger Wave Equation.   The start made by de Broglie was greatly elaborated upon by others, particularly by Schroedinger. The direct observation of the wave nature of matter raises the question of what it is that "waves," and what wave equation is to be satisfied by the "wave function" that represents the behavior of our particles.   The accepted interpretation for the wave function (which we shall write as $\Psi(x,t)$) is that $|\Psi(x,t)|^2 \, dx$ is the probability of finding the particle in the range dx at the point x.   It will turn out that this value is generally independent of t.   The practice of using only one spatial variable x simpli-

[3] T. H. Johnson, *J. Franklin Inst.*, **206**, 301 (1928).
[4] E. O. Wollan and C. G. Shull, *Nucleonics*, **3**, (1948).

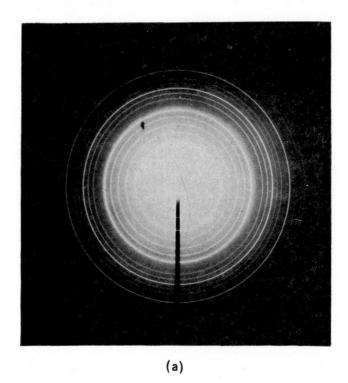

(a)

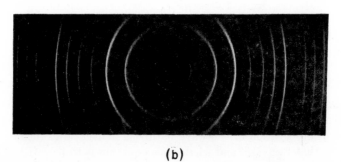

(b)

Fig. 11-6. Comparison of x-ray and electron diffraction. (a) Electrons diffracted (Thomson type) by thallous chloride. (b) x-rays diffracted (Debye-Scherrer type) by thallous chloride. The wavelength of the electrons was 0.055 Å. The wavelength of the x-rays was 1.54 Å. The different geometry of the two methods leads to the different appearance of the two figures, but the similarity of the patterns is still quite marked (Ernest F. Fullam, Inc.).

fies the expression.   All real situations require several variables to properly describe the situation.

In Chapter 10, we saw that the behavior of a displaced string could be described by the standard wave equation

$$v^2 \frac{\partial^2 y}{\partial x^2} = \frac{\partial^2 y}{\partial t^2},$$ (11–11)

which had solutions of the form

$$y = f(x \pm vt).$$ (11–12)

We were especially interested in the solutions of the form

$$y = A \cos 2\pi \left(vt - \frac{x}{\lambda} \right)$$ (11–13)

which have a frequency v and a wavelength λ that satisfy the relation $v\lambda = v$.   The constant v depended only upon the density of the string and the tension, not upon v.   It is important to note that the constant in the equation depends only upon the medium, not upon the state of vibration.

Let us see if this simple wave equation will work for matter waves for the case of freely moving particles having an energy K and momentum p where

$$K = \frac{p^2}{2m}.$$ (11–14)

From de Broglie's relations we expect the solution to have a certain wavelength λ and a frequency v so rewriting Eq. 11–13 as

$$\Psi(x,t) = A \cos 2\pi \left(vt - \frac{x}{\lambda} \right),$$ (11–15)

and requiring that de Broglie's relations hold, namely, $v = K/h$ and $\lambda = h/p$, Eq. 11–15 then becomes

$$\Psi(x,t) = A \cos 2\pi \left(\frac{K}{h} t - \frac{p}{h} x \right).$$ (11–16)

If Eq. 11–16 is put into Eq. 11–11 the wave equation will have the form

$$\frac{K^2}{p^2} \frac{\partial^2 \Psi}{\partial x^2} = \frac{\partial^2 \Psi}{\partial t^2}.$$ (11–17)

Since the ratio K^2/p^2 is *not* a constant independent of the state of vibration as required in Eq. 10–60, it is concluded that Eq. 11–11 is *not* a suitable wave equation for matter waves.   Some other equation must be found.

In any other approach to the problem of finding a suitable wave equation, Eq. 11–14 and the de Broglie relations must hold for matter waves so that

$$K = h\nu = \frac{1}{2m}\left(\frac{h}{\lambda}\right)^2 = \frac{1}{2m}p^2. \qquad (11\text{–}18)$$

In addition, it is preferable that traveling wave solutions result from the desired wave equation, so that the variables x and t should appear in the combination $(\nu t - x/\lambda)$ in the solutions. Under these conditions, if we try a *first* partial derivative with respect to t, and a second partial derivative with respect to x, then, since the product $\nu\lambda^2$ is a constant (see Eq. 11–18), a possible "wave" equation is

$$\frac{\partial\Psi}{\partial t} = (\text{constant})\frac{\partial^2\Psi}{\partial x^2}. \qquad (11\text{–}19)$$

This equation introduces some difficulties. If the function Ψ is assumed to be sinusoidal, neither the simple sine or cosine can be used. However, the complex exponential.

$$\Psi = A\exp\left[-2\pi i\left(\nu t - \frac{x}{\lambda}\right)\right] = A\exp\left[-i\left(\frac{K}{\hbar}t - \frac{p}{\hbar}x\right)\right], \qquad (11\text{–}20)$$

will satisfy Eq. 11–19 and Eq. 11–18 together, provided the constant in Eq. 11–19 is $ih/4\pi m = i\hbar/2m$, where $i = \sqrt{-1}$. Thus the equation

$$\frac{\partial\Psi}{\partial t} = \frac{i\hbar}{2m}\frac{\partial^2\Psi}{\partial x^2}, \qquad (11\text{–}21)$$

which contains only fundamental quantities, may serve as a suitable wave equation for matter waves. This equation is called the *time dependent Schroedinger wave equation* for the free particle. It is often written in the form

$$i\hbar\frac{\partial\Psi}{\partial t} = -\frac{\hbar^2}{2m}\frac{\partial^2\Psi}{\partial x^2}. \qquad (11\text{–}22)$$

There is nothing about the way we arrived at this equation that furnishes any very compelling reason for expecting it to work, but the experimental fact of the wave nature of matter and the appearance of only $\hbar$ and m in this equation make us hope it will be a useful equation. It is perhaps a bother that one must use complex quantities, but nature will have it no other way. A brief discussion of complex numbers will be found in Appendix B.

If the particle is not free but is subject to a force field described by a potential energy function $V(x)$, then Eq. 11–14 should be replaced by

$$W = K + V = \frac{p^2}{2m} + V. \qquad (11\text{–}23)$$

This leads to the more general time dependent Schroedinger wave equation

$$i\hbar \frac{\partial \Psi}{\partial t} = -\frac{\hbar^2}{2m}\frac{\partial^2 \Psi}{\partial x^2} + V\Psi. \tag{11-24}$$

In three dimensions, this becomes

$$i\hbar \frac{\partial \Psi}{\partial t} = -\frac{\hbar^2}{2m}\left(\frac{\partial^2 \Psi}{\partial x^2} + \frac{\partial^2 \Psi}{\partial y^2} + \frac{\partial^2 \Psi}{\partial z^2}\right) + V\Psi. \tag{11-25}$$

Eq. 11-20 which applied only to free particles is no longer a solution to this equation. The effect of the force responsible for $V(x)$ is to make the wavelength change with position. We can write the solution in the form

$$\Psi(x,t) = \exp\left(-i\frac{W}{\hbar}t\right)\psi(x), \tag{11-26}$$

since the time part of the function is $\exp(-iWt/\hbar)$ if the energy is definite. If this is put into Eq. 11-24, one gets

$$-i^2\frac{\hbar}{\hbar}W\exp\left(-i\frac{W}{\hbar}t\right)\psi = \exp\left(-i\frac{W}{\hbar}t\right)\left\{-\frac{\hbar^2}{2m}\frac{\partial^2 \psi}{\partial x^2} + V\psi\right\}$$

or

$$\frac{\partial^2 \psi}{\partial x^2} + \frac{2m}{\hbar^2}[W - V]\psi = 0. \tag{11-27}$$

The three dimensional form is

$$\frac{\partial^2 \psi}{\partial x^2} + \frac{\partial^2 \psi}{\partial y^2} + \frac{\partial^2 \psi}{\partial z^2} + \frac{2m}{\hbar^2}[W - V]\psi = 0. \tag{11-28}$$

These equations are to be solved for ψ after $V(x)$, or $V(x,y,z)$, is specified. It is the form of V that really describes the system, since it is determined by the forces. The results will also depend upon the value of the energy W. In fact, there are often situations for which only particular values of W provide for solutions that make sense in terms of our interpretation of ψ. These special values turn out to be the values for the energy that actually occur in nature. For example, in the problem of the hydrogen atom they are the Bohr levels. The limitations that should be imposed on ψ are straightforward and natural. They are,

1. ψ and its first derivatives must be continuous. (Otherwise ψ cannot be put back into the Schroedinger wave equation.)
2. ψ must be finite. (Otherwise the probability interpretation loses its meaning.)
3. ψ must be single valued at every point. (If it assumed more than one value, there would be the question of which was the correct value to use for the probability function.)

4. Certain special conditions may have to be satisfied for the system under consideration.

If ψ satisfies these conditions, it is said to be *well behaved.*

Quantum mechanics, then, is based on *finding well-behaved solutions of the Schroedinger wave equation.* All measurable mechanical characteristics can be found once one knows the well-behaved solutions of the Schroedinger wave equation. Each such solution is called a characteristic function or eigenfunction. The system can have only values of W which provide these well-behaved solutions. These values are called characteristic values or eigenvalues. Some examples will be examined a little later. Everything becomes self-consistent and natural once one accepts the significance of the Schroedinger wave equation and the role of its solution. No additional arbitrary rules are required. Thus a replacement, with quite equivalent generality, has been found for the old laws of mechanics.

It is important to note too that all of the predictions of wave mechanics reduce to the classical laws of motion when dealing with objects much larger than atomic size. This result is called Ehrenfest's theorem.

11-4. The Heisenberg Uncertainty Principle. Another individual who made many contributions to quantum mechanics was W. Heisenberg. He developed a form of quantum mechanics based on the use of matrices which was called *matrix mechanics.* Matrices are arrays of numbers in rows and columns. We will not elaborate on this, especially since it turns out to be equivalent to Schroedinger's method. In this article we want to present another of his ideas, the *uncertainty principle.*

This principle can be stated: *It is impossible to determine the position and momentum of a particle simultaneously with perfect accuracy. If the position x is determined to an accuracy Δx and the momentum in the x direction p_x to an accuracy Δp_x, then the product $\Delta x \Delta p_x$ cannot be less than a number of the order of $\hbar$.*

This can be derived in a number of different ways only one of which will be presented here. Consider a special microscope looking at a particle such as an electron. Because of diffraction effects, no microscope can tell the exact location of an object that is being viewed. A point object will look slightly "fuzzy" and there will be an uncertainty in location designated by Δx. If the diameter of the objective lens of the microscope subtends an angle θ at the object and the light being used has a wavelength λ, the value of the uncertainty is

$$\Delta x = \frac{\lambda}{2 \sin \dfrac{\theta}{2}}. \qquad (11\text{--}29)$$

See Fig. 11-7. There are two ways of decreasing this uncertainty. One is to make θ larger. The other is to use light of a shorter wavelength for illumination. In either case, since the illuminating light bounces off the particle before it enters the microscope, it disturbs the motion of the particle by the Compton effect; and since there is no way of knowing in which part of θ the photon went, there is no way of knowing exactly how

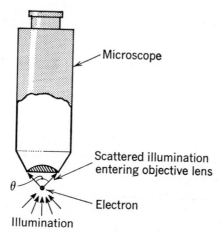

Fig. 11-7. Microscope experiment illustrating the uncertainty principle.

much the momentum was changed. There will be left an uncertainty as to the value of the x-component of momentum. We will call this uncertainty Δp_x. It can be as large as the largest x-component of momentum of any photon that can enter the microscope. This is

$$\Delta p_x = 2 \frac{h}{\lambda} \sin \frac{\theta}{2}.$$ (11-30)

The product of Δx and Δp_x is

$$\Delta x \Delta p_x = h > \hbar.$$ (11-31)

It can also be shown that

$$\Delta y \Delta p_y > \hbar,$$ (11-32)

$$\Delta z \Delta p_z > \hbar,$$ (11-33)

and that in a length of time Δt, one cannot simultaneously measure energy to an accuracy ΔE better than that given by

$$\Delta E \Delta t > \hbar.$$ (11-34)

The same results are obtained by considering the properties of matter waves. The uncertainty principle seems to be a fundamental law of nature. Note one essential aspect of it. If it is true, one can never quite know the exact position and momentum of a particle at any instant since any attempt to measure one always disturbs the value of the other in a way that is *unpredictable* to the extent of the uncertainty principle. This prevents one from predicting exactly what a particle will do. The laws of quantum mechanics are never causal, as contrasted to classical laws, instead, they tell only the probability of what may happen.

11–5. Bohr's Complementarity Principle. It is admittedly not easy to accept the wave-particle duality of electromagnetic radiation and of matter. Nevertheless, the experimental facts are not to be denied. Even though it may not seem sensible to say that light with a wavelength of 2536 Å has photons with an energy of 4.9 ev and a momentum of 2.49×10^{-27} kg m sec^{-1}, the fact is, that one can measure the energy and momentum of these particles, and the values quoted are observed. It also may not seem sensible to say that a beam of 300 v electrons has a frequency of 7.26×10^{16} vibrations sec^{-1} and a wavelength of 0.708 Å, but these also can be measured by experiment. It seems that if we consider only the wave nature of light, or only the particle nature of matter, we do not tell the whole story. We must complement the wave picture of light by adding a particle nature and we must complement the particle nature of matter by adding a wave nature. This view that both pictures are required is called the *complementarity principle*. It was first stated by Bohr.

The reluctance to use both wave and particle descriptions simultaneously is natural. Fortunately, it can be shown that the Heisenberg uncertainty principle makes it impossible to find a contradiction between any proper particle description and any proper wave description. The diffraction effects of the waves simply show the uncertainty in the original state of the particles.

In optics, the square of the electric field strength gives the intensity of the wave. This is consistent with the view that $E(x)^2\, dx$ is proportional to the probability of finding a photon in dx at x. In a similar way, we believe that $|\psi(x)|^2\, dx$ is proportional to the probability of finding the matter particle in dx at x. These interpretations and the uncertainty principle are all it takes to give a theory in which there is no possible experiment that might lead to a conflict between the particle part of the description and the wave part.

11–6. Eigenfunctions and Eigenvalues. It was pointed out in Art. 11–3 that the method of wave mechanics consists of finding well-behaved solutions of the Schroedinger wave equation, that is, upon finding eigenfunctions. These are possible for only certain values of the energy, that is, for eigenvalues of the energy.

Consider a particular potential energy function such as the one plotted in Fig. 11–8a. We write the Schroedinger wave equation, Eq. 11–27, in the form

$$\frac{d^2\psi}{dx^2} = \frac{2m}{\hbar^2} [V(x) - W] \psi. \qquad (11\text{–}35)$$

This shows that if a particular value of W is chosen, the second derivative of ψ is determined for all values of x. This can then be integrated twice, once to get $d\psi/dx$ and again to get ψ. We shall not look at this as a problem in solving a differential equation in closed form, but rather as a problem to be solved graphically. Let us therefore choose a particular value ψ_0 for ψ at $x = x_0$ and a particular value $(d\psi/dx)_0$ for the slope at that point. The actual value of ψ_0 is unimportant since it only changes the scale for ψ, and multiplication by a constant will preserve the essential shape of ψ. Let us also choose a particular value of energy W. At a and b (see Fig. 11–8a), $W = V$. To the left of a, $(V - W)$ is positive, so the second derivative of ψ has the same sign as ψ. Thus, if ψ is positive, it must also be concave upward; if it is negative, it must be concave downward. The same is true to the right of b. Between a and b the reverse is true.

Let us take the particular value ψ_0 and the particular value $(d\psi/dx)_0$ and see what shape function Eq. 11–35 leads to. With too small a value of $(d\psi/dx)_0$ a curve, such as A in Fig. 11–8b, that becomes infinite as x gets more negative may be formed. With too large a value of the slope, the curve may behave like the one labeled B. If the slope is just right, a curve like C can result.

The choice of suitable initial values ψ_0 and $(d\psi/dx)_0$ to get a well-behaved solution to the left of x_0, does not finish the problem. We must next follow the development of the function through the region ab and then on farther to the right. It is very unlikely that a well-behaved solution will result. The only way that we can get a solution such as that shown as C' is for W to be just right. If it is too low, a curve such as D would be formed; or if it is too high, the curve might develop like curve E.

The choice of W that leads to CC' is not the only one that can give a well-behaved solution. For example, two other energies W_1 and W_2 are shown in Fig. 11–8a with corresponding solutions FF' and GG' shown along with CC' in Fig. 11–8c.

If $W > V(x)$ everywhere, any value of W leads to a well-behaved solution because the curve is concave downward whenever ψ is positive and is concave upward whenever ψ is negative. This leads to an oscillatory behavior that does not become infinite. In such a case, W is said to have a continuous spectrum, while for the previous case, the spectrum of W is said to be discrete.

Eigenfunctions have two other important properties which involve integrals of the functions. Although we discussed these functions as if

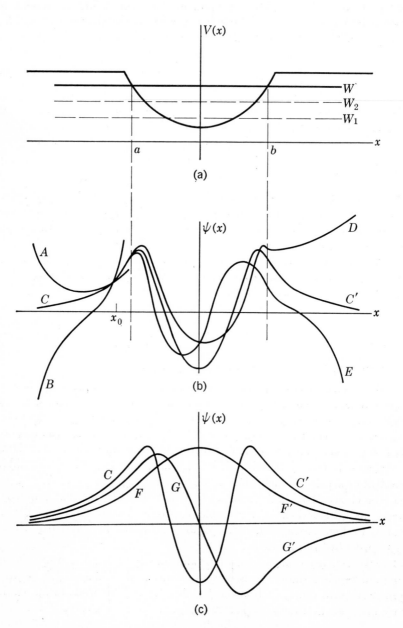

Fig. 11–8. Illustration of the special requirements to get an eigenfunction.

they were real functions, they may be complex. Suppose ψ_i is one such function and $\psi_i{}^*$ its complex conjugate, and suppose the ψ_j is another eigenfunction of the same Schroedinger wave equation and $\psi_j{}^*$ its conjugate. Then the first integral of interest is

$$\int_{-\infty}^{\infty} \psi_i{}^* \psi_i \, dx = \int_{-\infty}^{\infty} |\psi_i|^2 \, dx = C. \qquad (11\text{--}36)$$

By properly choosing a multiplier in ψ_i it is possible to make $C = 1$. When $C = 1$ the eigenfunction is said to be *normalized* and we have

$$\int_{-\infty}^{\infty} |\psi_i|^2 \, dx = 1. \qquad (11\text{--}37)$$

This is the first property referred to above, that is, the integral of the product of a wave function and its complex conjugate is unity. This corresponds to saying that the probability of the particle being somewhere is unity.

The second important property is obtained by integrating the product of one wave function and the complex conjugate of another. If the result of this integration is zero, that is,

$$\int_{-\infty}^{\infty} \psi_i{}^* \psi_j \, dx = \int_{-\infty}^{\infty} \psi_j{}^* \psi_i \, dx = 0, \qquad (11\text{--}38)$$

then the wave functions are said to be orthogonal.

11-7. Expectation Values. An eigenfunction of energy (that is, a solution of Schroedinger's wave equation) provides the key to all the information concerning the nature of the system when it has the amount of energy corresponding to the eigenvalue for energy corresponding to the eigenfunction. We say that the function *describes the state* of the system. The way one can use the function to determine any property of the system depends upon the definition of an *operator* appropriate to the quantity to be discussed. An operator operates on an operand. $d(\ )/dx$ is an operator. dy/dx is the result of $d(\ )/dx$ operating on the operand y. x is an operator. The product xy is the result of x operating on y. The rules of quantum mechanics call for two kinds of operators, those for quantities like the position x, and those for quantities like the momentum p. The operator for x is just x; but the operator for p is $-i\hbar \, d(\ )/dx$. Another example of an operator is the energy operator. The expression for the energy given in terms of p and of x is called the Hamiltonian. It is

$$H = \frac{p^2}{2m} + V(x). \qquad (11\text{--}39)$$

Thus the operator is

$$H_{\text{op}} = -\frac{\hbar^2}{2m}\frac{d^2}{dx^2} + V(x). \qquad (11\text{--}40)$$

If we let this operator operate on an operand $\psi(x)$, and set the result equal to the product of the constant W and ψ, we get

$$H_{\text{op}}\psi = -\frac{\hbar^2}{2m}\frac{d^2\psi}{dx^2} + V(x)\psi = W\psi, \qquad (11\text{--}41)$$

the Schroedinger wave equation. Similar operators are formed for other quantities.

One can define the *expectation value* for a dynamical variable as follows. If the quantity is represented by $S(p,x)$ and the operator formed using the rules just described is S_{op}, then the expectation value for S is $\langle S\rangle$, where

$$\langle S\rangle = \int_{-\infty}^{\infty} \psi^* S_{\text{op}}\psi \, dx. \qquad (11\text{--}42)$$

This gives the average to be expected of a large number of measurements of S. If a measurement of S always gives the same value, it can be recognized by the fact that $\langle S\rangle = S$, where S is an eigenvalue of the eigenfunction equation

$$S_{\text{op}}\psi = S\psi. \qquad (11\text{--}43)$$

We will now look at several examples which illustrate the principles discussed in this article and the previous one.

11–8. The Free Particle. A free particle with an energy W satisfies the Schroedinger equation

$$-\frac{\hbar^2}{2m}\frac{d^2\psi}{dx^2} = W\psi. \qquad (11\text{--}44)$$

This is the equation of simple harmonic motion since

$$\frac{d^2\psi}{dx^2} + \frac{2m}{\hbar^2}W\psi = 0. \qquad (11\text{--}45)$$

A solution of this is

$$\psi = A \exp i\frac{\sqrt{2mW}}{\hbar}x. \qquad (11\text{--}46)$$

It is well behaved no matter what the value of W is, so long as it is positive. Thus all positive energy values are possible. Any positive value of W is an eigenvalue and Eq. 11–46 is the corresponding eigenfunction. The wavelength is

$$\lambda = \frac{2\pi}{\dfrac{\sqrt{2mW}}{\hbar}} = \frac{h}{\sqrt{2mW}} = \frac{h}{p}. \tag{11-47}$$

Another solution of Eq. 11–45 is

$$\psi = A \cos \frac{\sqrt{2mW}}{\hbar} x. \tag{11-48}$$

Although it is an eigenfunction for the energy, it is not an eigenfunction for the momentum since

$$-i\hbar \frac{d\psi}{dx} = -i\hbar A \frac{d}{dx} \cos \frac{\sqrt{2mW}}{\hbar} x$$

$$= i\sqrt{2mW}\, A \sin \frac{\sqrt{2mW}}{\hbar} x \neq \sqrt{2mW}\psi. \tag{11-49}$$

If we compute the expectation value of p for this case, we get

$$\langle p \rangle = \int_{-n\lambda}^{+n\lambda} A^2 \cos kx \left(-i\hbar \frac{d}{dx} \cos kx \right) dx$$

$$= -i\hbar A^2 k \int_{-n\lambda}^{+n\lambda} \cos kx \sin kx \, dx = 0, \tag{11-50}$$

where $k = \sqrt{2mW}/\hbar = 2\pi/\lambda$.

This corresponds to electrons with the same energy moving both to the right and to the left. There is an equal chance of "catching" a particle with a positive momentum or with a negative momentum.

It is important and interesting to note that the value of $|\psi|^2\, dx = A^2\, dx$ is, for the case of the free particle, independent of x. The likelihood of finding the particle is the same anywhere. This is what would be predicted by Heisenberg's uncertainty principle, that is, since p (and W) is known exactly, $\Delta p = 0$ so $\Delta x = \infty$, and x is completely undetermined.

A Fourier synthesis (see Appendix C) of waves of a small range of wavelengths will lead to a wave packet such as that illustrated in Fig. 11–9 which shows $|\psi|^2$ versus x at a particular moment. Such a wave packet will advance at a speed (not equal to $\nu\lambda$) called the group velocity $d\omega/dk$. It turns out that this speed is just the mechanical velocity (see Prob. 11–18). It also turns out that the length of the packet Δx and the range of wavelength are so related that $\Delta p \Delta x \simeq h/2\pi$, in accord with the Heisenberg uncertainty principle. Thus the motion of a particle along the x direction is described in the wave picture as the motion of a wave packet which travels at the mechanical velocity. The uncertainty in position is the length of the packet and the uncertainty in momentum is associated with the range of wavelengths in the Fourier expansion of the packet.

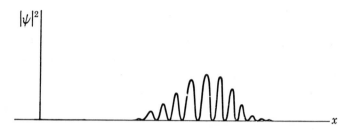

Fig. 11–9.   A wave packet.

11–9. A Particle in a Box with Infinite Walls.   Fig. 11–10 is a plot of the potential energy for a particle which can move freely from $x = -a$ to $x = +a$, but cannot exist in the regions $x > a$ or $x < -a$.   In the region $-a \leq x \leq +a$ the Schroedinger wave equation is

$$\frac{d^2\psi}{dx^2} + \frac{2m}{\hbar^2} W\psi = 0. \tag{11–51}$$

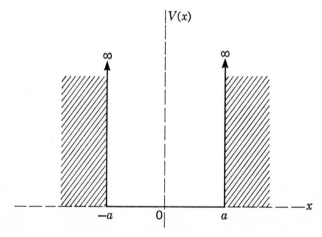

Fig. 11–10.   The potential energy for a "box" with infinitely high walls.

No formal expression can be given for the Schroedinger wave equation for the regions $x > a$ or $x < -a$, but in these regions the value of $\psi = 0$. Eq. 11–51 is again the equation of simple harmonic motion and a possible solution is

$$\psi(x) = A \cos kx + B \sin kx, \tag{11–52}$$

where $k^2 = 2mW/\hbar^2$.   For $\psi = 0$ at both $x = a$ and $x = -a$, either A or B must be equal to zero.   In addition, the constant k must be

$$k = \frac{n\pi}{2a} \qquad (11\text{--}53)$$

where n is an integer.   If n is odd, B must equal zero since $\sin \frac{1}{2}n\pi = \pm 1$; if n is even, A must equal zero since $\cos \frac{1}{2}n\pi = \pm 1$.   The limitation on k then leads to limitations on the permitted energy of the system, namely,

$$W_n = \frac{n^2\hbar^2\pi^2}{8ma^2} . \qquad (11\text{--}54)$$

These are the eigenvalues of the energy.

The values of A and B are determined by the requirement that

$$\int_{-a}^{a} |\psi|^2 \, dx = 1,$$

so that

$$A^2 \int_{-a}^{a} \cos^2 \frac{n\pi x}{2a} \, dx = 1;$$

$$B^2 \int_{-a}^{a} \sin^2 \frac{n\pi x}{2a} \, dx = 1. \qquad (11\text{--}55)$$

These give

$$A \text{ or } B = \sqrt{\frac{1}{a}} . \qquad (11\text{--}56)$$

Thus associated with each eigenvalue W_n we have an eigenfunction (a wave function),

$$\psi_n = \sqrt{\frac{1}{a}} \cos \frac{n\pi}{2a} x \quad (n \text{ odd}) \qquad (11\text{--}57)$$

or

$$\psi_n = \sqrt{\frac{1}{a}} \sin \frac{n\pi}{2a} x \quad (n \text{ even}). \qquad (11\text{--}58)$$

It is true that at $x = -a$ and $x = a$ the first derivative of ψ is discontinuous, but this does not matter because of the infinite discontinuity of the second derivative where $V(x)$ becomes infinite.

Note that the wave functions with odd values of n are symmetric about the origin, while those with even values of n are antisymmetric about the origin.   The behavior of a wave function with respect to a reflection in the origin is called its *parity*.   Thus these wave functions have *even* parity if n is odd, and *odd* parity if n is even.

The problem that has just been treated can be seen to be exactly similar to the problem of a string clamped at both ends, which was treated in Art. 10–12. The allowed energy values are related to the allowed frequencies of vibration of the string, and the wave functions correspond to the standing waves on the string. In this case, as well as for the string, there is a sinusoidal variation of the complete wave function with time, but in this case the frequency is given by $\nu = W_n/h$.

A plot of allowed energies and corresponding wave functions is given in Fig. 11–13a along with several other examples.

11–10. A Potential Well of Finite Depth.   Consider a potential function for a particle of mass m such as that shown in Fig. 11–11. Suppose that the

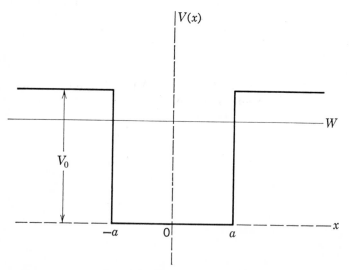

Fig. 11–11.   Potential function for a "well" of finite depth.

energy of the system is $W < V_0$. Then for $-a \leq x \leq +a$ the Schroedinger wave equation is

$$\frac{d^2\psi}{dx^2} + \alpha^2\psi = 0 \tag{11–59}$$

and for $x < -a$ or $x > +a$ it is

$$\frac{d^2\psi}{dx^2} - \beta^2\psi = 0. \tag{11–60}$$

$\alpha^2 = 2mW/\hbar^2$ and $\beta^2 = 2m(V_0 - W)/\hbar^2$ have been chosen so that they are both positive.

The solutions of Eq. 11–59 are sinusoidal and those for Eq. 11–60 are either exponentially increasing or decreasing functions. It is possible to choose solutions that remain finite everywhere and have continuous first derivatives as well as being continuous only if W has proper values. We shall not carry the analysis out in equation form. Instead we point out that this is an example of the situation discussed in Art. 11–6. It is just impossible to find an initial value of ψ and $d\psi/dx$ that will lead to a solution having the necessary continuity properties and also remaining finite except for a few special values of W, such as shown in Fig. 11–13b along with the corresponding eigenfunctions. The number of eigenvalues for $W < V_0$ is limited. However, if $W > V_0$, any value of W is possible. The solutions for such energies include traveling waves going both ways. This can be interpreted as reflection by the potential well. In order to match the wave functions and their slopes at $x = -a$ and at $x = +a$ the magnitude of the reflected wave depends considerably upon the value of the energy and the width of the well. This is an interference effect similar to the interference of light on reflection by a thin film.

11–11. The Harmonic Oscillator. Another problem can be solved completely by the Schroedinger equation, the problem of the *harmonic oscillator*. The potential function is $V = \frac{1}{2}kx^2$. (See Fig. 11–12.) Clas-

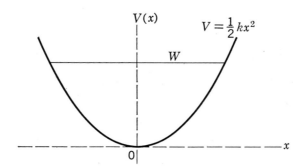

Fig. 11–12.   Potential function for harmonic oscillator.

sically, a mass m subject to this potential energy function can vibrate with simple harmonic motion at a frequency $\nu_0 = \sqrt{k/m}/2\pi$ with any amount of energy.

The Schroedinger wave equation is

$$\frac{d^2\psi}{dx^2} + \frac{2m}{\hbar^2}\left(W - \frac{1}{2}kx^2\right)\psi = 0. \tag{11–61}$$

The solution of Eq. 11–61 again illustrates the point of Art. 11–7. Well-

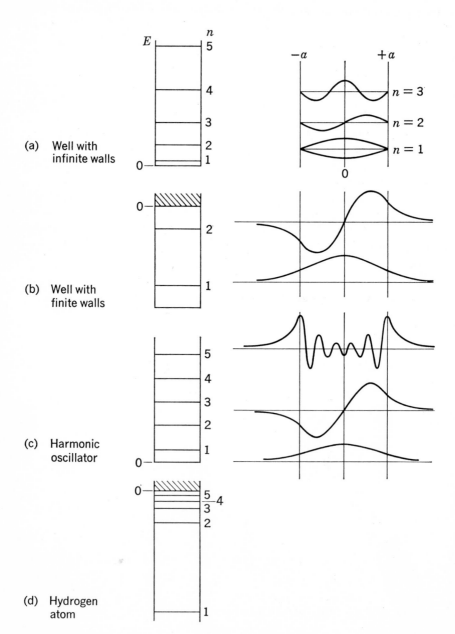

Fig. 11–13.   Eigenvalues and eigenfunctions for systems of bound particles.

behaved solutions are possible only if the energy is

$$W_n = \left(n + \frac{1}{2}\right) \hbar \sqrt{\frac{k}{m}} = \left(n + \frac{1}{2}\right) h\nu_0. \qquad (11\text{–}62)$$

The solutions are

$$\psi_n = A_n \exp\left(\frac{-\gamma^2 x^2}{2}\right) H_n(\gamma x). \qquad (11\text{–}63)$$

Where $\gamma = (mk/\hbar^2)^{\frac{1}{4}}$ and the function $H_n(\gamma x)$ is a polynomial of degree n in γx, called a Hermite polynomial. Both the eigenvalues and a few eigenfunctions are shown in Fig. 11–13c. Note that the lowest energy level is $\frac{1}{2}h\nu_0$, not zero.

In Fig. 11–13 we have collected diagrams illustrating both the eigenvalues of the energy and the corresponding eigenfunctions for the cases of the systems of bound particles that we have discussed. The eigenvalues for the hydrogen atom have been added as another example of bound energy states.

11–12. Barriers. In Fig. 11–14a, there is plotted a steplike potential function. When W is greater than V_0 (as in the case of W_2), a beam of

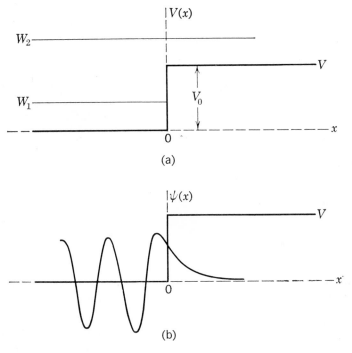

(a)

(b)

Fig. 11–14.   Potential function with a step and resulting wave function

particles from the left can pass to the right of $x = 0$, but some will be reflected. There is an abrupt increase in wavelength, of course, corresponding to the decrease in kinetic energy and momentum. When W is less than V_0 (as in the case of W_1), all the particles are reflected, but $\psi \neq 0$ for $x > 0$. The form of the solution is shown in Fig. 11–14b. The solution to the right decreases exponentially.

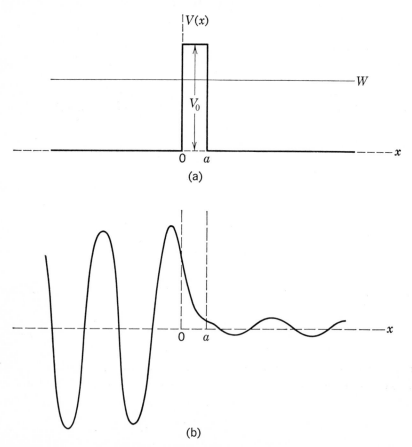

(a)

(b)

Fig. 11–15. Potential function and wave function for barrier tunneling.

If the potential looks like that in Fig. 11–15a, a solution such as that shown in Fig. 11–15b is possible. In this case, the small amplitude of ψ to the right of the barrier shows there is a certain, though small, probability of the particle beam penetrating the barrier, though this could not happen according to classical laws. This *tunneling effect* is predicted only by quantum mechanics. Several examples are known to occur. Alpha particle emission and field emission of electrons from a cold metal are two well-known cases. In addition, some solid state devices, notably the *tunnel diodes* make use of this effect.

This type of behavior has been known in other wave cases. One interesting case is that of total reflection in optics. Although no energy is transmitted beyond the reflecting surface, the electric and magnetic fields are not actually zero in that region. See Fig. 11–16a. Then if one brings

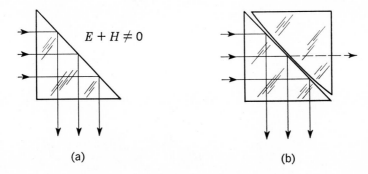

(a)   (b)

Fig. 11–16. Frustrated total reflection.

up another piece of glass so that it is almost in contact, there can be a small amount of energy transmitted when the air film is very thin. See Fig. 11–16b. This is referred to as frustrated total reflection.

11–13. The Hydrogen Atom. The Schroedinger wave equation in three dimensions for the potential

$$V = -\frac{Ze^2}{4\pi\epsilon_0 r} \qquad \left[V = -\frac{Ze^2}{r} \text{ (cgs)} \right]$$

appropriate to a hydrogen-like atom, can be solved without resorting to approximate methods. A sketch of the treatment is given in Appendix D. The results give a discrete set of negative energy states

$$W_n = \frac{-me^4 Z^2}{8\epsilon_0^2 n^2 h^2}, \qquad \left[W_n = \frac{-2\pi^2 me^4 Z^2}{n^2 h^2}, \right] \qquad (11\text{--}64)$$

where $n = 1, 2, 3, 4, \ldots$.

In addition, two other quantum numbers appear, namely, l and m_l, which do not affect the energy. The values of l are limited to $0, 1, 2, \ldots$, $(n - 1)$ and of m_l to $-l < m_l < +l$. The calculation of the angular momentum shows that

$$p_\theta^2 = l(l + 1)\hbar^2 \qquad (11\text{--}65)$$

and that

$$(p_\theta)_z = m_l \hbar. \qquad (11\text{--}66)$$

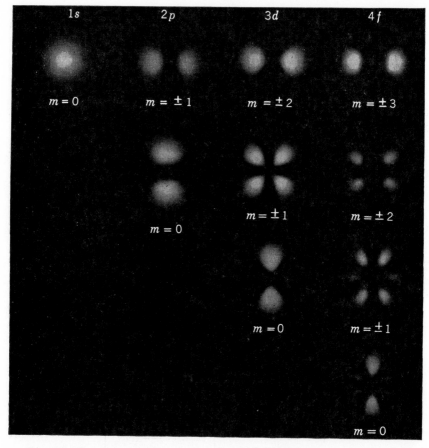

Fig. 11–17. Photographs of the electron probability density distribution (the "electron cloud") for several states of the hydrogen atom. (By permission from R. B. Leighton, *Principles of Modern Physics*. McGraw-Hill Book Co., Inc., New York, 1959.)

(Also see Appendix D.) This suggests that l is related to k of the Bohr theory. In fact $l = k - 1$. The distribution of several of the wave functions is shown in Fig. 11–17. The value of n determines the distance at which the probability of finding the electron is greatest. This distance is close to r_n of Bohr's theory.

For more complicated atoms the solutions of the wave equation cannot be found in closed form, but good approximations often can be found. The problem is often handled by replacing all the separate interactions between electrons by a non-coulomb field which may be considered as due to the nucleus and all the other electrons. Since the motion of each other

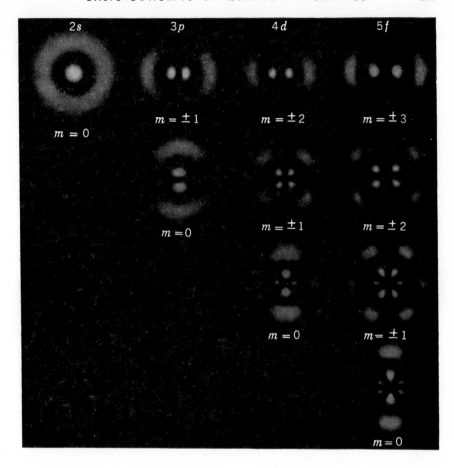

electron is similarly determined, it is necessary to find a distribution which will furnish the right field and also be a result of the field. Such a distribution is said to produce a "self-consistent field." The energy of an atom so composed depends upon the n and the l of each electron and upon other details of the arrangement of electrons in the atom.

PROBLEMS

11-1. Derive Eq. 11-4.

11-2. When an electron enters a certain metal at the surface, its potential drops by 16 v. Compute the relative index of refraction of the metal for electrons which have passed through 80 v in an electron gun.

11–3. Show that the circumference of a Bohr orbit contains an integral number, the principal quantum number, of wavelengths as determined by the de Broglie conditions.

11–4. Find the wavelength of: (a) a 10 gm mass having a velocity of 30 cm sec^{-1}, (b) a 3000 lb car traveling 60 mph (convert to metric units), (c) an electron which has fallen through 3000 v.

11–5. Determine that the constant in Eq. 11–10a is 12.27.

11–6. Calculate the wavelength of electrons that have fallen through a potential difference of 55 v.

11–7. Calculate the wavelength of electrons that have fallen through a potential difference of 55,000 v.

11–8. What is the wavelength of neutrons with a kinetic energy of 0.032 ev?

11–9. What energy protons have a wavelength of 3 Å?

11–10. With the aid of the de Broglie relation show that the wavelength of a particle depends upon the field of force through which it moves.

11–11. A beam of electrons which have fallen through 150 v strikes the surface of a metallic crystal, such as used in the experiment by Davisson and Germer, at an angle of 30° from the normal. For this metal W_0 is 20 v. What will be the direction of the beam within the crystal? What is the wavelength of the electrons within the crystal?

11–12. Electrons which have fallen through 80 v strike a crystal perpendicular to the face. The crystal planes are inclined 20° from the surface. The value for W_0 for this crystal is 10 v. The electrons are reflected by a Bragg diffraction process so that the reflected beam is most intense for the accelerating potential of 80 v. What is the spacing of the crystal planes? At what angle do the reflected electrons leave the surface?

11–13. A beam of electrons passes through a slit 10 Å wide. The beam then diverges about 5° on each side. What was the momentum of the incident electrons and what energy do they have?

11–14. Electrons which have been accelerated by a potential difference of 300 v pass through a narrow slit. The beam spreads about 2° to each side. How wide is the slit?

11–15. What is the uncertainty of momentum of an electron known to be located within a region of length of the order of 10^{-14} m? To what energy does this correspond?

11–16. What is the uncertainty of momentum of an electron known to be located within a region of length of the order of 10^{-10} m? To what energy does this correspond?

11–17. If one is sure that an electron is within an atom having a diameter 4×10^{-8} cm, what is the minimum uncertainty in its momentum? What is the energy of an electron having this momentum?

11–18. For a free particle $E = p^2/2m = \frac{1}{2}mv^2$. Using this find the relation between $\omega = 2\pi\nu$ and $k = 2\pi/\lambda$. Calculate the group velocity $d\omega/dk$. Change back to mechanical quantities and thus show that the group velocity is v.

11–19. Rewrite the Heisenberg uncertainty principle in terms of k and x rather than p and x. Compare with the relations shown in Appendix C. What is the uncertainty in wavelength when x is determined to an accuracy of Δx ($k = 2\pi/\lambda$ is the wave vector)?

11–20. Eq. 11–46 is the solution of the time independent Schroedinger equation for a free particle. Combine this equation with the time dependent term (see Eq. 11–26) and show that the result is a traveling wave.

11–21. Calculate the lowest 4 energy levels for an electron in a one-dimensional box with infinite walls and a length of 4 angstrom units.

11–22. Calculate the lowest three energy levels of a neutron in a one-dimensional box with infinite walls and a length of 10^{-14} m.

11–23. (a) Compute, according to quantum mechanics, the possible energy levels for the vibrating mass on a spring for which $k = 6.25 \times 10^4$ dyne cm^{-1} and $m = 49$ gm. (b) Compute the energy levels for a vibrating H_2 molecule for which $\nu_0 = 13.2 \times 10^{13}$ vibrations sec^{-1}.

11–24. Plot the probability function versus position for an electron in a one-dimensional box with infinite walls for the lowest two energy states.

11–25. Plot the probability function versus position for an electron in a one-dimensional box with infinite walls for the third and fourth energy levels.

11–26. Calculate the spacing for the energy levels for a molecule that behaves like a simple harmonic oscillator with a frequency of 4×10^{12} cps.

11–27. Calculate the spacing of the energy levels for a tuning fork with a frequency of 440 cps.

11–28. The lowest order eigenfunction for a harmonic oscillator given by Eq. 11–63 is (since for $n = 0$, $H_0 = 1$) $\psi = A_0 \exp -(\gamma^2 x^2/2)$. Show that this is a solution of the proper Schroedinger equation. Show that the solution has the form shown in Fig. 11–13. As an added exercise try $H_2 = 4\gamma^2 x^2 - 2$ in Eq. 11–63.

11–29. In Art. 11–7 the operator for the momentum p is given. Derive an operator for *energy* by taking Eq. 11–20, differentiating once with respect to time, and then using the expression for the energy of a photon. Similarly use Eq. 11–20, differentiated with respect to x, and the de Broglie relation to get the momentum operator p.

11–30. A flywheel has a kinetic energy $H = J^2/2I$ where J is its angular momentum and I is its moment of inertia, i.e., $J = I \, d\theta/dt$. Set up the Schroedinger wave equation for this system and find the eigenvalues for the energy and appropriate eigenfunctions. Is it possible to get eigenvalues for J? If so, what are they and what are the eigenfunctions?

11–31. Compute the difference $(px)_{op}\psi - (xp)_{op}\psi$. This is called the commutator of p and x and is written $[p,x]\,\psi$.

11–32. If ψ_i is an eigenfunction corresponding to W_i and ψ_j is one corresponding to W_j, prove, using the Schroedinger wave equation, that

$$\int_{-\infty}^{\infty} \psi_i{}^{*}\psi_j \, dx = 0.$$

11–33. Under what condition do the solutions of Problem 11–20 have a physical significance? What is this physical significance?

SELECTED REFERENCES

Sherwin, C. W. *Introduction to Quantum Mechanics.* Holt, Rinehart & Winston, Inc., New York, 1959. Chaps. 1, 2, and 3.

Powell, J. L. and B. Craseman. *Quantum Mechanics.* Addison-Wesley Publishing Co., Inc., Reading, Mass., 1961. Chap. 4.

Schiff, L. I. *Quantum Mechanics.* McGraw-Hill Book Co., Inc., New York, 1955. Chaps. 1 and 2.

Leighton, R. B. *Principles of Modern Physics.* McGraw-Hill Book Co., Inc., New York, 1959. Chap. 2.

12

Complex Optical Spectra

The extreme simplicity of the hydrogen atom is responsible for the comparatively simple spectrum we have already considered in Chapter 9. More complicated atoms produce spectra which are frequently very complex. In many cases, things seem so complicated that one can hardly believe there is any system in the spectrum at all. The spectrum of iron, shown in Fig. 12–1, is an example. In all cases, though, it is possible to find system and order in the wavelengths of the lines; and in most cases, the reasons for each particular wavelength are now quite well understood.

12–1. Spectral Series and Energy Levels. It is found that the lines group themselves into series similar to the Lyman, Balmer, etc., series in hydrogen. In addition, spectral lines are often found in groups of two, three, or more lines. Sometimes the wavelength separation of lines in such groups may be less than an angstrom, and sometimes as much as several hundred angstroms. Such groups are called multiplets (doublets, triplets, etc.). We shall also use the term in a slightly different sense. Another type of regularity that occurs frequently is a similarity between the spectra of elements having similar chemical properties. The alkali metals all have quite similar spectra. The spectra of the alkaline earths are also very much alike.

We already know, in a general way, the cause of optical spectra. We know that atoms consist of a massive nucleus with a positive charge surrounded by a swarm of electrons, for example, only one for hydrogen, two for helium, three for lithium, eleven for sodium, twenty-six for iron, and ninety-two for uranium. We know that such systems are subject to quantum laws and consequently can exist in only certain permitted energy states (energy levels). We know, furthermore, that the transition from one such state (or level) E_i to a lower one E_f corresponds to the emission of a photon. The frequency ν of the emitted light is such that the energy

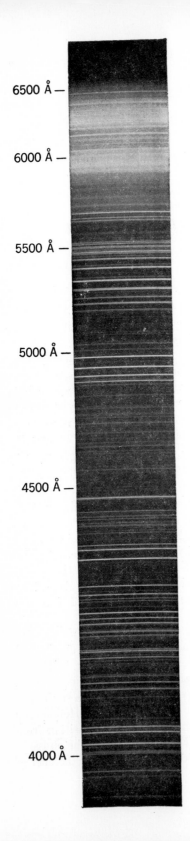

6500 Å —

6000 Å —

5500 Å —

5000 Å —

4500 Å —

4000 Å —

Fig. 12–1. The arc spectrum of iron.

of the photon is

$$h\nu = E_i - E_f. \tag{12-1}$$

We have already pointed out in Chapter 9 that spectroscopists find it inconvenient to work with the frequency ν, because it is such a large number (and cannot be measured directly). They prefer to work with the quantity called the wave number of a spectral line,

$$\bar{\nu} = \frac{1}{\lambda} = \frac{\nu}{c}.$$

The unit usually used by spectroscopists is the reciprocal centimeter, cm^{-1}. We will follow this practice for the rest of the chapter, temporarily leaving the mks system. Eq. 12-1 can then be rewritten

$$\bar{\nu} = \frac{\nu}{c} = \frac{E_i - E_f}{hc} = T_f - T_i, \tag{12-2}$$

where

$$T_i = -\frac{E_i}{hc} \quad \text{and} \quad T_f = -\frac{E_f}{hc}. \tag{12-3}$$

The quantities T_i and T_f are called the *initial term value* and the *final term value*. They too are usually given in reciprocal centimeters, as indicated in Eq. 12-2. The negative sign indicates that the lower the energy of a state, the larger the term value. The lowest energy state for hydrogen is -13.6 ev $= -21.76 \times 10^{-19}$ j. The corresponding term value is $+109,700$ cm^{-1}. As a brief exercise the reader should compute the energy of the next-to-ground state and the corresponding term value. Then determine the energy and term values of the lowest five levels and compute the wave number of two or three Balmer lines.

The problem in explaining spectra of complicated atoms is to find the explanation for the particular value of energy or the term value for each state (energy level). The correct way to do this requires the use of quantum mechanics. A great many of the results can also be described in more simple terms and in such a way as to provide considerable insight concerning the behavior of atoms.

It is also desirable to find a suitable way of labeling or designating the various energy levels of each atom. One could simply start at the bottom and count up. This would inform people as to which of two levels was higher, but would furnish no further information. A much more informative system has developed with the growth of spectroscopy and some of its features will be pointed out when needed. Its most useful feature is that it gives the values of the angular momenta associated with various parts of the atom. Perhaps this is not surprising in view of the constancy of angular momentum when there are no external torques acting on the atom.

The principal quantum number n and the azimuthal quantum number l are examples of possibilities for labels of states, although they are not adequate alone to provide a full label.

Our program will be to present certain important results of quantum mechanics. They make it possible to predict the term values for each element and thus to predict, in detail, the spectra of all the elements. We shall then illustrate all this with some special cases.

12–2. The Major Factors Influencing the Position of Energy Levels.

The treatment of the hydrogen atom has shown that the principal quantum number n, which determines the distance at which the wave function ψ is especially large, is the principal factor in determining the energy of the atom. It is true that several energy levels, differing only slightly in their value of energy, may exist for a given quantum number n. When this is so, the level, state, or wave function is said to be *degenerate*. Experimentally, degeneracy may be removed, that is, the levels may be spread apart, by applying the proper disturbance to the atom. A magnetic field is often used as such a disturbance.

However, the situation with a swarm of electrons is naturally much more complicated than the situation in hydrogen. One fact helps keep things on a reasonably simple basis—the inner electrons that make up the core of the atom are ordinarily almost unaffected by the changes responsible for optical spectra. Only in the production of x-rays do these inner core electrons change their motion appreciably. The presence of the core electrons, however, does have important consequences. First of all, these electrons screen much of the nuclear charge. If the nuclear charge is $+Ze$ and there are $Z - 2$ electrons in the core, the two remaining electrons "see" a central charge of less than $+2e$ when they are outside of the core since they even screen each other. Because of this, the potential function for an electron is different from that for a Coulomb field, and hence the degeneracy with respect to l no longer exists. The wave functions with $l = 0$ tend to have a higher probability for the electron to be close to the nucleus, and thus lead to more tightly bound states (lower energies). Wave functions with larger l lead to less tightly bound states since the probability of the electron being close to the nucleus is less.

Similar conclusions about the effects of n and l can be arrived at by using a model of elliptic orbits similar to the Bohr orbits. Larger n means larger semimajor axes, and hence less tightly bound electrons. Larger l means more nearly circular orbits that are less penetrating and consequently less tightly bound electrons.

A more tightly bound state has a more negative value of energy, and hence has a larger term value. This is indicated in the simple energy diagram of Fig. 12–2 for a fictitious atom. Use has been made of the fact that l can range from 0 to $n - 1$ for each value of n.

We can indicate these results by formulas for energy and for term values. Any one term is given by the expression

$$T_{nl} = \frac{R}{(n - \delta_l)^2}.$$ (12–4)

Corresponding to this we have an energy

$$E_{nl} = -hcT_{nl}.$$ (12–5)

R is the Rydberg constant (see Eq. 9–1 and Eq. 9–20). In these expressions δ_l depends only upon l, and usually δ_l is larger if l is smaller. Since $\delta_l = 0$ for hydrogen and since its effect is to give the appearance of chang-

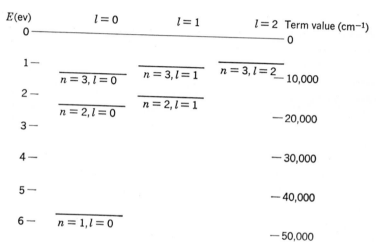

Fig. 12–2.　Energy levels of a hypothetical atom.

ing n to an effective principal quantum number, $n^* = n - \delta_l$, it has been called the "quantum defect" for the state. Eq. 12–4 gives quite good values for the terms of many spectra; so one often finds series of levels belonging together (those with the same l and different n). Such a grouping was indicated in Fig. 12–2.

Eq. 12–4 is a consequence of quantum mechanics. It was also derived earlier by an extension of Bohr's theory.

The relative orientation of the orbital angular momenta of the electrons in the atom affects the overlapping of the wave functions of the electrons, and therefore, affects the energy of the atom. Thus the total orbital angular momentum may also become important in determining the energy of the atom. Certain other features, especially the splitting of levels into a *fine structure*, not yet accounted for so far, are explained by other processes than the effect of electrostatic fields of the nucleus and electrons. The next article considers one important example.

12–3. Electron Spin and its Effects. Around 1925, it was suggested by Uhlenbeck and Goudsmit[1] that many of the peculiarities of optical spectra could be explained by postulating that each electron has a spin, an intrinsic angular momentum apart from that due to its orbital motion. The quantum number describing it is usually designated s and its value is $\frac{1}{2}$.

It was seen in Chapter 3 that a rotating charge produces a magnetic field and behaves much like a magnetic dipole. If the angular momentum is represented by the quantum number l, the magnetic moment is

$$\mu_l = \sqrt{l(l+1)}\,\mu_B, \tag{12–6}$$

where μ_B, the Bohr magneton defined in Eq. 3–42, has the value $\mu_B = 0.9273 \times 10^{-23}$ a-m^2 [$\mu_B = 0.9273 \times 10^{-20}$ emu (cgs)]. There is a similar magnetic moment associated with the spin. Its value is

$$\mu_s = 2\sqrt{s(s+1)}\,\mu_B. \tag{12–7}$$

The factors $\sqrt{l(l+1)}$ and $\sqrt{s(s+1)}$ appear because the rules of quantum mechanics show that these expressions should replace l and s. See Art. 11–13 and Appendix E. Modern theory and experiments show that the 2 should really be replaced by 2.0030, but we will ignore this in the discussions to follow. The direction of the magnetic moment is opposite to the angular momentum for both orbital motion and spin because of the negative charge of the electron. This is not shown in Eq. 12–6 and Eq. 12–7, which give magnitudes only.

In Article 12–8 we shall consider the effect of an external magnetic field, but first consider the interaction between the magnetic moment due to the spin and the magnetic field produced by the orbital motion of the electron. If you will imagine yourself "riding" on the electron, the nucleus of the atom will seem to swing around the electron. The magnetic field due to this will be lined up parallel to the vector representing the orbital angular momentum. If the spin magnet is lined up parallel to this field (i.e., s opposite to l), the energy will be lowest (as when a compass needle is aligned parallel to the earth's magnetic field). To turn it around so that s is in the same direction as l requires work. This means a higher energy. It can be shown that this energy is given (relative to s perpendicular to l) by

$$W_{ls} = \frac{1}{2m^2}\frac{l}{r}\frac{dV}{dr}(\mathbf{p}_{orb})\cdot(\mathbf{p}_{sp}),$$

$$\left[W_{ls} = \frac{1}{2m^2c^2}\frac{l}{r}\frac{dV}{dr}(\mathbf{p}_{orb})\cdot(\mathbf{p}_{sp}), \right] \tag{12–8}$$

[1] G. E. Uhlenbeck and S. Goudsmit, *Physica*, **5**, 266 (1925); *Nature*, **117**, 264 (1926).

where V stands for the function giving the potential energy of the electron. We have introduced the notation $(\mathbf{p}_{orb})$ and $(\mathbf{p}_{sp})$ to stand for the orbital and spin angular momenta. The letter J has a special meaning as a quantum number in spectroscopy; so we avoid its use here for angular momentum. Since $(\mathbf{p}_{orb})$ and $(\mathbf{p}_{sp})$ are related to l and s, Eq. 12–8 is sometimes abbreviated as

$$W_{ls} = A\mathbf{l} \cdot \mathbf{s}. \tag{12–9}$$

The magnitude of this effect is usually much less than those discussed in Art. 12–2.

If we now add this *spin-orbit* effect to our example of a fictitious atom shown in Fig. 12–2, we see that each term in that example may become two terms. The reason it is two rather than some other number is a result of the rules for adding angular momenta given by quantum mechanics.

We present a more detailed treatment (but still simplified) of the handling of angular momenta in Appendix E. The gist of the matter is that angular momenta are quantized—permitted values differing by integral amounts. The quantum numbers themselves may be integers or half integers, but a sequence must involve integral differences, thus, $0, 1, 2, 3, \ldots$, or $\frac{1}{2}, \frac{3}{2}, \frac{5}{2}, \ldots$, but *not* $0, \frac{1}{2}, 1, \frac{3}{2}, 2, \frac{5}{2}, \ldots$. If angular momentum is described by the quantum number j, then its magnitude is given by

$$p_{ang} = \hbar\sqrt{j(j+1)}, \tag{12–10}$$

and a component such as the z component is

$$(p_{ang})_z = m\hbar, \tag{12–11}$$

where

$$-j \leq m \leq j.$$

Let us apply these rules to our fictitious atom. We are interested only in a single electron. It has an orbital angular momentum described by the quantum number l and a spin angular momentum described by the quantum number $s = \frac{1}{2}$. If we follow our rules we can add these to get a resultant, or total, angular momentum represented by j, and j can only be $l + \frac{1}{2}$ or $l - \frac{1}{2}$, except that $j = \frac{1}{2}$ only when $l = 0$. If $j = l + \frac{1}{2}$, the spin magnet is aligned *against* the magnetic field at the electron due to the orbital motion, so the energy of the atom is greater than when $j = l - \frac{1}{2}$ and the spin magnet is aligned *with* the field. On this basis Fig. 12–2 is transformed into that shown in Fig. 12–3.

12–4. Notation for Representing Terms. The description and understanding of spectra is aided by a knowledge of the notation used by spectroscopists. This notation provides the following information regarding an atom in a particular energy state. It gives the value of the principal quantum number n and the azimuthal quantum number l, for each electron; if it is meaningful, it tells the resultant S of the spin angular momentum quantum numbers and the resultant L of the orbital angular momentum quantum numbers; and finally, it also gives J, the quantum number describing the total electronic angular momentum, including all spin and orbital angular momenta.

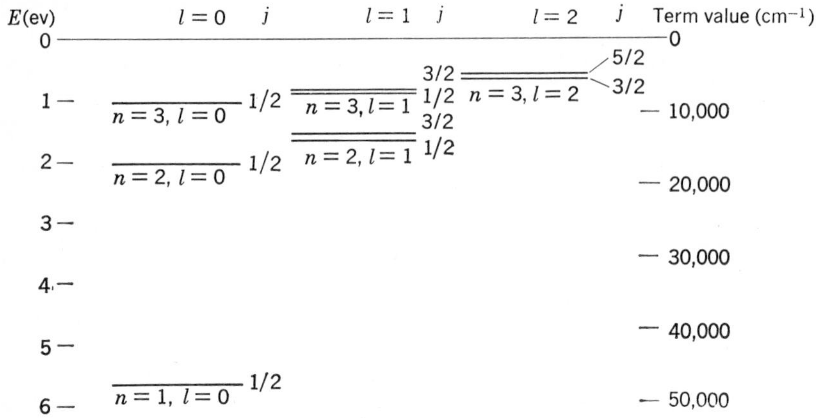

Fig. 12–3.   Energy levels of a hypothetical atom including spin-orbit interactions.

For historical reasons, letters are used to represent the values of the orbital angular momentum quantum numbers l. If $l = 0$, the letter used is s; if $l = 1$, the letter is p; if $l = 2$, it is d; if $l = 3$, it is f; if $l = 4$, it is g; and so forth, alphabetically. The same letters are used in capital letters to represent the values of L.

The symbol used to stand for a term value has two parts, though sometimes one is not written. The first part specifies the values of n and l for each electron. To see how this works, consider an atom with 11 electrons. Suppose that two have $n = 1$ and $l = 0$, two have $n = 2$ and $l = 0$, six have $n = 2$ and $l = 1$, and one has $n = 3$ and $l = 0$. This will be designated

$$1s^2 2s^2 2p^6 3s.$$

Note how the number of electrons of a particular sort is indicated by a superscript. We have now designated the *configuration* of the atom.

The next symbols tell L, S, and J. This finally specifies the particular term. All terms having the same value of L and S, but with different J's make up a multiplet. An example of the second part of the term designations is

$$^2S_{1/2}.$$

The capital letter represents the value of L; the pre-superscript (called the multiplicity) is $2S + 1$; the subscript is J. Thus our example has $S = \frac{1}{2}$, $L = 0$, and $J = \frac{1}{2}$. It would be read "doublet S one-half." The multiplet is called a *doublet*, even though in this case no other value of J is possible and there is only one term in the doublet. A term with a label $^3F_4$ has $S = 1$, $L = 3$, and $J = 4$, and is read "triplet F four." This triplet, "triplet F," can have three levels, those with $J = 4$ or 3 or 2.

The full designation of a term includes both the configuration and the term symbol. Thus we should write $1s^22s^22p^63s\ ^2S_{\frac{1}{2}}$. Another might have been $1s^22s^22p^63p\ ^2P_{\frac{1}{2}}$. They are often abbreviated $3s\ ^2S_{\frac{1}{2}}$ and $3p\ ^2P_{\frac{1}{2}}$ since the quantum numbers of the other electrons are likely to be well known. Spectroscopists use such symbols to stand for the *term value* itself. It thus does a double duty of representing a particular numerical value of a term and at the same time describes the atom in that particular state. The two examples just given apply to sodium. The spectrum of sodium shows that

$$3s\ ^2S_{\frac{1}{2}} = 41{,}449.0\ \text{cm}^{-1},$$

$$3p\ ^2P_{\frac{1}{2}} = 24{,}492.8\ \text{cm}^{-1}.$$

If the sodium atom was initially in the state represented by $3p\ ^2P$, and changed to $3s\ ^2S$ by radiating a photon, the transition could be indicated by

$$
\begin{aligned}
T_f - T_i &= 3s\ ^2S_{\frac{1}{2}} - 3p\ ^2P_{\frac{1}{2}} \\
&= 41{,}449.0 - 24{,}492.8 = 16{,}956.2\ \text{cm}^{-1}.
\end{aligned}
$$

Note how this formula tells both the numerical value of the wave number of the line and of the initial and final states, and also give a rather complete description of the atom in both states. Term values similar to the ones used here have been measured and identified for many states of many atoms and are recorded in the literature.[2]

12–5. The Spectrum of Sodium. Let us now see how the points we have discussed apply in the case of the spectrum of a simple system. Our choice is that of sodium. The spectrum is largely determined by the one outer electron, and is typical of all the alkali metals. Fig. 12–4 is a picture of the spectrum of sodium. Note how the lines tend to group in series. Three series show in this figure. They are called the *principal series*, the *sharp series*, and the *diffuse series*. The latter two overlap but have the same series limit. The fundamental series occurs in the infrared region so it is not shown here. The terms (energy levels) for this system are sketched in Fig. 12–5. Terms having different values of L, S, and J have been put into different columns. They could have been put in a single column, but

---

[2] See individual articles analyzing spectra and also compilations such as R. F. Bacher, and S. Goudsmit, *Atomic Energy States*, McGraw-Hill Book Co., Inc., New York, 1932.

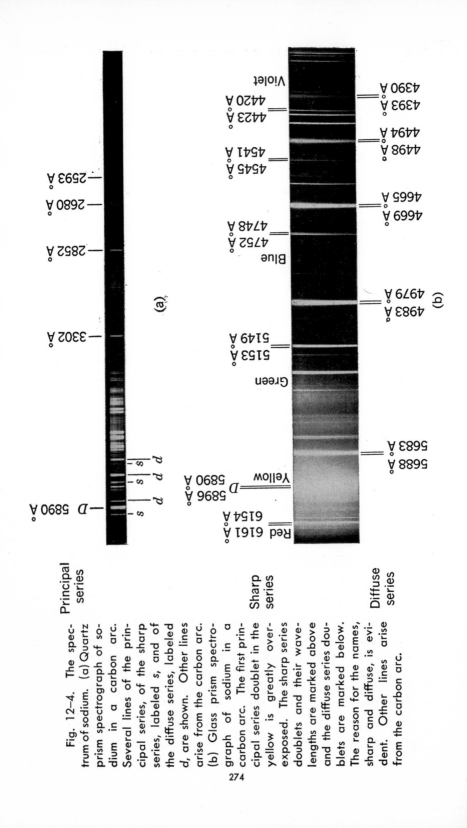

Fig. 12–4. The spectrum of sodium. (a) Quartz prism spectrograph of sodium in a carbon arc. Several lines of the principal series, of the sharp series, labeled *s*, and of the diffuse series, labeled *d*, are shown. Other lines arise from the carbon arc. (b) Glass prism spectrograph of sodium in a carbon arc. The first principal series doublet in the yellow is greatly overexposed. The sharp series doublets and their wavelengths are marked above and the diffuse series doublets are marked below. The reason for the names, sharp and diffuse, is evident. Other lines arise from the carbon arc.

274

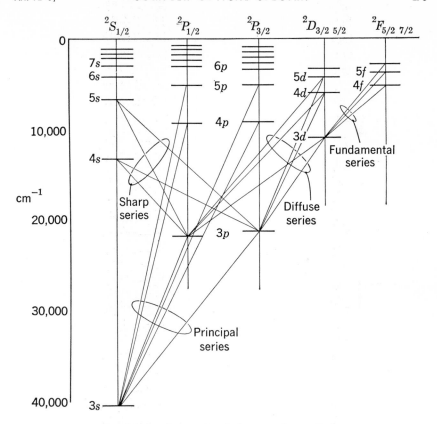

Fig. 12–5.   Energy level diagram for sodium.

this would make it confusing and difficult to interpret such a set of levels. The form we use is an elaboration on the one used in Fig. 12–3. The following points should be noted.

1. The series of ^2S terms are single terms with $J = \frac{1}{2}$ only. (They are still called doublets.)
2. The series of ^2P terms are actually doublets with $J = \frac{3}{2}$ and $J = \frac{1}{2}$.
3. The series of ^2D terms are also actually doublets with $J = \frac{3}{2}$ and $J = \frac{5}{2}$. They are not shown separated because they are so close together.
4. The series of ^2F terms are also actually doublets with $J = \frac{5}{2}$ and $J = \frac{7}{2}$.
5. The smaller the value of n, the lower the energy.
6. The smaller the value of L (also l), the lower the energy.
7. The lower the value of J, the lower the energy.

These points are all in accord with our previous discussion. The values of L, S, and J are appropriate. The most penetrating and hence most tightly bound states are s states; p states are less tightly bound; d states are still less tightly bound; etc. The magnetic interaction between spin and orbital magnetic fields provides the proper separation for the two different values of J in each multiplet.

It is not possible to have transitions between all terms. In Fig. 12–5, we have shown the important ones that actually occur. You will note that they form the four series of spectral lines:

The sharp series	$3p\ ^2P_{1/2} - ns\ ^2S_{1/2}$
	$3p\ ^2P_{3/2} - ns\ ^2S_{1/2}$
The principal series	$3s\ ^2S_{1/2} - np\ ^2P_{1/2}$
	$3s\ ^2S_{1/2} - np\ ^2P_{3/2}$
The diffuse series	$3p\ ^2P_{1/2} - nd\ ^2D_{3/2}$
	$3p\ ^2P_{3/2} - nd\ ^2D_{3/2}$
	$3p\ ^2P_{3/2} - nd\ ^2D_{5/2}$
The fundamental series	$3d\ ^2D_{3/2} - nf\ ^2F_{5/2}$
	$3d\ ^2D_{5/2} - nf\ ^2F_{5/2}$
	$3d\ ^2D_{5/2} - nf\ ^2F_{7/2}$

The first three are shown in the picture of the spectrum, Fig. 12–4. The first two lines of the principal series are the two yellow lines familiar to you since they occur in flames in which there is sodium. It takes a fairly good spectroscope to separate them since their wavelengths differ by only about six angstroms.

12–6. The Selection Rules. Quantum mechanics provides a scheme for calculating the light emitting characteristics of atoms. The classical expression for the electric field **E** of an electromagnetic wave emitted by an oscillating charge e is proportional to $e\mathbf{r}$, the electric moment of the oscillator where $\mathbf{r}$ is the vector displacement of the charge. This has a term that varies periodically with the time with a frequency ν. Thus

$$E = A \cos (2\pi\nu t). \tag{12–12}$$

The equivalent quantum mechanical expression for a transition between states of an atom is

$$\int \Psi_i{}^*(r,t)e\mathbf{r}\Psi_f(r,t)\ dv = \exp 2\pi i \left(\frac{W_i}{h} - \frac{W_f}{h}\right) t \int \psi_i{}^*(r)e\mathbf{r}\psi_f(r)\ dv \tag{12–13}$$

where $\Psi_i(r,t)$ and $\Psi_f(r,t)$ are the time dependent wave functions of the initial and final state. This expression, too, has a sinusoidal variation with time and the frequency is given by the Bohr rule, namely, $\nu = (W_i - W_f)/h$.

The integral involving the non-time-dependent wave functions determines the amplitude (or rather, the transition probabilities) for the spectral line. When it is large, the line is strong; when it is zero, the line cannot occur; and when it is small, the line is faint. The qualitative results of such a calculation provide what are called *selection rules*. For example, in Eq. 12–13, **r** has odd parity; so the integral will be zero unless the two wave functions have opposite parity. This rule and the others are as follows:

1. There must be a change in parity. It is possible to determine the parity by finding the sum of the l's of all the electrons. If this sum is even, the parity is even; if the sum is odd, the parity is odd. (Exceptions are known but are rare and in general are weak because they depend upon another mechanism for radiation.)
2. J may change by $+1, 0,$ or -1, but $J = 0$ to $J = 0$ is definitely forbidden.
3. L should change by $+1$ or -1. This is violated frequently.
4. S should not change. This, too, is violated often. Lines arising from states of different S are called *intercombination lines*.
5. There are no restrictions on the changes of n.

You will find that all the transitions listed in Art. 12–5 satisfy these rules.

12–7. The Spectrum of Mercury (Two Electron Systems). For atoms having a core and two external electrons, the effects of adding l's and s's and of the possible sums of L and S become apparent. Mercury is a good example (as are magnesium and calcium). The spectrum of mercury is shown in Fig. 12–6 and the energy level diagram is shown in Fig. 12–7 where some of the important spectral lines are indicated. The transition $6s^2\,^1S_0 - 6s6p\,^3P_1$ is the resonance line. It is an intercombination line, but it is the most important line of the spectrum of mercury. Two other familiar transitions are indicated by the wavelengths designation 5790 (in the yellow) and 5461 (in the green). There are also several strong blue lines.

The transition $6s^2\,^1S_0 - 6s6p\,^3P_0$ is strictly forbidden; so any atom that ends up in the $6s6p\,^3P_0$ state cannot radiate its excess energy. It can only lose the energy by non-elastic collisions. Such a state is called a metastable state.

12–8. The Zeeman Effect. When a source of an atomic spectrum is placed in a magnetic field, most single lines separate into several lines. The spacing is small and is proportional to the magnetic field strength. This effect is called the Zeeman effect. Classical theory predicts that each line should split into three. This is sometimes observed, but often more than three lines are observed. The prediction of classical theory is called the normal Zeeman effect, any other behavior is called the anomalous Zeeman effect. An additional aspect of the effect is the polarization of the light emitted. In Fig. 12–8, two experimental arrangements are shown. In one (labeled transverse effect), the light is viewed from a posi-

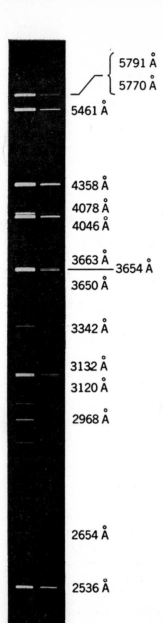

5791 Å
5770 Å
5461 Å

4358 Å
4078 Å
4046 Å

3663 Å
3654 Å
3650 Å

3342 Å

3132 Å
3120 Å

2968 Å

2654 Å

2536 Å

Fig. 12–6. The spectrum of mercury. The wavelengths of some of the prominent lines are indicated. Two different exposures are shown.

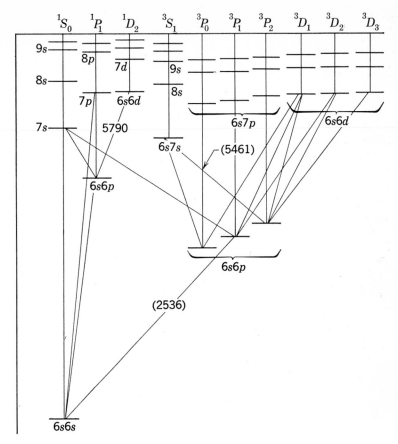

Fig. 12–7.   Energy level diagram for mercury.

tion on a line perpendicular to the magnetic field; in the other (labeled longitudinal effect), the light is viewed along the magnetic field. In the transverse effect, the lines are plane polarized, some parallel to the field (the undeviated line in the normal effect). In the longitudinal effect there is no undeviated line and all lines are circularly polarized. Some have right-hand polarization and some have left-hand polarization. The direction of polarization proves that the emitting object is negatively charged. The size of frequency shifts shows that the specific charge of the emitter is the same as for cathode rays. The inference should be clear—the particles responsible for the emission of light are electrons (as we have assumed all along).

The classical theory of the Zeeman effect is based upon the material presented in Art. 3–9, especially on Eq. 3–43. The expectation is that the

Larmor precession frequency should be added to or subtracted from the undeviated frequency. This frequency shift is

$$\Delta\nu = \frac{\omega_p}{2\pi} = \frac{e}{4\pi m}B = \frac{\mu_B}{h}B. \qquad \left[\Delta\nu = \frac{\omega_p}{2\pi} = \frac{e}{4\pi mc}B = \frac{\mu_B}{h}B.\right] \qquad (12\text{--}14)$$

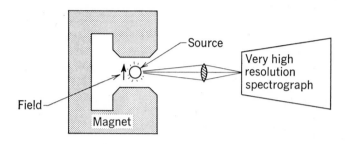

(a) Transverse effect

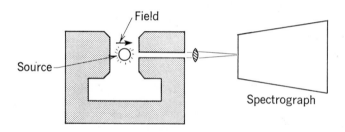

(b) Longitudinal effect

Fig. 12–8.   Apparatus for obtaining the Zeeman effect.

The quantum mechanical explanation considers the effect of the magnetic field on the energy of the atom. Because of the fact that the magnetic moment due to the spin has a factor 2 in it (see Eq. 12–7), we find that the average magnetic moment parallel to J is

$$\mu_{\text{eff}} = \mu_B \left\{1 + \frac{J(J+1) + S(S+1) - L(L+1)}{2J(J+1)}\right\} \sqrt{J(J+1)}. \qquad (12\text{--}15)$$

The factor in the bracket is called the Landé g-factor, so we write

$$\mu_{\text{eff}} = \mu_B g \sqrt{J(J+1)}. \qquad (12\text{--}16)$$

The energy change because of the magnetic field should be

$$\Delta E = -\boldsymbol{\mu}_{\text{eff}} \cdot \mathbf{B} = \mu_{\text{eff}} B \cos\theta, \qquad (12\text{--}17)$$

where θ is the angle between $\mathbf{J}$ and $\mathbf{B}$. The z direction is taken along $\mathbf{B}$;

$\cos \theta$ can be found from Eq. 12–10 and Eq. 12–11 (also see Appendix E); so

$$\Delta E = \mu_B g B \sqrt{J(J+1)} \cdot \frac{M_J}{\sqrt{J(J+1)}} = \mu_B B g M_J. \qquad (12\text{--}18)$$

M_J, the magnetic quantum number representing the component of the total angular momentum parallel to the external field, can take on values ranging from $-J$ to $+J$ separated by unity; so we see that a single energy level should split into $2J + 1$ levels, separated by $\mu_B B g$ ergs. Two cases are shown in Fig. 12–9, one for $J = 2$ and one for $J = \frac{3}{2}$. The spacing is small compared to the separation between levels in a multiplet.

The selection rule for M_J is that it can change by 0, 1, or -1. Now if $g = 1$ for both the initial and final states, we get the same results as predicted by classical theory. Their singlet states which have $g = 1$ lead to a *normal Zeeman effect*. The more general case is illustrated by the D lines, the yellow doublet of sodium. How it works is shown in Fig. 12–10.

When the magnetic field becomes large enough for the effect of the field to be as great as that due to different values of J, things become different. This case is called the *Paschen-Back* effect.

The case of really huge fields, though not of experimental importance, is of theoretical importance, as we shall see. Under extreme fields, the only quantum numbers affecting the energy are n, l, m_l, and m_s. The last two numbers are the projections of l and s along the field. L, S, and J no longer have any meaning. In fact, the quantities they represent are not constant when B is very great.

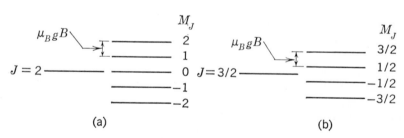

Fig. 12–9. Energy level splitting by a magnetic field, Zeeman effect. (a) For $J = 2$, (b) for $J = 3/2$.

12–9. The Stern-Gerlach Experiment.

The first conclusive evidence that angular momenta must have quantized projections (this is called space quantization) was provided by Stern and Gerlach. Silver atoms in a $^2S_{1/2}$ state were passed in a beam between the pole pieces of a magnet. The pole pieces were shaped to give a very non-homogeneous field (see Fig. 12–11). The rules of quantum mechanics require that the spins line

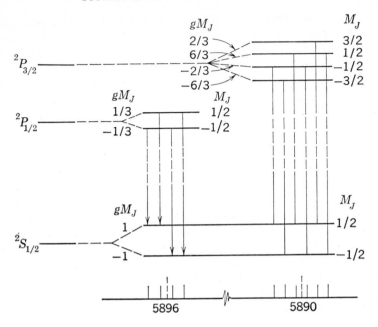

Fig. 12–10.   Zeeman effect for the D lines of sodium.

up either parallel to the field or antiparallel to the field.   No other orientations are permitted.   The atomic beam thus consists of two kinds of atoms.
One kind, those with spin angular momenta parallel to the field ($M_s = \frac{1}{2}$),
have the magnetic moment against the field and as a result are deflected

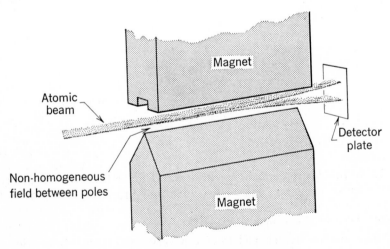

Fig. 12–11.   Stern-Gerlach experiment.

toward the weak part of the field. The others, those with spin angular momenta antiparallel to the field ($M_s = -\frac{1}{2}$) have magnetic moments parallel to the field and are deflected toward the strong part of the field. The fact that the beam does split into just two portions verifies the quantum mechanical limitation on the orientation of the spins. The magnetic field must be non-homogeneous to produce any deflection at all. A magnetic moment in a uniform field may experience a *torque*, but no resultant *force*.

12–10. Hyperfine Structure. Very high resolution spectrographs show that many apparently single lines have a structure much smaller than that due to variations in J. This structure is called *hyperfine structure*. There are several causes of hyperfine structure. Among these is the fact that the different reduced masses for different isotopes of an element lead to slightly different energies. This is particularly important for light atoms (see Art. 9–3). There are other more complicated interactions between the electron field and the nucleus that cause detectable variations in energy with isotopes for heavier atoms.

Another major reason is that many nuclei have a nuclear spin and a nuclear magnetic moment. This is usually of the order of

$$\mu_N = \frac{eh}{4\pi M_p} = \frac{\mu_B}{1836}. \qquad \left[\mu_N = \frac{eh}{4\pi M_p c} = \frac{\mu_B}{1836}.\right] \qquad (12\text{--}19)$$

Here M_p is the mass of a proton, approximately 1836 times the mass of an electron. The nuclear spin quantum number is usually designated by I. The resultant of J and I is designated by F. The addition of J and I follow the same rules as L and S. The knowledge of I and of μ_I are important in the study of nuclei.

PROBLEMS

12–1. In this chapter we have seen that the angular momentum of an atomic system is the central factor in untangling complicated structure. Review the concepts covered in Chapter 3.

12–2. (a) Compute the magnetic moment of an electron in the first Bohr orbit. (b) Using the mass of an electron and its orbital radius and velocity in the first Bohr orbit compute the value of the angular momentum. (c) Compare the computed value found in (b) to the value obtained from (a) and the known value of the Bohr magneton. Draw a diagram of this atom and place on it the angular momentum and magnetic moment vectors.

12–3. What is the multiplicity of an $L = 3$, $S = 1$ state? Show why it is $2S + 1$.

12-4. Some of the term values in cm^{-1} for potassium are: 22,021, 10,304, 6009, 3934 cm^{-1}. Transitions between these levels and a level having the term value 35,006 cm^{-1} lead to a series. Calculate the wavelength of each line.

12-5. Some of the term values for rubidium are: 25,110, 9974, 5854, 3854 cm^{-1}. Transitions between these levels and a level having the term value 33,689 cm^{-1} lead to a series. Calculate the wavelength of each line.

12-6. Compute the energy of each of the levels of Problem 12–4 in electron volts and in joules (or ergs).

12-7. Compute the energy of each of the levels of Problem 12–5 in electron volts and in joules (or ergs).

12-8. Four important spectroscopic lines have the following wavelengths:

D_1 of sodium	5896 Å
D_2 of sodium	5890 Å
Green mercury line	5461 Å
Mercury resonance line	2537 Å

Calculate the wave number for each of these lines.

12-9. Two energy states for sodium are

$$-8.22 \times 10^{-12} \text{ ergs,}$$
$$-4.86 \times 10^{-12} \text{ ergs.}$$

Calculate the corresponding energies in electron volts. Calculate the corresponding term values in per centimeter units.

12-10. Use the data of Problem 12–9 to calculate the wave number and wavelength of the line originating from a transition between these states.

12-11. Find the one value of δ_l so that the expression of Eq. 12–4 gives the best approximation to the term values of the initial states of Problem 12–4 where $n = 4, 5, 6$, etc.

12-12. Find the one value of δ_l so that the expression of Eq. 12–4 gives the best approximation to the term values of the initial states of Problem 12–5 where $n = 5, 6, 7$, etc.

12-13. A state with angular momentum $\frac{1}{2}$ is said to be twofold degenerate. How many fold degenerate is a state with angular momentum of $\frac{5}{2}$?

12-14. A configuration is $1s^2 2s^2 2p^6 3s^2 3p^3$. What does this tell about the atom?

12-15. An atom has 14 electrons. Two electrons have $n = 1$ and $l = 0$; 2 have $n = 2$ and $l = 0$; 6 have $n = 2$ and $l = 1$; 2 have $n = 3$ and $l = 0$; 1 has $n = 3$ and $l = 1$; 1 has $n = 3$ and $l = 2$. Write the symbol describing the configuration.

12-16. List the values of S, L, and J for the terms $^3P_2$, $^1D_2$, $^4P_{3/2}$, $^6F_{9/2}$, $^1S_0$.

12-17. List the values of S, L, and J for the terms $^1P_1$, $^2D_{5/2}$, $^3F_4$, $^2S_{1/2}$, $^5D_1$.

12-18. Two electrons have orbital angular momentum quantum numbers (azimuthal quantum numbers) $l_1 = 2$ and $l_2 = 3$. What are possible values of S? What are possible values of L? For each combination of L and S, find the possible values of J.

12–19. Two electrons have orbital angular momentum quantum numbers (azimuthal quantum numbers) $l_1 = 1$ and $l_2 = 3$. What are the possible values of S? What are possible values of L? For each combination of L and S, find the possible values of J.

12–20. Treat the case of Problem 12–18 by adding each l and s to get j. Find the possible values of each of j_1 and j_2. For each compute the possible values of $\mathbf{J} = \mathbf{j}_1 + \mathbf{j}_2$. Compare the results with those of Problem 12–18.

12–21. Treat the case of Problem 12–19 by adding each l and s to get j. Find the possible values of each of j_1 and j_2. For each compute the possible values of $\mathbf{J} = \mathbf{j}_1 + \mathbf{j}_2$. Compare the results with those of Problem 12–19.

12–22. List all the terms originating from each of the following configurations $2s3p$, $4d5p$.

12–23. List all the terms originating from each of the following configurations $2p3p$, $3s3p4p$.

12–24. An atom has an angular momentum vector $\frac{3}{2}\,\hbar$. When the atom is in a magnetic field B the angular momentum is constrained to such a direction as to keep the component of angular momentum in the direction of B equal to $\frac{1}{2}\,\hbar$. (a) Make a diagram showing the direction of the angular momentum vector and B. (b) What is the angle between the angular momentum and B? (c) What other orientations are possible for the angular momentum under the quantum rules?

12–25. An atom has a magnetic moment of 2 Bohr magnetons. If it is aligned with a magnetic field of 1.0 weber m^{-2}, how much work will be required to reverse its direction?

12–26. Compute the torque on the atom of Problem 12–25 if its magnetic moment vector is at an angle of 60° with the field.

12–27. If the angular momentum of the atom of Problem 12–25 were $2\hbar$, at what rate would this vector precess?

12–28. Calculate the Landé g factor for the state $^3S_1$ and for $^3P_2$. Plot the energy levels and determine the nature of the Zeeman patterns for a transition from the $^3S_1$ state to the $^3P_2$ state.

12–29. Calculate the Landé g factor for the states $^3P_1$ and for $^3D_2$. Plot the energy levels and determine the nature of the Zeeman pattern for a transition from the $^3D_2$ to the $^3P_1$ state.

12–30. If $B = 0.7$ weber m^{-2} calculate the actual separation between the levels for each state of Problem 12–28.

12–31. If $B = 1.2$ weber m^{-2} calculate the actual separation between the levels for each state of Problem 12–29.

12–32. The normal Zeeman effect occurs for one of the yellow lines of mercury ($\lambda = 5791$Å). Calculate the separation for a field of 4000 gauss (a) in wave numbers, (b) in frequency, (c) in wavelength.

12-33. The figure shows a few of the energy levels and corresponding table of term values for magnesium. List all allowed transitions in standard spectroscopic notation and find the wave numbers for the first 4 of the lines.

		cm^{-1}
$3s^2$	$^1S_0$	61,672.1
$3s3p$	$^3P_0$	39,821.3
	$^3P_1$	39,801.4
	$^3P_2$	39,760.5
	$^1P_1$	26,620.7
$3s4s$	$^3S_1$	20,474.5
	$^1S_0$	18,169.0
$3s3d$	$^1D_2$	15,268.9
$3s3d$	$^3D_{3,2,1}$	13,714.7 (not resolved)

SELECTED REFERENCES

HERZBERG, G. *Atomic Spectra and Atomic Structure.* Dover Publications, Inc., New York, 1944. Chap. 2.

LEIGHTON, R. B. *Principles of Modern Physics.* McGraw-Hill Book Co., Inc., New York, 1959. Chap. 8.

RICHTMYER, F. K., E. H. KENNARD, and T. LAURITSEN. *Introduction to Modern Physics.* McGraw-Hill Book Co., Inc., New York, 1955. 5th ed., chap. 7.

WHITE, H. E. *Introduction to Atomic Spectra.* McGraw-Hill Book Co., Inc., New York, 1934. Chaps. 12 and 14.

13

The Periodic Table and X-Rays

If the chemical elements are arranged in order of atomic number, certain regularities or repeatable patterns of chemical and physical properties are displayed. This discovery by Mendeléef is an important milestone in chemical history. The *atomic number* is the number of positive electronic charges on the nucleus of the atom and, consequently, also the number of electrons in the swarm about the nucleus. The value of the atomic number Z of an atom can be inferred from the atomic weight of the element, from the chemistry of the element, from the results of a Rutherford scattering experiment, and from its optical and x-ray spectra. The naturally occurring elements have values of Z ranging from 1 for hydrogen to 92 for uranium. There are no naturally occurring elements with atomic numbers 61, 85, or 87. These elements have been produced artificially, as have elements with atomic numbers from 93 to 103.

13–1. The Periodic Table. Table 13–1 is a table of the chemical symbols of the chemical elements arranged in order of atomic number. When hydrogen and helium are placed as shown and by considering the elements enclosed within the parentheses to be special, all elements in each column possess very similar chemical and physical properties. Following hydrogen and helium there is a group of eight elements showing a regular progression of chemical properties. They are Li, Be, B, C, N, O, F, and Ne. This is followed by another group of eight elements, chemically remarkably like the ones just listed. They are Na, Mg, Al, Si, P, S, Cl, and A. These are followed by two more, namely, K and Ca, that behave as if a third group was being started, but the next ten elements are quite unlike any previous ones. These are Sc, Ti, V, Cr, Mn, Fe, Co, Ni, Cu, and Zn. These are then followed by Ga, Ge, As, Se, Br, and Kr that seem to finish the group started by K and Ca. Again we get a long group Y, Zr, etc., to Cd, followed by the completion of the group of eight with In to Xe.

TABLE 13-1

The Periodic Arrangement of the Elements

H							He										
Li	Be	B	C	N	O	F	Ne										
Na	Mg	Al	Si	P	S	Cl	A										
K	Ca	Ga	Ge	As	Se	Br	Kr	Sc	Ti	V	Cr	Mn	Fe	Co	Ni	Cu	Zn
Rb	Sr	In	Sn	Sb	Te	I	Xe	Y	Zr	Nb	Mo	Tc	Ru	Rh	Pd	Ag	Cd
Cs	Ba	Tl	Pb	Bi	Po	At	Rn	(La	Hf	Ta	W	Re	Os	Ir	Pt	Au	Hg
	Ce	Pr	Nd	Pm	Sm	Eu	Gd										
								Tb	Dy	Ho	Er	Tm	Yb	Lu			
Fr	Ra							(Ac									
	Th	Pa	U	Np	Pu	Am	Cm										
								Bk	Cf	E	Fm	Mv	No	Lw)			

The same pattern seems to start over again with Cs and Ba, followed by the start of a long group by La, but suddenly fourteen more elements, the rare earths (lanthenum is also usually included in the rare earths), interpose themselves to be followed by the rest of the long group Hf to Hg. Then the group of eight started with Cs and Ba is completed with Tl to Rn. Another start is then made on a group of eight with Fr and Ra, followed by Ac and a new "rare earth" group Th, etc.

The explanation of this behavior is given in the article that follows. Basically, the chemical properties of elements, and hence this table, are the result of each atom tending to exist in the lowest possible energy state permitted by quantum mechanics and the Pauli exclusion principle.

13–2. The Pauli Exclusion Principle. There are several ways of formulating the principle. Perhaps the easiest way, at least for our purpose, is the following:

In any one system, such as an atom, no two particles can have an identical set of quantum numbers.

Alternatively, if the form of quantum mechanics called wave mechanics is being used, the exclusion principle can be stated by saying that the wave function must change sign if the coordinates of two particles are interchanged. This can be rephrased as follows:

Nature can be described only with wave functions which are antisymmetric in an interchange of any pair of similar particles.

In quantum mechanics, the specification of the values of all appropriate quantum numbers provides all the information possible about any part of the system. If two parts of the system had the same full set of quantum numbers, they would be doing identical things, would be occupying the same space, etc. One may consider the Pauli exclusion principle as being the quantum mechanical equivalent of the old principle that two bodies cannot occupy the same space simultaneously. The validity of this idea may be questionable, but there is no known case of a violation of the Pauli exclusion principle.

13–3. Sizes of Shells and Subshells. The particular set of quantum numbers that are appropriate depends upon the system. The systems of interest here are atoms, each with a swarm of Z electrons moving around a nucleus. The rules of quantum mechanics are often difficult to apply, except in extreme situations. We will create such an extreme situation for our discussion by imagining that each atom has been put into a suitably strong magnetic field. Then there will be no L, S, or individual j because the magnetic field is strong enough to break all coupling between electrons. This is the Paschen-Back effect mentioned in Chapter 12. The only quantum numbers of individual electrons that can mean anything, then, are n, l, m_l, and m_s. The energy associated with each electron in this case is lowest when each of these quantum numbers is the lowest it can be. n has the greatest effect, then l, and finally m_l and m_s are still less and are about equal.

We shall call a group of electrons all having the same value of n a *shell*. Electrons within a shell which all have the same value of l will be called a subshell—an s-, p-, d-, or f-subshell, if l is 0, 1, 2, or 3, respectively. The exclusion principle limits the number of electrons in any subshell. Let us now see how this is so.

First, consider s-electrons. Since $l = 0$, m_l must be zero. The only possible way of having non-equal quantum numbers in a stated subshell is to have the values of m_s different. There are only two possible values of m_s, namely, $-\frac{1}{2}$ and $+\frac{1}{2}$. So we can have only two s-electrons in any shell.

In the case of p-electrons with $l = 1$, there are three possible values of m_l, -1, 0, and $+1$, and for each of these there can be two values of m_s. This allows six p-electrons in a shell.

You should now be able to show that there can be ten d-electrons in a shell and fourteen f-electrons.

Of course atoms are not ordinarily found in huge magnetic fields, but this does not change the limitation on the maximum number of electrons in any subshell of a certain type because a fundamental theorem of quantum mechanics requires the *number* of levels to be independent of external fields. Thus, as an external field changes, the energy and other properties of a state or level may change but the number of states or levels does not change. We are, therefore, now ready to determine the configuration of the normal (lowest energy) state of any atom. In Tables 13–2 and 13–3, we shall summarize the next article and also give both the configuration and the state description under the assumption that there is Russell-Saunders coupling, although this latter fact is incidental to the point of this chapter. Russell-Saunders coupling is discussed in Appendix E.

13–4. Building the Periodic Table. We shall first consider the first eighteen elements. Then we shall present the rest of the periodic table with a few comments.

The simplest atom is hydrogen. n should be 1 for the lowest energy state, so l must be 0. The configuration of H is $1s$. If we make $Z = 2$ to get helium, n is again 1 and $l = 0$. The configuration of He is $1s^2$. When we look at lithium and ask if we can add another electron with $n = 1$, the answer is no, since a third electron with $n = 1$ must certainly violate the exclusion principle. So we must shift to $n = 2$. We can then keep $l = 0$, so the configuration for lithium is $1s^2 2s$. (Note that we have an s-electron outside a "closed shell.") For beryllium, we can have the configuration $1s^2 2s^2$. Now we see that we have a closed subshell, and our next electron must be a $2p$-electron, giving boron the configuration $1s^2 2s^2 2p$.

For carbon we can have $1s^2 2s^2 2p^2$, etc. Table 13–2 shows the configuration of these and the remaining elements through argon.

Using the table, you will note how the sequence Na, Mg, Al, Si, P, S, Cl, and A is similar to that of Li, Be, B, C, N, O, F, and Ne. The chemical similarity of corresponding pairs of these is well known and we used this similarity in constructing Table 13–1.

TABLE 13–2

Configurations and Ground States of Elements 1 to 18

Z	Element	Symbol	Configuration	Ground state
1	Hydrogen	H	$1s$	$^2S_{1/2}$
2	Helium	He	$1s^2$	$^1S_0$
3	Lithium	Li	$1s^2 2s$	$^2S_{1/2}$
4	Beryllium	Be	$1s^2 2s^2$	$^1S_0$
5	Boron	B	$1s^2 2s^2 2p$	$^2P_{1/2}$
6	Carbon	C	$1s^2 2s^2 2p^2$	$^3P_0$
7	Nitrogen	N	$1s^2 2s^2 2p^3$	$^4S_{3/2}$
8	Oxygen	O	$1s^2 2s^2 2p^4$	$^3P_2$
9	Fluorine	F	$1s^2 2s^2 2p^5$	$^2P_{3/2}$
10	Neon	Ne	$1s^2 2s^2 2p^6$	$^1S_0$
11	Sodium	Na	$1s^2 2s^2 2p^6 3s$	$^2S_{1/2}$
12	Magnesium	Mg	$1s^2 2s^2 2p^6 3s^2$	$^1S_0$
13	Aluminum	Al	$1s^2 2s^2 2p^6 3s^2 3p$	$^2P_{1/2}$
14	Silicon	Si	$1s^2 2s^2 2p^6 3s^2 3p^2$	$^3P_0$
15	Phosphorus	P	$1s^2 2s^2 2p^6 3s^2 3p^3$	$^4S_{3/2}$
16	Sulphur	S	$1s^2 2s^2 2p^6 3s^2 3p^4$	$^3P_2$
17	Chlorine	Cl	$1s^2 2s^2 2p^6 3s^2 3p^5$	$^2P_{3/2}$
18	Argon	A	$1s^2 2s^2 2p^6 3s^2 3p^6$	$^1S_0$

Before going on, it is well to point out that the closed subshells, particularly the s- and p-subshells, are especially stable configurations. A single electron or two outside of such a closed subshell is not very tightly bound. Conversely, the filling of an almost closed shell leads to a low energy configuration. The familiar chemical properties of the alkali metals and the halogens are largely the result of these last two facts.

When we proceed to develop the rest of the periodic table, certain questions arise that were not present when considering the first group of elements. For example, there is the question of whether the next electron to be added after the last $3p$-electron should be a $3d$-electron or a $4s$-electron. The question may be restated as follows: Of two alternatives, (a) keeping n fixed at 3 and increasing l to 2, or (b) increasing n to 4 and decreasing l to 0—which gives the lower energy level? It is possible to compute the answer and the result agrees with nature—the next electron to be added is a $4s$-electron. We get another alkali metal. Even the next is another $4s$-electron, giving another alkaline earth. But the next electron will be a $3d$-electron rather than a $4p$-electron, since such an electron gives a lower energy level. In fact, all the next nine electrons will have lower energies if they are $3d$-electrons rather than $4p$-electrons. In the case of chromium and copper it is even favorable to lose a $4s$-electron and have an extra $3d$-electron. All of these ten cases have an entirely different electronic structure from any before and, consequently, a different chemistry. They make up the first *long group*. Other irregularities arise as electrons are added.

TABLE 13–3

Configurations and Ground States of Elements 19–103

Z	Element	Symbol	Configuration	Ground state
19	Potassium	K	$1s^22s^22p^63s^23p^64s$	$^2S_{1/2}$
20	Calcium	Ca	$1s^22s^22p^63s^23p^64s^2$	$^1S_0$
21	Scandium	Sc	$1s^22s^22p^63s^23p^63d4s^2$	$^2D_{3/2}$
22	Titanium	Ti	$1s^22s^22p^63s^23p^63d^24s^2$	$^3F_2$
23	Vanadium	V	$1s^22s^22p^63s^23p^63d^34s^2$	$^4F_{3/2}$
24	Chromium	Cr	$1s^22s^22p^63s^23p^63d^54s$	$^7S_3$
25	Manganese	Mn	$1s^22s^22p^63s^23p^63d^54s^2$	$^6S_{5/2}$
26	Iron	Fe	$1s^22s^22p^63s^23p^63d^64s^2$	$^5D_4$
27	Cobalt	Co	$1s^22s^22p^63s^23p^63d^74s^2$	$^4F_{9/2}$
28	Nickel	Ni	$1s^22s^22p^63s^23p^63d^84s^2$	$^3F_4$
29	Copper	Cu	$1s^22s^22p^63s^23p^63d^{10}4s$	$^2S_{1/2}$
30	Zinc	Zn	$1s^22s^22p^63s^23p^63d^{10}4s^2$	$^1S_0$
31	Gallium	Ga	$1s^22s^22p^63s^23p^63d^{10}4s^24p$	$^2P_{1/2}$
32	Germanium	Ge	$1s^22s^22p^63s^23p^63d^{10}4s^24p^2$	$^3P_0$
33	Arsenic	As	`"` $4s^24p^3$	$^4S_{3/2}$
34	Selenium	Se	`"` $4s^24p^4$	$^3P_2$
35	Bromine	Br	`"` $4s^24p^5$	$^2P_{3/2}$
36	Krypton	Kr	`"` $4s^24p^6$	$^1S_0$
37	Rubidium	Rb	`"` $4s^24p^65s$	$^2S_{1/2}$
38	Strontium	Sr	`"` $4s^24p^65s^2$	$^1S_0$
39	Yttrium	Y	(Core to $3d^{10}$)$4s^24p^64d5s^2$	$^2D_{3/2}$
40	Zirconium	Zr	`"` $4s^24p^64d^25s^2$	$^3F_2$
41	Niobium	Nb	`"` $4s^24p^64d^45s$	$^6D_{1/2}$
42	Molybdenum	Mo	`"` $4s^24p^64d^55s$	$^7S_3$
43	Technetium	Tc	`"` $4s^24p^64d^55s^2$	$^6S_{5/2}$
44	Ruthenium	Ru	(Core to $3d^{10}$)$4s^24p^64d^75s$	$^5F_5$
45	Rhodium	Rh	`"` $4s^24p^64d^85s$	$^4F_{9/2}$
46	Palladium	Pd	`"` $4s^24p^64d^{10}$	$^1S_0$
47	Silver	Ag	`"` $4s^24p^64d^{10}5s$	$^2S_{1/2}$
48	Cadmium	Cd	`"` $4s^24p^64d^{10}5s^2$	$^1S_0$
49	Indium	In	`"` $4s^24p^64d^{10}5s^25p$	$^2P_{1/2}$
50	Tin	Sn	`"` $4s^24p^64d^{10}5s^25p^2$	$^3P_0$
51	Antimony	Sb	`"` $4s^24p^64d^{10}5s^25p^3$	$^4S_{3/2}$
52	Tellurium	Te	`"` $4s^24p^64d^{10}5s^25p^4$	$^3P_2$
53	Iodine	I	`"` $4s^24p^64d^{10}5s^25p^5$	$^2P_{3/2}$
54	Xenon	Xe	`"` $4s^24p^64d^{10}5s^25p^6$	$^1S_0$
55	Caesium	Cs	(Core to $4d^{10}$)$5s^25p^66s$	$^2S_{1/2}$
56	Barium	Ba	`"` $5s^25p^66s^2$	$^1S_0$
57	Lanthanum	La	`"` $5s^25p^65d6s^2$	$^2D_{3/2}$

TABLE 13–3 (Continued)

Z	Element	Symbol	Configuration	Ground state
58	Cerium	Ce	" $5s^2 5p^6 4f^2 6s^2$	$^3H_4$
59	Praseodymium	Pr	" $5s^2 5p^6 4f^3 6s^2$	$^4I_{9\frac{1}{2}}$
60	Neodymium	Nd	" $5s^2 5p^6 4f^4 6s^2$	$^5I_4$
61	Promethium	Pm	" $5s^2 5p^6 4f^5 6s^2$	$^6H_{5\frac{1}{2}}$
62	Samarium	Sm	" $5s^2 5p^6 4f^6 6s^2$	$^7F_0$
63	Europium	Eu	" $5s^2 5p^6 4f^7 6s^2$	$^8S_{7\frac{1}{2}}$
64	Gadolinium	Gd	" $5s^2 5p^6 4f^7 5d 6s^2$	$^9D_2$
65	Terbium	Tb	" $5s^2 5p^6 4f^9 6s^2$	$^6H_{15\frac{1}{2}}$
66	Dysprosium	Dy	" $5s^2 5p^6 4f^{10} 6s^2$	$^5I_8$
67	Holmium	Ho	" $5s^2 5p^6 4f^{11} 6s^2$	$^4I_{15\frac{1}{2}}$
68	Erbium	Er	" $5s^2 5p^6 4f^{12} 6s^2$	$^3H_6$
69	Thulium	Tm	" $5s^2 5p^6 4f^{13} 6s^2$	$^2F_{7\frac{1}{2}}$
70	Ytterbium	Yb	(Core to $4d^{10}$)$5s^2 5p^6 4f^{14} 6s^2$	$^1S_0$
71	Lutetium	Lu	" $5s^2 5p^6 4f^{14} 5d 6s^2$	$^2D_{5\frac{1}{2}}$
72	Hafnium	Hf	(Core to $5p^6$)$4f^{14} 5d^2 6s^2$	$^3F_2$
73	Tantalum	Ta	" $4f^{14} 5d^3 6s^2$	$^4F_{3\frac{1}{2}}$
74	Wolfram (Tungsten)	W	" $4f^{14} 5d^4 6s^2$	$^5D_0$
75	Rhenium	Re	" $4f^{14} 5d^5 6s^2$	$^6S_{5\frac{1}{2}}$
76	Osmium	Os	(Core to $4f^{14}$)$5d^6 6s^2$	$^5D_4$
77	Iridium	Ir	" $5d^7 6s^2$	$^4F_{9\frac{1}{2}}$
78	Platinum	Pt	" $5d^9 6s$	$^3D_3$
79	Gold	Au	" $5d^{10} 6s$	$^2S_{1\frac{1}{2}}$
80	Mercury	Hg	" $5d^{10} 6s^2$	$^1S_0$
81	Thallium	Tl	" $5d^{10} 6s^2 6p$	$^2P_{1\frac{1}{2}}$
82	Lead	Pb	" $5d^{10} 6s^2 6p^2$	$^3P_0$
83	Bismuth	Bi	" $5d^{10} 6s^2 6p^3$	$^4S_{3\frac{1}{2}}$
84	Polonium	Po	" $5d^{10} 6s^2 6p^4$	$^3P_2$
85	Astatine	At	" $5d^{10} 6s^2 6p^5$	$^2P_{3\frac{1}{2}}$
86	Emanation	Em	" $5d^{10} 6s^2 6p^6$	$^1S_0$
87	Francium	Fr	" $5d^{10} 6s^2 6p^6 7s$	$^2S_{1\frac{1}{2}}$
88	Radium	Ra	(Core to $5d^{10}$)$6s^2 6p^6 7s^2$	$^1S_0$
89	Actinium	Ac	" $6s^2 6p^6 6d 7s^2$	$^2D_{3\frac{1}{2}}$
90	Thorium	Th	" $6s^2 6p^6 6d^2 7s^2$	$^3F_2$
91	Protactinium	Pa	(Core to $6p^6$)$5f^2 6d 7s^2$	$^4K_{11\frac{1}{2}}$
92	Uranium	U	" $5f^3 6d 7s^2$	$^5L_6$
93	Neptunium	Np	" $5f^4 6d 7s^2$	$^6L_{1\frac{1}{2}}$
94	Plutonium	Pu	" $5f^5 6d 7s^2$	$^7F_0$
95	Americium	Am	(Core to $6p^6$)$5f^7 7s^2$	$^8S_{15\frac{1}{2}}$
96	Curium	Cm	" $5f^7 6d 7s^2$	$^9D_2$
97	Berkelium	Bk	" $5f^8 6d 7s^2$	$^8H_{17\frac{1}{2}}$
98	Californium	Cf	" $5f^9 6d 7s^2$	$^5I_8$
99	Einsteinium	E	" $5f^{10} 6d 7s^2$ (?)	$^4I_{15\frac{1}{2}}$ (?)
100	Fermium	Fm	" $5f^{11} 6d 7s^2$ (?)	$^3H_6$ (?)
101	Mendelevium	Mv	" $5f^{12} 6d 7s^2$ (?)	$^2F_{7\frac{1}{2}}$ (?)
102	Nobelium	No	" $5f^{13} 6d 7s^2$ (?)	$^1S_0$ (?)
103	Lawrencium	Lw	" $5f^{14} 6d 7s^2$ (?)	$^2D_{3\frac{1}{2}}$ (?)

The rest of the arrangement is given in Table 13–3. After the addition of ten $3d$-electrons, adding $4p$-electrons gives the sequence Ga to Kr which is similar to the sequence Al to A. Then again, it requires less energy to add a 5s-electron than a 4d one, but finally the 4d's lead to lower energy giving the next long group as the 4d's are added. There follows the addition of 5p's and then another alkali and alkaline earth, caesium and barium are formed. Next a 5d-electron is best, as you might expect, but then it requires less energy to add 4f-electrons. Fourteen of these can be added. They have small orbital radii spending most of their time far inside the atom, and therefore have very little effect on the chemistry of these elements, the *rare earths*. The rest of the table proceeds in the same manner including even the formation of a second rare-earth-like group, the actinides, the final group of known atoms.

All of this makes up one of the notable successes of the quantum theory. We have not mentioned many other features, such as the ability to predict the magnetic and chemical properties of the atoms from this.

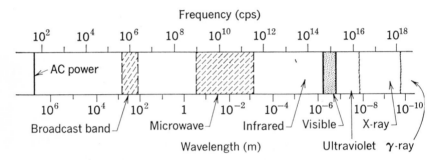

Fig. 13–1.   The electromagnetic spectrum.

13–5. X-Rays. The emission of electromagnetic radiations has been discussed at a number of points in this book. Reference has been made to infrared, visible, and ultraviolet radiation. It should be understood that these wavelengths make up only a portion of the complete, known electromagnetic spectrum. There are longer wavelengths, usually produced by electronic devices, and shorter wavelengths, x-rays and gamma rays. Fig. 13–1 identifies these various types of radiation relative to each other. The plot is logarithmic with respect to wavelength and frequency.

Our immediate interest here is x-rays, electromagnetic radiation with a wavelength shorter than 100 Å. This range of wavelengths includes electromagnetic radiation emitted by nuclei. Such radiations from nuclei are usually called *gamma rays*, while the term *x-rays* generally refers to radiation produced by machines. X-rays can be produced in a number of ways. The most common way is to have electrons with high kinetic energy strike a solid anode within a highly evacuated tube. The electrons are accelerated from the hot tungsten filament ($\simeq 2000°C$) to the anode by a potential difference of approximately 20 to 250 kv. The anode, or target (a metal, such as copper, nickel, molybdenum) is usually water cooled and for industrial and medical use is sometimes rotated so that it is not destroyed by the steady intense bombardment by electrons (see Fig. 13–2).

For research purposes, x-rays of very short wavelength are often desirable. For shorter wavelengths, higher energy electrons are needed. Such electrons are obtained in *betatrons* and *synchrotrons* (see Chapter 16).

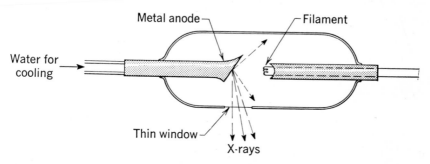

Fig. 13–2.   An x-ray tube.

Betatrons and synchrotrons are also now used in medical therapy work, and for radiographing large industrial castings. The use of x-rays for radiography (making shadow pictures through living bodies and other objects) and the use of x-rays for medical therapy are so familiar that there is no need for further discussion here.

X-rays can also be produced by irradiating matter with other x-rays. Such secondary x-rays may be the only kind obtainable from gaseous or highly volatile materials.

13–6. Characteristics of X-Rays.   X-rays are short wavelength electromagnetic waves. They are much more penetrating than radiation in the visible wavelength range. An important technique for determining the energy of x-rays is to measure their absorption in materials. They can be diffracted and polarized; they cause fluorescence in certain crystals; they are usually detected either by their ability to ionize gases (in ionization chambers) or by photographic techniques. A further interesting characteristic is that the index of refraction of materials for x-rays is often less than unity. This fact makes possible the use of reflection grating spectrometers discussed in Art. 6–3 as devices used for measuring x-ray wavelengths. We also recall from that article that most crystals have a spacing between atomic planes d which is suitable for interference effects with x-rays. They can be used in crystal spectrometers to measure wavelengths using the Bragg relation

$$n\lambda = 2d \sin \theta, \tag{13-1}$$

derived in Art. 6–3. Fig. 13–3 is a schematic diagram of a *rotating crystal spectrometer* using an ionization chamber as a detector. By carefully

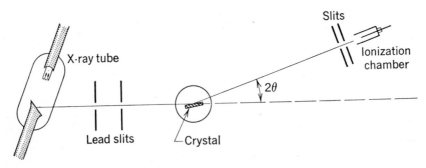

Fig. 13–3. X-ray spectrometer.

rotating the crystal and detector so that the angles of reflection and incidence are both θ, the variation of intensity with wavelength is easily observed, i.e., the x-ray spectrum is obtained.

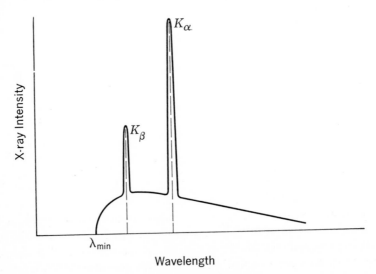

Fig. 13–4. X-ray spectrum.

A spectrum such as might be obtained from a molybdenum target is shown in Fig. 13–4. The typical features include a comparatively low intensity of radiation at all wavelengths longer than a certain minimum wavelength, and an intense radiation at certain particular wavelengths. These peaks constitute the *line spectrum* or *characteristic x-radiation*. The lines are very sharp, are about 10,000 times more intense than the continuous spectrum, and their wavelength and number depend on the target material.

The presence of these lines indicates once again the existence of discrete energy levels in atoms. However, the photon energy associated with x-ray lines of wavelength approximately 1 Å, have energies

$$hv = h\frac{c}{\lambda} \simeq 2 \times 10^{-15} \text{ j} \simeq 12{,}000 \text{ ev.}$$

Therefore, the energy levels in atoms that produce visible light (and are separated only by a few electron volts) are somewhat different in arrangement from those producing x-rays (and separated by thousands of electron volts). In the next articles, we shall apply our knowledge of the quantum rules to these x-ray energy levels.

13–7. Moseley's Law. In 1913–14, Moseley[1] made a brilliant study of the x-ray spectra of the elements. (Shortly afterwards, Moseley was unfortunately killed while serving in the British army during World War I.)

He used potassium ferrocyanide as the crystal and used thirty different elements as targets in the x-ray tube. He detected the x-rays by letting them fall on a photographic plate.

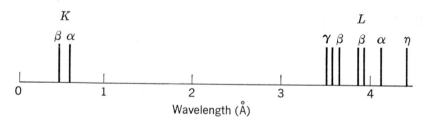

Fig. 13–5.   X-ray spectrum of silver.

He found that the characteristic lines occurred principally in two groups. First, a group at shorter wavelengths that he called K lines; second, a group of longer wavelengths that he called L lines. The members of the group were designated as K_α, K_β, and L_α, L_β, etc. The approximate positions of these lines for a silver target are shown in Fig. 13–5.

In addition, he observed that, unlike optical spectra, x-ray spectra are all very much alike. The actual wavelengths are the distinguishing features.

[1] H. G. J. Moseley, *Phil. Mag.*, **26**, 1024 (1913) and *Phil. Mag.*, **27**, 703 (1914).

For the elements aluminum through silver, Moseley noted a regularity in the wavelengths of the K_α lines. Guided by the recently published work of Bohr which gave for the frequency of a spectral line,

$$\nu = AZ^2, \tag{13-2}$$

(see Eq. 9–18) he plotted the square root of the frequency versus Z and obtained a straight line as illustrated in Fig. 13–6. The equation of the

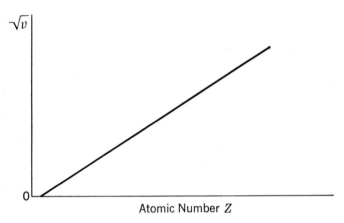

Fig. 13–6. Moseley's law.

line instead of being Eq. 13–2 was actually closer to

$$\nu = A(Z - 1)^2. \tag{13-3}$$

The value of A was obtained from the slope and found to be (again see Eq. 9–18 and set $n_2 = 1$, $n_1 = 2$)

$$A = \frac{me^4}{8\epsilon_0^2 h^3}\frac{3}{4}. \qquad \left[A = \frac{2\pi^2 me^4}{h^3}\frac{3}{4}.\right] \tag{13-4}$$

Moseley also tried analyzing his data on the basis of atomic weight, but found the results did *not* give the regularity given by the atomic number. He concluded that for x-ray characteristic lines, atomic number is a more valuable quantity as contrasted to Mendeléef's emphasis on atomic weight in formulating the periodic arrangement of the atoms. Measurement of the wavelength of x-ray lines thus provides information for obtaining the atomic number Z.

He also extended his work for elements from zirconium through gold, using the L series. In terms of wave numbers, $\tilde{\nu} = \nu/c$, we write the results of this experimental work (Moseley's laws) as

$$K_\alpha: \tilde{\nu} = \left(\frac{1}{1^2} - \frac{1}{2^2}\right) R(Z-1)^2, \tag{13-5}$$

$$L: \tilde{\nu} = \left(\frac{1}{2^2} - \frac{1}{3^2}\right) R(Z-7.4)^2. \tag{13-6}$$

Improved methods have extended Moseley's work to even heavier elements, and additional series, the M and N series of even longer wavelengths have been found.

13–8. X-Ray Spectra and Atomic Structure. We have just seen that we should expect each atom to have 2 electrons in the $n = 1$ shell and 8 electrons in the $n = 2$ shell, and so on. One of these innermost electrons may be removed by a high energy electron striking the target of an x-ray tube. The atom is then ionized, that is, it has lost an electron, and the vacancy is in (say) the $n = 1$ shell. The K series can be accounted for as an electron drops into this vacancy in the $n = 1$ shell, leaving a vacancy in an outer shell. An atom with an electron *absent* from its $n = 1$ shell is said to be in the K *quantum state of the ion.* An electron dropping from the $n = 2$ shell changes the ion from the K quantum state to the L quantum state. The difference in energy appears as an x-ray photon. For this reason, the innermost shells of atoms have acquired the following notation.

For n equal to 1, 2, 3, . . . , the shell is a K-, L-, M-, . . . shell.

An electron which is changing from the L-shell to the K-shell is "inside" all the other electrons in the atom except the single electron still remaining in the K-shell. Therefore, the nuclear charge that the changing electron "sees" is not Z but rather the screened value $(Z-1)$. This accounts for this term in Eq. 13–5. By this same reasoning, the factor should be $(Z-7)$ in Eq. 13–6 for a transition from the M to the L-shell (and hence for the L series). The effective nuclear charge is less than the actual because of the screening by electrons.

13–9. X-Ray Energy Level Diagrams. It is customary in drawing x-ray energy level diagrams to take the normal (i.e., ground) state of the atom as the energy state of zero energy. Energetic electrons striking the atom and removing electrons *add* energy to the atom, so that the K quantum state of the ion lies high above the ground state. As we pointed out in Art. 13–6, these levels are thousands of electron volts apart, as contrasted with the several-volt separations in optical spectra. Fig. 13–7 shows a simplified x-ray energy level diagram. When the atom is in a K state it has one K-electron missing. A transition to an L state means that an L-electron has left its usual orbit and filled in the gap of the missing K-electron. One might think of a transition from a K state to an L state as a jump of a *hole* (a shortage of an electron) from the K-shell to the L-shell.

When a K-electron is missing there is only one possible state. In this state the angular momentum of orbital motion for the core electrons is still zero since a K-electron must have $l = 0$. Because of its spin it leaves a

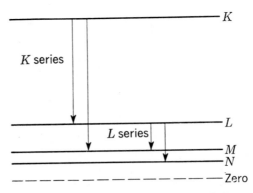

Fig. 13–7.   Simplified x-ray energy level diagram.

total angular momentum represented by $j = \frac{1}{2}$. When an L-electron is missing there are three possibilities. These are indicated by the symbols L_I, L_{II}, and L_{III}. The first of these is the state in which a $2s$ electron is missing; so $l = 0$ and $j = \frac{1}{2}$. The second and third are states in which a $2p$-electron is missing. Then $l = 1$ and j is either $\frac{1}{2}$ or $\frac{3}{2}$, respectively. The five M levels arise for similar reasons since l can be 0, 1, or 2. These details have been plotted schematically in Fig. 13–8. The scale of this figure is not uniform for the spacing between K, L, M, etc., states should be much more than the spacing between members of each group. Transitions are controlled by selection rules very similar to those controlling transitions in the optical region, namely,

$$\Delta l = \pm 1; \quad \Delta j = 0 \quad \text{or} \quad \pm 1. \tag{13–7}$$

A number of possible transitions are indicated in Fig. 13–8 with the standard line designation shown. Thus the K_α and K_β lines are seen to be doublets.

13–10. The Continuous X-Ray Spectrum. We have discussed the characteristic or line, part of the x-ray spectra, so let us now turn our attention to the continuous background radiation. This is a relatively low intensity radiation, characterized by a maximum value of intensity and by the cut-off wavelength represented in Fig. 13–4 by λ_{min} the intersection on the wavelength axis. Both the maximum intensity and the short wavelength cut-off are a function of the voltage applied to the tube.

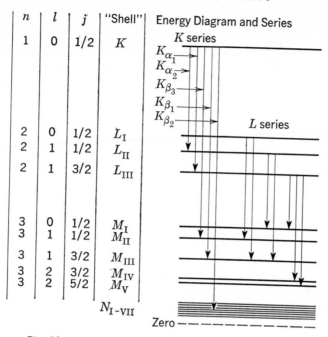

Fig. 13–8. Schematic x-ray energy level diagram.

Increasing the voltage increases the maximum intensity and gives a shorter wavelength cut-off.

Classical electromagnetic theory predicts that radiation will occur when high speed electrons are decelerated as they pass the nuclei of atoms in the target of the x-ray tube and the spectrum should be continuous. Quantum rules say that if the electron loses an amount of energy ΔE in passing a nucleus and h is Planck's constant the frequency of radiation will be

$$\nu = \frac{\Delta E}{h}. \tag{13–8}$$

If the electron has been accelerated through a potential difference V, then the maximum possible energy loss is

$$\Delta E = eV,$$

and therefore the cut-off frequency (i.e., the maximum frequency corresponding to the minimum wavelength) is

$$\nu_0 = \frac{eV}{h}. \tag{13–9}$$

A measurement of ν_0 thus gives another determination of h/e.

This type of continuous background radiation has been given the German name "Bremsstrahlung." It may be translated approximately as "braking radiation" or "deceleration radiation."

13–11. The Interaction of X-Rays with Matter. X-rays lose their energy by several mechanisms as they pass through matter. This loss is measured experimentally by a determination of the *absorption coefficient* μ.

If I is the intensity of x-rays incident on a piece of material of thickness dx, and dI is the decrease in intensity of the x-rays because of their passage through the material, then μ is defined as the fractional decrease in intensity per unit thickness, i.e.,

$$\mu = -\frac{dI}{I\,dx}, \tag{13–10}$$

so

$$\frac{dI}{I} = -\mu\,dx$$

and, integrating over a thickness from 0 to x, setting $I = I_0$ at $x = 0$,

$$I = I_0 \exp -\mu x. \tag{13–11}$$

In this *absorption law*, μ may be called the linear absorption coefficient. Eq. 13–11 is also often written

$$I = I_0 \exp - \left(\frac{\mu}{\rho}\right)\rho x = I_0 \exp -\sigma w \tag{13–12}$$

where ρ is the density of the absorber and $\sigma = \mu/\rho$ is called the *mass absorption coefficient*. The variable $w = \rho x$ is the mass per unit area that the x-rays have traversed.

The absorption coefficient is quite dependent upon wavelength. In fact, Eq. 13–11 will not hold well unless the x-rays are monochromatic. In general, x-rays of longer wavelength are more easily absorbed (μ is large) and are said to be *soft*; those of short wavelengths are more penetrating (μ is small) and are said to be *hard*.

Any mechanism that removes energy from the x-ray beam contributes to the absorption. These mechanisms may be (a) excitation of atoms, or (b) ionization with the production of x-ray photoelectrons, (c) scattering by bound electrons or (d) by the Compton effect discussed in Art. 8–7.

Fig. 13–9 shows the variation of μ with wavelength for nickel. The abrupt decrease in μ at K, and L_I, L_{II}, and L_{III} occur when $h\nu$ becomes too small to remove a K-, L_I-, L_{II}-, or L_{III}-electron.

Items (a), (b), and (d) above all lead to the ejection of an electron from the system, i.e., result in ionization. It is this ionization that produces most of the detectable effects of x-rays. It will make a silver halide crystal developable (easily reduced to metallic silver by a weak reducing agent), the photographic effect; it disturbs the chemistry of living cells, the biologic effects; etc.   The amount of ionization produced, thus, may serve as a measure of exposure, and the rate of production of ions may serve as a measure of intensity.   The unit of this measure is called the

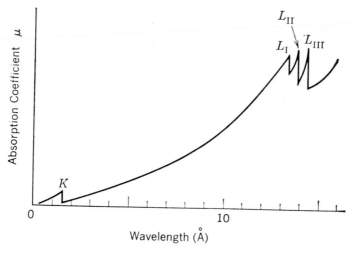

Fig. 13–9.   X-ray absorption spectrum for nickel.

roentgen r.   It is that amount of exposure to x-rays (or other ionizing radiation) such that 1 statcoulomb ($\frac{1}{3} \times 10^{-9}$ coulombs) of ions of either sign is produced in 0.001293 g of dry air (1 cm^3 at a pressure of 76 cm of mercury and at 0°C).   On the average each ion pair requires about 32 ev of energy to produce it.   Thus an exposure of 1 r means that 1.07×10^{-8} j of energy are absorbed per cm^3 of air at standard pressure and temperature.   This is 8.4×10^{-3} j per kg of air.   Other materials will absorb different amounts, but water, animal tissue, and vegetable tissue absorb quite similar amounts per unit mass as air.

A human body is considered able to accept 250 mr per week without serious injury.   A single whole body dose may result in serious injury. The survival probability following a dose of 400 r over the whole body is about 0.5.

The photoelectrons emitted by process (b) can be used to measure the energy of the photons themselves.   The kinetic energy K of the photoelectron can be measured by its deflection in a magnetic field.   See Fig. 13–10.   Then

$$h\nu = K + W, \tag{13–13}$$

where W is the energy required to remove the electron from the system.

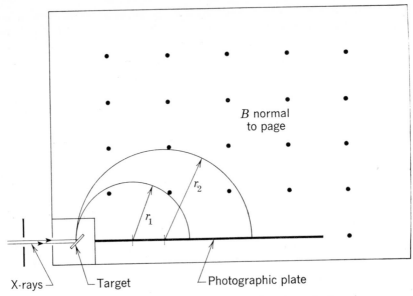

Fig. 13–10. Magnetic spectrometer for photoelectrons.

PROBLEMS

13–1. Show that 10 d-electrons are possible in an electronic shell.

13–2. Show that 14 f-electrons are possible in an electronic shell.

13–3. Show that the angular momentum vectors for electrons in a closed 3 p-shell add to zero.

13–4. The least amount of energy required to remove an electron completely from a particular shell has been determined experimentally in electron volts for some of the atoms in the periodic table. Among these are

	K	L		M			N	
	$1s$	$2s$	$2p$	$3s$	$3p$	$3d$	$4s$	$4p$
Argon	3200	325	248	29.1	15.6			
Potassium	3600	378	292	35.3	16.3		4.35	
Scandium	4500	492	408	48.9	36.7	7.34	6.80	

What is the ionization potential for each of these atoms? What is the wavelength of their K x-ray lines?

13–5. What electrons will the (a) sodium ion (b) cupric ion (c) ferrous ion (d) Mn^{+7} ion contain?

13-6. Roughly sketch the orbits for the $4s$, $4p$, $4d$, and $4f$ electrons to show the relative shape and amount of penetration. According to the Bohr-Sommerfeld theory for hydrogen the ratio of semi-major to semi-minor axes $a/b = n/k$.

13-7. (a) Compute the kinetic energy of electrons in a 50 kv x-ray tube (in electron volts and ergs). (b) The copper target area in this tube has dimensions 0.08 cm by 0.01 cm. If the beam current is 15 ma, how much power is dissipated in this area? (c) The tube is water cooled. Show how the 50 kv high voltage must be connected to the tube.

13-8. Compute the energy in electron volts of a photon with a wavelength of 1.0 angstroms.

13-9. X-rays are produced in a tube across which the potential difference is 30,000 v. What is the shortest wavelength of x-ray that can be emitted?

13-10. The shortest wavelength emitted by an x-ray tube has a wavelength of 0.345 Å. What is the potential difference across the tube?

13-11. A set of crystal planes in calcite has a separation distance $d = 3.03$ Å. At what angle will the K_α line of molybdenum be diffracted? K_α line = 0.710 Å.

13-12. A set of crystal planes in rock salt has a separation distance $d = 2.81$ Å. What will be the Bragg diffraction angle for the K_α line of platinum? K_α line = 0.19 Å.

13-13. The K_α line for copper has a wavelength of 1.54 Å. For molybdenum it is 0.710 Å. What is the wavelength of the K_α line for arsenic?

13-14. The K_α line for iron has a wavelength of 1.93 Å. For platinum it is 0.19 Å. What is the wavelength of the K_α line for tin?

13-15. The K_α line for an element is 0.56 Å. What is the value of Z for that element? Use the data from Problems 13-13 and 13-14.

13-16. The K_α line for an element is 0.39 Å. What is the value of Z for that element? Use the data from Problems 13-13 and 13-14.

13-17. The linear absorption coefficient for zinc for the K_α line of copper is 418 cm^{-1}. What fraction of the incident x-rays of that wavelength will penetrate 0.1 mm of zinc?

13-18. What is the linear absorption coefficient for aluminum for the K_α line of molybdenum if a film 0.71 mm of aluminum permits 37.8% of the x-rays of that line to be transmitted?

13-19. Calculate the mass absorption coefficient for zinc using the data of Problem 13-17. The density of zinc is 7.14 gm cm^{-3}.

13-20. Calculate the mass absorption coefficient for aluminum using the data of Problem 13-18. The density of aluminum is 2.7 gm cm^{-3}.

13-21. The K_α line of tungsten ($\lambda = 0.71$ Å) falls on tin. The L_I absorption edge is 2.77 Å. If a $2s$ electron of tin is ejected by the photon, what energy will it have?

13–22. The K_α line of tantalum ($\lambda = 0.22$ Å) falls on palladium. The L_I absorption edge is 3.42 Å. If a $2s$ electron of palladium is ejected by the photon, what energy will it have?

13–23. X-ray dosages are measured in roentgens. One roentgen will produce ions carrying 1 statcoulomb of electrical charge in 1 cm³ of air at standard conditions. Notice that this definition is not a *rate* definition. One statcoulomb could be produced in 1 cm³ of air by even a very weak x-ray beam if the exposure were long enough. An ionization chamber for measuring x-ray dosage consists of a parallel-plate capacitor of capacitance C = 25 statfarad and volume 25 cm³. If it is charged to 300 v and exposure to x-rays removes 50% of the initial charge, calculate the x-ray dosage.

SELECTED REFERENCES

Clark, G. L. *Applied X Rays.* McGraw-Hill Book Co., Inc., New York, 1955. 4th ed., chap. 8.
Compton, A. H., and S. K. Allison. *X-Rays in Theory and Experiment.* D. Van Nostrand Co., Inc., Princeton, N. J., 1935. 2d ed., chap. 1.
Leighton, R. B. *Principles of Modern Physics.* McGraw-Hill Book Co., Inc., New York, 1959. Chap. 12.
Richtmyer, F. K., E. H. Kennard, and T. Lauritsen. *Introduction to Modern Physics.* McGraw-Hill Book Co., Inc., New York, 1955. 5th ed., chap. 7.

14

The Solid State

The properties of solid materials have long been of interest to the engineer, and much practical experience in such areas as strength of materials, thermal properties and electrical characteristics, has been obtained by workers in these fields. The advent of atomic theory, quantum mechanics, and computing aids has made possible a more fundamental approach to solids. Using these aids, physicists have turned their attention to developing general laws applicable to solid materials. Arbitrary subdivisions in this broad field of solid state physics might be made along the following lines.

1. Bonding in solids—a subdivision based on a study of the type of force that binds the atoms of a solid together. We may note four important types of bonding forces, namely, ionic, covalent, metallic, and molecular bonding.
2. The structure of solids—a subdivision arising from a study of the location of atoms and their electrons in the solid. This study combines newer techniques of x-ray, electron, and neutron diffraction, with the older concepts of crystallography.
3. Imperfections in solids—a subdivision involving a study of how departures from ideal crystal structure affect both the growth and structure of solids.
4. The gross properties of solids—a subdivision in which are included studies of the electrical, thermal, magnetic, and optical properties of solids.

Unavoidable overlap exists in this arbitrary grouping since many of the properties are interconnected.

The concepts of bonding, and the electronic band theory of solids will be discussed in this chapter. Both of these topics properly reside in the realm of theoretical solid state physics and tend to be abstract and mathematically involved. A detailed study is beyond the level of this text but it is hoped that the descriptive treatment given here will whet the appetite for more and at the same time lay a foundation of understanding about solids. The band theory of solids, which describes how the electrons behave in the solid, has proven particularly useful in the study of the optical, thermal, magnetic and electrical properties of solids. It therefore plays a central role in solid state physics at the present time. Here, however, the problem of how solids are held together will be examined first.

Some preliminary reference must be made to the structure of the solids that will be discussed. The type of solid to be considered here is the *crystalline* solid. The atoms of a crystal are arranged in a regular array such as have been suggested in Chapters 6 and 13. Sometimes the crystals have a large size and some minerals and gems are examples of this. Sometimes the crystals are small and randomly oriented and interlocking. Metals are especially likely to be of this sort. But even just a single microcrystal contains a very large number of atoms or molecules, so the study of the organized arrangement is of particular importance. This is not to say that amorphous solids (i.e., uncrystallized solids, such as glass) are not important. On the contrary, there is an active branch of solid state physics devoted to their study.

As previously noted, binding forces may be classified into four types, ionic, covalent, metallic, and molecular. In actuality, any one solid depends to some extent on all four types, yet one or the other is likely to predominate. Each of the four will be discussed in turn, each preceded by a discussion of the simpler problem of what holds two atoms together to form a molecule.

14–1. Ionic Binding. Elements Li, Na, K, Rb, Cs in the first column of the periodic table, plus Cu, Ag, Au are "monovalent metals" exhibiting a single s-electron outside the noble-gas closed-shell electronic structure

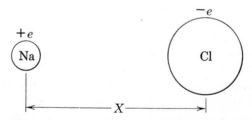

Fig. 14–1.   A positive and negative ion pair.

of He, Ne, A, Kr, Xe (plus d^{10} electrons for Cu, Ag, and Au). See Tables 13–2 and 13–3. These elements are easily ionized, leaving behind a positive ion with noble-gas closed shells. A noble-gas structure is spherically symmetric and hence the ion appears to be a spherical cloud of electrical charge with a reasonably defined radius as roughly indicated in Fig. 14–1.

On the other hand, elements F, Cl, Br, and I of column 7 of the periodic table are converted to the noble-gas closed-shell structure by the addition of just one electron. This produces negative ions because of the excess negative charge. These ions also have a clearly defined charge distribution about the nucleus. Fig. 14-1 shows such a pair of positive and negative ions separated by a distance X. The charge on each is $+e$ and $-e$, respectively. We have chosen sodium and chlorine only for the sake of definiteness in the next several paragraphs.

Since these are oppositely charged ions, we see at once that the electrostatic force of attraction is extremely important in binding these two together. Instead of discussing forces directly, we turn to the potential energy V which is just as descriptive as the force, since we know that

$$F = - \frac{dV}{dX}.$$

(14-1)

It is convenient to divide the range of possible values of X into three regions, X very large, X intermediate, and X small. Different processes are acting in these three regions. The results are shown in Fig. 14-2 in which the three regions are shown separately in Fig. 14-2a and are then combined in Fig. 14-2b to give the complete potential energy function.

When X is very large the potential energy between the ions is very small, but if we wish to make the comparison between neutral atoms of sodium and chlorine it is necessary to take into account the energy of forming the ions. It requires 5.14 ev to remove an electron from a neutral sodium atom. The addition of an electron to a neutral chlorine atom releases 3.82 ev. Thus it requires a total of $5.14 - 3.82 = 1.32$ ev to form the ion pair even when they are remote from each other.

For intermediate distances we can add the potential energy V_c from the coulomb forces. This is

$$V_c = - \frac{e^2}{4\pi\epsilon_0 X}. \qquad \left[V_c = - \frac{e^2}{X}. \right]$$

(14-2)

In the region where X is small other forces become important. There is a small effect due to the repulsion of the nuclei, but the most important effect comes from an application of the exclusion principle. If the two sets of electronic clouds overlapped appreciably, it would be necessary for two electrons to have the same set of quantum numbers (or for more than one electron to occupy the same region of space). Thus a very large amount of work must be done against this "force" arising because of the exclusion principle to bring the atoms very close together. This is a purely quantum mechanical effect that is not known in classical physics, but the behavior of molecules makes it very clear that it occurs. It is

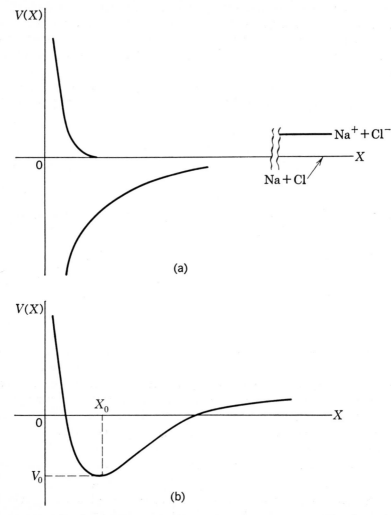

Fig. 14–2. The potential energy of an ionic molecule.

found that it is possible to represent this repulsion approximately by a reciprocal ninth power law,

$$V(X) = +\frac{b}{4\pi\epsilon_0 X^9} \cdot \qquad \left[V(X) = +\frac{b}{X^9}\cdot\right] \qquad (14\text{–}3)$$

When these three effects are combined as is done in Fig. 14–2b it becomes apparent that the potential function will have a minimum value V_0 when $X = X_0$. For this equilibrium separation there is no force between the two ions. An attempt to separate them produces an attractive force between them and an attempt to bring them closer creates a repulsive force. The first force arises because electrostatic forces of attraction predominate, and the second arises because exclusion-principle repulsive forces predominate.

The potential function resulting from other types of forces are similar; thus Fig. 14–2b shows the general behavior of all diatomic molecules. If the spacing between the atoms does not become too different from X_0, the shape of the potential curve can be approximated by a parabola. A parabola is the potential function for a harmonic oscillator and the energy states will be quantized as was discussed in Chapter 11, giving energy levels

$$E_v = (n + \tfrac{1}{2})h\nu_0. \tag{14–4}$$

Transitions between these states lead to emission of what is called the vibration spectrum of the molecule. This occurs generally in the infrared region. The energy levels are not quite uniformly spaced because the oscillator is not truly simple harmonic. The molecule can also rotate as a dumbbell might. Quantum mechanics tells us that the energy levels will be at

$$E_r = \frac{J(J + 1)\hbar^2}{2I}. \tag{14–5}$$

Transitions between these states lead to a rotation spectrum in the extreme infrared region. There can be disturbances in the electronic structure of a molecule similar to that in an atom and transitions between these states lead to light in the visual or ultraviolet region. Because the vibrational and rotational energies can be superimposed on such electronic states, the spectra of molecules appear very complicated with many lines very close together. These are called *band spectra*.

14–2. Ionic Solids. Materials such as NaCl, KBr, ZnO, BaSO$_4$ are examples of ionic solids. The description of molecule formation in the previous article leaves a strong dipole structure. Such dipoles would be found in vapors at high temperatures. As the temperature decreases these dipoles will begin to attract one another. The details of the mechanism beyond this point are not as yet well known. Because of the spherical symmetry of the ions, the ionic bond is non-directional and this fact gives us a general rule for assimilation and stability of the ions in the solid. This rule is that each ion will be surrounded by as many ions of opposite charge as possible and ions of like charge will be as far away from one another as possible. Actual distances are determined by the magnitude of the charges and atomic radii. Each ion tends to settle into the crystal in such a way that its surroundings are identical with that of any other ion, and a continuous lattice or network is constructed. This is shown in

Fig. 14-3 representing the structure of common salt. X-ray diffraction studies confirm this structure for the compounds listed. It is clear that the forces we have described for ionic molecules exist in the ionic solid since calculations of total crystal energy based on these forces agree with the measured values. Examples are given in Table 14-1. Ionic solids are strong, hard, and often are characterized by high melting points.

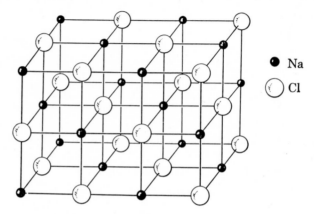

● Na

◯ Cl

Fig. 14-3.   Lattice structure for sodium chloride.

TABLE 14-1

Calculated and Measured Lattice Energies (kcal/mole)

	Calculated	Measured
NaCl	180	183
KBr	158	156
ZnO	968	966
ZnS	819	851

14-3. Covalent Binding. The concept of covalent bonds arose in chemistry shortly after Bohr put forward his theory of the atom. It was suggested by Lewis and Langmuir[1] that like or unlike *neutral* atoms could form molecules by pairing off unpaired valence electrons. No attempt was made to explain at that time why only two electrons should appear in a bond. Other problems were left unanswered, such as why carbon, which has a configuration for the ground state of $1s^2 2s^2 2p^2$, should form four bonds as it does.

The development of quantum mechanics made it possible to find the explanation for such problems. The work of Heitler and London[2] is par-

[1] G. N. Lewis, *JACS*, **38**, 762 (1916); I. Langmuir, *JACS*, **41**, 868 (1919).
[2] W. Heitler, F. London, *Z. f. Physik*, **44**, 455 (1927).

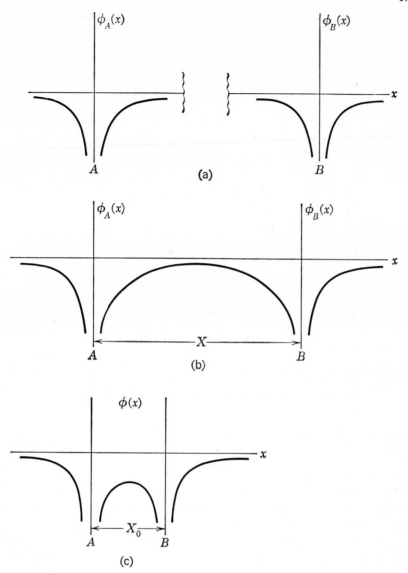

Fig. 14-4. The potential function for the electrons in a diatomic molecule.

ticularly noteworthy. We will indicate how Heitler and London combined individual atomic wave functions to get suitable molecular wave functions and thus "explain" the covalent bond. Fig. 14-4a shows the potential energy function $\phi(x)$ for the electrons of two neutral, but distant atoms. These atoms are assumed to each possess one valence electron responsible for the covalent bond. Fig. 14–4b shows the potential function as the atoms approach, and finally Fig. 14–4c shows the potential function when the two atoms settle at their equilibrium position X_0.

The procedure now is to solve the Schroedinger wave equation for the given potential functions illustrated in Fig. 14–4. Two types of wave functions $\psi_+(x)$ and $\psi_-(x)$ are well behaved. These wave functions and their squares are plotted in Fig. 14–5. It will be noted that for ψ_+ there

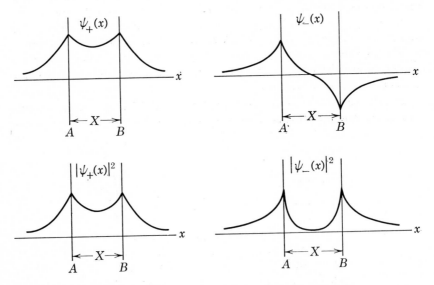

Fig. 14–5. Wave functions for a diatomic molecule.

is a considerable probability $|\psi_+|^2$ of finding the electrons in the regions between the two atoms where according to Fig. 14–4c the potential energy is low. On the other hand, with ψ_- there is a small probability $|\psi_-|^2$ in this low energy region.

The implication of the quantum mechanical solution should now be clear. ψ_+ is likely to be the solution that describes the electrons in the molecule since it predicts a low energy state. (All systems in nature tend toward a low energy state.) The energy of this state becomes even smaller as X decreases because $\phi(x)$ in Fig. 14–4c will become smaller in the region between A and B as the atoms approach one another. This tendency of the energy to decrease is interpreted as an attractive force between the atoms.

Bonding by this mechanism is known as *covalent bonding*, since two electrons usually are involved. It is characteristic of the covalent bond that the wave functions from the two atoms overlap between them as was shown in Fig. 14–5. Then the wave function ψ_+ can satisfy the Pauli exclusion principle only if the spins of the two electrons are opposite. This limits the covalent bond to the sharing of only two electrons, one from each atom. No third electron can be accommodated in this theory.

Carbon has four bonds because the energies of the electrons in the $2s$ and $2p$ states are very nearly the same. As a result the carbon atom in a molecule is likely to have its four outer shell electrons distributed in a wave function containing a combination of one $2s$ and three $2p$ states, and all of the spins are free to align with those from other atoms. Thus four unpaired electrons are available for the four covalent bonds of carbon.

The repulsive force which arises if the two atoms are pushed too closely together is again due to the Pauli exclusion principle. The explanation is identical with that given for the ionic bond.

Finally, note that the charge distribution in the case of covalent bonds is far from spherical as it is in ionic binding. In Fig. 14–6 a model of the

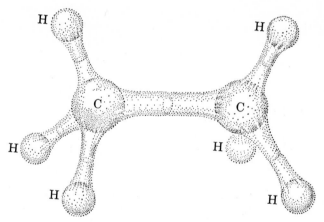

Fig. 14–6.   The ethane molecule, CH_3–CH_3.

ethane molecule C_2H_6 illustrates this. The right combinations of $2s2p^3$ wave functions extend toward the corners of a tetrahedron for each of the carbon atoms.

14–4. Covalent Solids. The number of solids which contain covalent bonds *alone* is very few in spite of the importance of the covalent bond in organic chemistry.

In the formation of the solid we must remember that the bonds are "saturated." That is, two valence electrons make a fairly strong bond and another electron cannot be added. Such a molecule can be bound to another only by a weak, fluctuating dipole interaction—a force which is called a *van der Waals force*. Such molecules as H_2 and O_2 which are bound to similar atoms only by this weak force can be liquids or solids only at very low temperatures. Organic compounds on the other hand are often liquid at ordinary temperatures because the carbon atom has four electrons to share and can thus form long lines of atoms that are called "chains" by the chemist. In other materials such as crystals of diamond, germanium, and silicon, the valence bonds form spirals and various three-dimensional structures. They hold this form tightly and are characterized by hard crystal structure and very high melting points.

14–5. The Metallic Bond. Approximately three-quarters of the elements in the periodic table solidify as metals. Moreover, many materials alloy to form a large number of metallic structures. Thus the structure of metals is extremely important. Unfortunately, the structure is difficult to explain. The fact that the atoms are all alike shows that no ionic structure can be responsible. On the other hand, the high electrical conductivity indicates that a large number of free electrons exist in the crystal. The idea that each atom contributes one or more free electrons to the metal was proposed by Drude before the development of quantum mechanics. While this is most useful in explaining the electrical and thermal conductivities of metals, it does not account for the forces that hold the metal together. It also raises a problem about the specific heat of the metal, for if there is a "gas" of free electrons, one might expect them to acquire a large amount of kinetic energy as the temperature is raised. This would lead to a value of specific heat considerably larger than that known for any metal. This latter point was explained by the fact that electrons have a Fermi-Dirac distribution of energy and do not follow the law of equipartition of energy. Thus only a few free electrons gain kinetic energy when the metal is heated, yet all are available for electrical conduction.

The explanation of the metallic bond comes from quantum mechanical considerations. An early treatment by Wigner and Seitz only partially accounted for metallic bonding. A somewhat similar model by Pauling pictured a rather weak valence bond in which an electron is shared by all atoms of the solid and is free to move from one site to another. An equivalent classical picture of the metallic bond is that the attractive force arises between the positive ions and all the conduction electrons regarded as a "smeared out" cloud. The repulsion between atoms again arises from exclusion forces amongst the inner-shell electrons. Although this leads to a fair representation of the metallic bond and predicts reasonable melting points and heats of vaporization, there still is no completely satisfactory theory of the metallic bond.

14–6. Molecular Solids. The last class of solids arises as a result of the van der Waals force. This is the force of attraction that exists between electric dipoles both induced and permanent. Permanent dipoles are found in many molecules and induced dipoles appear in others because the charge is free to move.

The van der Waals force is a very weak force so that molecular solids are weak. For example, the rare gases (argon, neon) crystallize into molecular crystals. Carbon dioxide is a simple molecular crystal while the paraffin hydrocarbons are long chain molecular crystals and the high polymers are even more complex molecular solids. We shall not study them any further although they are of great commercial interest.

This completes our survey of how atoms are put together to form solids. We conclude by saying that the situation, in the general case, is *not* as clear cut as these four subdivisions show. Often solids combine all types of binding since groups of atoms are held together by one bond and in turn groups are held to other groups by some other type of bond.

14–7. The Band Theory of Electrons in Solids. In the remainder of this chapter the theory that satisfactorily accounts for many phenomena exhibited by solid materials, other than strength or rigidity, will be reviewed. This theory is called the *band theory of solids.* Some of the phenomena are electrical conduction, electrical insulation, semiconduction, heat capacity, thermal conductivity, thermal expansion, ferromagnetism, photoconductivity, luminescence, thermionic emission, contact potential difference, secondary emission, and the photoelectric effect. Because of successes in these areas, it has replaced the Drude electron gas theory mentioned in an earlier article although the latter is at times useful for metals.

The band theory determines the allowed energy states for the electrons in the solid and then describes how the available electrons are distributed amongst these energy levels. Both of these points require the application of quantum mechanics. In the case of simple systems, such as atoms, only certain energy levels are permitted and large regions of energy are forbidden. Similar results are obtained when atoms come together to form a solid, but because of the proximity of other atoms and because of their regular arrangement in the crystal lattice all electron energy levels are modified. In particular, the valence electron levels are profoundly changed into bands of permitted energy with forbidden regions in between.

The calculation of the allowed energy levels or bands can be done by direct use of the Schroedinger wave equation. In order to obtain a solution the potential energy function $V(x)$ that the electron would have inside the solid must be known. A suitable function can be obtained by the now familiar technique of simplification and idealization. It is necessary to replace the solid by a simplified system, a single line of atoms, with the nuclei regularly spaced a distance R_0 apart, at rest, and with the line infinitely long so that the ends of the line (i.e., the "surface" of the crystal) can be neglected. Under these conditions a potential function such as $V(x)$ shown in Fig. 14–7a arises from the Coulomb electrostatic force between

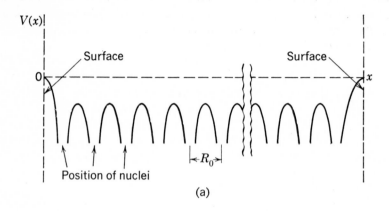

(a)

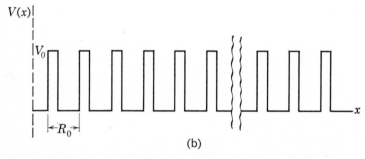

(b)

Fig. 14–7.   (a) A linear model of the solid.   (b) The Kronig-Penney model.

the electron and the nuclei. A particular variation of this that can be solved completely is shown in Fig. 14–7b where we have further idealized this Coulomb potential energy. Notice in Fig. 14–7b that the problem has been simplified to one of regularly repeating square-wells and that the surfaces of the solid have been neglected. The approximation shown in Fig. 14–7b is known as the Kronig-Penney[3] model of a solid. It is a one-dimensional approximation.

The solution of the Schroedinger equation with this approximation, though algebraically tedious, can be carried out in closed form. It can be

[3] R. de L. Kronig and W. G. Penney, *Proc. Roy. Soc.* (London), **A 130**, 499 (1931).

shown that a well-behaved solution is possible only if the energy W is limited to values that fit the relation

$$\frac{P \sin \alpha R_0}{\alpha R_0} + \cos \alpha R_0 = \cos k R_0 \qquad (14\text{-}6)$$

where P is a constant, $\alpha = \sqrt{2mW/\hbar^2}$, and $k = 2\pi/\lambda$, the propagation constant of the electron, a quantity essentially proportional to the momentum. We now examine this equation to see what restrictions it places on the energy.

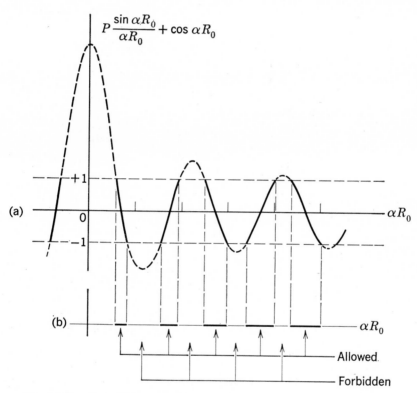

Fig. 14-8. The allowed regions of αR_0 for the Kronig-Penney model.

Since the right-hand side of the equation is a simple cosine function, its value can only lie between -1 and $+1$. The left-hand side of Eq. 14-6 is plotted in Fig. 14-8a. The solid portions indicate those values satisfying Eq. 14-6.

Fig. 14-8b shows the range of αR_0 (and therefore W) over which Eq. 14-6 is satisfied. Thus we see that the system has ranges or *bands* of allowed energy separated by forbidden regions of energy and the width of the allowed bands of energy increase with increasing energy.

From Fig. 14–8, we can find the values of α that are permitted. In addition, we know the value of k corresponding to each value of α; therefore we can deduce the total energy W as a function of k. The results are shown in Fig. 14–9a. The allowed and forbidden energy bands are also shown in Fig. 14–9b.

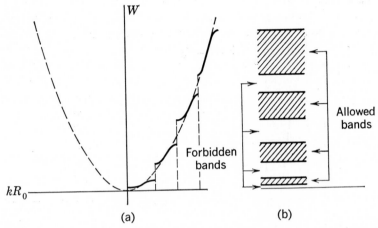

(a)   (b)

Fig. 14–9. The energy of an electron in a periodic potential (solid line) compared with the energy of a free electron (dotted line) as a function of momentum.

The discontinuities occur when $\cos kR_0 = +1$, that is, when

$$k = \frac{n\pi}{R_0} \qquad n = 1, 2, 3, \ldots,$$

and if we substitute for k, we get

$$\frac{2\pi}{\lambda} = \frac{n\pi}{R_0}$$

or

$$n\lambda = 2R_0, \tag{14-7}$$

which is the Bragg diffraction law if $\theta = 90°$. Thus we see that the discontinuities represent a location at which the electron waves are reflected backward. The three-dimensional equivalent using the true Bragg law leads to very similar energy bands and critical values of both the magnitude and direction of $\mathbf{k}$. The ranges of $\mathbf{k}$ and its components are called Brillouin zones. These bands contain an infinite number of levels, but only because there is no end to the line of atoms as the problem was set up. If there are only N atoms in the line, there will be N levels in each band.

The same result can be obtained by a completely different approach consisting of a consideration of the energy levels of individual atoms. The atoms are then brought together to form the solid. The total number of energy levels does not change as the atoms are brought together. Thus if N atoms are far apart and we consider the five lowest levels, there are actually $5N$ levels, N identical sets of 5 levels. When the atoms are brought together the levels are no longer the same, but spread into five groups of N levels all close together. If N is large enough, each group becomes a band of practically continuous permitted energy levels. The

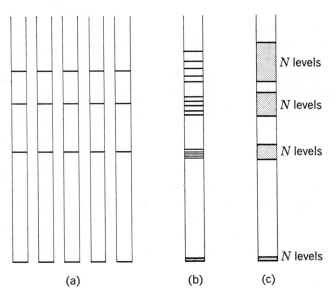

Fig. 14–10.   (a) Energy levels of five separated atoms.   (b) Energy levels of five atoms close together.   (c) Energy levels of a large number of atoms close together.

lowest levels do not change much corresponding to the electrons which are bound to their own particular atom, while the upper levels may spread into wide bands corresponding to electrons not especially identified with any particular atom, similar to the previous discussion of metals in which each electron is subject to the full potential function of all atoms. This is illustrated in Fig. 14–10 where the levels of five atoms when separate (see Fig. 14–10a) are compared with five close together (see Fig. 14–10b), and finally with a large number having the same spacing (see Fig. 14–10c). The N levels form the equivalent of a continuous band in the last case.

If there are n electrons for each of the N atoms, nN of the levels will be occupied in accordance with the Pauli exclusion principle. At low temperatures the bottom nN levels will be occupied, but at higher temperatures it may be possible that some higher ones are occupied leaving a few vacancies just below the nNth level. This will depend upon how much energy is required to get to these higher levels, for there can only be a Fermi-Dirac distribution of the electrons among the levels.

14–8. Conductors, Insulators, and Semiconductors. With different atoms and with different crystal structures, there will be different arrangements of the bands. Fig. 14–11 shows four possible situations. In Fig. 14–11a the band A is not completely occupied. By this is meant, not all energy states are occupied by electrons. In Fig. 14–11b bands A and B overlap so it doesn't matter whether A is completely occupied so long as B is not. If a small electric field is applied across the crystal of a material with a band system such as shown in Fig. 14–11a or b, it is easy for that field to accelerate the electron and move it into a higher energy level. Such a material is a good conductor of electricity and band systems such as these two are found in metals.

The situation shown in Fig. 14–11c and d is quite different from that in Fig. 14–11a and b. The former two cases are characterized by an occupied set of energy levels A, and an almost empty set of energy levels B, separated by an "energy gap" or a forbidden region of energy. The band B in the figure is called the *conduction band*. The band A, since it represents, in Fig. 14-11c and d, energy levels filled by the outer electrons of atoms, is called the *valence band*.

Band systems such as shown in Fig. 14–11c and d are found in insulators and semiconductors, respectively. Fig. 14–11c represents an insulator since no electrons are free to move unless they are taken across the wide energy gap. Ordinary electric fields cannot impart enough energy to electrons in the limited space available inside the crystal lattices of insulators. In diamond, for example, the required energy (which is the gap width) is approximately 7 ev. No current can therefore flow since there are no energy states to which the electrons can move. In insulators, it is possible to force electrons to jump the energy gap by using electromagnetic radiation, i.e., a photon, which has the proper frequency and therefore energy $h\nu$. These electrons leave behind in the valence or filled band a *hole* which is simply an empty energy state. This hole makes possible conduction amongst the valence electrons since there is now available an empty energy state into which the electrons can move.

Fig. 14–11d is similar to Fig. 14–11c except that the forbidden energy gap is much narrower. Semiconducting materials such as germanium and silicon have band systems such as this. In germanium, for example, the

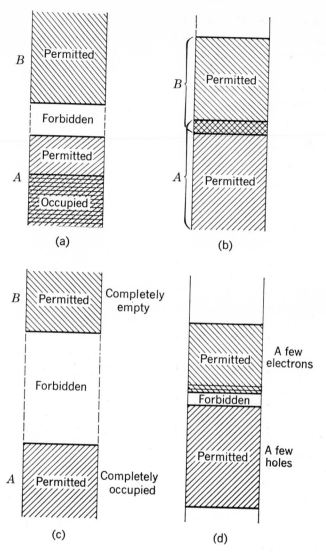

Fig. 14–11. Four energy band arrangements.

gap width is approximately 0.7 ev. Because of the narrow gap it is relatively easy to move electrons across the forbidden region. In fact, at
room temperatures, the thermal energy of the electrons can cause electrons to cross. Photons of the proper frequency can also be used.

Two examples of energy band systems calculated from the band theory
are shown in Fig. 14–12 and Fig. 14–13. Fig. 14–12 shows the band sys-

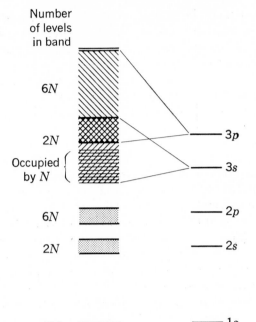

Fig. 14–12.   Energy bands for sodium.

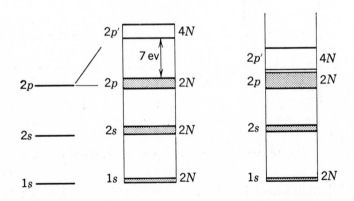

Fiq. 14–13.   Energy band system for carbon.

tem for metallic sodium. The 3s band is only half filled and in addition the
3p band overlaps the 3s band; so sodium, a metal, is a good electrical
conductor. Fig. 14–13a and Fig. 14–13b provide schematic representa-
tions of crystalline carbon. In both cases there are two separate parts to
the 2p band. In the case of diamond, there is a wide gap and only the
lower band has electrons in it, just filling it. In the case of graphite,
the gap is narrow. Diamond is a good insulator, and graphite is a
semiconductor.

Before turning to the next point it must be stated that the picture of
conductors given here does not explain their resistance. Resistance to
current flow, that is, to the motion of electrons being accelerated by applied
electric fields, consists of a loss of electron energy to the atoms of the
lattice. Theoretical studies show that this loss only occurs if there are
irregularities in the lattice. The important irregularities are thermal
vibrations of the lattice, impurities in the lattice, and crystal grain boundaries in the lattice. The first effect suggests that the resistance of a conductor should increase with increasing temperature, a well-known behavior
of conductors. Because of grain and crystal irregularities we would not
expect zero resistance at absolute zero. Most conductors behave this way
but some have the interesting property of becoming perfect conductors at
temperatures above absolute zero, say $\simeq 2°$K. Such *super-conductors* are
very interesting.[4] The theory depends upon subtle quantum effects and is
only now being developed. An important feature is that as the magnetic
field in the conductor increases, the temperature at which the super-con-
ducting state sets in is lowered.

The variation of resistance with temperature for *semiconductors* is determined principally by its effect on the population of the conduction band.
Although increasing the temperature will increase the loss of energy to the
crystal lattice, the effect of increasing the number of electrons in the
allowed band is more important. This leads to a decrease in resistance
with increase in temperature, a distinguishing and important behavior for
semiconductors.

14–9. The Fermi Distribution. The temperature effects discussed above
are the result of the influence of temperature on the distribution of electrons with energy, designated $n(E)\,dE$. This expression $n(E)\,dE$ means
the number of electrons per unit volume occupying states in the energy
range between E and $E + dE$ in some system at a fixed absolute temperature T. Alternatively, we can define $n(E)\,dE$ as the number of occupied
states per unit volume in the energy range between E and $E + dE$ at
equilibrium temperature T. These two are equivalent because the number
of occupied states per unit volume is the same as the number of electrons
per unit volume.

[4] B. T. Matthian, *Sci. Am.*, Nov., 1957, or H. A. Bourse, *Am. Jour. Phys.* **27**, 47 (1959).

$n(E)\,dE$ is obtained by taking the product of two factors. The first of these, the *density of states* giving the total number of states per unit volume between E and $E + dE$ we designate as $S(E)\,dE$. The second, the *Fermi factor* (see Eq. 5–49) which gives the fraction of these states occupied, we designate as $f(E)$ dropping the subscripts "FD" used in Eq. 5–49. Thus the number of states occupied $n(E)\,dE$ equals the total number of states $S(E)\,dE$ times the fraction occupied $f(E)$, i.e.,

$$n(E)\,dE = f(E)\,S(E)\,dE \qquad (14\text{–}8)$$

The Fermi factor $f(E)$ is obtained from quantum statistical mechanics. Derivations can be found in various treatments of the subject.[5] An important feature of the Fermi distribution is that, since the particles are electrons, Pauli's exclusion principle holds, so only one electron can occupy each state or energy level. This latter fact makes a great difference in the

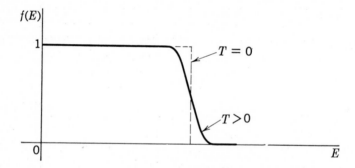

Fig. 14–14.   The Fermi factor for $T = 0$ and $T > 0$.

energy of the system, since the Maxwell-Boltzmann statistics allows many electrons to be at low energies while the Fermi statistics prevents this because of the exclusion principle. The result of the derivation is

$$f(E) = \cfrac{1}{\exp\left(\cfrac{E - E_f}{kT}\right) + 1}, \qquad (14\text{–}9)$$

where $k =$ Boltzmann's constant and $E_f =$ the Fermi level. (See Art. 5–11.) $f(E)$ is plotted in Fig. 14–14 for two values of absolute temperature, $T = 0$ and $T > 0$. Note from Eq. 14–9 that for $E < E_f$, the exponential in the denominator is negative and as $T \to 0$, the exponential approaches

[5] For example, A. J. Dekker, *Solid State Physics*, Prentice-Hall, Inc., Englewood Cliffs, N. J., 1957, p. 529.

zero so that $f(E) = 1$, as shown in Fig. 14–14. When $E > E_f$, and $T = 0$, then the exponential approaches exp $(+\infty)$ and $f(E) = 0$. This is also shown in the plot for $T = 0$. If $T > 0$ and $E \gg E_f$, then the exponential term is large compared with the unity in the denominator so that $f(E) \sim$ exp $[-(E - E_f)/kT]$. Since this is essentially the Maxwell-Boltzmann energy relation, the "tail" of the $T > 0$ curve must be similar to the high energy portion of the classical curve.

When $E = E_f$, $f(E)$ is one-half. Thus one interpretation of the Fermi level E_f is that it is the energy value for which there is an occupation probability of one-half.

The other function in Eq. 14–8 $S(E)$, the density of states, must now be discussed. For the case of metals $S(E)$ can be computed by considering the electrons to be free and non-interacting, the result is

$$S(E) \, dE = CE^{\frac{1}{2}} \, dE, \tag{14–10}$$

where the constant $C = 4\pi (2m/h^2)^{\frac{3}{2}}$. For most semiconductors and insulators, $S(E)$ is not known, although the more advanced Brillouin zone treatment gives some help.[6] Some approximation, such as using a constant for $S(E)$ or treating the bottom part of the conduction band like a metal, is usually made. Hence the importance of Eq. 14–10.

The determination of three Fermi distributions is shown in Fig. 14–15 where the Fermi factor and the density of states function are plotted below the resulting $n(E)$. This is carried out for the three cases discussed earlier, i.e., for a conductor, an insulator, and an intrinsic semiconductor. The diagrams show the opportunity for a redistribution by an applied electric field in the case of the conductor in Fig. 14–15a, the impossibility of a change in distribution by the field for the insulator in Fig. 14–15b, and the limited opportunity for redistribution for the semiconductor in Fig. 14–15c.

It must be remembered that the use of Eq. 14–8 is restricted by the condition that the total number of occupied states must equal the total number of electrons. This integration of Eq. 14–8 is often useful; for example, the determination of the Fermi level E_f in the case of a metal can be done easily for $T = 0$. If N is the total number of free electrons in the metal, and V is the volume, then

$$N = V \int_0^\infty n(E) \, dE = V \int_0^\infty S(E) f(E) \, dE$$

$$= CV \int_0^\infty \frac{(E)^{\frac{1}{2}} \, dE}{\exp \left(\dfrac{E - E_f}{kT} \right) + 1}.$$

---

[6] A. J. Dekker, *op. cit.*, Chap. 10.

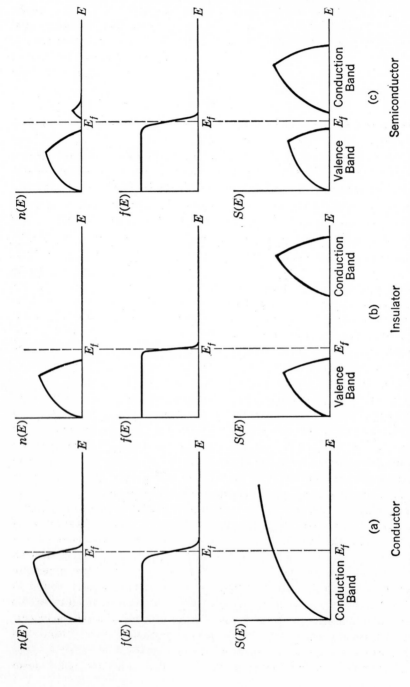

Fig. 14–15.   The Fermi level and bands for (a) a conductor, (b) an insulator, and (c) a semiconductor.

If T is set equal to zero, $f(E) = 1$ for $E < E_f$ and $f(E) = 0$ for $E > E_f$; so we get

$$N = CV \int_0^{E_f} \sqrt{E} \, dE,$$

from which

$$E_f = \frac{h^2}{2m} \left(\frac{3N}{8\pi V} \right)^{2/3}. \tag{14–11}$$

14–10. Holes, Hole Conduction, and Impurities. In Fig. 14–11 and Fig. 14–15c we saw the energy band picture of an intrinsic semiconductor with its characteristic narrow forbidden gap. At very low temperatures semiconductors are insulators, since no electrons can have enough energy to exist in any but the lowest band which is completely filled. As the temperature of the solid is increased, electrons in the filled band can acquire enough thermal energy to jump the forbidden gap and appear in the conduction band. This gives a comparatively free electron to contribute to the conductivity, but in addition, it leaves an empty state in the filled band. Thus the electrons in the filled band can also move and contribute to the conductivity. However, rather than investigate the motion of all the electrons in the filled band, it is much simpler to observe the motion of the empty state. This empty state is called a *hole* and its contribution to the conduction is called *hole conduction*. Experiments actually show the presence of such holes in semiconductors. They behave as positive current carriers rather than the expected negative electrons. Fig. 14–16 shows the hole concept as pictured by the band theory.

Impurities in a crystal, like other imperfections, have a profound effect on its properties. One of the most common types of impurities is an atom that is adjacent in the periodic table to the material that makes up the main body of the crystal. In the case of germanium, the neighbors are gallium and arsenic. The presence of one of these atoms at a crystal lattice site in the otherwise pure germanium crystal provides energy levels that lie between the valence band and the conduction band.

For example, arsenic with a configuration of $4s^2 4p^3$ outside a closed shell has one more electron than germanium which has a configuration of $4s^2 4p^2$. Thus the presence of an arsenic atom as a replacement for a germanium atom in a crystal of germanium provides both a spare electron and a nuclear charge greater by unity, than for the rest of the immediate region of the crystal. The additional electron is only loosely bound to the extra positive charge of the arsenic atom. At room temperatures, the distribution function may make it easy for this electron to leave the arsenic atom and occupy one of the states in the conduction band. Since the arsenic atom has given the electron to the crystal it is called a *donor impurity* and the bound states in the forbidden band are called *donor states.* A crystal with small amounts of such an impurity can conduct electricity because of the presence of electrons in the conduction band without the formation of holes; so it is called an *n-type* semiconductor.

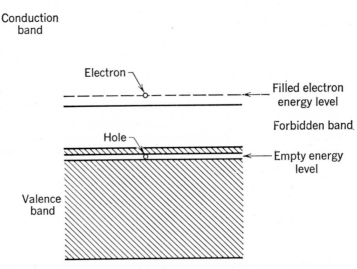

Conduction band

Electron

Filled electron energy level

Forbidden band

Hole

Empty energy level

Valence band

Fig. 14–16.   An electron excited into the conduction band leaving a hole.

On the other hand, if the impurity atom is a gallium atom with a configuration of $4s^2 4p$, it tends to take an electron from its neighbors. This leaves a shortage of electrons, a hole, which is loosely bound to the now excessively negative gallium atom. Again the energy level of such a system lies in the forbidden region between the valence band and the conduction band. What has happened is that this level is now occupied by an electron, thus leaving a hole in the valence band. Because the hole is not tightly bound, it can wander throughout the crystal and provide conduction. Since the gallium atom takes on an extra electron, it is called an *acceptor impurity* and the local energy level that becomes occupied to form a hole is called an *acceptor level.* The conduction that results from the motion of holes behaves like conduction due to positive carriers, so such a material is called a *p-type* semiconductor.

Only small amounts of such impurities, a few parts per million, are required to produce these effects. They can be found in naturally occurring materials, but are now produced under carefully controlled conditions to obtain predictable behavior. Fig. 14–17 represents the situation for both n-type and p-type semiconductors using the common diagrammatic representation.

Surface boundaries between metals and semiconductors and between n-type and p-type semiconductors have interesting electrical properties. Among these is a marked difference in conductivity depending upon the direction of the applied electric field. Thus metal-semiconductor interfaces and p-n junctions can serve as rectifiers. A p-n junction can be formed by carefully changing the impurities in the melt from which the semiconducting crystal is being grown.

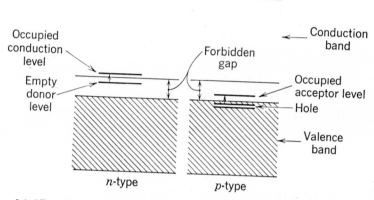

Fig. 14–17. Electron energy levels for *n*-type and *p*-type semiconductors.

If a sandwich of semiconductor types, such as n-p-n or p-n-p, is formed, current though one junction may influence the current through the other one. This can produce amplification. Such devices, known as *transistors*, have the advantage of requiring no filament heating and are practically instantaneous in their action. They operate at comparatively low voltages and draw little current. They can be very small and tend to be more rugged than vacuum tubes, though they are more sensitive to temperature effects. At the present time, they can control only a few watts, and that at radio frequencies. They are capable of working in the low UHF region if they do not need to handle appreciable power. Further information concerning the manufacture and theory of operation of semiconductor rectifiers and transistors can be found in many of the present books on electronic devices.

PROBLEMS

14–1. An ionic molecule requires 0.86 ev to produce the ion pair from free remote atoms. The equilibrium separation is 2.63 Å. The energy to dissociate into ions is 4.33 ev. What is the energy of formation of the molecule? What is the energy due to repulsive forces at the position of equilibrium?

14-2. An ionic molecule requires 6.15 ev to dissociate it into ions. The energy of formation of the molecules is 5.80 ev. What energy is required to produce a remote ion pair? The equilibrium separation is 2.1 Å. What is the energy due to repulsive forces at the position of equilibrium?

14-3. (a) The electron affinity of chlorine is 3.82 ev. The ionization energy of potassium is 4.34 ev. If we remove 1 electron from K and add it to Cl with $r = \infty$, do we have a stable configuration? If not, why not? (b) The dissociation energy of KCl is 4.40 ev. Compute an approximate (neglecting repulsion) equilibrium internuclear separation for KCl. (c) By x-ray diffraction the KCl $r_0 = 2.79$ Å. Compute the potential energy of repulsion in electron volts.

14-4. The reduced mass for the atoms of a diatomic molecule is 1.5×10^{-26} kg. The vibrational spectrum of the molecule shows that the spacing of vibrational levels is 3.5×10^{-2} ev. What is the shape of the potential function of the molecule close to the equilibrium separation?

14-5. Calculate the reduced mass for the molecule HCl. The vibration spectrum of this molecule shows that the spacing of vibrational levels is 0.371 ev. What is the shape of the potential function of the molecule close to the equilibrium separation?

14-6. A simple cubic crystal has cubes with sides 3.2 Å long. Calculate two critical wavelengths for electrons moving parallel to the crystal axes and two critical wavelengths for electrons moving along a direction making 45° with two axes and 90° with the third.

14-7. A simple cubic crystal has cubes with sides 2.9 Å long. Calculate two critical wavelengths for electrons moving parallel to the crystal axes and two critical wavelengths for electrons moving along a direction making 45° with two axes and 90° with the third.

14-8. The valence band and conduction band for several crystals are separated by the following: 6.6 ev, 1.6 ev, 0.04 ev, 0.96 ev, 0.00 (overlap). Characterize the type of electrical conductivity of each crystal.

14-9. The valance band and conduction band for several crystals are separated by the following: 8.0, 0.03 ev, 1.06 ev, 0.00 (overlap). Characterize the type of electrical conductivity of each crystal.

14-10. Calculate the Fermi level for a simple cubic metal with 1 free electron per atom and a crystal spacing of 3.2 Å.

14-11. The Fermi level of a metal is 4.6 ev. What is the electron density of the metal?

14-12. A hole-electron pair is produced when radiation of the proper frequency is incident on a pure solid. Germanium, a semiconductor, has a forbidden gap width of 0.72 ev. What photon wavelength will create a hole-electron pair? What temperature will create such a pair?

14–13. Diamond has a forbidden gap width of approximately 7 ev. What frequency of electromagnetic radiation will just move an electron from the filled band to the conduction band? What temperature might move such an electron?

14–14. The experimentally measured activation energy for arsenic donor atoms in silicon is 0.049 ev. (a) Make an energy level diagram roughly to scale for this situation if the gap width of silicon is 1.12 ev. (b) What temperatures would fill these levels?

14–15. (a) Compute the radius of the first Bohr orbit for a donor electron trapped at an arsenic atom. The dielectric constant of silicon is 11.9. (b) Compute the binding energy for this electron. (c) How does it compare with the activation energy? (d) How low a temperature is required for this trapping?

14–16. The Fermi Factor: (a) Set $E = E_f$ in Eq. 14–9 and evaluate $f_{FD}(E)$. On the basis of this value give a definition for the Fermi level E_f. (b) To what does $f_{FD}(E)$ reduce for values of energy significantly greater than E_f? (c) Plot $f_{FD}(E)$ for $T = 0$.

14–17. Evaluate the Fermi factor for values of electron energy $2kT$, $3kT$, and $10kT$ above the Fermi level in order to show how quickly the Fermi factor falls to zero at ordinary temperatures. To minimize the labor, take the value of kT at room temperature = 0.025 ev.

14–18. Evaluate E_f in electron volts for Ag (a monovalent metal) at $T = 0°K$.

14–19. (a) Prove that the average energy of conduction band electrons in a metal at 0°K is $\frac{3}{5} E_f$. (*Hint:* Use your knowledge of distribution functions.) (b) Compute the rms thermal speed.

14–20. Compute the separation of germanium atoms in a solid lattice assuming a simple cubic structure (germanium actually has a diamond lattice structure). For germanium the density is 5.33 gm cm^{-3} and the atomic weight is 72.6. Compare the result with the measured value of 2.43 Å.

14–21. The mean free path for electrons in germanium is approximately 10^{-5} cm. (a) Compare this with the interatomic spacing. (b) What would you expect electrons to collide with in a lattice and hence produce resistance?

14–22. When a low electric field is applied to a solid the electrons "drift" at a speed v_d given by $v_d = \mu E$ where E is the applied electric field and μ is the mobility. The mobility of electrons in silver is 5.6×10^{-3} m^2 v^{-1} sec^{-1}. Compare the drift velocity when E is 2 volt m^{-1} with the electron thermal velocity of Problem 14–19.

14–23. A conductor of cross-section A carries a current I. (a) Derive an expression for the current density in terms of n the number of charge carriers per unit volume, e the electronic charge, and v_d the drift velocity. (b) Using the definition of mobility in Problem 14–22 find an expression for the conductivity of the material. (c) What is the resistivity?

14–24. A piece of n-type silicon has 10^{13} negative charge carriers per cm^3. If the electron mobility is 1250 cm^2 v^{-1} sec^{-1} compute the current through a 2 cm by 1 mm by 1 mm bar when 1 v is applied across the bar.

14–25. What is the drift velocity for the electrons in the metal of Problem 14–11 if there is 1 amp flowing in a conductor with a cross-section of 1 mm^2?

14–26. What is the drift velocity for the electrons in the metal of Problem 14–10 if there is 1 amp flowing in a conductor with a cross-section of 1 mm^2?

14–27. Would you expect selenium doped with a small amount of arsenic to be a p- or n-type semiconductor?

14–28. Would you expect silicon doped with a small amount of aluminum to be a p- or n-type semiconductor?

SELECTED REFERENCES

BRATTAIN, W. H. "Development of Concepts in Semiconductor Research," *Am. Jour. of Phys.*, **24**, 421/425 (1956).
DEKKER, A. J. *Solid State Physics.* Prentice-Hall, Inc., Englewood Cliffs, N. J., 1957. Chaps. 10 and 12.
DUNLAP, W. C. *An Introduction to Semiconductors.* John Wiley & Sons, Inc., New York, 1957. Chap. 5.
HEMENWAY, C. L., R. W. HENRY, and M. CAULTON. *Physical Electronics.* John Wiley & Sons, Inc., New York, 1962. Chaps. 2 and 3.
KITTEL, C. *Introduction to Solid State Physics.* John Wiley & Sons, Inc., New York, 1956. 2d ed., chap. 3.
LEIGHTON, R. B. *Principles of Modern Physics.* McGraw-Hill Book Co., Inc., New York, 1959. Chap. 11.

15

Radioactivity

In all the earlier chapters there has been a marked emphasis on the characteristics of matter that depend upon the electronic structure of atoms. In the remaining chapters the interest will tend to be centered on the properties of matter that depend upon the nuclei of atoms. The nucleus of an atom is small, of the order of 10^{-15} m, but it contains most of the mass of the atom. In addition, large amounts of energy (of the order of 10^6 ev) are involved when changes occur in the structure of a nucleus. The understanding of nuclei has proceeded rapidly since the time of Rutherford's discovery of the nuclear nature of atoms, and many important developments have resulted.

The mass and charge of the nucleus are obviously important gross properties. From the earliest probings of chemists into atomic structure, it was clear that nearly all atoms had masses which were integral multiples of the hydrogen mass. This fact, combined with the Rutherford result of a massive nucleus and very light electrons, strongly suggested that all nuclei were made up of hydrogen nuclei. Since the hydrogen nucleus is a single proton, all nuclei appeared to be made up of protons. The number of protons in a nucleus was designated by Z and called the *atomic number*, a concept that we used in Chapter 13. By the above evidence, Z should be equal to the mass number A, where A is the mass of the nucleus in atomic mass units (amu). One atomic mass unit equals $\frac{1}{16}$ of the mass of an oxygen 16 atom (see Art. 17–2).

Experimental work by Barkla and Moseley with x-rays, however, definitely indicated that the atomic number Z was approximately only one-half of the mass when the mass was expressed in units of hydrogen mass. This result pointed out that particles other than protons were present in nuclei, but not until 1932 were these other particles established to be neutrons—particles with a mass approximately equal to the mass of the proton but with zero charge. The number of neutrons in the nucleus

335

is N, the *neutron number*. Hence the *mass number* $A = N + Z$. The particles inside nuclei (neutrons and protons) are called *nucleons*.

Other names are used to describe special groupings of nuclei. The most important groups are:

Isotopes—same Z, different N.
Isomers—same Z, same A.

Finally, nuclei belonging to a particular nuclear species are called *nuclides*.

The first observed manifestation of nuclear transformations was the natural radioactivity of certain elements. This makes a natural point to begin the study of nuclear phenomena.

15–1. The Nature of Radioactivity. Radioactivity, originally discovered in uranium by Becquerel (1896), is the breaking up or disintegration of the nuclei of atoms. It is spontaneous (natural) in all of the nuclides with atomic numbers greater than 83 (bismuth), in some isotopes of Bi, Pb, and Tl and a few others, namely, K^{40}, V^{50}, Rb^{87}, In^{115}, La^{138}, Ce^{142}, Nd^{144}, Sm^{147}, Lu^{176}, Re^{187}, and Pt^{192}. It can be induced (artificial) in most of the other elements in the periodic table by creating unstable isotopes of these elements.

When a nucleus spontaneously disintegrates, charged particles with high energy are emitted, often accompanied by short wavelength electromagnetic radiation called gamma rays. These particles leave behind a transformed nucleus. An important example is the radioactive decay of radium which is customarily written

$$_{88}Ra^{226} \rightarrow {}_{86}Rn^{222} + {}_2He^4.$$

Here the chemical symbol indicates the individual nucleus while the subscript is the *atomic number Z*, and the superscript is the *mass number A*. The product nucleus $_2He^4$ is called an *alpha particle*, and the reaction is known as an *alpha decay*. In this, and all other nuclear reactions, the total charge and total mass on both sides of the equation balance.

Another example of natural radioactivity is

$$_{90}Th^{234} \rightarrow {}_{91}Pa^{234} + {}_{-1}e^0.$$

Here we see that a negative electron, called a *beta particle*, is given off, converting the thorium nucleus to a protactinium nucleus. The decay is known as a *beta decay*.

Gamma rays are emitted when the product nucleus is left in an excited energy state. The excited nucleus emits its extra energy in the form of gamma rays and drops to lower energy states much like the emission of light or x-rays by the electronic structure of the atom.

15–2. The Decay Law. Assume that we have a few grams of a radioactive material. Experimentally, we find that the rate of transformation of the nuclei in our mass is unaffected by external effects such as temperature and pressure and the past history of the sample. As a result of these observations, we assume that the decay of a particular nucleus is purely a matter of chance and that the probability of a decay is the same for all nuclei of the same kind. Let this probability be p. The only factor that affects p for this nucleus is the length of time Δt that we observe the nucleus. Then, the probability of decay is

$$p = \lambda \, \Delta t, \tag{15–1}$$

where λ = a constant, called the *disintegration constant*, which is characteristic of the decaying nuclei.

The probability of *not* disintegrating is

$$P_1 = 1 - \lambda \, \Delta t. \tag{15–2}$$

If the nucleus we are observing survives this first time interval, the probability of surviving a second interval Δt is again

$$P_1 = 1 - \lambda \, \Delta t.$$

The probability of surviving both intervals is

$$P_2 = (1 - \lambda \, \Delta t)^2, \tag{15–3}$$

and for n intervals,

$$P_n = (1 - \lambda \, \Delta t)^n. \tag{15–4}$$

Let the total observation time t be $t = n \, \Delta t$ then Eq. 15–4 becomes

$$P_n = \left(1 - \lambda \, \frac{t}{n}\right)^n. \tag{15–5}$$

Let Δt go to zero and n increase without limit, giving

$$P_n = \lim_{n \to \infty} \left(1 - \lambda \, \frac{t}{n}\right)^n. \tag{15–6}$$

Since

$$\lim_{n \to \infty} \left(1 - \frac{x}{n}\right)^n = \exp -x,$$

we get for the probability of a nucleus surviving for a time t without disintegrating,

$$P_t = \exp -\lambda t. \tag{15–7}$$

If we multiply this probability by the number of nuclei originally present N_0, we should expect the result to be the number of nuclei surviving after time t. Thus the number of atoms N at time t is

$$N = N_0 \exp -\lambda t. \tag{15–8}$$

Eq. 15–8 is the law of radioactive decay. As noted previously, the constant λ is called the disintegration constant.

This derivation emphasizes the importance of chance or probability in describing radioactive transformations. The same law can be derived by formulating and solving a differential equation, as follows. If the number of nuclei at any moment is N, the number transforming in a differential time interval dt should be proportional to N and to dt, if the process is one determined by chance. If we let the proportionality constant equal λ, we can write for the number of nuclei expected to transform

$$dN = -\lambda N \, dt. \tag{15–9}$$

The negative sign indicates that the number remaining is decreasing. This can be rewritten as

$$\frac{dN}{N} = -\lambda \, dt.$$

Its integral is

$$\ln N = -\lambda t + C.$$

At $t = 0$, $N = N_0$; so $C = \ln N_0$ and we have

$$N = N_0 \exp -\lambda t. \tag{15–10}$$

The time derivative of Eq. 15–8 or Eq. 15–10 is

$$\frac{dN}{dt} = -\lambda N. \tag{15–11}$$

dN/dt is called the *activity* or the *intensity* of radioactivity and it is the quantity measured by electronic ratemeters. The unit of activity is named the *curie* after Madame P. Curie. The curie is that *amount* of radioactive material that will give 3.70×10^{10} disintegrations per sec. This is close to the number of disintegrations per second for 1 gm of radium.

15–3. The Half-Life—The Mean-Life. Eq. 15–8 enables us to compute the time T required for one-half of the nuclei to disintegrate. Setting $N = N_0/2$ and $t = T$

$$\frac{N_0}{2} = N_0 \exp -\lambda T,$$

or

$$\ln \frac{1}{2} = -\lambda T$$

$$T = \frac{0.693}{\lambda}. \tag{15–12}$$

T is called the *half-life* of the nuclei and it is one of the chief characteristics of any kind of radioactive nucleus. It is easily determined experimentally for those nuclei which do not have very short or very long half-lives by simply measuring the activity versus time. Half-lives range in values from 10^{10} yr to 10^{-8} sec.

The differential of Eq. 15–8 is, of course,

$$dN = -\lambda N_0 \exp -\lambda t \, dt. \tag{15–13}$$

We can calculate an average or mean-life in the usual way, namely,

$$t_{\text{av}} = \frac{\displaystyle\int_0^{N_0} t \, dN}{\displaystyle\int_0^{N_0} dN} = \frac{\displaystyle\int_0^{\infty} t\lambda N_0 \exp -\lambda t \, dt}{N_0}$$

$$= \lambda \int_0^{\infty} t \exp -\lambda t \, dt. \tag{15–14}$$

Integration by parts will show that this gives

$$t_{\text{av}} = \frac{1}{\lambda}. \tag{15–15}$$

We see from Eq. 15–13 and Eq. 15–10 that the half-life and the mean-life are related, namely,

$$T = 0.693 t_{\text{av}}. \tag{15–16}$$

Since the activity is proportional to the amount of radioactive material present we may use the intensity of emission as a measure of N. Suppose we observe the counting rate (see Art. 15–10) for a particular nuclide and plot the counting rate versus time. An exponential curve should result. It is more useful to plot the logarithm of the counting rate versus time since this should lead to a straight line. Such a plot is particularly easy to perform with semilogarithmic graph paper. An example is shown in Fig. 15–1, where the counting rate from a sample of Na^{24} is presented in a semilogarithmic plot. Note how the half-life can be determined.

15–4. The Natural Radioactive Series. The elements above $Z = 80$ have received intensive study by chemists and physicists and have been found to lie in three series of elements named the uranium, actinium, and thorium series. In these series the nuclei spontaneously decay from one to the other and eventually all three series end as one of the isotopes of lead. Each transformation consists of the emission of an alpha particle or a beta particle. Since the mass of an alpha particle is close to 4 amu, and the mass of a beta particle is $1/1836$ amu, the emission of an alpha particle decreases the mass number by 4 while the emission of a beta particle does not change the mass number. Within a given series the mass numbers

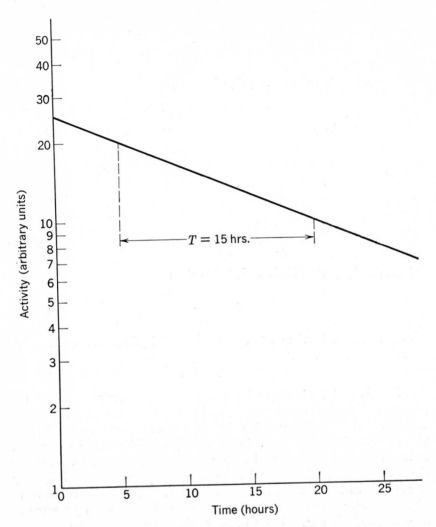

Fig. 15–1.   A decay curve for Na^{24} in a semilogarithmic plot.

will all fall in one of the four classes, $A = 4n$, $A = 4n + 1$, $A = 4n + 2$, or $A = 4n + 3$, where n is an integer.   The $4n$ series is the thorium series, the $4n + 2$ series is the uranium series, and the $4n + 3$ series is the actinium series.   The $4n + 1$ series is not found occurring naturally but a full series has been produced in the laboratory.   It is called the neptunium series. The reason for its absence in nature can be seen by examining Table 15–4. Tables 15–1, 15–2, 15–3 and 15–4 give the four series.   The history of the discovery of various members of these series led to the use of names differ-

TABLE 15–1

Uranium Series

Nuclide	Common name	Particle emitted	T	E (Mev)
$_{92}U^{238}$	Uranium I	α	4.51×10^9 yr	4.18
$_{90}Th^{234}$	Uranium X$_1$	β	24.1 days	0.19, 0.10
$_{91}Pa^{234}$	Uranium X$_2$	β	1.18 min	2.31
$_{91}Pa^{234}$	Uranium Z	β	6.66 hr	0.5
$_{92}U^{234}$	Uranium II	α	2.50×10^5 yr	4.76
$_{90}Th^{230}$	Ionium	α	8.0×10^4 yr	4.68, 4.61
$_{88}Ra^{226}$	Radium	α	1620 yr	4.78, 4.59
$_{86}Em^{222}$	Radon	α	. 3.825 days	5.48
$_{84}Po^{218}$	Radium A	α	3.05 min	6.00
$_{82}Pb^{214}$	Radium B	β	26.8 min	0.7·
$_{83}Bi^{214}$	Radium C	β α	19.7 min	β 1.6, 3.17 α 5.5–10.5
$_{84}Po^{214}$	Radium C′	α	1.6×10^{-4} sec	7.68
$_{81}Tl^{210}$	Radium C″	β	1.32 min	1.9
$_{82}Pb^{210}$	Radium D	β	20 yr	0.02
$_{83}Bi^{210}$	Radium E	β	5.0 days	1.17
$_{84}Po^{210}$	Polonium	α	138 days	5.30
$_{82}Pb^{206}$	Radium G	stable		

SOURCE: *Chart of the Nuclides*, 5th ed. (1956), The General Electric Company.

TABLE 15–2

Actinium Series

Nuclide	Common name	Particle emitted	T	E (Mev)
$_{92}U^{235}$	Actinouranium	α	7.1×10^8 yr	4.40, 4.58
$_{90}Th^{231}$	Uranium Y	β	25.6 hr	0.09, 0.30, 0.22
$_{91}Pa^{231}$	Protoactinium	α	3.4×10^4 yr	5.0, 4.63–5.05
$_{89}Ac^{227}$	Actinium	β	22 yr	0.046
$_{90}Th^{227}$	Radioactinium	α	18.2 days	5.97, 5.65–6.03
$_{88}Ra^{223}$	Actinium X	α	11.6 days	5.70–5.68
$_{86}Em^{219}$	Actinon	α	3.92 sec	6.82, 6.56
$_{84}Po^{215}$	Actinium A	α	1.8×10^{-3} sec	7.36
$_{82}Pb^{211}$	Actinium B	β	36.1 min	1.4, 0.5
$_{83}Bi^{211}$	Actinium C	α β	2.15 min	α 6.62, 6.27 β 0.35
$_{81}Tl^{207}$	Actinium C″	β	4.78 min	1.45
$_{84}Po^{211}$	Actinium C′	α	0.52 sec	7.43
$_{82}Pb^{207}$	Actinium D	stable		

SOURCE: *Chart of the Nuclides*, 5th ed. (1956), The General Electric Company.
There is also branching at Actinium and Ac A.

TABLE 15-3

Thorium Series

Nuclide	Common name	Particle emitted	T	E (Mev)
$_{90}\text{Th}^{232}$	Thorium	α	1.39×10^{10} yr	3.99, 3.93
$_{88}\text{Ra}^{228}$	Mesothorium₁	β	6.7 yr	<0.02
$_{89}\text{Ac}^{228}$	Mesothorium₂	β	6.13 hr	1.11, 0.45-2.18
$_{90}\text{Th}^{228}$	Radiothorium	α	1.90 yr	5.42, 5.34
$_{88}\text{Ra}^{224}$	Thorium X	α	3.64 days	5.68, 5.44
$_{86}\text{Em}^{220}$	Thoron	α	52 sec	6.28, 5.75
$_{84}\text{Po}^{216}$	Thorium A	α	0.16 sec	6.77
$_{82}\text{Pb}^{212}$	Thorium B	β	10.64 hr	0.34, 0.58
$_{83}\text{Bi}^{212}$	Thorium C	β α	60.5 min	β 2.25 α 6.05, 6.09
$_{84}\text{Po}^{212}$	Thorium C'	α	3×10^{-7} sec	8.78
$_{81}\text{Tl}^{208}$	Thorium C''	β	3.1 min	1.79, 1.28
$_{82}\text{Pb}^{208}$	Thorium D	stable		

SOURCE: *Chart of the Nuclides*, 5th ed. (1956), The General Electric Company.
Branching also occurs at Th A.

TABLE 15-4

Neptunium Series

Nuclide	Particle emitted	T	E (Mev)
$_{93}\text{Np}^{237}$	α	2.2×10^{6} yr	4.79, 4.52-4.87
$_{91}\text{Pa}^{233}$	β	27.4 days	0.26, 0.14, 0.57
$_{92}\text{U}^{233}$	α	1.62×10^{5} yr	4.82, 4.78, 4.73
$_{90}\text{Th}^{229}$	α	7300 yr	4.85, 4.94, 5.02
$_{88}\text{Ra}^{225}$	β	14.8 days	0.32
$_{89}\text{Ac}^{225}$	α	10 days	5.80
$_{87}\text{Fr}^{221}$	α	4.8 min	6.30, 6.07
$_{85}\text{At}^{217}$	α	1.8×10^{-2} sec	7.02
$_{83}\text{Bi}^{213}$	β α	47 min	β 1.39 α 5.90
$_{84}\text{Po}^{213}$	α	4.0×10^{-6} sec	8.34
$_{81}\text{Tl}^{209}$	β	2.2 min	1.8, 2.3
$_{82}\text{Pb}^{209}$	β	3.3 hr	0.62
$_{83}\text{Bi}^{209}$	stable		

SOURCE: *Chart of the Nuclides*, 5th ed. (1956), The General Electric Company.

ent from those which would be given now, but the historical names persist. The second column in each table gives the historical or common name. The column headed T gives the half-life and the column headed E gives the energy of the most important alpha particle groups emitted or that of the most energetic beta particles, both in Mev.

The behavior of Radium C which can either emit a β becoming Ra C' or emit an α becoming Ra C'' is called "branching." It is now known to also occur at Ra A and Ra E, facts not shown in Table 15-1. Uranium X_2 and Uranium Z have the same Z and A and are examples of isomers. UZ is formed when UX_2 emits a gamma ray. It is interesting to speculate on the marked similarities of the different series such as the branching that always occurs at $_{83}$Bi.

The other naturally occurring radioactive materials mentioned at the beginning are nuclides with very long half-lives. $_{19}K^{40}$ is a beta emitter with a half-life of 1.2×10^9 yr; $_{49}In^{115}$, another beta emitter, has a half-life of 6×10^{14} yr; $_{60}Nd^{144}$, an alpha emitter, has a half-life of 3×10^{15} yr, for example.

15-5. Successive Transformations. It should be clear from looking at the radioactive series that one should expect some mixture of the product nuclides to develop along with any parent nuclide. Let us look at the mathematics relating the various proportions of parent and daughter nuclides. We first suppose that we can chemically isolate an amount of a particular nuclide and look at how the various amounts develop. To make things concrete, let us consider a chain of three nuclei in which the third one formed is stable.

Let us start with a number $N_1{}^0$ of the first material at time $t = 0$. For this first member we have an amount N_1 at any time satisfying

$$\frac{dN_1}{dt} = -\lambda_1 N_1. \tag{15-17}$$

The second member is formed from the first at a rate $\lambda_1 N_1$ and at the same time decays, so the net rate is

$$\frac{dN_2}{dt} = \lambda_1 N_1 - \lambda_2 N_2. \tag{15-18}$$

For the non-radioactive third member

$$\frac{dN_3}{dt} = \lambda_2 N_2. \tag{15-19}$$

Since $N_1{}^0$ is the original amount of nucleus 1 at time $t = 0$, the integral of Eq. 15-17 is just

$$N_1 = N_1{}^0 \exp -\lambda_1 t. \tag{15-20}$$

If this result is substituted into Eq. 15-18, the result is

$$\frac{dN_2}{dt} = \lambda_1 N_1{}^0 \exp (-\lambda_1 t) - \lambda_2 N_2 \tag{15-21}$$

or

$$\frac{dN_2}{dt} + \lambda_2 N_2 = \lambda_1 N_1{}^0 \exp -\lambda_1 t. \tag{15-22}$$

If both sides are multiplied by $\exp +\lambda_2 t$, Eq. 15–22 becomes

$$\exp (+\lambda_2 t) \frac{dN_2}{dt} + \lambda_2 N_2 \exp (+\lambda_2 t) = \lambda_1 N_1{}^0 \exp (\lambda_2 - \lambda_1)t.$$

The left side is now a complete differential, so

$$\frac{d}{dt} (N_2 \exp \lambda_2 t) = \lambda_1 N_1{}^0 \exp (\lambda_2 - \lambda_1)t. \tag{15-23}$$

Integrating once gives,

$$N_2 \exp \lambda_2 t = \frac{\lambda_1}{\lambda_2 - \lambda_1} N_1{}^0 \exp (\lambda_2 - \lambda_1)t + C. \tag{15-24}$$

Since $N_2 = 0$ when $t = 0$,

$$C = - \frac{\lambda_1}{\lambda_2 - \lambda_1} N_1{}^0,$$

and

$$N_2 \exp \lambda_2 t = \frac{\lambda_1}{\lambda_2 - \lambda_1} N_1{}^0 [\exp (\lambda_2 - \lambda_1)t - 1],$$

so

$$N_2 = \frac{\lambda_1}{\lambda_2 - \lambda_1} N_1{}^0 [\exp (-\lambda_1 t) - \exp (-\lambda_2 t)]. \tag{15-25}$$

When this expression is substituted into Eq. 15–19 the integration of the result gives

$$N_3 = N_1{}^0 \left[1 + \frac{\lambda_1}{\lambda_2 - \lambda_1} \exp (-\lambda_2 t) - \frac{\lambda_2}{\lambda_2 - \lambda_1} \exp (-\lambda_1 t) \right]. \tag{15-26}$$

Eqs. 15–20, 15–25, and 15–26 give the number of nuclei remaining after a time t for each of the three types of nuclei. This analysis can be extended to any number of successively radioactive atoms although this calls for a consequent increase in the mathematical labor. A special case of particular interest occurs when the amount of parent nuclide remains constant, either because so little is depleted or because as much is formed as decays. In this case, if one waits long enough, the amount of daughter nuclide will become constant and an equilibrium condition will result. This can be represented by the equation,

$$\frac{dN_2}{dt} = \lambda_1 N_1 - \lambda_2 N_2 = 0. \tag{15-27}$$

A daughter of nuclide 2 might be in equilibrium as well and a similar expression would hold and so on.

These equations will be only approximately true when no parent is being formed but it is a good approximation if λ_1 is very small. In either case we say we have *secular equilibrium*.

Since

$$\lambda_1 N_1 = \lambda_2 N_2,$$

we have a technique for determining very long half-lives.

15–6. Radioactive Dating. It should be apparent that if one can get a piece of material into which the full radioactive series is trapped one can determine how much parent material was originally there by measuring the amount of daughters present, especially the lead isotope. The amount of helium formed (by alpha particles) is also indicative. Thus one can find the length of time that the parent has been entrapped. Studies of minerals and rocks based upon this indicate times of the order of, but not in excess of, 5×10^9 yr. Some theoretical cosmologists picture the formation of our universe some 5 to 10×10^9 years ago and our solar system must have condensed soon after. In any case, the entrapment times indicate that its condensation must have occurred several billion years ago.

Another example of the use of radioactivity depends upon the formation of C^{14} from N^{14} by cosmic-ray bombardment. If we assume that the fraction of C^{14} in CO_2 in the atmosphere has been relatively constant in the last few tens of thousands of years, we can determine the age of any carbon bearing object formed by a living organism. The carbon was deposited in the existing proportions while the organism was alive. Since its death the only change in concentration occurs by radioactive decay. The half-life of C^{14} is 5568 yr; so the determination of the age of material by this method is successful only back to about 30,000 years ago. These measurements fit historical dating very well and many significant historical ages have been determined using this method. The method was developed by W. F. Libby.

In the remainder of this chapter we shall examine some of the properties of the energetic particles and rays emitted by naturally radioactive materials.

15–7. Alpha-Particle Decay. The characteristics of alpha particles which are of interest are their energy, their range in matter, and their effects. Knowledge of their energy, in particular, helps us to understand the possible energy levels that a nucleus may have.

Alpha-particle energies may be determined by observing their deflection by a magnetic field in instruments called magnetic spectrographs using the principles described in Art. 6–6. Alpha particles from various nuclei have the relatively limited range of energies which range between 4.5 to 9.0 Mev.

This corresponds to velocities which range from approximately 1.5×10^7 m sec^{-1} to 2.0×10^7 m sec^{-1}. For a given nuclide, however, the energy of an alpha particle emitted has a characteristic value. Some nuclides may emit alpha particles having more than one characteristic value. Several such cases are found in the tables of the four series.

Although the alpha particle is energetic, it is easily absorbed. It may require only a few thousandths of a centimeter of aluminum or several centimeters of air to do this. The distance traveled before the alpha is converted to a neutral helium atom is called its *range*. The alpha particle has a short range because it ionizes the atoms of the material through which it passes and hence loses its energy. For instance, in air, on the

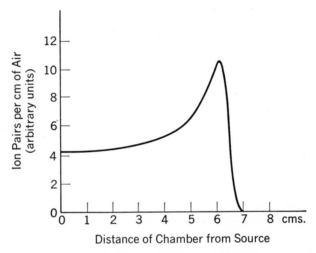

Fig. 15–2. Variation of ionizing power of alpha particles along their path.

average, each ionizing collision removes 32.5 ev energy from the alpha particle. As the alpha particle loses energy, it slows down and the ionizing collisions become more frequent, since the alpha particle has a longer time to interact with the atoms that it passes. This increase in ionization near the end of its path is clearly seen in a cloud chamber as an increase in the thickness of the track at its terminus. Electronic measurements of ionization along the track show the same result. Fig. 15–2 shows this.

The range of alpha particles is also short in human tissue. For instance, a 5 Mev alpha particle penetrates about 45 microns of tissue. However, alpha emitters are very dangerous when taken into the body by inhalation, ingestion, or other means. Radium, for instance, concentrates in the bones where the alpha particles destroy the marrow.

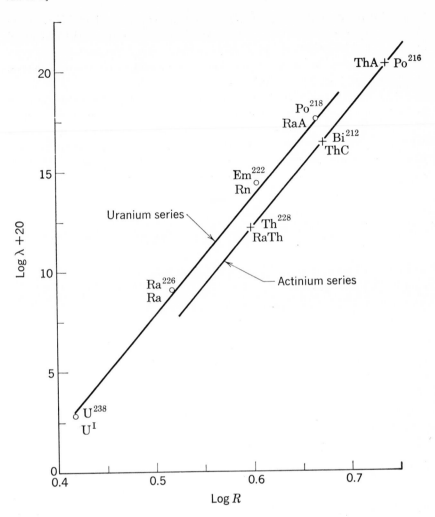

Fig. 15–3. The Geiger-Nuttall law for two of the naturally radioactive series.

An empirically determined relation between the range of alpha particles in air R and the decay constant λ called the *Geiger-Nuttall law* is

$$\log R = A + B \log \lambda, \tag{15–28}$$

where A and B are constants. Fig. 15–3 shows the experimental results from which the law was inferred. We see that the law has slightly different intercepts for each of the three radioactive series but the constant B

is practically the same for all three. The Geiger-Nuttall law tells us that the shorter the half-life ($\sim 1/\lambda$) the higher the range, and hence the energy, of the particle emitted.

Alpha-particle emission and the Geiger-Nuttall law have been satisfactorily explained by assuming the existence of alpha particles within nuclei and assuming that they are subject to a potential function similar to that shown in Fig. 15–4. Outside the nucleus, the potential must lead

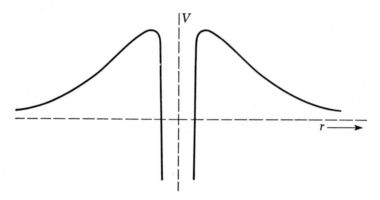

Fig. 15–4.   The potential function for an alpha particle in a nucleus.

to a Coulomb inverse square force of repulsion as indicated by the Rutherford scattering experiment. Inside the nucleus, the form of the potential is not known but it must be very deep and the fall very sudden indicating a strong attractive force. In this manner, the barrier or potential wall shown in Fig. 15–4 is formed at the nuclear surface. The wide range of λ's found for alpha emitters is successfully predicted on the basis of quantum mechanical "tunneling" of this barrier. If the energy of the alpha particle inside the nucleus is high, it will be in an energy level near the top of the barrier. At this energy level, the barrier is narrow and the probability of escape of the alpha particle is much greater than if it were in a lower energy level. Thus λ depends on the energy state in which the alpha is located. The discrete form of the energy spectra of nuclei indicates the existence of levels for the alpha particles within the nucleus as would be expected for a potential energy function such as that in Fig. 15–4.

15–8. Beta-Particle Decay.   The spectrum of the energy of alpha particles emitted from a particular nuclide consists usually of a single discrete "line" or (rarely) two or three distinct lines. In contrast, the spectrum of the energy of the betas from a particular nuclide show a continuous energy spread as shown in Fig. 15–5. An important feature of this curve

is the maximum or "end-point energy" representing the highest energy
that an electron can carry away from a particular nucleus.

The energy of beta particles is measured in a variety of beta-ray
spectrometers using magnetic fields to determine the momentum of the
beta rays, and hence their energy. The range of betas in matter is much
greater than for alphas. In air a beta particle with an energy of 3 Mev
will travel 10 m or so before being stopped. They too lose energy by
ionizing the atoms of material through which they pass, but are much less
likely than an alpha to ionize any given atom. The range also is much
less definite than for alphas.

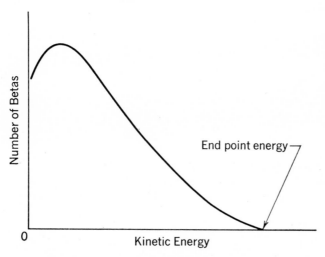

Fig. 15–5.   A typical beta-ray spectrum.

Fermi explained the continuous distribution of energy by suggesting
that beta particles were formed at the instant of emission, along with
another particle called the *neutrino*. These two particles are produced
from the neutron according to the reaction

$$_0n^1 \rightarrow {}_1H^1 + {}_{-1}e^0 + \nu$$

where ν represents the neutrino, a particle of zero charge and probably
zero rest mass. The total energy of the transformation, which is a fixed
value, can be shared between the electron and the neutrino in such a way
that the electron can acquire any energy from zero up to the maximum
as shown by the curve of Fig. 15–5.

15–9. Gamma-Ray Decay. Gamma rays are electromagnetic waves
with wavelengths shorter than x-rays, so that their properties are much

different from those of the alpha and beta particles. They originate when an excited nucleus changes its energy state to a lower one. They are extremely penetrating.

Gamma rays are absorbed in materials according to the absorption law

$$I = I_0 \exp -\mu x$$

that we discussed in connection with x-rays. The concepts associated with this absorption are important. Gamma rays are absorbed (that is, the beam intensity is reduced) by (1) the *photoelectric effect*, in which gamma-ray photons eject bound electrons from atoms, (2) *Compton scattering*, in which gamma-ray photons collide with *free* electrons and hence are deflected from the beam, and (3) *pair production*, in which the gamma ray disappears and a negative and positive electron (electron and positron) are produced. This latter effect is a prime example of the conversion of energy into mass. More will be said about this process in Chapter 20.

Gamma-ray energies may be accurately measured by measuring their wavelength with a crystal spectrometer or by the use of a scintillation detector and photomultiplier as described in Art. 15–10. A third method measures the energy of the photoelectrons ejected by the gamma rays using a beta-ray spectrometer. In fact these photoelectrons sometimes give the appearance of a line spectrum for the beta particles. Of course these photoelectrons are not true beta particles.

The spectrum of gamma rays is always a line spectrum. The energy of a gamma ray is equal to the difference in energy between two nuclear energy levels just as the energy of a photon in the optical region is equal to the difference in energy between two electronic levels. The spectroscopy of nuclei is very similar to that for the electronic structure of atoms. For instance, similar selection rules hold. Sometimes an excited state cannot radiate to reach lower levels or will have a long half-life. Such a state is said to be metastable, and since nuclei in such states have the same Z and the same A, the states are referred to as *isomeric states*. Uranium X_2 and Uranium Z are such isomers.

15–10. Radiation Detectors. The instruments used to detect radioactive radiation, cosmic rays, and the other high energy charged particles all depend upon the fact that such radiation produces ionization. Since the number of ions produced is related to the intensity of radiation, it is possible to determine the intensity of radiation by measuring the ionization current produced. It is also possible to detect the passage of individual particles through the detectors, measure their energy, and count them directly.

Total ionization chambers consist of two electrodes, which may have a variety of shapes, insulated from each other. The space between them is filled with a gas often merely air, at a convenient pressure which may be less than, equal to, or greater than atmospheric pressure. If a high speed of response is required, the gas used is argon. A typical circuit is shown in Fig. 15–6. The radiation ionizes the gas in the ionization chamber

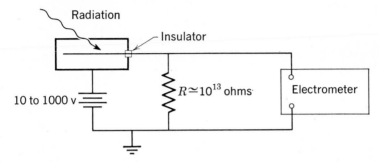

Fig. 15–6. Ionization chamber and current measuring circuit.

and the voltage V separates the charge causing a current to pass through R. The potential difference across R is measured with the electrometer or an electrometer vacuum-tube amplifier. An even simpler version involves an electroscope with a scale on it. The electroscope is charged to a potential indicated by a mark on the scale. As radiation discharges it, the total exposure can be determined by the motion of the pointer on the scale. Such chambers can be made in a very rugged form and with very good insulation so that a person can carry one in his pocket for days (if needed) to determine the total exposure to radiation. Note that the amount of discharge is measured by the decrease in potential. This, in turn, is proportional to the charge (the integral of the ionization current) that has been formed by the radiation.

Individual counters of charged particles are now very common. The detecting chamber of the instrument usually consists of a very fine wire anode concentric with an outer conducting cylindrical cathode. The chamber is filled with a gas sometimes mixed with an organic vapor such as ethyl alcohol or, alternatively, a halogen gas. The pressure is usually less than atmospheric, often about 10 cm of mercury and the behavior of the chamber is quite sensitive to changes in this pressure. The operation depends upon the voltage applied but the circuit is nearly always that shown in Fig. 15–7. The detector may have thick walls if it is to detect very penetrating radiation, but the walls must be thin if alphas or low energy betas are to be observed. Often a thin end window is used which permits the particles to enter the end of the cylindrical cathode.

The operation is quite complicated and depends upon the applied potential difference. The primary action is the production of ion pairs by the passage of an alpha particle, a beta particle, or the photoelectrons ejected by a gamma ray (or other photon). If V is small, only these ions participate in the current through R and a small pulse of potential difference across R is produced. By increasing V an amplification effect is produced. Each primary ion produces secondary ones, and these still more, as they move toward the anode. If V is not too great the amplification is constant and the size of the pulses, though much greater than before, is still proportional to the number of primary ions produced. It is possible to distinguish whether an alpha, a beta, or a gamma produced the pulse. The chamber is then said to be a *proportional counter*.

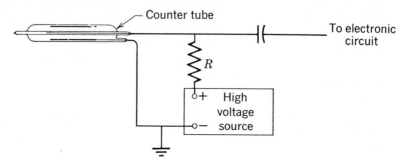

Fig. 15–7.   Counter tube circuit.

Increasing V still further leads to a situation in which so many secondary ions are formed that the whole gas volume in the chamber becomes conducting. The current pulse, and hence potential pulse across R, becomes much larger, and is independent of the original source. The discharge would, in fact, continue principally because of electrons knocked out of the cathode by the bombardment by positive ions, if it were not for the presence of the organic vapor, or halogen gas, which quenches the discharge by absorbing any secondary photons, electrons, or photoelectrons. The plot of pulse height versus V in Fig. 15–8 shows the typical behavior for all the chambers we have discussed. V must not exceed V_c.

An important type of operation occurs when the chamber is operated at a voltage at the center of the plateau. This type of operation is called Geiger-Mueller operation and the chamber is known as a *Geiger-Mueller tube* (*G-M tube*).

A second important type of radiation detection system depends upon the light flash or scintillation created as a high energy particle passes into certain solids. Certain crystals containing small amounts of impurities, e.g., ZnS with impurities and NaI with impurities (especially small amounts of thallium), will produce a scintillation when sufficient energy is transferred to them. The scintillation arises as electrons in the solid are excited to high energy states directly by the incoming radiation or by secondary ions, photoelectrons or Compton electrons or electron pairs. The brightness of the flash is proportional to the total energy absorbed. If a crystal is attached to a photomultiplier, (see Fig. 15–9) the current produced will

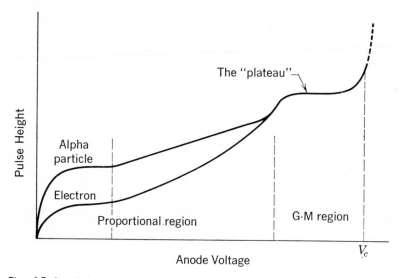

Fig. 15–8. Pulse height versus applied voltage for a particle detecting chamber.

indicate the flash. The size of the voltage pulse across a resistor is a measure of the energy of the particle producing the flash.

We shall not discuss the circuitry used to count or measure these pulses. Counting-rate meters, scaling circuits, coincidence circuits and pulse height analyzing circuits are commonly used.

Another class of detector shows the actual paths of charged particles. One of these is a photographic emulsion. An ordinary film will do, but special ones are manufactured for the purpose. If a charged particle (alpha, beta, proton, etc.) passes through a microscopic crystal of a silver halide and loses some energy to it, the crystal becomes developable, i.e., is easily reduced chemically to metallic silver. A fine line of such crystals is easily identified in the emulsion and shows the path of the particle. Fig. 15–10 shows a reproduction of a photographic emulsion exposed to billion-volt particles from the Brookhaven cosmotron. The dotted tracks left to right were formed by energetic protons and the emulsion shows at the right a "star" where a nucleus (perhaps silver or bromine) exploded after being struck by a proton.

Cloud chambers and bubble chambers are a second type of detector showing the actual path of the particle. In a cloud chamber, sudden cooling of a saturated vapor will supersaturate it. If an energetic charged particle passes through this vapor, ion pairs are formed along its track and these ion pairs form condensation "nuclei" on which the vapor changes to

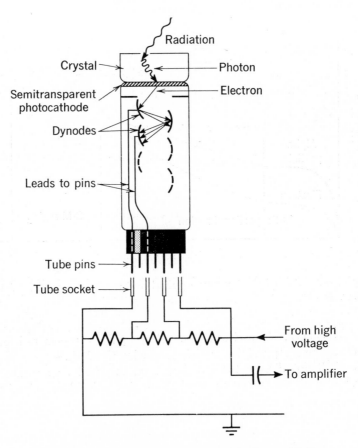

Fig. 15–9.   A scintillation detector with photomultiplier.

a liquid. The droplets that are formed leave a visible track. In a cloud chamber, the sudden cooling is produced by expansion. It was done first by C. T. R. Wilson and the device is known as a *Wilson cloud chamber*.

A supersaturated vapor cloud can also be created by carefully controlling the temperature gradient above a liquid. Such a chamber is called a *diffusion cloud chamber*. Fig. 15–11 is a photograph of nuclear tracks taken with the aid of such a chamber. In the figure, the streaks running right to left are energetic protons from a target outside the chamber which was bombarded by 2.2 Bev protons from the Brookhaven cosmotron. The pronged track at the right, which seems to originate from nothing, is believed to be a disintegration caused by a neutron (zero charge, therefore, leaves no tracks) also coming from the target. A strong magnetic field has been applied to the chamber producing a curvature in the tracks.

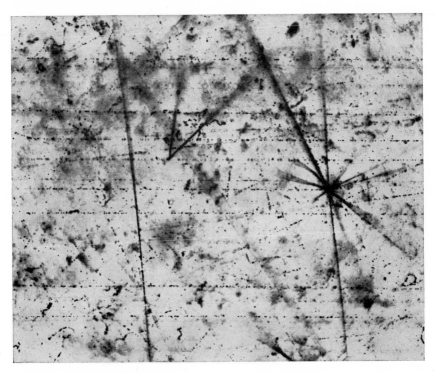

Fig. 15–10. Photographic emulsion exposed to billion-volt particles from Brookhaven cosmotron (Brookhaven National Laboratory).

The final type of detector showing actual paths is the bubble chamber, invented by D. A. Glaser in 1952. In this chamber, a liquid is superheated under conditions which prevent vaporization (or "bubbling") until there is a nucleus on which the vapor can form. As in the cloud chambers, energetic particles passing through the chamber provide such nuclei and a train of bubbles indicate the particle track. Fig. 15–12 shows tracks made in such a chamber. In this figure a 2.85 Bev proton from the Brookhaven Cosmotron has collided with a proton in the liquid. The liquid used was liquid hydrogen. Six prongs emerge from the collision site.

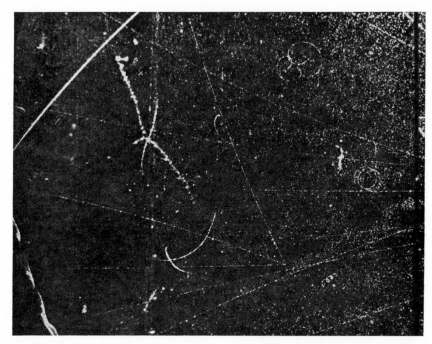

Fig. 15–11. Neutron-proton collision in a diffusion cloud chamber (Brookhaven National Laboratory).

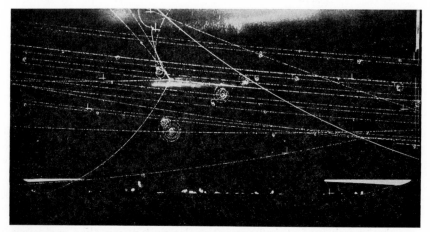

Fig. 15–12. A bubble-chamber photograph (Brookhaven National Laboratory).

PROBLEMS

15-1. Calculate the probability of throwing (a) 5, using a single die (b) 7, using 2 dice, (c) "snake-eyes," using 2 dice.

15-2. If $4.0 \times 10^{+18}$ nuclei have transformed in a given time in a sample originally containing $12.0 \times 10^{+18}$ nuclei, what is the probability of survival for this given time?

15-3. If the time required for the transformation in Problem 15-2 is 2 hours, what is the half-life for the process?

15-4. The disintegration constant of radon ($_{86}\mathrm{Em}^{222}$) is $2.10 \times 10^{-6} \sec^{-1}$. If the original sample weighed 1 mg, compute (a) the number of nuclei that have decayed in 1 day (b) in 3.82 days.

15-5. Compute the percentage of the original amount of material left after 10 half-lives of any radioactive material.

15-6. If 1 mg of radium is sealed in a container, calculate the amount of helium produced in 1 yr (in cubic centimeters at standard temperature and pressure).

15-7. A speculator hears that the Atomic Energy Commission plans to double the price of Po^{210} next January 1st. He rushes out today and buys $10,000 worth. He plans to sell it January 1st at the higher price. Does he gain or lose on the deal? How much?

15-8. Show that 1 gm of radium has an activity of 1 curie.

15-9. What is the activity of 1 kg of U^{238}?

15-10. What mass of thoron has an activity of 1 millicurie? What volume will it occupy at standard temperature and pressure?

15-11. What mass of radon has an activity of 1 millicurie? What volume will it occupy at standard temperature and pressure?

15-12. The counting rate for a radioactive material taken every minute is 14,600, 4050, 1120, 310, and 88 counts per min. Make a suitable semilogarithmic plot of these data, determine the half-life, the mean-life, and the disintegration constant for this material.

15-13. The counting rate for a material taken every hour is 450, 250, 140, 78, 44, and 24 counts per min. Make a suitable semilogarithmic plot of these data, determine the half-life, the mean-life, and the disintegration constant for this material.

15-14. Plot Eqs. 15-20, 15-25, and 15-26 all on the same graph. Let the x-axis be the time in hours, plot for a 24 hr period, and take $T_1 = 1$ hr, $T_2 = 6$ hr.

15-15. Suppose the initial amount of a radioactive material is N_0, and it has a disintegration constant $\lambda_1 = 0.5$ per day forming a material with a disintegration constant $\lambda_2 = 1.5$ per day which disintegrates to a stable material.

Plot N_1/N_0, N_2/N_0, and N_3/N_0 as a function of time for a period of 6 days, where N_1, N_2, and N_3 are the amounts of the first, second, and third materials, respectively.

15–16. Suppose the initial amount of a radioactive material is N_0, and it has a disintegration constant $\lambda_1 = 1.2$ per day forming a material with a disintegration constant $\lambda_2 = 0.4$ per day which disintegrates to a stable material. Plot N_1/N_0, N_2/N_0, and N_3/N_0 as a function of time for a period of 5 days, where N_1, N_2, and N_3 are the amounts of the first, second, and third materials, respectively.

15–17. What is the equilibrium amount of radon associated with 1 gm of radium? If all the radon is pumped away, what fraction of this equilibrium amount has formed again after 2 days, 1 week, 1 month?

15–18. What is the equilibrium amount of thoron in equilibrium with 1 gm of thorium X? If all the thoron is pumped away, what fraction of this equilibrium amount has formed again after $\frac{1}{2}$ min, 1 min, 5 min, 15 min?

15–19. If a sample of 1 kg of uranium is analyzed with a mass spectrograph how much U^{234} should be found if it all originated from U^{238}?

15–20. In a 1 kg sample of thorium, how much mesothorium$_1$ and mesothorium$_2$ should be found?

15–21. A sample of carbon-bearing material shows 4 counts per min. How old was the sample if an equivalent sample of modern material shows 6.5 counts per min?

15–22. A sample of carbon-bearing material shows 0.6 counts per min. How old was the sample if an equivalent sample of modern material shows 2.8 counts per min?

15–23. Rocks containing 2 gm of U^{238} per ton show 0.33 gm of Pb^{206}. How old are the rocks? How much helium might be found if all alphas were trapped?

15–24. Rocks containing 6 gm of U^{238} per ton show 1.2 gm of Pb^{206}. How old are the rocks? How much helium might be found if all the alphas were trapped?

15–25. Determine A and B of the Geiger-Nuttall law for the uranium series using the data of Fig. 15–3. Suggest a reformulation of the law so that there will be no problem of units.

15–26. The range-energy for some selected alpha emitters is given below.

Energy (Mev)	Range (cm in standard air)
4.05	2.49
4.88	3.30
5.59	4.05
6.89	5.64
8.95	8.57

Make a log-log plot of these data. What is your conclusion about how the range of an alpha particle is related to its energy?

15–27. An ionization chamber containing air is used to detect alpha particles. If a 4.78 Mev alpha loses 34 ev of energy for each ion-pair produced in the chamber, how much negative charge is produced when the alpha is stopped in the chamber?

15–28. 4.78 Mev alphas from radium enter an ionization chamber at a rate of 1000 alphas min^{-1}. If each ion-pair formed required 34 ev of energy, what current in amperes flows in the chamber?

15–29. The absorption coefficient of the most energetic gamma rays from Thorium C'' ($_{81}Tl^{208}$) in lead is 0.46 cm^{-1}. Calculate the thickness of lead required to reduce the intensity of these gamma rays to 1/100 of its original value.

15–30. Use the absorption law to find an expression for the half-thickness $x_{1/2}$, i.e., the absorber thickness required to absorb half the gamma-ray photons.

15–31. A G-M tube is filled with argon gas at a pressure of 10 cm of Hg. It operates with a high voltage of 800 v. The mean free path of electrons in argon at this pressure is 15×10^{-4} cm and the ionization potential of argon is 15.7 ev. (a) What electric field is necessary to ionize an argon atom? (b) Design a tube that will provide this field using reasonable parameters. Use cylindrical geometry for the tube.

SELECTED REFERENCES

BECQUEREL, H. "The Radiation from Uranium," and CURIE, M., and P. CURIE. "Polonium and Radium." In *A Source Book in Physics*, W. F. Magie, ed. McGraw-Hill Book Co., Inc., New York, 1935. Pp. 610 and 613, respectively.

BEYER, R. T. *Foundations of Nuclear Physics*. Dover Publications, Inc., New York, 1949. This contains some very interesting reproductions of original papers dealing with various aspects of nuclear physics.

BLEULER, E., and G. J. GOLDSMITH. *Experimental Nucleonics*. Holt, Rinehart & Winston, Inc., New York, 1952. Parts I and III.

KAPLAN, I. *Nuclear Physics*. Addison-Wesley Publishing Co., Inc., Reading, Mass., 1955. Chaps. 10 and 12.

LAPP, R. E., and H. L. ANDREWS. *Nuclear Radiation Physics*. Prentice-Hall, Inc., Englewood Cliffs, N. J., 1954. 2d ed., chap. 4.

LIBBY, W. F. *Radiocarbon Dating*. Univ. of Chicago Press, Chicago, 1955. (A brief account of the work done in this field.)

PRICE, W. J. *Nuclear Radiation Detection*. McGraw-Hill Book Co., Inc., New York, 1958. Chaps. 4, 5, and 6.

RUTHERFORD, E., J. CHADWICK, and C. D. ELLIS. *Radiation from Radioactive Substances*. The Macmillan Co., New York, 1930. Chap. 1.

SEGRE, E., ed. *Experimental Nuclear Physics*. John Wiley & Sons, Inc., New York, 1953. Vol. I.

16

Accelerators

Our knowledge of the nucleus has been acquired in a variety of ways. The nuclear charge, for example, was originally inferred from the chemical behavior of atoms, while some magnetic moments and spin angular momenta were deduced from the physical observation of optical spectra. An example of a more direct experiment with nuclei is the classic scattering experiment of Rutherford discussed in Chapter 7—an experiment which gave a rough measure of nuclear radii. The mass spectrometer, which gives very precise information about nuclear masses, is a further example of highly refined external measurements on the nucleus.

These measurements of size, mass, charge, and momenta are about all that can be obtained without disturbing the nucleus in some way. By a fortunate chance, some nuclei are unstable and some information of the interior structure of those nuclei which are naturally radioactive can be obtained. However, to investigate the interior of the remainder of the nuclei, some probe, or some means of disturbing the nucleus, is needed.

16–1. Some Problems in Nuclear Experimentation. It is not easy to tamper with the nucleus. Consider a collision experiment and examine first the size of the nucleus. The diameter of aluminum, for example, may be taken to be about 8×10^{-15} m. If we define the nuclear cross-section σ (see Art. 7–3) to be simply the cross-sectional area of the nucleus, then $\sigma = 0.5 \times 10^{-28}$ m^2 = 0.5×10^{-24} cm^2 for each aluminum nucleus. (Nuclear cross-sections are generally of the order of 10^{-28} m^2 = 10^{-24} cm^2; so for convenience this unit of area is called a *barn*. Thus the nuclear cross-section of an aluminum nucleus is 0.5 barns.) Now a cubic centimeter of aluminum contains $2.7/27.0 \times 6.02 \times 10^{23} \simeq 6 \times 10^{22}$ atoms. (The density of aluminum is 2.7 g cm^{-3} and its atomic weight is 27.) Thus, if we consider a cube of aluminum 1 cm on a side, the nuclei obscure only $0.5 \times 10^{-24} \times 6 \times 10^{22} = 0.03$ cm^2 = 3% of the 1 cm^2 area of the face. Since the number of atoms per unit volume times the thickness equals the number per unit area, then the nuclei of any sheet of aluminum

1 cm thick obscure only 3% of the area. Since this percentage is so small the chance of an incoming particle colliding with a nucleus is correspondingly small. This admittedly is a rough calculation since the value of the nuclear cross-section is not necessarily the value used here and in fact differs for different nuclear processes. However the small size of the nucleus leads to the conclusion that only a small fraction of the incident particles will participate in any nuclear process.

There are additional difficulties. It is often desirable to disturb a nucleus by forcing a charged particle into the nucleus. Electrons are not very good for this purpose because their small mass means a comparatively long wavelength, and the uncertainty principle makes it difficult to try

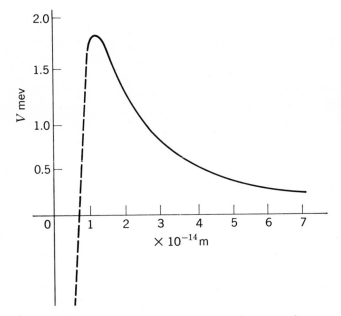

Fig. 16–1.   Potential of the proton as a function of distance from an aluminum nucleus.

to pin an electron down to such a small region as a nucleus. Photons in the gamma-ray or extreme x-ray region can be used, but it will be seen that their production requires elaborate machinery. This leaves only other nuclei to use as bombarding particles to disturb a nucleus. (There are two other important particles that can disrupt a nucleus, neutrons and mesons, but we will postpone their discussion.)

The trouble with bombarding nuclei with other nuclei is that both are charged. Consider the problem of bombarding an aluminum nucleus with the nucleus of hydrogen (a proton), the simplest of all possible nuclei to use. Fig. 16–1 shows the potential energy as a function of the distance between the center of the proton and the center of the nucleus. In the region $r < 0.8 \times 10^{-14}$ m which would be somewhere inside the nucleus, the potential energy of the entering proton apparently is negative since the proton, in order to stay so close to the other protons in the nucleus, must experience some kind of attractive force. For $r > 2 \times 10^{-12}$ cm the potential energy is given by

$$V = \frac{Ze^2}{4\pi\epsilon_0 r} \cdot \qquad \left[V = \frac{Ze^2}{r} \cdot \right] \qquad (16\text{-}1)$$

In the intermediate range, the potential energy is hard to predict, but it must behave like the potential energy shown in Fig. 16–1 in order to meet the potential function in the other two regions. From this figure, you can see that if a proton is to enter the aluminum nucleus it must have a kinetic energy of about 1.5 Mev. An alpha particle because of its larger charge would need a larger energy than this. The atomic number of aluminum is only 13. For nuclei with values of Z much greater, still higher energies are required.

The most direct way to give a bombarding particle kinetic energy is to let it accelerate through a potential difference. But it is not easy to provide potential differences of the magnitude required. A whole series of devices have been developed for accomplishing this. They go by the general term of *accelerators* since their principal purpose is to accelerate charged particles to a high kinetic energy. Some of these devices will be described.

16–2. Transformer-Rectifier Systems. Ordinary step-up transformers can be used to get high alternating potentials. The use of rectifiers and filters can change this to a unidirectional, fairly steady value. It is even possible to use rectifiers and capacitors to double or quadruple the potential difference as is shown in Fig. 16–2. Accelerating machines which impart energy to a particle by making it pass once through a large steady potential difference are known as *electrostatic* accelerators. One of the earliest of these systems, developed by Cockroft and Walton at the Cavendish Laboratory, produced a potential difference of 150,000 v. Later it was increased to give 800,000 v.

With such electrostatic generators the principal problem is to obtain adequate insulation. For example, the filaments of the rectifier tubes must be heated by currents from transformers not shown in Fig. 16–2 and the windings must be insulated for the full voltage, as must the capacitors. This leads to a large and complicated structure. In some modern rectifier systems, stacks of solid-state rectifiers are used, and radio-frequency transformers are used rather than 60-cycle transformers.

After such a potential difference has been produced, it is still necessary
to use it to accelerate the protons. This is done in an accelerator tube,
such as the one shown in Fig. 16–3. A small amount of hydrogen gas
enters the ion gun at the top of the column. An electric discharge through
the hydrogen gas between electrodes A and B produces hydrogen ions in

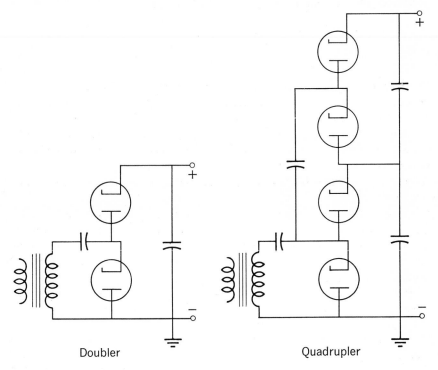

Doubler   Quadrupler

Fig. 16–2.   A.C. to D.C. conversion circuits with voltage multiplication.

the middle. Some of these are attracted by the negative electrode C and
begin to move down the tube. They are accelerated additional amounts
as they cross the gaps between C and D, D and E, E and F, and F to
target. Thus they eventually gain the full amount of kinetic energy
appropriate to the potential difference through which they pass. The
accelerating field between each pair of electrodes, such as D and E, has
such a shape that it not only accelerates the protons but also keeps the
beam from spreading out. This focusing action is very important. The
success of a particular tube may depend largely on the design of the electrodes. Many variations of this scheme have been used so that some .
columns have many electrodes and others just a few. Various types of
ion sources are also in use.

The resistor R determines the potential distribution along the column. It prevents having nearly all the potential drop across a short distance which might lead to a breakdown in the insulators.

Sometimes it is important that only one type of accelerated particle collide with the target, while the beam may contain several kinds of ions. For example, there might be hydrogen molecules as well as hydrogen atoms

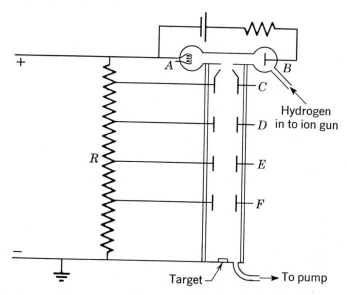

Fig. 16–3.   Schematic diagram of an accelerating tube.

If it is necessary to segregate just one kind, the target is moved back and the beam is permitted to pass between the poles of a magnet. Ions having different masses will be deflected different amounts. After this sorting, the chosen ions are directed to the target.

Transformer-rectifier systems have the advantage of stability, high current capacity, and comparative simplicity, but they are not capable of a very high potential difference. It is very difficult to get more than 800,000 ev of energy.

16–3. Van de Graaff Accelerators.   Other types of electrostatic generators have been developed. One of the simplest and most effective consists of a hollow conductor supported on an insulating stand. A belt of insulating material driven by a motor rides over an idler pulley located inside the hollow spherical conductor. Fig. 16–4 shows the arrangement. A charge is sprayed on the belt. As the belt moves, the charge is carried up to the hollow conductor where the charge then moves from the belt onto

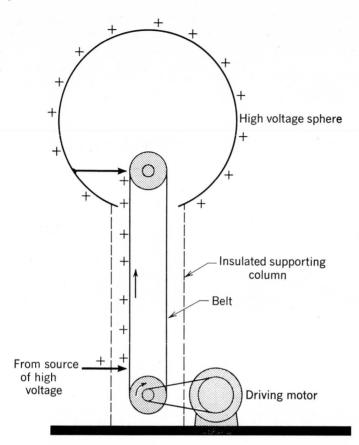

Fig. 16–4. Schematic diagram of the charging system of a Van de Graaff generator.

the conductor. If the conductor is large and smooth enough, the potential can be raised to a high value before the air around it breaks down and begins to conduct in a corona discharge. An ion source and an accelerating tube can be connected between the conductor and the ground to produce a beam of high energy ions as is done in the previously described electrostatic generators.

In order to increase the maximum attainable potential difference, the whole system can be placed in a large tank and the air or gas pressure increased a number of atmospheres to increase its insulating strength. The addition of freon or carbon tetrachloride to the air will also help. Potentials of about 4×10^6 v are possible. The value can be maintained and will be very stable. The Van de Graaff generator provides a source of precisely determined energetic particles at quite useful current densities and at the present time is widely used both by itself and as an *injector* or starter for very high energy machines.

16–4. The Cyclotron. In 1932, E. O. Lawrence at the University of California developed a device to give particles a high energy by accelerating them over and over again. Only 10,000 v applied 100 times will impart 1 Mev of energy to a particle. One scheme for doing this consists of

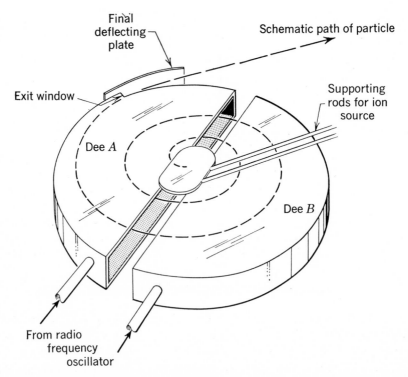

Fig. 16–5. The electrode system for a cyclotron. (The particle actually makes many more revolutions than are shown.)

applying a radio-frequency potential difference of say 10,000 v to two **D**-shaped electrodes, as shown in Fig. 16–5. The **D**'s are enclosed in a chamber that is evacuated and the whole system is placed between the poles of a large constant field magnet. Ions from an ion source are first accelerated across the gap between the **D**'s. The magnetic field makes the ions travel in a circular path, so they return to the gap again after a half turn. If the electric field has been reversed by the oscillator during the time the ions are completing their first half circle they will be accelerated again. This can continue many times. An accelerating device of this form is known as a *cyclotron* and the basic relations governing its action will now be investigated.

The path of an ion will be a circle because of the magnetic field. The radius of the circle is

$$R = \frac{Mv}{Be}, \qquad \left[R = \frac{Mvc}{Be} \right] \tag{16-2}$$

since

$$Bev = \frac{Mv^2}{R}. \qquad \left[\frac{Bev}{c} = \frac{Mv^2}{R}. \right] \tag{16-3}$$

The time required to make one half turn is

$$T_{\frac{1}{2}} = \frac{\pi R}{v} = \frac{\pi M}{Be}. \qquad \left[T_{\frac{1}{2}} = \frac{\pi Mc}{Be}. \right] \tag{16-4}$$

Thus if the frequency of the oscillator is set to

$$\nu = \frac{1}{2T_{\frac{1}{2}}} = \frac{Be}{2\pi M} \qquad \left[\nu = \frac{Be}{2\pi Mc} \right] \tag{16-5}$$

everything will be just right for the particle to reach the gap every half period regardless of its speed. When the ion reaches a value of R near the maximum permitted by the apparatus it is usually deflected to hit a target or to escape in a beam outside the apparatus. If the radius of largest possible orbit is R_m, the maximum energy that can be given to a particle is

$$E = \frac{B^2 R_m{}^2 e^2}{2M}. \qquad \left[E = \frac{B^2 R_m{}^2 e^2}{2Mc^2}. \right] \tag{16-6}$$

The magnet for such an instrument must be very large since its radius is determined by R_m. A typical one with a pole face 4 ft in diameter weighs 180 tons. It requires 16 kw to produce 1.6 weber m^{-2}. For protons, the oscillator should have a frequency of 12 megacycles. The maximum gap potential difference is 200 kv, and up to 70 kw are required for the oscillator. This is a very severe power and frequency requirement for an electronic oscillator.

Protons can be accelerated to 8 Mev, deuterons (the nuclei of heavy hydrogen) to 16 Mev, and alpha particles (nuclei of helium) to 32 Mev. These values are representative of standard designs.

Eqs. 16–2 to 16–6 depend upon the constancy of M. We know from the special theory of relativity that as the speed of the particle increases, M also increases since

$$M = \frac{M_0}{\sqrt{1 - \beta^2}}. \tag{16-7}$$

Thus, there is an upper limit to normal cyclotron operation. In order to reach higher energies, it is necessary to work with pulses of ions. It can be seen from Eq. 16–5 that a decrease in the frequency will accommodate for the change in mass of the particles. Such frequency modulated cyclotrons (also called synchrocyclotrons) have been built to accelerate protons to about 400 Mev.

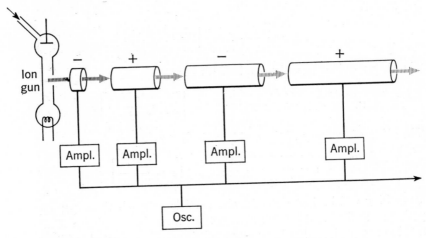

Fig. 16–6.   Electrode arrangement in a linear accelerator.

An important difficulty with devices such as the cyclotron is to keep the beam focused into a narrow region. A careful study shows that the orbit may involve vertical and radial oscillations. The shape of the electric field helps to some extent as does the slight decrease in magnetic field strength at the edge of the **D**. However, unless these fields are carefully adjusted the whole orbit may become unstable.

In contrast with the circular cyclotrons, *linear accelerators* have been constructed which also accelerate ions to high energies by many small increments. The small increments in energy are delivered as the particles pass between tubular electrodes arranged in a line. The arrangement is shown schematically in Fig. 16–6. A master oscillator drives separate amplifiers connected between the individual electrodes. The phases of the amplifiers are carefully controlled so that the polarities of the electrodes alternate in a proper succession. The electrodes provide a suitable accelerating field as the particle passes between the electrodes. Because of the absence of a large magnetic field, linear accelerators hold the promise of very high energies at relatively low cost. However, the severe electronic requirements of the oscillator and amplifiers as well as problems of focusing have prevented the full realization of their hoped-for performance.

Fig. 16-7.   The Yale University linear accelerator (Yale University Physics Department).

Linear accelerators however provide beams of high current density and are particularly good for accelerating heavier nuclei. Fig. 16–7 shows a view of the Yale University linear accelerator. It produces high energy ions with mass numbers ranging from 4 to 40 with energies of about 10 Mev per nucleon. Thus it will provide approximately 40 Mev alphas and 400 Mev argon ions. Yale University is planning to build an 800 Mev proton linear accelerator with an average current of 100 μa approximately 100 times the current now available at such energies.

16–5. The Betatron. There are only a few applications for the direct use of high energy electrons, but x-rays of high energy, produced when electrons strike a target, are of considerable use. One device to accelerate electrons to high energies is called the *betatron.*

Let us consider an electron moving in a circular orbit (as if it were in a wire loop the shape of the orbit). Let a changing magnetic field be enclosed by this orbit or loop. Therefore, an emf

$$V = \frac{d\Phi}{dt} \qquad \left[V = \frac{1}{c}\frac{d\Phi}{dt} \right] \qquad (16\text{--}8)$$

is developed around the loop where Φ is the magnetic flux enclosed by the orbit. This corresponds to a tangential electric field intensity E_t such that

$$2\pi R E_t = V, \qquad (16\text{--}9)$$

where R is the radius of the orbit. Such a tangential electric field will give an electron a tangential acceleration since, if the momentum is p

$$\frac{dp}{dt} = eE_t, \qquad (16\text{--}10)$$

where by the special theory of relativity

$$p = mv = \frac{m_0 v}{\sqrt{1 - \beta^2}}.$$

It is therefore seen that a changing magnetic field will accelerate an electron. At the same time, because it is in a magnetic field, the electron will continue to move in a circular orbit and if the magnetic flux density is B_0 at the orbit, then

$$p = mv = B_0 eR. \qquad \left[p = \frac{B_0 eR}{c}. \right] \qquad (16\text{--}11)$$

According to this equation, if it is necessary to keep the radius of the orbit R constant as the electron is accelerated and v increases, B_0 the field at the orbit must be increased. A betatron is the accelerating machine in which this is done, that is, an electron is accelerated in a circle, whose radius is constant, by changing the flux that passes through the orbit.

The restriction that must exist on B_0 for this to be done is now easily found. From Eqs. 16–8 to 16–11

$$\frac{d\Phi}{dt} = 2\pi R^2 \frac{dB_0}{dt}. \qquad \left[\frac{1}{c}\frac{d\Phi}{dt} = \frac{2\pi R^2}{c}\frac{dB_0}{dt}.\right] \qquad (16\text{–}12)$$

If both Φ and B_0 start at zero, integrating Eq. 16–12 will give

$$\Phi = 2\pi R^2 B_0. \qquad (16\text{–}13)$$

Letting

$$\Phi = \pi R^2 \bar{B}, \qquad (16\text{–}14)$$

where $\bar{B}$ is an average flux density, and substituting this in Eq. 16–13 we find

$$\bar{B} = 2B_0. \qquad (16\text{–}15)$$

Therefore, if an electron is started in a circular path and if B_0 is increased while $B_0 = \bar{B}/2$, it will be possible to accelerate the electron by this electromagnetic induction and still keep it in the same orbit. To increase B_0 a changing current is required in the field coils of a magnet. It is found convenient to cyclically change B_0 and hence to accelerate groups or bursts of electrons. In order to satisfy the requirement of Eq. 16–15, the pole pieces may be shaped as shown in Fig. 16–8.

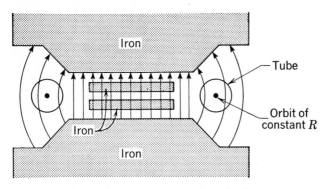

Fig. 16–8.   The magnet and tube of a betatron.

The extra iron in the center makes $\bar{B} = 2B_0$. The details of the requirement for a stable orbit are more complicated than we have shown, but they can be met. Betatrons capable of producing 100 Mev electrons have been built. Generally the electrons themselves are made to strike a target after they have been accelerated, and it is the x-rays produced that are used, but some betatrons use the electrons directly.

16–6. Synchrotrons. In Art. 16–4 we saw that in order to keep the particles "in step" with the accelerating electric field in accordance with the equation

$$\nu = \frac{Be}{2\pi M} \qquad \left[\nu = \frac{Be}{2\pi Mc} \right] \qquad (16\text{–}5)$$

we could decrease ν the frequency of the electric field when the relativistic mass increase began to be felt. We indicated that the machine in which this is done was the *synchrocyclotron* or frequency modulated cyclotron.

Eq. 16–5 also gives us an alternative method of keeping the relativistic particles in step with the electric field. Instead of changing the frequency of the electric field, it is possible to increase the magnetic field B. Under this condition the particles gain just enough energy from the oscillating electric field, as they pass through it once each turn, to accommodate for the steadily increasing magnetic field and thus satisfy Eq. 16–3 with R constant. The accelerator in which this is done is called a *synchrotron.* An important feature of the operation of a synchrotron and similar machines is that they depend upon the principle of *phase stability* discovered independently by McMillan, by Veksler, and by Oliphant. Phase stability occurs because, if a particle passes the accelerating gap at the moment the field is zero, it is unaccelerated and if its orbital frequency agrees with the applied radio-frequency accelerating field as shown in Eq. 16–5, it will coast at constant speed. But if it reaches the gap so that it is slowed down, the radius of its path becomes enough smaller that it will get around in time to be accelerated; and if it gets accelerated too much, the radius of its path is increased and it arrives enough later to be slowed down. It thus tends to stay in phase with the radio-frequency accelerating field. If B is slowly increased, the particles travel faster and faster, or rather gain more and more energy and mass, always keeping in phase in accordance with the phase stability principle. This technique is put into operation when the particles become relativistic (i.e., attain a velocity close to the velocity of light). If electrons are given an energy of a few million electron volts, they are relativistic, so such a device works well with electrons. Synchrotrons for electrons have been built giving energies of several hundred million electron volts.

It is more difficult to do this with protons, but by changing both the field and the frequency, it is possible to accelerate them to high energies. At Brookhaven, the cosmotron has produced 3 Bev protons. The University of California bevatron has produced 7 Bev protons, while the highest energy in machines of this type is produced by a 10 Bev machine in Russia which contains 36,000 tons of magnet.

16–7. Alternating-Gradient Synchrotrons. The most recent and highest energy machines are synchrotrons employing the *strong focusing* or *alternating-gradient* principle suggested by E. D. Courant, M. S. Livingston and H. S. Snyder and independently by N. C. Christofilos. Two machines, one at Brookhaven and one near Geneva, Switzerland, are operating in the 25 to 30 Bev region. Both have fundamentally the same design in which the particles are held in a constant circular path by increasing the

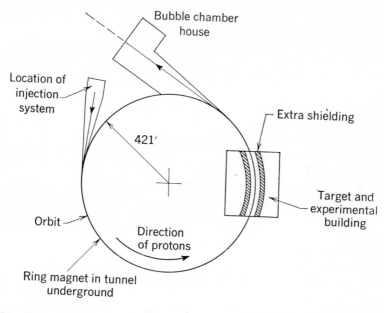

Fig. 16–9.   Schematic plan view of the Brookhaven alternating-gradient synchrotron.

magnetic field as the energy is increased. The strong focusing involves the use of an alternating sequence of focusing and defocusing magnetic fields that have a net focusing effect. These magnetic fields compress the beam into a region only a few inches wide thus reducing the requirements on the large magnet which keeps the particles in orbit. For example, the Geneva accelerator requires only 3200 tons of magnet and the Brookhaven machine 4000 tons. A diagram of the Brookhaven machine is found in Fig. 16–9. Note the over-all size of the machine. The other major components of the Brookhaven machine are a 750 Kev transformer-rectifier system fed by protons from an ion source which in turn injects these particles into a 50 Mev linear accelerator. The linear accelerator passes the already high energy protons into the main synchrotron magnet ring through complicated focusing equipment. This latter injection equipment is shown in Fig. 16–10.

Fig. 16–10. The injection system of the Brookhaven alternating-gradient synchrotron. The main magnet ring is seen in the background at right. The four inch pipe in the foreground leads the proton beam from the linear accelerator located behind the shielding wall in the left background to the main magnet ring. The men are aligning the beam at special viewing boxes (Brookhaven National Laboratory).

Still higher energy machines are on the drawing boards. A 45 Bev linear electron accelerator 10,000 ft long has been approved to be built by Stanford University. California Institute of Technology is designing a 300 Bev proton AGS and an internationally sponsored 1000 Bev proton AGS is being considered for Brookhaven. The limit seems to be set not by man's ingenuity but by his willingness to finance such ventures. In the past and present his optimism in proceeding has been justified by the knowledge obtained.

PROBLEMS

16–1. The simplest electrostatic accelerator consists of two metal plates with an electric field between them. Design a system to give electrons a velocity of 3×10^9 cm sec^{-1} subject to the condition that the system must be confined to an evacuated region such that the electric field cannot exceed 17.5 kv m^{-1}. Include a discussion of how the voltage might be obtained.

16–2. Explain the operation of the circuits in Fig. 16–2.

16–3. Average beam currents from Cockroft-Walton machines are about 1 ma. How many singly ionized particles arrive per second in such a beam?

16–4. Beam currents of 1 ma can be obtained from Van de Graaff generators. (a) How many alpha particles per second will reach the target in such a beam? (b) If a potential of 6×10^6 v can be obtained with a certain Van de Graaff generator, with what energy will alpha particles reach the target?

16–5. Consider an isolated sphere in air carrying an electric charge. If the breakdown electric field for air is 30 kv cm^{-1}, what is the surface charge density on a sphere 0.70 cm in radius?

16–6. The surface charge density σ on a belt in air in a Van de Graaff accelerator is $\sigma = \epsilon E$ [$\sigma = E/4\pi$] where E is the electric field at the surface of the belt. If 30 kv cm^{-1} is the breakdown potential in air what is the maximum charge that a belt will carry on one side? How long will it take to charge a sphere of 0.70 cm radius to the breakdown limit if the belt travels at 15 m sec^{-1} and is 30 cm wide if the belt carries only 0.01 of the limiting charge? Assume that all charge is removed from the belt.

16–7. What must be the kinetic energy of a proton to be able to approach to within 10^{-14} m of a phosphorus nucleus in a head-on collision?

16–8. What must be the kinetic energy of a deuteron (the nucleus of hydrogen of atomic weight 2) to be able to approach to within 10^{-14} m of a copper nucleus?

16–9. Protons from a Cockroft-Walton system having an energy of 8×10^5 ev can produce a nuclear reaction with Li. Such a reaction can thus occur when the nuclei have what separation?

16-10. Deuterons from a low voltage system that gives them an energy of 10^5 ev can react with tritium (hydrogen of atomic weight 3). Such a reaction can thus occur when these nuclei have what separation?

16-11. Calculate the proper frequency for a cyclotron for protons when the flux density is 1 weber m^{-2}.

16-12. Calculate the proper frequency for a cyclotron for deuterons when the flux density is 1.2 weber m^{-2}.

16-13. What will be the radius of the path of a proton having an energy of 4 Mev in a magnetic flux density of 1 weber m^{-2}?

16-14. What will be the radius of the path of a deuteron having an energy of 6 Mev in a magnetic flux density of 1.2 weber m^{-2}?

16-15. Prove that the energy of a particle accelerated in a cyclotron is

$$E = \frac{B^2 R_m^2 e^2}{2M}, \qquad \left[E = \frac{B^2 R_m^2 e^2}{2Mc^2}, \right]$$

where R_m is the maximum possible radius in the machine.

16-16. The Swedish cyclotron has the following dimensions: maximum diameter 88 in., magnetic field 1.80 webers m^{-2}, beam current 250 μa. Compute the frequency, the particle energy for alpha particles, and the number of alphas striking the target per second. What would be the result for protons?

16-17. At what energy does the mass of a proton become 10% greater than its rest mass?

16-18. At what energy does the mass of a helium nucleus become 5% greater than its rest mass?

16-19. Calculate the proper frequency for an FM cyclotron having a flux density of 1.5 weber m^{-2} for protons with low energy, with 100 Mev, with 200 Mev, and with 300 Mev.

16-20. Calculate the proper frequency for an FM cyclotron having a flux density of 1.6 weber m^{-1} for deuterons with low energy, with 100 Mev, with 200 Mev, and with 300 Mev.

16-21. Electrons are accelerated in a betatron. (a) What percentage of the speed of light is their speed when their energy reaches 3 Mev? (b) At 100 Mev energy approximately how many revolutions will they make per second in a betatron of 125 cm radius?

16-22. What flux density at the orbit of a betatron is required when the electrons have an energy of 50 Mev and the radius is 0.8 m? Approximately how many revolutions will an electron make in reaching this energy in 3×10^{-3} sec?

16-23. The circular portions of the path in the 3 Bev proton synchrotron has a radius of 10 m. What is the final flux density of the magnetic field in these portions of the orbit? If you neglect the straight portions of the orbit (which are actually quite short) what frequency accelerating field should be used?

16–24. The University of California at Berkeley linear proton accelerator was designed to produce 32 Mev particles. Because of losses this requires a total input voltage of 36 megavolts. If the impedance of the device is 316 megohms, what is the peak power requirement in watts of the r-f voltage source? If the machine produces pulses of length 300 μsec at a rate of 15 sec^{-1}, what is the average power requirement?

SELECTED REFERENCES

BEYER, R. T. *Foundations of Nuclear Physics.* Dover Publications, Inc., New York, 1949. P. 692.

GREEN, A. E. S. *Nuclear Physics.* McGraw-Hill Book Co., Inc., New York, 1955. Chap. 3.

LIVINGSTON, M. S. *High Energy Accelerators.* Interscience Publishers, Inc., New York, 1954. A concise yet complete description of accelerators.

17

Nuclear Reactions and the Neutron

The Rutherford scattering experiment was probably the first experiment in which energetic nuclear particles were directed toward other nuclei. Rutherford in 1919 bombarded nitrogen atoms with the alphas from $_{83}Bi^{214}$ (Ra C) to obtain the first recorded nuclear reaction. Some of the alphas disappeared and long range particles, identified as protons, were found.

It was concluded that the alpha particle penetrated the nucleus of nitrogen where it formed a complex and excited nucleus which in turn broke up to give off the proton which was observed. This earliest nuclear reaction can be written

$$_2He^4 + _7N^{14} \rightarrow [_9F^{18}] \rightarrow _8O^{17} + _1H^1$$

where the fluorine symbol represents a compound nucleus, and the oxygen, a product nucleus. The reaction is known as an "alpha-proton reaction" and it is convenient to abbreviate the equation to $N^{14}(\alpha,p)O^{17}$. The first symbol represents the target nucleus, the symbols in the parentheses give, first, the bombarding particle, next, the light particle released, and finally, the last symbol denotes the new nucleus which has been formed. Note how the total number of protons (in this case 9) is the same on both sides of the equation as is the total number of nucleons, the sum of the mass numbers (here 18).

Since this first transmutation of nitrogen into oxygen was accomplished in the laboratory, a large number of similar reactions have been produced. We shall describe several types of reactions and point out some aspects of their importance. First though, it is necessary to discuss the *neutron*, a particle found in all nuclei heavier than H^1.

17–1. The Discovery of the Neutron. In 1930, Bothe and Becker[1] observed a very penetrating form of radiation coming from beryllium and boron when these nuclei were bombarded by alpha particles. In 1932, further study of this radiation by Mme. Curie and F. Joliot[2] showed that the radiation was very likely to knock protons out of any material which contains a considerable amount of hydrogen. They concluded that the radiation was gamma rays and that the gamma rays had an energy of about 50 Mev in order to cause the protons to recoil as observed. Chadwick[3] then discovered that the same radiation would also knock nitrogen nuclei out of matter. He realized that if the radiation was gamma rays, the energy of the gammas would have to be much greater than 50 Mev. This is an impossible conclusion since the mass difference between beryllium plus a 5 Mev alpha particle, and the product nucleus (carbon of atomic weight 13) is equivalent to approximately only 16 Mev, much less than the required 50 Mev or greater.

Chadwick was therefore led to the assumption that the radiation was not electromagnetic. He decided also that because of its very high penetrating power it was probably not charged particles, but was made up of neutral particles of considerable mass. With this hypothesis, everything about the radiation seems to fit into a consistent picture.

A rough determination of the mass of these neutral particles was made in the following manner. For a head-on collision (producing a maximum forward velocity) the forward velocity of the recoil proton will be

$$V_H = V_0 \frac{2M_0}{M_0 + 1}, \tag{17–1}$$

where V_0 is the velocity of the particle and M_0 is its mass in atomic mass units. In the case of a similar head-on impact with a nitrogen nucleus

$$V_N = V_0 \frac{2M_0}{M_0 + 14}. \tag{17–2}$$

This gives

$$\frac{V_H}{V_N} = \frac{M_0 + 14}{M_0 + 1}. \tag{17–3}$$

The experimental values for V_H and V_N lead to the value $M_0 = 1.15 \pm 10\%$.

Chadwick called the particles making up this radiation *neutrons*. He proposed that they were produced by the following reaction:

$$_4\text{Be}^9 + _2\text{He}^4 \rightarrow _6\text{C}^{12} + _0\text{n}^1.$$

[1] W. Bothe and H. Becker, *Zeit. f. Phys.*, **66**, 289 (1930); *Naturwiss*, **19**, 753 (1931).
[2] I. Curie and F. Joliot, *Compt. Rend.*, **194**, 273 (1932), and **198**, 254 (1934).
[3] J. Chadwick, *Nature*, **129**, 312 (1932); *Proc. Roy. Soc.*, **A136**, 692 (1932).

17-2. The Properties of the Neutron. The discovery of the neutron was a tremendous help in understanding the structure of nuclei. It is now clear that neutrons and protons are the principal constituents of nuclei. In fact, a nucleus of atomic number Z and mass number A consists of Z protons and $A - Z$ neutrons.

Among the neutron properties whose values have been measured are the following:

Mass $= 1.008982 \pm 0.000003$ amu
Charge $= 0.000 \ldots$
Angular momentum $=$ a spin of $\frac{1}{2}$
Magnetic moment $= 1.91354$ nuclear magnetons $\left(1 \text{ nuclear magneton} = \dfrac{\hbar e}{2M_p} \right.$

$= 0.50504 \times 10^{-26}$ amp m$^2 \Big)$

$\left[1 \text{ nuclear magneton} = \dfrac{\hbar e}{2M_p c} = 0.50504 \times 10^{-23} \text{ erg gauss}^{-1}. \right]$

Free neutrons are beta emitters with a half-life of approximately 13 minutes.

The mass just quoted is measured from nuclear reactions. For example, gamma rays of sufficient energy cause deuterons (the nuclei of $_1$H^2) to disintegrate into a proton and a neutron. The sum of the energy of the original material and the total energy after the reaction must be the same. Thus, using the equivalence of mass and energy from special relativity theory, and if K is the total kinetic energy of the neutron and proton, then

$$M_D c^2 + h\nu = M_H c^2 + M_n c^2 + K. \qquad (17\text{--}4)$$

Everything in this equation is known except M_n and K. In addition, we know that $M_n \simeq M_H$. In the experiment, the photon has very little momentum, so after the photo-dissociation of the deuteron the momenta of the proton and neutron are almost equal, i.e.,

$$|M_H V_H| \simeq |M_n V_n|. \qquad (17\text{--}5)$$

This also means that their kinetic energies are almost equal,

$$K_H \simeq K_n \qquad (17\text{--}6)$$

and since K_H can be measured, then the total kinetic energy of the neutron and proton,

$$K = K_H + K_n,$$

is determined. Eq. 17-4 can now be quantitatively examined. Experimentally it is found that gamma rays with an energy $h\nu$ of 2.62 Mev will cause the reaction to proceed and to give the proton a measured kinetic energy K_H of 0.20 Mev. Since, as we have seen, the neutron has an equal kinetic energy, then the total energy $K = K_H + K_n$ is 0.40 Mev.

Then $h\nu - K = 2.22$ Mev (a more precise value is 2.226 Mev) is the energy required to just separate the neutron and proton.

To complete the determination of the mass of the neutron, Eq. 17–4 requires the masses of hydrogen and deuterium. Nuclear masses are accurately measured by the high precision mass spectrometers which were briefly mentioned at the end of Chapter 6. Table 17–2 on page 386 is a table of nuclear masses for some of the lighter nuclei. In this table it will be seen that the mass values are almost integral values when the value of the most abundant isotope of oxygen is taken to be 16 units exactly. This practice, which gives a physical scale of mass, is slightly different from that used in chemistry where the mass 16 is assigned to ordinary atmospheric oxygen, a mixture of isotopes. The choice is arbitrary and although in 1961 an international standards committee decided to use carbon 12 as a base, in this text we will use the older physical scale based on oxygen 16, since most tables of nuclear masses use this base. The atomic mass unit (1 amu) in this scale is defined to be $\frac{1}{16}$ of the mass of one atom of oxygen 16. Therefore

$$1 \text{ amu} = \frac{16}{16(6.02 \times 10^{23})} = 1.66 \times 10^{-24} \text{ g}$$

$$= 1.66 \times 10^{-27} \text{ kg}.$$

Since the equivalence of mass and energy from the special relativity theory may be applied,

$$1 \text{ amu} = 931 \text{ Mev}.$$

Now returning to the disintegration of the deuteron, since 2.22 Mev equals 0.00239 amu, then Eq. 17–4 gives

$$M_n = M_D + \left(\frac{h\nu - K}{c^2}\right) - M_H$$

$$= 2.01474 + 0.00239 - 1.00814$$

$$= 1.00899 \text{ amu}.$$

(The mass of the electron included in the deuterium atom is just balanced by the mass of the electron in the hydrogen atom.) You will also note that a gamma ray with less than 2.226 Mev cannot dissociate a deuteron.

17–3. Thermal Neutrons. Neutrons have one advantage over most other bombarding particles—the fact that they are uncharged. As a result, they are not repelled by nuclei. In fact, when they get very close to a nucleus they are generally attracted by the nucleus. Therefore, it is not necessary for them to be given a high kinetic energy in order to participate in nuclear reactions. It may even be better for them to be slowed down so that they spend a greater time near the nucleus. This can be accomplished by letting the neutrons collide with nuclei with which they do not interact. They will then give up energy to the other nucleus and finally slow down to the thermal energy of the material. Materials containing hydrogen, deuterium, and carbon are very good for this purpose and water, paraffin, and graphite are most commonly used. Such a material is called a *moderator*.

How a moderator slows down a neutron can be seen by calculating the energy of a neutron following an elastic collision with the nucleus of the moderator. The most effective collision is a head-on collision. In such a case we get the following results shown in Table 17–1 for four

TABLE 17–1

Moderator Effectiveness

	Hydrogen	Deuterium	Beryllium	Carbon
Approximate mass of moderator (amu)	1	2	9	12
V of neutron after collision	0 (very small)	$\frac{1}{3} V$	$\frac{8}{10} V$	$\frac{11}{13} V$
Energy of neutron after collision	0 (very small)	$\frac{1}{9} E$	$0.64 E$	$0.71 E$
Energy of moderator after collision	E	$\frac{8}{9} E$	$0.36 E$	$0.29 E$

different moderators when the initial velocity of the neutron is V and its energy is E. We have assumed here that the nucleus of the moderator was at rest and we have neglected the difference in mass from whole numbers. Neither of these make much difference, except to make it very unlikely that the final velocity of the neutron becomes zero. In fact, the result of many collisions leads to neutrons having a distribution of speeds appropriate to the temperature of the moderator. The advantage of the two isotopes of hydrogen is clear from Table 17–1. Ordinary hydrogen combines with some of the neutrons to form deuterium and, therefore, is not really as good a moderator as deuterium.

Lithium and boron both have high absorbing power for neutrons and cannot be used as moderators. Helium is gaseous at ordinary temperatures; hence its use is unlikely. One can also see in this table the reason for the prominent effect of high energy recoil protons when high energy neutrons bombard hydrogen.

The actual physical arrangement usually used to obtain thermal neutrons is to imbed a neutron source in a large block of paraffin or graphite or to immerse the source in ordinary, or heavy water. A fairly large fraction of the neutrons will be slowed to thermal velocities if the moderator is only a few inches thick.

17–4. Neutron Sources. The production of neutrons can be carried out using any of the nuclear reactions in which neutrons are produced.

Certain ones have special advantages over others. Among the commonly used ones are the reactions

$$_4\text{Be}^9 + _2\text{He}^4 \rightarrow _6\text{C}^{12} + _0\text{n}^1$$

and

$$_4\text{Be}^9 + h\nu \rightarrow 2 \,_2\text{He}^4 + _0\text{n}^1.$$

The former was the reaction which led to the discovery of the neutron. Finely divided beryllium is intimately mixed with a salt of radium or polonium or other alpha emitting material and enclosed in a tight metallic capsule. Typically, 1 millicurie to 1 curie of radium may be used. One curie of radium mixed with beryllium will produce about 10^7 neutrons per second. The rather strong gamma emission from the radium and its daughters may be inconvenient or dangerous and a polonium source of alphas may then be superior.

The second reaction above actually uses a strong gamma emitter to produce the neutrons. Strong gamma sources may be much less expensive than radium-beryllium sources and they have an additional advantage of producing monoenergetic neutrons. Both of these sources produce fast, high energy, neutrons. A moderator can then be used to slow the neutrons to intermediate or thermal speeds.

Other neutron sources depend upon particles which have been given high energy by an accelerator. However, the most intense sources of neutrons are the result of the fission reaction. Reactors, to be described in Chapter 19, can produce tremendous neutron fluxes of both high speed and thermal neutrons. One can even get fairly monoenergetic neutrons from a reactor by using Bragg diffraction to obtain neutrons of a particular wavelength. Another scheme used to sort out neutrons of a particular velocity is to use a "chopper" such as that indicated schematically in Fig. 17–1. Absorbing disks with slits in them rotate on a common shaft of length L. The slits are not in line. Instead, the first slit passes in front of the beam of neutrons first and then after the shaft has turned through an angle θ the second slit comes to alignment. Thus, only neutrons with a speed $v = L/t$, where t is the time for the shaft to turn through the angle θ, can get through the device. Cadmium is a very good absorber of slow neutrons and hence is the material used for the construction of any slit system such as this.

17–5. Neutron Detectors. Because neutrons have no electric charge they have practically no effect on the electronic structure of an atom. They will, therefore, not produce directly any ionization in ordinary ionization chambers, proportional counters, or Geiger-Mueller tubes. Nor will they produce directly any darkening of a photographic film or any scintillation in regular scintillation crystals. It is necessary to make use of secondary particles such as the recoil protons which led to the discovery of

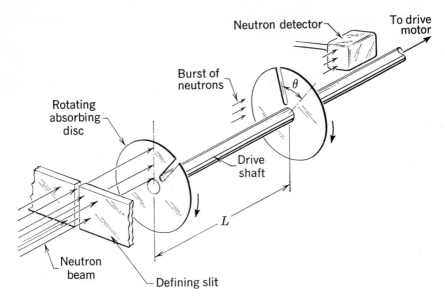

Fig. 17–1.   Schematic diagram of a fast neutron chopper.

neutrons or other charged secondaries produced by many nuclear reactions.   Finally the fission process may be used.

Two possible types of neutron detectors are ionization chambers lined with paraffin to produce protons or lined with U^{235} to produce fission fragments.   The protons or fission fragments are then observed by the ionization they produce.

Another common detector is a Geiger-Mueller type tube filled with BF_3, a gas at ordinary temperatures.   The reaction used here is

$$_5B^{10} + {}_0n^1 \rightarrow {}_3Li^7 + {}_2He^4.$$

Both the lithium nucleus and the alpha particle produce ions in the G-M tube and thus trigger off a discharge.

Scintillation crystals also can be doped with materials such as $_5B^{10}$ to produce scintillation from the secondaries produced by neutrons.

17–6. Energy Considerations.   Now we turn to a more general discussion of nuclear reactions.   An important feature of most nuclear reactions is the redistribution of energy.   In Chapter 2, while discussing collisions, most of the considerations were directed toward perfectly elastic collisions. All nuclear collisions in which some nuclear transformation occurs are inelastic collisions.   The energy of reaction, the Q-value of Chapter 2, becomes especially important.   The mass of the particles is a manifestation of their energy.   Precision mass spectrographs make it possible to measure their masses very well; thus we can expect to compare the values so obtained with the requirements of the dynamics of the interactions.

Consider a nuclear reaction in which the target nucleus of rest mass M_t is originally at rest. Let the incoming particle have kinetic energy K_i and rest energy $m_i c^2$. (See Fig. 17-2.) M_p designates the rest mass of the

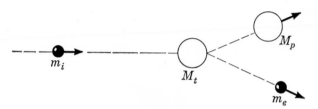

Fig. 17-2.   Essentials of a nuclear reaction.

product nucleus and m_e the rest mass of the emitted particle. The law of conservation of energy requires that

$$(K_i + m_i c^2) + M_t c^2 = (K_p + M_p c^2) + (K_e + m_e c^2),$$

or

$$[(M_t + m_i) - M_p - m_e] c^2 = (K_p + K_e) - K_i. \qquad (17\text{-}7)$$

The right hand side of Eq. 17-7 is the Q of the reaction, as defined earlier in Eq. 2-63. If Q is positive, the sum of the final masses is less than the sum of the initial masses. Mass has disappeared by being converted into the excess kinetic energy of the product nucleus and the recoil particle over the kinetic energy of the bombarding particle. If Q is negative, then mass has been formed and it can only come from the energy of the incoming particle. This latter reaction will not be possible until the kinetic energy of the bombarding particle is above a *threshold* characteristic of the reaction.

The unit of mass used in the calculations of Q values is the amu. Table 17-2 gives the masses of some of the lighter isotopes in the periodic table in amu as measured by mass spectrographs.

17-7. Types of Nuclear Reactions. Before we examine particular reactions let us make some generalizations. Very often these reactions are accompanied by gamma rays. These gamma rays originate in and are emitted from the product nucleus and serve as definite evidence of nuclear energy levels. Also, in general, only one particle is emitted in a nuclear reaction. There are, however, exceptions, especially in reactions at very high energies. Again, in a great many of these reactions the phenomenon of *resonance* is found. That is, as the energy of the incoming particle is

TABLE 17-2

The Masses of Light Nuclei

Element	Mass number	Atomic mass	Element	Mass number	Atomic mass
n	1	1.008982	F	17	17.007505
			F	18	18.006651
H	1	1.008142	F	19	19.004456
H	2	2.014735	F	20	20.006350
H	3	3.016997			
			Ne	19	19.007952
He	3	3.016977	Ne	20	19.998777
He	4	4.003873	Ne	21	21.000504
He	6	6.020833	Ne	22	21.998358
			Ne	23	23.001768
Li	6	6.017021			
Li	7	7.018223	Na	21	21.004286
Li	8	8.025018	Na	22	22.001409
			Na	23	22.997055
Be	7	7.019150	Na	24	23.998568
Be	8	8.007850			
Be	9	9.015043	Mg	23	23.001453
Be	10	10.016711	Mg	24	23.992628
			Mg	25	24.993745
B	9	9.016190	Mg	26	25.990802
B	10	10.016114	Mg	27	26.992876
B	11	11.012789			
B	12	12.018162	Al	27	26.990071
			Al	28	27.990760
C	11	11.014916			
C	12	12.003804	Si	28	27.985767
C	13	13.007473	Si	29	28.985650
C	14	14.007682	Si	30	29.983237
			Si	31	30.985140
N	13	13.009858			
N	14	14.007515	P	30	29.987896
N	15	15.004863	P	31	30.983550
			P	32	31.984016
O	15	15.007768	P	33	32.982166
O	16	16.000000			
O	17	17.004533	S	32	31.982183
O	18	18.004857	S	33	32.981881

varied, it is found that at particular energies the yield of emitted particles is sharply increased over the yields at nearby energies. These maxima in the yield curves are known as resonances. Finally, as was mentioned previously, the mass numbers and charge must balance.

Nuclear reactions can be classified by the type of bombarding particle. These bombarding particles may be alphas, protons, deuterons, neutrons, gamma rays, or heavy nuclei such as carbon. The charged particle reactions are brought about, usually, by placing foils of the materials in the beams coming from nuclear accelerators. Neutrons, because they are neutral, penetrate easily into nuclei, and we shall consider them separately.

A rather important classification of reactions has to do with the time for the reaction. First, those of shortest time occur when only a part of the bombarding particle enters the target nucleus and a portion is left behind. Examples are those for which a deuteron (1 neutron plus 1 proton) may leave one part, say the neutron, in the target nucleus while the other, here the proton, proceeds onward. The time required for this is of the order of the time for the particle to pass the nucleus, namely 2×10^{-15} m/2 $\times$ 10^7 m sec^{-1} = 10^{-22} sec. An example of such a "stripping" reaction is the reaction $_{11}\mathrm{Na}^{23}$ (d,p) $_{11}\mathrm{Na}^{24}$. The inverse of this type, a *pick-up* reaction, is also possible. A second class of reaction is much more common. An example is given at the beginning of this chapter where the incident particle enters the nucleus and forms an excited compound nucleus which later emits the product particle, thus forming a new nucleus (usually in an excited state). The time for such events is much longer than for the stripping reactions, but is still very short, namely, of the order of 10^{-15} sec. The third class requires much longer times such as 10^{-6} sec to hours and even days. These are the reactions of spontaneous decay—of radioactive transformations.

Incoming particles with energies between 1 Kev and 0.5 Mev will react with intermediate ($A < 80$) nuclei, but energies greater than 0.5 Mev are required for heavier nuclei. When the incoming energy is above 10 Mev, the reaction may include the possible complication of more than one particle being emitted.

17-8. Alpha-Particle and Proton Reactions. Because of their positive charge, alphas and protons must, in general, have greater energies than 0.1 Mev in order to cause a transmutation. We have already mentioned an important one when we discussed the (α,p) reaction on nitrogen. A second important type of reaction with these charged particles is known as "radiative capture" in which the particle is absorbed and only a gamma ray is emitted. $\mathrm{Al}^{27} (p,\gamma)$ Si^{28} is an example of this. At increased energies (p,n), (α,n), $(p,2n)$, and $(\alpha,2n)$ reactions occur.

Resonance effects are quite evident in proton reactions. An example is shown in Fig. 17-3 which is a plot of a portion of the curve showing gamma-ray intensity resulting from bombardment of $_{13}\mathrm{Al}^{27}$ with protons with carefully controlled energies.[4] These results furnish much information concerning the energy levels of $_{13}\mathrm{Al}^{28}$.

17-9. Deuteron Reactions. Deuterons are useful because of their mass of two amu and their single electronic charge. Protons, alphas, neutrons, and gammas have been observed as emitted particles. We have already mentioned the stripping reaction. At low enough energies, the Coulomb repulsion keeps the proton in the deuteron away from the target nucleus,

---

[4] K. J. Brostrom, T. Huus, R. Tangen, *Phys. Rev.*, **71**, 661 (1947).

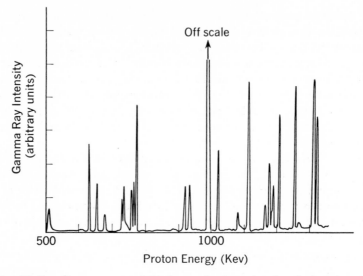

Fig. 17–3.   Gamma ray yield from aluminum bombarded with variable energy protons.

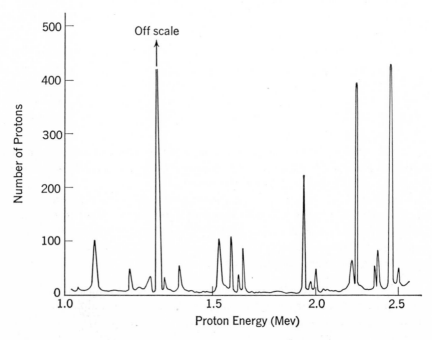

Fig. 17–4.   Proton yield from an aluminum target under bombardment by monoenergetic deuterons.

but the neutron may enter, be captured, and tear away from the proton. Or at high energies the proton enters, is captured, and leaves the neutron to continue its way. The direction of motion is seldom modified very much; so a collimated beam of particles appears from this stripping action in contrast to the more isotropic release of particles in a reaction in which a compound nucleus is formed. The deuteron reactions are particularly valuable for producing isotopes not found in nature. The d-p reactions form nuclei with an excess of neutrons and the d-n reactions form nuclei with an excess of protons.

Again, we can gain information on the details of the energy level of nuclei. As an example, the reaction $_{13}Al^{27}$ (d,p) $_{13}Al^{28}$ can be produced with monoenergetic deuterons. When this is done, it is observed that the protons which are ejected come off with definite amounts of energy as indicated in Fig. 17–4 which sketches the results of Eng, Buechner, and Sperduto.[5]

17–10. Gamma Reactions. Nuclei will be disintegrated when an incident gamma-ray photon has sufficient energy. A most important experiment of this type is the so-called photodisintegration of the deuteron which we discussed in Art. 17–2.

Reactions of the gamma-n type have now been found in many nuclei. If we assume that all the neutrons of a particular nucleus are not bound in with the same amount of energy, then the γ-n reaction probably gives a measure of how much energy is required to remove the most lightly bound or "last" neutron. These energies lie between 5 and 13 Mev, except for the deuteron and for $_4Be^9$. In $_4Be^9$ a very low value ($\sim$1.66 Mev) is believed to indicate that the beryllium nucleus is formed of essentially two alpha particles and in the case of $_4Be^9$, that the extra neutron is very lightly bound to this structure.

17–11. Neutron Reactions. Neutron reactions are probably the most widely studied reactions in nuclear physics. It is now possible to obtain beams of neutrons from nuclear reactors and to select neutrons with energies ranging from very low values to millions of electron volts. The measurement of cross-sections (or probability of reaction) for neutron reactions and their theoretical explanation have been highly developed for a wide range of values of neutron energy.

Low and intermediate energy neutrons (0 to 500 Kev) undergo chiefly elastic scattering and radiative capture with the lighter nuclei ($A < 80$). These reactions are (n,n) and (n,γ) reactions. The total cross-section σ_t includes the possibility of scattering and capture, but for light nuclei, the elastic scattering probability is much greater than the capture probability.

[5] H. A. Eng, W. W. Buechner, A. Sperduto, *Phys. Rev.*, **88**, 963 (1952).

Low energy neutrons are also chiefly scattered elastically or are captured by radiative capture by heavy nuclei. At certain resonant energies, however, the capture cross-section predominates.

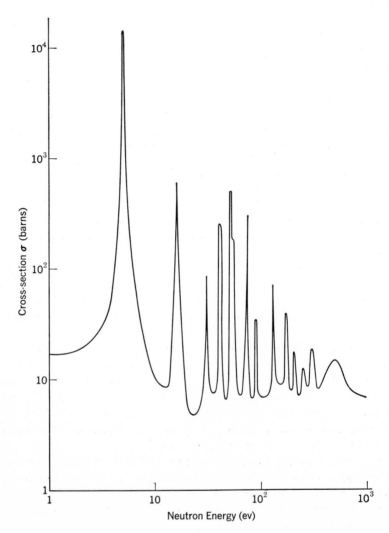

Fig. 17–5.   Neutron resonance phenomenon in silver.

Fig. 17–5 shows the total neutron cross-section of silver and illustrates the resonance phenomenon. Such resonances, as in the other cases, represent definite energy levels in the nuclei.

Neutrons in a moderator, because of the slowing-down process, will soon reach an equilibrium state with the atoms of the moderator. Because of this thermal equilibrium the neutrons are said to be *thermal neutrons.* They then exhibit the properties of gases at ordinary temperatures and particularly the Maxwell distribution of velocities. As a result, their average kinetic energy is

$$\bar{K} = \tfrac{3}{2}kT. \tag{17–8}$$

Another important energy is the energy corresponding to the most probable *velocity* v_0 and this is

$$K_0 = \tfrac{1}{2}mv_0{}^2 = kT. \tag{17–9}$$

Thermal neutrons are customarily described in terms of this latter energy. Cross-sections for thermal neutrons are given for a velocity of 2200 m sec^{-1} or 0.025 ev of energy, the values corresponding approximately to $T = 20°C$.

Neutrons in this range are likely to be scattered elastically or absorbed by an n-γ capture. The total cross-section is

$$\sigma_t = \sigma_s + \sigma_a, \tag{17–10}$$

where σ_s represents the scattering probability and σ_a the absorption probability. Fig. 17–6 shows the cross-sections of boron and cadmium for low energy neutrons.

The straight line on this log-log plot has a slope of $\tfrac{1}{2}$ and it indicates that the neutron cross-section for boron has a $1/v$ dependence. This might be expected (and is certainly common) since the chances of absorption should be proportional to the time spent close to the nucleus, i.e., to $1/v$.

Notice the large resonance in the cadmium cross-section just above thermal energies. This arises from a cross-section for $_{48}Cd^{113}$ for 0.025 ev neutrons of 20,800 barns, very, very much larger than one finds for most nuclei or even for cadmium at other energies. Only 12% of natural cadmium is $_{48}Cd^{113}$ so the effect is partially masked in Fig. 17–6. It is this large cross-section that makes cadmium such a good shield or absorbing screen for thermal neutrons in particular.

Neutrons having energies of the order of 1 Mev or greater are called high-energy neutrons. These neutrons can undergo inelastic scattering or cause the emission of charged particles or neutrons.

At very high energies (>10 Mev), the following reactions are found, $(n,2n)$, (n,np), and $(n,3n)$.

17–12. Induced Radioactivity. Often the product nuclei in radioactive transformations are unstable. Such nuclei are said to exhibit induced, or artificial radioactivity. Although induced activity may be almost identical to ordinary beta emission, it may differ from natural radioactivity in that positive electrons, or *positrons,* may be emitted. The theory of positrons is discussed briefly in Chapter 20. Mme. Curie and Joliot reported the discovery of the first production of induced radio-

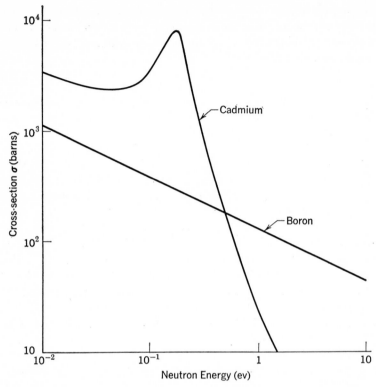

Fig. 17-6.   Total slow neutron cross-section of cadmium and boron.

activity in 1934 when they investigated the reaction

$$_{13}\text{Al}^{27} + {}_2\text{He}^4 \rightarrow {}_{15}\text{P}^{30} + {}_0\text{n}^1.$$

The product was radioactive with a half-life of 2.5 min and the decay
equation was

$$_{15}\text{P}^{30} \rightarrow {}_{14}\text{Si}^{30} + {}_{+1}\text{e}^0.$$

Usually, in induced radioactivity, a single emission leads directly to a
stable nucleus, in contrast to the naturally radioactive series.

This reaction shows a decay in which the nuclear charge is decreased
by unity. Artificial nuclei can decay and reduce the nuclear charge in
still another manner that is also unknown in naturally radioactive materials. This mode of decay is known as *K-capture* and it occurs when an
extra-nuclear electron enters the nucleus from the *K*-shell of the atom
and converts a proton into a neutron. This event is detected by the *K*
x-ray that is emitted from the atom as another electron replaces the
missing electron.

The energies involved determine whether or not positron or electron emission or orbital electron capture occurs in artificial nuclei. As an example consider the positron emission of the example above. The energy of the reaction is

$$Q = M_P - M_{Si} - m, \tag{17–11}$$

where M_P and M_{Si} representing *nuclear* masses and m the electron mass. Nuclear masses are not usually measured but instead the atomic masses are. We might designate these

$$M_{aP} = M_P + 15m,$$

and

$$M_{aSi} = M_{Si} + 14m,$$

so Eq. 17–11 becomes

$$Q = (M_{aP} - 15m) - (M_{aSi} - 14m) - m = M_{aP} - M_{aSi} - 2m. \tag{17–12}$$

For the reaction to be possible, the Q must be positive. Eq. 17–12 shows that for Q to be positive, the mass of the phosphorus atom must be at least two electron masses heavier than the silicon atom. Reference to Table 17–2 gives $M_{aP} = 29.987896$ and $M_{aSi} = 29.983237$. Since $2m = 0.001089$, we see that $Q = 29.987896 - 29.983237 - 0.001089 = 0.003570$, a positive number.

Induced radioactivity has furnished the research worker with several valuable tools. One of these is the availability of strong radioactive sources, especially beta and gamma sources. This has made it possible to observe the effects of intense radiation on matter and has provided more convenient sources for medical and therapeutic uses. Another is to provide *labeled* atoms. The chemistry of various isotopes of an element is practically independent of their mass number. By adding some atoms of a radioactive isotope into the ingredients it becomes possible to trace the chemical behavior in considerable detail. The careful application of this technique has cleared up many uncertain points regarding chemical reactions and chemical structure. It has also aided in tracing the details of many processes in the field of biology. One other use comes about because of the selective chemical action of certain organs of living systems. As an example, the thyroid concentrates nearly all the iodine that enters a body and uses it to produce thyroxin. Thus radioactive iodine can be used to study the activity and possible malfunctioning of the thyroid. It can also be used to concentrate radiation in the thyroid for therapeutic purposes. Many other similar examples can be found.

17–13. The Transuranium Elements. Of especial interest to us are those nuclei found above $_{92}U^{238}$ in the periodic table. Fermi suggested in 1934 that neutrons probably would penetrate the very heavy nuclei and that perhaps in the rearrangement an element with Z greater than 92 would be formed.

In 1940, it was found that *low* energy neutrons yielded

$$_{92}U^{238} + {}_0n^1 \rightarrow {}_{92}U^{239} + \gamma$$

and that $_{92}U^{239}$ was artificially radioactive giving

$$_{92}U^{239} \rightarrow {}_{93}Np^{239} + {}_{-1}e^0 \qquad (T_{1/2} = 23.5 \text{ min})$$

where Np is the symbol for neptunium and that

$$_{93}Np^{239} \rightarrow {}_{94}Pu^{239} + {}_{-1}e^0 \qquad (T_{1/2} = 2.33 \text{ days})$$

where Pu = plutonium (half-life 24,300 yr). It is an important material in the construction of nuclear reactors and nuclear bombs.

Other transuranium isotopes were quickly formed, for example, with energetic deuterons,

$$_{92}U^{238} + {}_1H^2 \rightarrow {}_{93}Np^{238} + 2\,{}_0n^1,$$

with energetic neutrons

$$_{92}U^{238} + {}_0n^1 \rightarrow {}_{92}U^{237} + 2\,{}_0n^1,$$

and with energetic (120 Mev) carbon nuclei

$$_{92}U^{238} + {}_6C^{12} \rightarrow {}_{98}Cf^{244} + 6\,{}_0n^1,$$

where Cf is the symbol for californium.

Similar reactions have produced ten isotopes of $_{93}Np$, fifteen isotopes of $_{94}Pu$, ten isotopes of $_{95}Am$ (americium), twelve of $_{96}Cm$ (curium), eight of $_{97}Bk$ (berkelium), eleven of $_{98}Cf$ (californium), eleven of $_{99}E$ (einsteinium), seven of $_{100}Fm$ (fermium), one isotope of $_{101}Mv$ (mendelevium), one of $_{102}No$ (nobelium), and one of $_{103}Lw$ (lawrencium). These are probably not the end, though the life of elements of still higher Z are likely to be very short.

17–14. Nuclear Fission. Slow neutrons when absorbed by $_{92}U^{235}$ cause the U^{235} nucleus to split, usually into two nearly equal parts—a process known as *fission*. The products of this reaction are sometimes equal in mass but an unequal division has a larger probability. The actual distribution is shown in Fig. 17–7 in which is graphed the yield versus the mass number for the fission reaction. In addition, a certain number of neutrons are also released. The reaction might be written ($\sigma = 580$ barns)

$$_{92}U^{235} + {}_0n^1 \rightarrow F_1 + F_2 + \eta\,{}_0n^1 + Q,$$

where F_1 and F_2 represent the *fission fragments* and η represents the average number of neutrons emitted per fission. The neutrons are high energy neutrons, with an average energy of 2 Mev; 99% are *prompt* neutrons, i.e., they are emitted within about 10^{-12} sec after the fission and their average number, $\eta = 2.33$ per fission. The other approximately 1% of neutrons are *delayed* neutrons and are emitted as excess neutrons from the unstable fission fragments.

The most likely fission fragments are $_{38}Sr^{95}$ and $_{54}Xe^{139}$ (strontium and xenon).

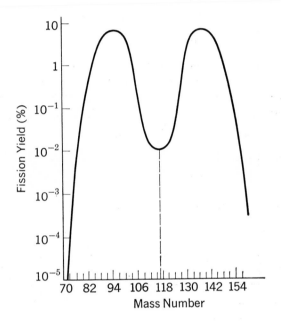

Fig. 17-7.   Distribution of fission fragments for thermal neutrons incident on U^{235}.

A calculation of the Q of the fission reaction indicates the large amount of energy released. This energy appears as kinetic energy of the fission fragments, neutron energy, beta energy, neutrino energy, and gamma-ray energy. That this is so can be seen by looking at Fig. 17-8 which is a plot of the packing fraction P. If M is the actual mass of a nuclide in amu and A is the mass number

$$P = \frac{M - A}{A}.$$ (17-13)

If the internal energy is low, the mass defect $(M - A)$ is low and hence P is low. In fact P is negative for the most stable nuclides. Sr^{95} and Xe^{139} are marked by x's on the curve and U^{235} by an o. The fission fragments are unstable and give characteristic decay curves, some with long half-lives, for example $_{38}Sr^{90}$, 25 yr, emitting 0.6 Mev betas and no gammas or $_{43}Tc^{99}$, 9.4×10^5 yr, an element unknown in the periodic table before the fission process was discovered. An important short life fragment is $_{54}Xe^{133}$, half-life 5.3 days emitting both betas and gammas. This isotope is produced in quantity (see Fig. 17–7) and is very active. It therefore presents a problem of storage and disposal, and because of its gaseous nature, care must be taken to avoid leakage into the atmosphere.

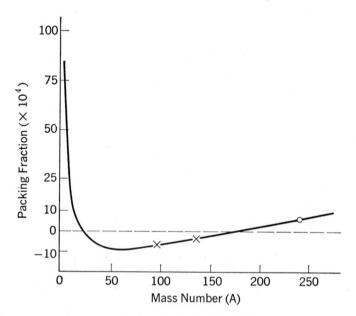

Fig. 17–8. The packing fraction curve.

17–15. Fusion. Fig. 17–8 suggests another way of obtaining energy from nuclei. This is to make two light nuclei combine to form a heavier one. This process is called *fusion*. An example is the tritium-proton-alpha reaction

$$_1H^3 + {}_1H^1 \rightarrow {}_2He^4 + Q.$$

The value of Q is approximately 20 Mev. There are several such reactions (another is $_1H^3 + {}_1H^2 \rightarrow {}_2He^4 + {}_0n^1 + Q$). Extremely high temperatures are required to keep such reactions going—temperatures to be found only in stars or in reactions started by fission reactions. Controlled processes are being studied by many groups in the hopes of using fusion as a source of energy. Some aspects of the theory of both fission and fusion will be discussed in greater detail in Chapter 19.

PROBLEMS

17-1. Use the uncertainty principle to compute the energy an electron might have if it were inside a nucleus.

17-2. Theory and experiment give the nuclear radius r to be $r = 1.40\,A^{1/3} \times 10^{-15}$ m where A is the atomic weight. Using this relation compute the geometrical cross-section of boron, copper and uranium. Express the answers in barns.

17-3. List two cross-sections that a nucleus might have for neutrons that could contribute to a total cross-section.

17-4. Derive the absorption law for neutrons passing through a material. To do this consider a beam of n neutrons cm^{-2} sec^{-1} incident normally on a surface. Let N be the number of atoms per unit volume in the target and σ be their cross-section.

17-5. A beam of neutrons is incident normally on natural uranium. What thickness will reduce the intensity of the neutrons by 36.6%? (Density of uranium = 18.7 gm cm^{-3}, cross-section = 16.0 barns).

17-6. The density of boron is 2.34 gm cm^{-3} and its thermal neutron absorption cross-section is 750 barns. What thickness of boron will reduce a neutron flux of 10^{13} neutrons cm^{-2} sec^{-1} to 10^2 neutrons cm^{-2} sec^{-1}?

17-7. Derive Eqs. 17-1 and 17-2.

17-8. Neutrons from a source strike protons giving them a maximum forward kinetic energy of 3 Mev. Neutrons from the same source strike nitrogen atoms giving them a maximum forward kinetic energy of 0.85 Mev. What is the approximate mass of the neutron?

17-9. Neutrons from a source strike protons giving them a maximum forward kinetic energy of 4.0 Mev. Neutrons from the same source strike beryllium atoms giving them a maximum forward kinetic energy of 1.50 Mev. What is the approximate mass of the neutron?

17-10. Calculate the recoil energy for both proton and neutron resulting from the photo-disintegration of the deuteron by gamma rays having an energy of 2.83 Mev.

17-11. Calculate the recoil energy for both deuteron and neutron resulting from the photo-disintegration of the nucleus of tritium by gamma rays having an energy of 6.75 Mev.

17-12. Check the validity of Table 17-1 by computing the values shown for beryllium.

17-13. One curie of radium mixed with beryllium will produce about 10^7 neutrons sec^{-1}. How many alpha particles are "wasted" each second in such a source?

17–14. A source of neutrons is the d-n reaction with tritium. Calculate the energy of the neutrons if the deuterons have a kinetic energy of 100 Kev.

17–15. Neutrons have been slowed by a moderator to an equilibrium condition at a temperature of 300°K. If the chopper of Fig. 17–1 has a length $L = 1$ m, and is rotating at 9000 rpm, what angle must there be between the slits to pass neutrons at the speed corresponding to the average kinetic energy?

17–16. The second slit in a chopper (see Fig. 17–1) is displaced 5° from the first. L is 1.2 m. At what speed must the chopper rotate to pass neutrons having an energy corresponding to the average for a temperature of 600°K?

17–17. Fill in the missing items in the symbols for the reactions shown and rewrite as reaction equations: $N^{14}(d,p)?$, $Na^{23}(p,n)?$, $?(n,\gamma)Cd^{114}$, $Li^7(?,\alpha)He^4$, $Mg^{25}(\gamma,?)Na^{24}$, $N^{14}(\alpha,n)?$.

17–18. Fill in the missing items in the symbols for the reactions shown and rewrite as reaction equations: $Al^{27}(n,\alpha)?$, $Fe^{58}(p,?)Co^{58}$, $?(\alpha,n)F^{17}$, $Cu^{63}(n,?)Cu^{64}$, $Ga^{69}(d,p)?$, $Br^{79}(?,n)Kr^{80}$.

17–19. Determine the Q for those reactions of Problem 17–17 for which there are data in Table 17–2.

17–20. Determine the Q for those reactions of Problem 17–18 for which there are data in Table 17–2.

17–21. The absorption cross-section for 0.025 ev neutrons for Cd^{113} is 20,800 barns. What thickness of natural cadmium (12% Cd^{113}) is required to absorb 10% of 0.025 ev neutrons? Neglect the absorption due to the other isotopes of cadmium. The density of cadmium is 8.65 gm cm^{-3}.

17–22. The absorption cross-section for 0.025 ev neutrons for Cd^{113} is 20,800 barns. What thickness of natural cadmium (12% Cd^{113}) is required to absorb 20% of 0.025 ev neutrons? What thickness is required to absorb 90%? The density of cadmium is 8.65 gm cm^{-3}.

17–23. An alpha entering a $_{11}Na^{23}$ nucleus forms a compound nucleus. What is it? List 5 possible product nuclei and the light particles associated with them.

17–24. An alpha entering a $_{12}Mg^{24}$ nucleus forms a compound nucleus. What is it? List 5 possible product nuclei and the light particles associated with them.

17–25. The cross-section for the reaction $Cu^{63}(p,pn)Cu^{62}$ is 0.83 barn if the energy of the proton is 23 Mev. How many Cu^{62} nuclei will be found in 2 hr if a cyclotron current of 1 μa of 23 Mev protons strike a copper target 0.08 mm thick? Natural copper is 69% Cu^{63}. The half-life of Cu^{62} is 9.9 min. Is there any point in activating the Cu target for so long?

17–26. The cross-section for the reaction $Cu^{63}(p,n)Zn^{63}$ is 0.50 barn if the energy of the protons is 11 Mev. How many Zn^{63} nuclei will be formed in 1 hr if a cyclotron current of 1.4 μa of 11 Mev protons strike a copper target 0.12 mm thick? Natural copper is 69% Cu^{63}. The half-life of Zn^{63} is 38 min. How close to saturation is the activity of Zn^{63}?

17–27. Is $_{11}Na^{24}$ a beta emitter? If so, what is the product nucleus? What will be the maximum energy of the betas?

17–28. Is Si^{31} a beta emitter? If so, what is the product nucleus? What will be the maximum energy of the betas?

SELECTED REFERENCES

CURTISS, L. F. *Introduction to Neutron Physics*. D. Van Nostrand Co., Inc., Princeton, N. J., 1959. Chaps. 1, 2, and 3.

DEVONS, S. *Excited States of Nuclei*. Cambridge Univ. Press, London, 1949. Chaps. 1 and 2.

ENDT, P. M., and M. DEMEUR. *Nuclear Reactions*. North-Holland Publishing Co., Amsterdam, 1959. Vol. 1, chaps. 6 and 8.

HALLIDAY, D. *Introductory Nuclear Physics*. John Wiley & Sons, Inc., New York, 1955. 2d ed., chap. 13.

HUGHES, D. J. *Pile Neutron Research*. Addison-Wesley Publishing Co., Inc., Reading, Mass., 1953. Chap. 1.

KAPLAN, I. *Nuclear Physics*. Addison-Wesley Publishing Co., Inc., Reading, Mass., 1955. Chap. 11.

LAPP, R. E., and H. L. ANDREWS. *Nuclear Radiation Physics*. Prentice-Hall, Inc., Englewood Cliffs, N. J., 1954. 2d ed., chap. 12.

SEMAT, H. *Introduction to Atomic and Nuclear Physics*. Holt, Rinehart & Winston, Inc., New York, 1954. 3d ed., chap. 11.

18

Descriptive Theories of Nuclei

A dual role is served by the constantly increasing number of phenomena associated with nuclei. These phenomena not only raise questions needing answers and explanations, but also furnish the evidence needed to substantiate earlier assumptions. The familiar pattern of observation, hypothesis, test, successful result (or failure), prediction of new effects, verification (or not), and revision, has certainly been evident in this field. Fro n these efforts there has grown an elaborate model, or theory, of the nucleus. Perhaps it would be more accurate to say that there has grown a *set* of models, for no all-encompassing model has been devised. No one would suggest that the picture is final. Probably every item will require revision, yet, as in the case of the Bohr theory of the atom, the present models contain a great deal of insight and will undoubtedly be very useful in furthering our understanding of the nature of nuclei.

No attempt will be made to present more than a descriptive summary of these models, but some of the observed effects which we have already discussed will be seen to fit into the picture well. The purpose will not be to provide a formulation for predicting quantitatively, but rather to make some things seem plausible and to provide qualitative predictions in some areas.

18–1. Nuclear Sizes. Experiments involving the scattering of neutrons, charged particles (alphas, protons, and electrons), along with other observations permit the making of estimates of nuclear sizes. In all cases, the radius turns out to be nearly proportional to $A^{1/3}$, or the volume to A. It is true that different methods give slightly different estimates, but on the whole, the agreement is good. We may therefore write

$$R = R_0 A^{1/3} \tag{18–1}$$

where R_0 is close to 1.4×10^{-15} m.

The implication of this result is that the nucleons can be thought of as little particles of definite size closely packed together within a certain region. They may be pictured as a "handful of marbles." Fig. 18–1 shows this. The shaded spheres represent protons and the unshaded ones neutrons. It is obvious that nucleons do attract each other because they do stick together. But the attractive force has a short range, and a strong repulsive force develops for extremely small inter-

Fig. 18–1.   Schematic representation of a nucleus.

nucleon distances. The latter effect is probably a result of an exclusion principle for nucleons similar to the exclusion principle for electrons that plays the major role in limiting the closeness of approach of atoms in molecules.

18–2. Nuclear Masses and Binding Energies.   For nearly all the stable nuclei, it requires energy to remove a nucleon from the nucleus. In the light of the special theory of relativity, the sum of the mass of the resulting nucleus and the nucleon should be greater than that of the original nucleus. Many experiments have verified this. The amount of energy required to remove one nucleon from a nucleus is the *binding energy* for that nucleon in that nucleus, and the energy required to separate a nucleus into individual nucleons divided by the number of nucleons is the *average binding energy per nucleon*, thus

$$\bar{B} = \frac{[M_p Z + M_N N - M] c^2}{A}.$$

Here M_p and M_N are the masses of proton and neutron, M is the actual mass of the nucleus, Z is the atomic number, and N is the *neutron number* (the number of neutrons in the nucleus). A plot of B versus A is given in Fig. 18–2. The fact that $\bar{B}$ becomes almost independent of A is evidence that the forces "saturate." Gravitational forces *do not* saturate. For example, six equal particles with mass M have a total "binding energy"

$$E = GM^2 \left(\frac{1}{r_{12}} + \frac{1}{r_{13}} + \frac{1}{r_{14}} + \frac{1}{r_{15}} + \frac{1}{r_{16}} + \frac{1}{r_{23}} + \frac{1}{r_{24}} + \frac{1}{r_{25}} \right.$$

$$\left. + \frac{1}{r_{26}} + \frac{1}{r_{34}} + \frac{1}{r_{35}} + \frac{1}{r_{36}} + \frac{1}{r_{45}} + \frac{1}{r_{46}} + \frac{1}{r_{56}} \right), \quad (18–2)$$

where G is the universal gravitational constant and each r_{ij} is the distance between the ith and the jth particle. In this type of force, the addition of an extra particle increases the total binding energy by an amount proportional to the number already present. Electrostatic forces also do *not* saturate.

An example of other forces that *do* saturate is the case of chemical forces holding atoms together in molecules, in liquid drops, or in solids. In those cases, the addition of a molecule adds only a fixed amount to the total energy, and in general the energy is increased proportional to the amount of material added independent of the amount already present.

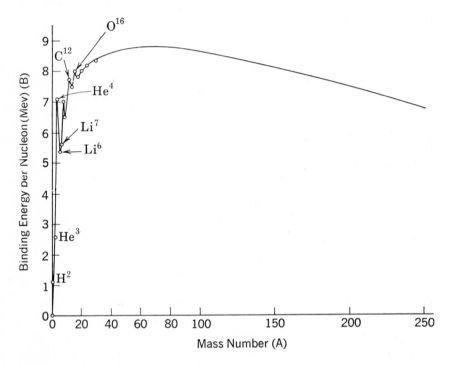

Fig. 18–2.   The average binding energy per nucleon as a function of mass number.

Two features of Fig. 18–2 should be noted: (a) The value for $\bar{B}$ for many elements is close to 8.3 Mev and (b) the most tightly bound nuclei are in the range of $A = 30$ to $A = 130$. Consequently, we see again that energy should be released by the fission of large nuclei and by the fusion of very light nuclei.

18–3. Charge Independence of Nuclear Forces.   The electric forces between protons tend to lead to a reduction of the binding energy. The electric forces do not saturate, so they become more and more important as Z increases. But if one allows for the repulsion due to the electric charges, it turns out that the other kind of force, specifically the nuclear force that holds the nucleons together in the nucleus, is nearly independent of whether the nucleons are protons or neutrons.

It might seem that the most desirable situation would be to have a large number of neutrons and few protons, but this is not the case. For light nuclei there is a strong tendency to have $Z = N$. Since protons and neutrons are different particles, it is possible to have them in very similar energy states; and since the states for protons are much like those for neutrons, the low energy arrangement would be to have them come in pairs. The addition of a proton to form a new nuclide is most likely to be followed by the addition of a neutron, and vice versa. Another way of saying this is to say that the proton and neutron are simply two different forms of a nucleon. Which form the nucleon is in can be stated by giving a quantum number one of two values. That only two values are possible suggests an analogy to spin, so the number is called the *isotopic spin* and is represented by the letter τ. It is usually assigned the value $\frac{1}{2}$, and can have two projections, $\tau_\zeta = +\frac{1}{2}$ (a proton) and $\tau_\zeta = -\frac{1}{2}$ (a neutron). An exclusion principle applies here in which the two values of τ_ζ are arranged with other more familiar quantum numbers. Thus neutron-proton pairs tend to result. As we proceed to heavier nuclei, the effect of the electrical repulsion then tends to make N increase more rapidly than Z. This is shown in Fig. 18–3, where the neutron number N is plotted versus atomic number Z.

The ratio N/Z determines the stability of the nucleus with respect to beta production. For low values of Z, the ratio is almost unity. For larger values of Z the ratio increases slightly, as we have just seen. If N/Z for some nucleus is larger than this proper value, the nucleus is likely to emit ordinary electrons (a neutron turns into a proton); if it is smaller, the nucleus is likely to emit positive betas (a proton is converted into a neutron). These two processes force the N/Z ratio toward the proper value.

Since the energy E of a nucleus depends both upon Z and N, a plot of E versus Z and N will give a surface in a three-dimensional plot. This surface will be a valley-shaped surface with a minimum running along the line of stable nuclides shown in Fig. 18–3. This has been sketched schematically in Fig. 18–4. Nuclei represented by points distant from the stable condition have very high energies, so the figure has been truncated after getting away from the lower part of the valley. The surface is not as smooth and simple as has been suggested in the figure since a number of factors play roles of varying amounts in the final determination of the energy. A brief reference is made to this in Art. 18–9. The intersecting surface AA (and those parallel to it that show the shape of the valley) is a surface which includes nuclides having the same mass number A. Such nuclides are called *isobars*.

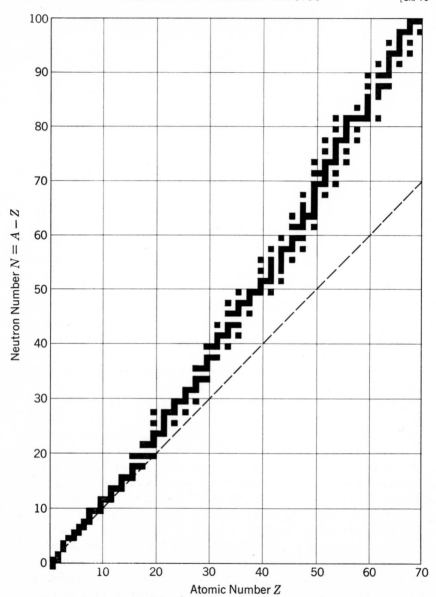

Fig. 18–3.   Chart of the stable nuclei.

18–4. The Liquid-Drop Model.   One of the models (or theories) of
nuclei that describes and accounts for many nuclear phenomena is usually
referred to by the term *liquid-drop model*.   The saturation of nuclear

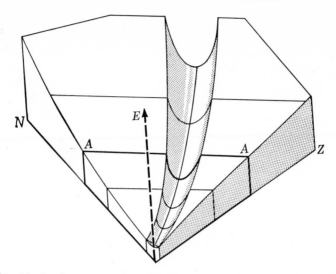

Fig. 18–4.   Energy surface (schematic) as a function of N and Z.

forces and the fact that the nucleons have a finite radius suggests that the "handful of marbles" may be considered analogous to a tiny drop of liquid. It is true that the number of nucleons in a nucleus is much smaller than the number of molecules in a liquid droplet, but the features of constant volume and saturated forces are similar.

A drop of liquid displays the phenomenon of *surface tension*. To move an interior particle (molecule in the case of a liquid, nucleon in the case of a nucleus) to the surface requires that work be done against the attraction of the remaining interior particles. Any attempt to increase the surface of a drop requires such a movement of some particles from interior to surface. The effect is to make the surface appear like an elastic diaphragm resisting any attempt to stretch it and attempting to shrink to a condition of minimum area and minimum energy. Because of this, a drop tends to be spherical. Presumably, nuclei also tend to be spherical. An attempt to flatten or elongate the drop or nucleus requires work. If extra energy is added to the system, such a distortion may result. The drop may oscillate between oblate and prolate shapes, both of which have extra potential energy. For intermediate shapes part of the extra energy is kinetic energy. The situation is not unlike that of a harmonic oscillator. The quantum mechanical treatment shows that nuclei should have discrete closely spaced energy levels resulting from this type of motion.

An additional possible motion of the liquid drop is rotation. The energy levels of such rotation also seem to fit into some observed situations.

The concept of the compound nucleus mentioned in Art. 17–7 can be seen to have an explanation in the liquid-drop model. Since the individual nucleons move around, constantly colliding with each other, the chance of a nucleon obtaining a large amount of extra energy and escaping through the surface is very small. Even if a nucleus is given excess energy by an incoming particle, probably a long time and many collisions will be required before some other nucleon will acquire sufficient energy to escape. Thus a compound nucleus exists during this time. Of course the excess energy might be lost by radiation, as gamma-ray radiation, before this happens.

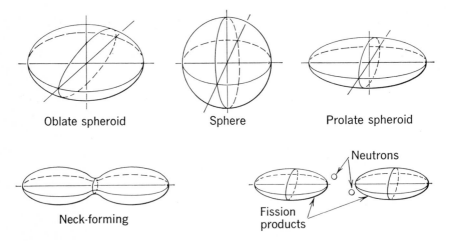

Oblate spheroid   Sphere   Prolate spheroid

Neck-forming   Fission products   Neutrons

Fig. 18–5. Fission—schematically shows that violent vibration can lead to break-up.

The liquid-drop model is also useful for the explanation of fission. As has been seen, the nucleus will be set in oscillation by the absorption of energy when either a gamma ray or a nucleon is absorbed. Under some special circumstances, the oscillation may be so violent that the prolate spheroid pinches and splits into two liquid drops. Usually some single neutrons separate at the same time. Fig. 18–5 suggests the process.

18–5. The Central Force Model. A second model used to picture the nucleus differs from the liquid-drop model in several respects. It attempts to treat the nucleus in a manner similar to the treatment of the electronic structure of atoms. It is assumed that the nuclear forces acting on the nucleons can be derived from a potential energy function symmetric about the center of the nucleus. For this reason it is called the *central force model*.

Although it is clear that no central force comparable to that for the case of an electron in an atom really fits the case of nuclei, there are some occasions when it is desirable to treat the nucleus as a central force problem. Reasonable potential functions can be developed.

One particular feature of the central force formulation is that the angular momentum of the nucleus should be a constant of the motion and therefore should be a useful quantum number in the description of the state of a nucleus. Since individual nucleons have a spin $(s = \frac{1}{2})$ and may have an "orbital" angular momentum l, the same sort of notation may be used as was used to describe the electronic structure (except that only j-j coupling holds). The total angular momentum is usually designated by the letter I.

A shell structure can be shown to develop. Although the details are somewhat different, the shell structure resembles that for electrons in atoms. Table 18–1 lists the labels of the shells and tells how many nucleons can be in each level.

TABLE 18–1

Nuclear Shell Structures

Level	No. per level	No. for a full shell	Total number
$nl\ j$	$2j+1$		
$1s\ \frac{1}{2}$	2	2	2
$1p\ \frac{3}{2}$	4		
$1p\ \frac{1}{2}$	2	6	8
$1d\ \frac{5}{2}$	6		
$1d\ \frac{3}{2}$	4		
$2s\ \frac{1}{2}$	2	12	20
$1f\ \frac{7}{2}$	8		
$1f\ \frac{5}{2}$	6		
$2p\ \frac{3}{2}$	4		
$2p\ \frac{1}{2}$	2		
$1g\ \frac{9}{2}$	10	30	50
$1g\ \frac{7}{2}$	8		
$2d\ \frac{5}{2}$	6		
$2d\ \frac{3}{2}$	4		
$3s\ \frac{1}{2}$	2		
$1h\ \frac{11}{2}$	12	32	82
$1h\ \frac{9}{2}$	10		
$2f\ \frac{7}{2}$	8		
$2f\ \frac{5}{2}$	6		
$3p\ \frac{3}{2}$	4		
$3p\ \frac{1}{2}$	2		
$1i\ \frac{13}{2}$	14	44	126

The numbers 2, 8, 20, 50, 82, and 126 which appear in the last column of the table are known as the *magic numbers*. Nuclei having Z or N equal to any of these are known to be particularly stable.

Another sign of stability has to do with whether Z, N, or A is even or odd. The significance is indicated in Table 18–2. Each column shows

TABLE 18–2

The Odd-Even Effect

A	Even	Even	Odd	Odd
Z	Even	Odd	Even	Odd
N	Even	Odd	Odd	Even
Number of naturally occurring stable nuclides	162	4	55	53

whether A, Z, or N is even or odd. From this table, the preference for having N and Z even is evident. The case of the alpha particle is the most significant one. The combination of a pair of neutrons and a pair of protons is so stable that it tends to maintain an entity of its own in many nuclei.

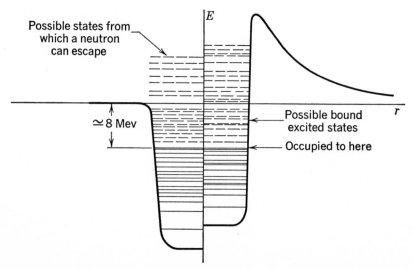

Fig. 18–6. Idealized nuclear energy states. Both proton and neutron states are shown.

18–6. Nuclear Energy Levels. Regardless of the models used to describe them, the energy levels of numerous nuclei are now known in great detail.[1] A somewhat idealized situation is shown in Fig. 18–6 where

[1] For example, a compilation for light nuclei is given in F. Ajzenberg and T. Lauritsen, *Rev. Mod. Phys.*, **27**, 72 (1955).

energy levels for protons are shown on the right and those of neutrons are shown on the left. The shapes of the respective potential functions, of course, are only approximations. The electrostatic repulsion outside the nucleus is clearly indicated and the sudden drop at the surface of the

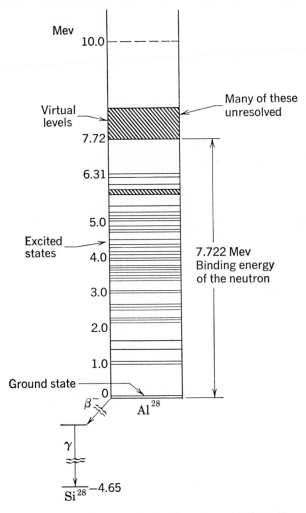

Fig. 18–7.   Actual excited energy levels for $_{13}Al^{28}$.

nucleus is what might be expected for strong short-range forces. The flat bottom suggests that a nucleon in the inner portions is subject to uniform forces from all sides, hence, to negligible resultant force.

For comparison with Fig. 18–6, an actual set of energy levels is shown in Fig. 18–7. The case is for $_{13}Al^{28}$. The levels have been identified by

$(n,\gamma)^2$ and $(d,p)^3$ reactions with $_{13}Al^{27}$. The binding energy for a neutron is 7.72 Mev. The levels above these are "quasi-stationary" states. The absorption of a neutron with such an energy is especially likely. The nucleus may then exist a significant time ($\simeq 10^{-15}$ sec) in such a level before gamma emission occurs and the new nucleus finally is definitely formed. The nucleus may lose a nucleon by "evaporation" before this happens, as mentioned in Art. 18–4. But in either case, the increased likelihood of something happening when the bombarding particle possesses an energy close to one of these levels accounts for the resonance effects in nuclear reactions.

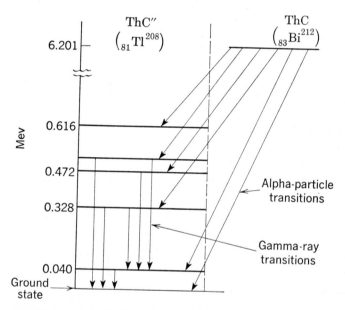

Fig. 18–8. Energy levels and alpha particles in Th C'' and Th C.

We have just seen that the alpha particle is a particularly stable grouping of nucleons. They may exist as a complete entity in some nuclei and have their own energy levels. This is particularly true in the case of the heavy nuclei. The energy diagram appropriate to Th C and Th C'' is shown in Fig. 18–8. Note how the alpha-particle energies from Th C are explained and also the gamma-ray energies which arise from Th C''. The transitions which do not occur are forbidden by selection rules.

Some of the nuclear energy levels are extremely sharp and the gamma rays that originate from them should be equally sharp. It should be possible to obtain resonant absorption and reradiation or scattering of such

[2] R. L. Henkel, and H. H. Barschall, *Phys. Rev.*, **80**, 145 (1950).
[3] H. A. Enge, W. W. Beuchner, and A. Sperduto, *Phys. Rev.*, **88**, 961 (1952).

gamma rays. The trouble is that the nucleus emitting the gamma rays recoils in order to conserve both energy and momentum. Consequently, the energy of the gamma rays is reduced, and the energy levels of a nucleus at rest are too sharp to permit the absorption of a photon of this decreased energy. However, it was discovered by Mössbauer[4] that both emitting and absorbing nuclei could be so firmly attached to a solid crystal lattice as to prevent any significant recoil loss. Thus photons emitted from $_{26}Fe^{57}$, for example, have an energy of 14.4×10^3 ev and the line width, i.e., the uncertainty in the position of the energy level is only 4.6×10^{-9} ev. Therefore, anything that might shift the wavelengths or frequency by 1 part in 3×10^{12} will have a profound effect on the absorption of this line by other $_{26}Fe^{57}$ nuclei. Actually, it is possible to observe to about 1/100 of this shift in frequency or to 1 part in 3×10^{14}. It is this tremendous accuracy that is being put to use to test relativistic effects, as was mentioned in Chapter 4. Many other materials can be used in Mössbauer effect experiments and much detailed information about nuclei can be obtained from it.

Before we proceed to other points, we should look at the possibility of describing the lowest energy level (the ground state) of nuclei with a formula. It is easiest to do this by giving the mass of the nucleus. Several formulas have been proposed. One of these is[5]

$$M(Z,A) = 939.526A - 0.784Z - 15.7A + 17.8A^{\frac{2}{3}} + 23.6(A - 2Z)^2 A^{-1}$$

$$+ 0.712Z(Z - 1)A^{-\frac{1}{3}} \pm 132A^{-1} \quad \left(\begin{array}{c} \text{odd-odd} \\ \text{even-even} \end{array} \right)$$

$$= ZM_H + NM_n - E_B. \tag{18-3}$$

These masses are given in millions of electron volts (1 amu = 931.141 Mev). The various terms in Eq. 18–3 arise from the following contributions to the binding energy E_B.

1. A volume effect $= \alpha A$ (due to the short range saturating forces).
2. A surface effect $= -\beta A^{\frac{2}{3}}$ (due to "surface tension").
3. An isotope effect $= -(N - Z)^2 f(A)$ (this makes neutron-proton pairs advantageous).
4. The Coulomb law effect $= -\gamma Z(Z - 1)A^{-\frac{1}{3}}$ (due to electrical forces).
5. An even-odd effect $= +\delta(A)$ both N and Z even, $-\delta(A)$ both N and Z odd, 0 one even the other odd.

Experiment has shown that[6]

$$\alpha = 15.7 \text{ Mev} \qquad f(A) = 23.6/A \text{ Mev}$$
$$\beta = 17.8 \text{ Mev} \qquad \delta(A) = 132/A \text{ Mev}.$$
$$\gamma = 0.712 \text{ Mev}$$

[4] R. L. Mössbauer, Z. Physik, **151**, 124 (1958), and see a summary article by H. Lustig; Am. Jour. Phys., **29**, 1 (1961).

[5] E. Feenberg, Rev. Modern Phys., **19**, 239 (1947).

[6] A. E. S. Green, Phys. Rev., **95**, 1006 (1954).

18–7. Nuclear Forces and Mesons. A particularly important problem
is to find some suitable explanation of the forces between nucleons. These
forces are short range, charge independent, and they saturate. A proposal
made by the Japanese physicist Yukawa has been generally accepted as
the explanation. Its elaboration has been difficult, but steady progress
is being made.

The proposal is to consider that the force between two nucleons is the
result of the emission and reabsorption of particles. (This concept itself
was not radical since it was known that electromagnetic forces can be
explained in terms of the emission and absorption of photons. The fact
that the photons have no rest mass leads to an inverse square law.) If the
particles have a rest mass different from zero, the force does not follow
an inverse square law, but contains an additional exponential factor which
introduces a range dependent upon the mass of the particle. The potential
due to nucleon, according to this theory, has the form

$$V(r) = \frac{1}{r}\exp - (mc/\hbar)r. \qquad (18–4)$$

The range of the forces is $R = \hbar/mc$. From this we can see that the ratio
of the mass of this particle to the mass of an electron is just the Compton
wavelength divided by $2\pi R$. If we take $R = 1.4 \times 10^{-15}$ m, the result is
a mass for this particle of 275 electronic masses.

In order to describe completely some of the peculiarities of the forces
between nucleons, it is actually necessary to postulate the existence of
three such particles: a neutral particle, a positively charged particle, and
a negatively charged particle. These particles have been observed in
large numbers and can be produced by any of the accelerators capable of
producing kinetic energies greater than about 300 Mev. They are called
pi-mesons and are designated by π^0, π^+, and π^-. The first has a mass of
$263m_e$ while the last two each have masses of $273m_e$ (where m_e is the mass
of an electron). The charges are either $+e$ or $-e$. The meson theory of
nuclear forces is not entirely developed, but it goes a long way in accounting for the details of nuclear forces.

The pi-mesons have their own peculiar properties. For example, they
are unstable, changing into a mu-meson in the case of π^+ or π^- or into
two photons in the case of π^0. The average life for a pi-meson is very
short; $\bar{T} = 1/\lambda = 2.54 \times 10^{-8}$ sec for $\pi^\pm$ and $\bar{T} < 5 \times 10^{-14}$ sec for π^0.
The mu-mesons μ^+ or μ^- do not play any role in nuclear forces, but they
do produce some interesting effects. Their mass is $206m_e$ and they have
an average life of 2.22×10^{-6} sec, decaying into an electron and two
neutrinos (see Table 20–1). They do not interact with nuclei, so they
have a great penetrating power (half of the cosmic rays at sea level are
mu-mesons). They have been known to be captured in orbits by nuclei,

thus forming "mesonic" atoms. They have even formed mesonic molecules; under some circumstances this can lead to bringing two protons or
a proton and a deuteron close enough together to produce fusion.

The pi-mesons naturally react strongly with nucleons. They are
quickly absorbed, often producing violent disruptions of the nucleus that
absorbed them.

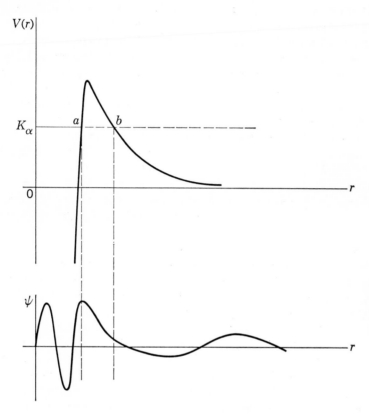

Fig. 18-9.   Potential energy and wave function for alpha emission.

18-8. Alpha-Particle Emission. In Chapter 11, the theory of alpha
emission was included among the examples of tunneling. There is good
reason to believe that the alpha particles exist as separate permanent
entities within some nuclei and that they may exist in various energy
levels within the nucleus. It is possible to identify the difference in energies
with the energy of gamma rays emitted from the nuclei.

Fig. 18-9 is a plot of a possible potential energy function for an alpha
particle in or out of a nucleus and it is assumed that the level labeled K_α
is occupied by an alpha particle. Classical theory will not permit an

alpha particle to exist in the region $r = a$ to $r = b$, nor will it permit one inside with an energy such as K_α to escape. In the lower part of the figure there is a schematic plot of a possible solution to the Schroedinger wave equation. The existence of a sinusoidal solution outside the nucleus indicates the possibility of an alpha particle escaping with a kinetic energy K_α. If K_α is closer to the top of the figure and hence if a and b are closer together, the amplitude of the wave outside is larger. This shows that more energetic alpha particles should be more likely to escape. In fact the escape probability is very sensitive to the position of K_α. The details of the relations predict what is observed very well, even to details not given in the Geiger-Nuttall law.

18–9. Beta-Particle Emission. The emission of beta particles is an entirely different matter. It is impossible for electrons to exist within a nucleus. The beta particles must be created during the process. Either negative electrons or positive electrons may be the beta particles, and the theory is similar in both cases. One can determine whether a negative or positive electron will be emitted by the position of the parent nuclide on the energy surface of Fig. 18–4. If the nuclide is on the high N side, it will be a negative emitter; and if it is on the high Z side, it will be a positive emitter. There is a situation in which the nuclide may be either a positive or negative emitter, and often is both. The difference is shown in Fig. 18–10. Two curves are shown, both of them are the intersection of the energy surface with a plane for a particular isobar like AA of Fig. 18–4. If A is odd, then either N is odd and Z even, or N is even and Z is odd. In either case it makes no difference and a curve such as that of Fig. 18–10a results. In this case, $A = 85$. $_{35}Br^{85}$ emits a β^-, forming $_{36}Kr^{85}$, which is also a β^- emitter. The final product, $_{37}Rb^{85}$, is stable. On the other side, $_{39}Y^{85}$ emits a β^+ to form $_{38}Sr^{85}$, another β^+ emitter. Again, the final stable product is $_{37}Rb^{85}$. The other situation arises when A is even. The two possibilities (both N and Z odd or both even) lead to two different curves because of the odd-even effect. In fact, the two curves of Fig. 18–10b are separated by $2\delta(A)$. The example with $A = 64$ shows how $_{29}Cu^{64}$ can emit either a β^- or a β^+ to form two stable nuclides.

There are several other peculiarities about beta emission. The most important problems are the apparent violations of the laws of conservation of energy, of momentum, and of angular momentum. The spectrum of the betas, as shown in Fig. 15–5, illustrates the difficulty with respect to energy. The parent nuclei all have the same energy, the daughter nuclei also all have the same energy, but the beta particles come off with different amounts of energy.

If a beta particle leaves the nucleus, the nucleus should recoil to conserve the momentum. However, many experiments show that the recoil

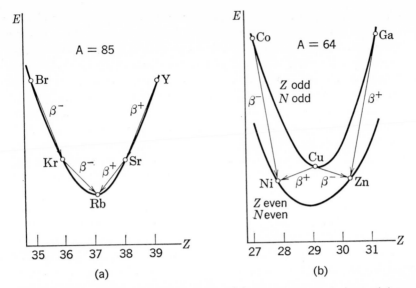

Fig. 18–10.   Possible beta transitions.   (a) Mass number, A, odd.   (b) Mass number, A, even.

is seldom appropriate to the momentum of the beta particle.   It often recoils as sketched in Fig. 18–11.

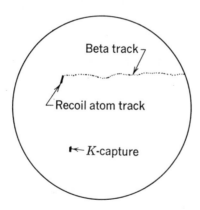

Fig. 18–11.   Schematic diagram of a beta-particle emission and K-capture.

Since K-capture (Art. 17–12) is equivalent to the emission of a positive beta ray, one would expect a similar behavior.   No beta ray leaves the atom; the nucleus simply recoils as shown in Fig. 18–11.   Such experiments make it clear that the nucleus and beta particles do not conserve linear momentum.

A similar apparent failure of the law of conservation of angular momentum occurs. The spin of the parent nucleus, that of the daughter nucleus, and of the electron are all known. In no case of beta decay can the angular momentum of the daughter nucleus and the electron be combined to be equivalent to that of the parent. Thus all three of the most important conservation laws seem to be violated.

Pauli pointed out that all of these difficulties can be resolved if another particle is part of the process. It could carry off the extra energy and could provide for the proper balance of both linear momentum and angular momentum. The only trouble is that no such particle is actually observed. However, it would have to be electrically neutral and hence should not have much interaction with matter. The theory was actually developed by E. Fermi and it is capable of explaining most of the things that actually happen, such as the shape of the spectrum and the half-lives of various nuclei.

Fermi suggested that this necessary, but unknown, particle be called the *neutrino*. It has no charge, it has a spin of $\frac{1}{2}$, its rest mass is less than $0.0005m_e$, and is probably actually zero. Its interaction with matter is so small that the cross-section for absorption by a nucleon $\sim 10^{-48}$ m^2. There are probably two kinds of neutrinos: the one emitted with the negative beta is called an antineutrino, the other is the neutrino.

Thus theory and experiment now indicate that the beta-emission of a negative electron from a nucleus, as discussed in Art. 15–8, can be described better by the reaction

$$n \rightarrow p + e^- + \bar{\nu}$$

where $\bar{\nu}$ stands for the antineutrino. A positron emission consists of

$$p \rightarrow n + e^+ + \nu$$

where ν stands for the neutrino.

It would be useful if one could demonstrate the existence of ν or $\bar{\nu}$. Reines and Cowan[7] have succeeded in detecting the particle by the inverse process

$$\bar{\nu} + p \rightarrow n + e^+.$$

This was done by placing a large tank containing a hydrogenous liquid, a scintillating material, and some cadmium salt dissolved in it, close to a big nuclear reactor which serves as the source of neutrinos. A large number of photomultipliers look at the contents of this tank and detect any scintillations.

[7] F. Reines, and C. L. Cowan, *Nature*, **178**, 446 (1958), and P. Morrison, *Sci. Am.*, **195**, 59 (1956).

The positron will be detected immediately by its annihilation. The neutron is detected by absorption by cadmium in the solution. This reaction is

$$\text{Cd}^{113} + n \rightarrow \text{Cd}^{114} + \gamma,$$

and the γ makes a scintillation. The two pulses look different and one should expect a delay of a few microseconds. The number of such events should be proportional to the beta activity. This was found to be the case and the cross-section turns out to be $6 \times 10^{-48}\,\text{m}^2$.

The experiment has now been run enough to be well established. There seems to be no reason to doubt that the neutrino has been detected by its absorption.

PROBLEMS

18–1. Eq. 18–1 is often claimed as evidence that nuclear matter is incompressible. Explain why it shows this.

18–2. Calculate the "radius" of the nucleus of Fe^{56}.

18–3. Calculate the "radius" of the nucleus of Pb^{207}.

18–4. On the basis of the nuclear shell structure theory, what spin I would you expect for the nuclei $_3\text{Li}^7$, $_{20}\text{Ca}^{40}$, $_{21}\text{Sc}^{45}$, and $_{49}\text{In}^{113}$? See Table 18–1.

18–5. What spin would you expect for the nuclei of $_4\text{Be}^9$, $_{38}\text{Sr}^{87}$, $_{50}\text{Sn}^{122}$, and $_{51}\text{Sb}^{123}$? See Table 18–1.

18–6. Pairs of nuclei such as $_3\text{Li}^7$ and $_4\text{Be}^7$ are called *mirror nuclei*. The energy due to electrical forces and the difference in mass of the neutron and proton appear to be the sole source of difference in energy between such mirror pairs. List three other such mirror pairs.

18–7. If nucleons crowd together in nuclei, what is the arrangement which would put the nucleons closest together? How many nearest neighbors would each interior nucleon have? If it is assumed that the nucleons are bonded together in this arrangement, how many bonds would each nucleon have?

18–8. How many bonds does a surface nucleon lack as compared with an interior nucleon under the considerations of Problem 18–7?

18–9. The deuteron has only 2 nucleons and therefore 1 bond. In Art. 17–2 this bond energy was shown to be approximately 2.23 Mev. Using Problem 18–7, compute a rough approximation to the *volume binding energy*, neglecting surface effects, of aluminum $_{13}\text{Al}^{27}$. Compare this with the value obtained from the appropriate expression in Art. 18–6.

18–10. The energy due to surface tension effects for a drop of radius r is $E_s = 4\pi r^2 S$, where S is a surface tension coefficient. Show that this term for the energy of nuclei has the form $\beta A^{2/3}$. The value of β is of the order of 17 Mev. What is the corresponding surface tension S?

18-11. Assuming that the spin of the neutron and proton is $\frac{1}{2}$, can the force holding them together be magnetic? Can it be gravitational?

18-12. If a nucleon occupies a diameter of the order of 10^{-13} cm in a nucleus, what kinetic energy might it have? Combine this result with the average binding energy per nucleon to get a rough approximation of the average potential energy in which the nucleon moves.

18-13. Use Eq. 18-3 to predict the mass of $_{11}Na^{23}$. Compare with its known value.

18-14. Use Eq. 18-3 to predict the mass of $_{13}Al^{27}$. Compare with its known value.

18-15. Plot a potential function of Eq. 18-4 for values of r ranging from $0.2R$ to $5R$ where $R = \hbar/mc$.

18-16. Assume that an alpha particle within a nucleus has a kinetic energy $K = 25$ Mev. How many round trips per second will it make across a radon nucleus? Use Eq. 18-1 to compute the diameter of the nucleus. From the known decay constant calculate the probability of escape on each impact with the surface of the nucleus.

18-17. Calculate the thickness of iron required to give 50% absorption for neutrinos if the absorption cross-section is 6×10^{-20} barns.

18-18. A tank contains 8 m³ of water. Every hour five of the hydrogen nuclei absorb a neutrino forming a neutron and a positive electron. If the cross-section for each event is 6×10^{-20} barns, what neutrino flux is passing through the tank?

SELECTED REFERENCES

HALLIDAY, D. *Introductory Nuclear Physics.* John Wiley & Sons, Inc., New York, 1955. 2d ed., chap. 11.

KAPLAN, I. *Nuclear Physics.* Addison-Wesley Publishing Co., Inc., Reading, Mass., 1955. Chap. 17.

LEIGHTON, R. B. *Principles of Modern Physics.* McGraw-Hill Book Co., Inc., New York, 1959. Chap. 18.

19

Nuclear Energy Sources

Throughout all history man has needed and put to use energy from outside sources. Up to 1942 the sources of energy were basically solar. Man's food and fuels all were the result of photosynthesis, and even water and wind power are fundamentally the result of solar heating. Solar energy has a nuclear origin, as we shall see, but it is completely beyond the control of man except in its final application. On December 2, 1942 when the first controlled nuclear reactor started operating under the stands at Stagg Field at the University of Chicago a new energy source came into being—the direct, controlled release of nuclear energy. Although the fission reaction does not seem to provide the best source of energy, it was the first, and is still the only controllable source; so we shall look at it first.

19–1. The Fission Process. A fission reaction releases a large amount of energy. It also releases neutrons. Since neutrons can produce further fission under proper conditions, there is the possibility of a chain reaction. Since the reaction can be kept under control, it provides the opportunity for a very attractive energy source. The device in which such a process is carried out is called a *nuclear reactor.*

In each fission nearly 200 Mev of energy, mostly kinetic, is released. It is divided very roughly in the following way:

1. Fast neutrons, 5 Mev
2. Beta particles, 9 Mev
3. Neutrinos, 9 Mev
4. Fission fragments, 166 Mev
5. Gamma rays, 10 Mev

The fission fragments, therefore, carry off most of the kinetic energy. They lose it as heat to the structure surrounding the fissionable material and this heat is the energy that the military uses as a bomb, and that is

used for propelling ships and producing electrical power. If we assume
that all except the energy of the fission fragments is lost, the remaining
166 Mev is still a considerable amount of energy. One mg of U^{235} is about
4×10^{-6} g-atoms or about 24×10^{17} atoms. If 1 mg of U^{235} is made to
fission, the heat available for a heat engine is then $24 \times 10^{17} \times 166 =
4 \times 10^{20}$ Mev $= 4 \times 10^{20} \times 1.6 \times 10^{-13} = 6.4 \times 10^7$ j. A heat engine
should convert at least one-third of this into mechanical energy. Thus
1 mg of U^{235} should furnish over 2×10^7 j, or over 5 kw-hr of useful work.

The problem, then, is to determine how to obtain such a reaction,
how to control it, and how to extract the energy released.

19–2. Nuclear Reactor Principles. There are a number of nuclides
which can be made to fission. Some of these require a large amount of
energy either furnished by high energy neutrons or gamma rays, but some
can be made to fission merely by the addition of the binding energy of a
neutron. Such nuclides are the ones needed for a nuclear reactor. A
thermal neutron is much more likely to be absorbed than a high speed
neutron. Three nuclides are particularly suitable for use in a nuclear
reactor. Table 19–1 shows some of the properties of these nuclides. The
column headed by ν gives the number of neutrons released per fission.

TABLE 19–1

Properties of Possible Nuclear Reactor Fuels

	ν	η	σ_f (barns)
Natural $_{92}U$	2.55	1.34	4.2
$_{92}U^{235}$	2.46	2.33	580.
$_{92}U^{233}$	2.54		533.
$_{94}Pu^{239}$	2.88	2.70	750.

Since not all neutrons absorbed by the material produce fission, a
constant that is perhaps a better indicator of the usefulness is the one
given in the column headed by η. It gives the number of neutrons released
per neutron absorbed in the material. The fission cross-section σ_f is
strongly dependent upon the speed of the neutrons and the values quoted
in the last column are the values for thermal neutrons. The natural
mixture of uranium isotopes is also included. The absorption of neutrons
without fission by U^{238} is responsible for the somewhat lower value of η
for the mixture.

For these materials to be used as "fuels" in reactors they must be
available in quantity. Natural uranium contains 0.72% U^{235} and the
remainder is U^{238}. The separation of these two isotopes is carried out
chiefly at Oak Ridge in Tennessee where a gaseous uranium compound is
forced through semipermeable membranes with the result that the lighter

isotopes move more quickly and become separated from the heavier. The transuranium element plutonium $_{94}Pu^{239}$ is mass produced at the Hanford, Washington, works of the General Electric Company where neutrons in nuclear reactors are used to make or "breed" the plutonium from U^{238} according to the reactions,

$$_{92}U^{238} + _0n^1 \rightarrow _{92}U^{239} + \gamma,$$

$$_{92}U^{239} \rightarrow _{93}Np^{239} + _{-1}e^0 + \bar{\nu} \qquad (T_{1/2} = 23 \text{ min}),$$

$$_{93}Np^{239} \rightarrow _{94}Pu^{239} + _{-1}e^0 + \bar{\nu} \qquad (T_{1/2} = 2.3 \text{ days}).$$

(The symbol $\bar{\nu}$ in these equations stands for the antineutrino and is not to be confused with ν the number of neutrons produced.) The first of these is the reaction which makes $\eta < \nu$ for natural uranium.

The possibility of a chain reaction using these fuels depends on a careful balance between competing processes for the neutrons. These processes are:

1. production—from fission
2. escape—from the structure
3. capture—non-fission capture by the structure
4. capture—non-fission capture by the fuel
5. capture—resulting in fission

Items 2, 3, and 4 remove neutrons of item 1 thus decreasing the occurrence of item 5. In general the effects of items 3 and 4 can only be decreased by care in design and choice of materials; but the effect of item 2 can be diminished by increasing the size of the reactor. The rate of escape of neutrons is proportional to the external area of the reactor. This increases as the square of its "radius." The rate of production is proportional to the volume available and hence to the cube of its "radius"; so if the reactor is larger than a certain *critical* size a reaction that is self-maintaining is possible. It is possible to have as many neutrons that can cause fissions produced as are used in the fission process.

Although it may be easier to use thermal neutrons for certain applications, it is also possible to produce a chain reaction with higher speed neutrons. Thus we can classify nuclear reactors by the speed of the neutrons used by the reactor.

1. *Thermal nuclear reactors* make use of thermal neutrons for fission. These reactors are the most common, but they tend to be of large size because of the material needed to slow the neutrons down. Their use is thus limited to large electrical power stations or possibly ship or submarine propulsion.
2. *Intermediate nuclear reactors* make use of intermediate energy neutrons. They are somewhat smaller but hard to handle. This type has been tried in at least one submarine.

3. *Fast neutron reactors* are experimental only but are compact. Atomic bombs may be thought of as fast neutron reactors.

We shall confine our discussion to thermal nuclear reactors.

19–3. Thermal Nuclear Reactors. Let us now examine the behavior of the neutrons in a chain reaction. Consider a fuel consisting of a mixture of U^{238} and U^{235} either in natural proportions or enriched with U^{235}. Let us start with the fission of a U^{235} nucleus by a thermal neutron. In this fission, ν fast neutrons appear. A small fraction of these collide with U^{238}, cause these nuclei to fission, and therefore create additional neutrons. Therefore, instead of ν fast neutrons, we will have $\nu\epsilon$ fast neutrons where ϵ, the *fast fission factor* is greater than unity. (An approximate value is $\epsilon = 1.03$, a 3% increase in ν.)

Some of these fast neutrons escape the structure entirely. Let the fraction escaping be l_f. Therefore, we have $\nu\epsilon(1 - l_f)$ fast neutrons left.

We must now reduce the energy of these neutrons as quickly as possible and have them re-enter the U^{235} at thermal energies before they are absorbed in other materials. This is done by collisions with the atoms of a moderator like graphite or heavy water. During the slowing-down process, the neutron energy passes through intermediate values. Some of these intermediate energy neutrons are captured when they have energies corresponding to resonances in the U^{238}. If we let $p = $ *resonance escape probability* be the fraction escaping such capture, we get, for the number of neutrons reaching thermal energies, $\nu\epsilon(1 - l_f)p$.

Some of these thermal neutrons escape. This fraction of thermals we denote as l_t. We then have left $\nu\epsilon(1 - l_f)p(1 - l_t)$.

Of these thermal neutrons, a fraction f is absorbed in U^{235}, where f is called the *thermal utilization factor*. Of those absorbed in U^{235}, some cause fission, but some form U^{236}, and therefore the fraction causing fission will be σ_f/σ_a, where σ_f is the fission cross-section and σ_a is the total absorption cross-section.

Therefore, the number of fissions in U^{235} per original fission of U^{235} is

$$k = \nu\epsilon(1 - l_f)p(1 - l_t)f\frac{\sigma_f}{\sigma_a}. \qquad (19\text{–}1)$$

This ratio k is called the *multiplication factor*.
If we let

$$\eta = \nu\frac{\sigma_f}{\sigma_a}, \qquad (19\text{–}2)$$

the number of fast fission neutrons produced per thermal neutron absorbed (Table 19–1), then the multiplication factor is

$$k = \eta\epsilon pf(1 - l_f)(1 - l_t). \qquad (19\text{–}3)$$

For a chain reaction to be sustained, k must be at least unity. When k is equal to unity, the reactor is said to be *critical* and the chain reaction is operating at a steady state. In actual practice it is difficult to fix k at unity and if it becomes slightly greater than unity, the reaction rate increases exponentially. If k is then made slightly less than unity, the reaction rate decreases exponentially. This variation in k is managed by withdrawing or reinserting control rods of a neutron absorbing material. The reaction rate thus varies as shown in Fig. 19–1. Safety rods which

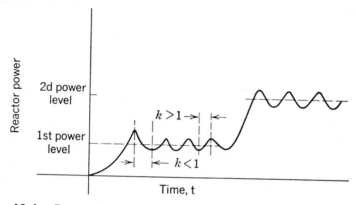

Fig. 19–1.   Time variation of reactor power as control rods are varied.

can be rapidly inserted to reduce k well below unity are also provided. They make it possible to shut the reactor down very quickly, a process known in reactor terminology as "scram."

The possibility of controlling a reactor is dependent upon the fact that not quite all of the neutrons are released immediately ($\sim 10^{-14}$ sec) in the fission process. About $\frac{3}{4}$ of one per cent are *delayed* neutrons. The half-lives of the reactions responsible for these delayed neutrons range from 0.43 sec to 55.6 sec. The value of k must not exceed a certain value or the prompt neutrons will lead to a disastrous "run away" of the reactor. For U^{235} the reactor becomes "prompt critical" when $k > 1.0075$. For U^{233} or Pu^{239} the safe range is even less.

For theoretical purposes, it is often useful to consider a reactor of infinite extent. In such a case $l_f = l_t = 0$ and the multiplication factor becomes

$$k_\infty = \eta \epsilon p f. \tag{19–4}$$

Eq. 19–4 is often known as the *four-factor formula*. The design of reactor structures requires close consideration of the resonance escape probability p and the thermal utilization factor f. The arrangement of the fuel and moderator in the reactor determines the value of p. The amount and distribution of absorbing material determines the value of f.

The problem of withdrawing the energy from the reactor is taken care of by circulating some coolant through the reactor. Care must be taken to use a material with low neutron absorbing power and the location of the pipes must be carefully planned.

19-4. Moderators. The moderator plays such an important role in a thermal reactor that we should look at some of the features involved. You will recall that a moderator is a substance in which fast neutrons will be converted to slow neutrons by making them undergo elastic collisions with light nuclei. Since absorption of the neutrons must be avoided, a moderator must have a small absorption cross-section compared to the scattering cross-section. Water, paraffin, and graphite are relatively inexpensive moderators while heavy water (D_2O) and beryllium are considerably more expensive.

If a neutron of mass m_N and initial velocity v_0 collides head-on with a stationary target of mass Am_N where A is the atomic weight, then conservation of energy and momentum give for an elastic collision

$$v_0 = -v + AV,$$
$$v_0{}^2 = v^2 + AV^2,$$

(19-5)

where v is the new velocity of the neutron after the collision and V is the velocity of the target. If we eliminate V, then,

$$\frac{E}{E_0} = \frac{v^2}{v_0{}^2} = \left(\frac{A-1}{A+1}\right)^2;$$

(19-6)

and if we let $[(A-1)/(A+1)]^2 = \alpha$ then the fractional energy loss in the collision is

$$\frac{\Delta E}{E_0} = \frac{4A}{(1+A)^2} = 1 - \alpha.$$

(19-7)

TABLE 19-2

Moderating Materials

Element	SDP	σ_a (barns)
H	1.32	0.33
D	0.16	0.46×10^{-13}
Li	0.017	70
Be	0.11	0.010
B	0.09	750
C	0.064	4.5×10^{-3}
O	0.016	very small

For a moderator of hydrogen, $\alpha = 0$, so $\Delta E/E_0 = 100\%$, while for a moderator of carbon, $\Delta E/E_0 = 28\%$.

Also important for moderator consideration are the number of nuclei per unit volume N, the scattering cross-section σ_s, and the absorption cross-section σ_a. The *slowing down power* (*SDP*) of the moderator is defined as the product of N, σ_s, and the average logarithm of energy change per collision. It is a very good indicator of moderator quality. Table 19–2 lists the SDP and the σ_a (thermal neutrons) for several possible moderators. The advantages of H, D, Be, and C are evident.

19–5. Thermal Reactor Types.

1. *Heterogeneous natural uranium reactors.* If natural uranium is arranged in a lattice of chunks or rods with the moderator filling the space between them, a chain reaction can be sustained. Natural uranium cannot be used in one large piece because the U^{238} captures too many neutrons without fissioning. Fermi's first reactor at the University of Chicago was of this type and used graphite as the moderator. Air is generally used as a coolant. For power reactors, a coolant with better heat transfer properties is required.

2. *Heterogeneous enriched uranium reactors.* Increasing the U^{235} content of the fuel to about 90% increases the value of η to approximately 2 and makes possible a sustained reaction in a much smaller volume since the fuel can be used in the form of plates. Water is used as both moderator and coolant. The swimming pool reactor is an example of this type.

3. *Homogeneous enriched uranium reactors.* In these reactors a uranium salt, enriched with U^{235} is dissolved in water (light or heavy). The solution is placed in a vessel and is then circulated. The fission heats the solution and this heat is removed by a heat exchanger. Continual refueling and chemical purification is possible.

4. *Boiling water reactors.* Reactors of type 2 or 3 can be operated at temperatures at which boiling of the water occurs. The resultant steam can be used directly. The advantages of boiling are the relatively low pressure on the reactor tank and the elimination of pumps and heat exchangers. In addition, such reactors have an intrinsic stability since an accidental prompt critical condition leads to an expansion of the moderator automatically shutting down the system.

5. *Breeder reactors.* Reactors which create additional fissionable fuel are breeder reactors. They may be of several of the types listed above, but are included here as a separate type because of their possible future importance. Unless more fuel can be produced in breeders the amount of U^{235} is the sole source of fission energy. We have already met one breeding reaction used to produce Pu^{239} and the Hanford reactors may be thought of as breeder reactors. Another reaction transforms thorium

into U^{233}. The reaction is

$$_{90}\text{Th}^{232} + {}_0\text{n}^1 \rightarrow {}_{90}\text{Th}^{233} + \gamma,$$

$$_{90}\text{Th}^{233} \rightarrow {}_{91}\text{Pa}^{233} + {}_{-1}\text{e}^0 + \bar{\nu}, \qquad (T_{\frac{1}{2}} = 23.3 \text{ min})$$

$$_{91}\text{Pa}^{233} \rightarrow {}_{92}\text{U}^{233} + {}_{-1}\text{e}^0 + \bar{\nu}. \qquad (T_{\frac{1}{2}} = 27.4 \text{ days})$$

The $_{92}\text{U}^{233}$ formed is a fission fuel. Several breeder reactors are being built. It is very desirable that the most successful breeding arrangement be found that is also compatible with obtaining energy from the reactor at the same time.

19–6. Thermonuclear Reactions. The source of energy for the sun has been a puzzle for a long time. The surface temperature is about $6000°\text{K}$ and the internal temperature is estimated as $2 \times 10^{7}°\text{K}$. Fission in the sun cannot be the source of these temperatures because the sun is composed principally of hydrogen (74% by mass) and helium (24%). The remainder of the mass is distributed among the other elements.

It is believed that the basic reaction providing the energy is the combining of four protons to give a helium nucleus. At the temperature of $20 \times 10^{6}°\text{K}$ the kinetic energy $(\frac{3}{2}kT)$ of the particles due to thermal motion would be approximately 1 Kev. At such temperatures appreciable numbers of nuclei have an energy high enough to produce fusion reactions called *thermonuclear reactions*.

The principal cycle that converts four protons to helium is now believed to be the *proton-proton chain*. It is

$$2(\text{H}^1 + \text{H}^1 \rightarrow \text{H}^2 + {}_1\text{e}^0 + \nu + 0.42 \text{ Mev}),$$

$$2(\text{H}^1 + \text{H}^2 \rightarrow \text{He}^3 + \gamma + 5.5 \text{ Mev}),$$

and

$$\text{He}^3 + \text{He}^3 \rightarrow \text{He}^4 + 2\text{H}^1 + 12.8 \text{ Mev}$$

and the net result is

$$4\text{H}^1 \rightarrow \text{He}^4 + 2\,{}_{+1}\text{e}^0 + 2\gamma + 2\nu$$

with a net Q of 26.7 Mev. About 0.5 Mev of this is carried away by the neutrinos.

Another possible variation is for some of the He^3 to combine with He^4 as follows:

$$\text{He}^3 + \text{He}^4 \rightarrow \text{Be}^7 + \gamma$$

$$\text{Be}^7 + {}_{-1}\text{e}^0 \rightarrow \text{Li}^7 + \nu$$

$$\text{Li}^7 + \text{H}^1 \rightarrow \text{He}^4 + \text{He}^4$$

or

$$Be^7 + H^1 \rightarrow B^8 + \gamma$$

$$B^8 \rightarrow Be^8 + {}_{+1}e^0 + \nu$$

$$Be^8 \rightarrow He^4 + He^4.$$

Bethe,[1] in 1939, proposed the *carbon-nitrogen cycle* as an alternative method to explain the conversion. This reaction is

$$C^{12} + H^1 \rightarrow N^{13} + \gamma$$

$$N^{13} \rightarrow C^{13} + {}_{+1}e^0 + \nu$$

$$C^{13} + H^1 \rightarrow N^{14} + \gamma$$

$$N^{14} + H^1 \rightarrow O^{15} + \gamma$$

$$O^{15} \rightarrow N^{15} + {}_{+1}e^0 + \nu$$

$$N^{15} + H^1 \rightarrow C^{12} + He^4.$$

The remarkable thing about this reaction is that carbon and nitrogen appear only as catalysts and are not consumed. It is now believed that our sun principally uses the proton-proton chain but that many other stars in the universe, with higher internal temperatures, use the carbon-nitrogen cycle.

The fusion reaction is a much more difficult reaction to run in the laboratory than the fission reaction. Basically, the reason for this is that in fusion the nuclei that must come together are charged, and high kinetic energies are required to overcome the Coulomb repulsion. The energies can be achieved without difficulty with the nuclear accelerators that we discussed earlier but these machines produce beams of very low density so that more energy is expended than is received from the reaction. Even in the sun, the rate of reaction is very low since only 1% of the hydrogen is used in a billion (10^9) years.

Fission bombs produce temperatures estimated at $50 \times 10^{6}°$K. Such bombs produce a furnace of sufficient time duration that fusion reactions between the *rarer* heavier isotopes of hydrogen can proceed even though the slower proton-proton chain and the carbon-nitrogen cycle do not. One possibility for such a reaction is

$$H^2 + H^3 \rightarrow He^4 + n^1 + 17.6 \text{ Mev,}$$

and there are several other similar ones. It is interesting and terrifying to realize that *fission* bombs are limited in size (essentially the critical size) but that *fusion* bomb size depends only on the amount of fuel that

[1] H. A. Bethe, *Phys. Rev.*, **55**, 434 (1939).

the designer can build into them. Tritium (H^3) is now manufactured in quantity throughout the world by using nuclear reactors to provide neutrons probably for the reaction

$$3Li^6 + {}_0n^1 \rightarrow (3Li^7) \rightarrow {}_1H^3 + {}_2He^4.$$

At the time of this writing, intensive research is well under way on laboratory methods for producing thermonuclear reactions. This research is at present directed toward magnetic methods of holding ions close together. It is developing a whole new field in physics called *magneto-hydrodynamics* or the motion of plasmas (collections of ions) in magnetic fields.

PROBLEMS

19-1. How many collisions with beryllium $_4Be^9$ will reduce a neutron's energy from 2 Mev to 0.025 ev?

19-2. How many collisions with graphite $_6C^{12}$ will reduce a neutron's energy from 2 Mev to 0.025 ev?

19-3. Calculate the speed of the neutrons emitted by fission if their energy is 2 Mev.

19-4. Neutrons emerge from a reactor with an energy corresponding to the equipartition value for thermal equilibrium at 400°K. Find their velocity and de Broglie wavelength.

19-5. How many neutrons per unit volume are contained in a collimated beam flux of 10^{12} neutrons cm^{-2} sec^{-1} of 2 Mev neutrons? Of 0.025 neutrons?

19-6. If the neutron flux in a reactor is 4×10^{14} neutrons cm^{-2} sec^{-1} and if their mean velocity is the rms velocity for 320°K, what is the density of neutrons in the reactor?

19-7. A thermal neutron detector depends on the fission produced in a foil of pure U^{235} which has a thickness of 0.08 mm. What fraction of the neutrons entering the foil will produce a fission? Density of uranium is 18.7 gm cm^{-3}.

19-8. Assuming that a beam of n particles passes through a material containing N target particles per unit volume with a scattering cross-section σ, derive the average distance a particle goes before it undergoes a collision (the mean free path).

19-9. Compute the mean free path for absorption of thermal neutrons in boron (density 2.5 gm cm^{-3}, cross-section 750 barns).

19-10. (a) How many grams of U^{235} are consumed to give a megawatt-day of energy? (b) If this heat could be converted to electricity with a conversion efficiency of 33%, what energy in kilowatt-hours would it yield?

19–11. (a) Compute the energy in ergs liberated in the fission of one U^{235} atom. (b) Compute the number of tons of TNT equivalent to 1 kg of U^{235} if it could undergo complete fission. Take 1 ton of TNT equal to 1×10^6 kilocalories. (c) Compute the number of fissions of U^{235} per second required to give one watt of power. This is a convenient number to remember since the answer is numerically the velocity of light.

19–12. Calculate the amount of mass converted into other forms of energy for a megaton bomb (20 kiloton $= 8 \times 10^{13}$ j). What mass of U^{235} would be required if it was a pure fission bomb? What mass of $H^3 + H^2$ would be required for the $H^3(d,n)He^4$ reaction? Assume 100% conversion.

19–13. If 100 gm of U^{235} is in a steady flux of 10^{13} thermal neutrons $cm^{-2}\,sec^{-1}$, what mass of uranium will fission in 10 days (density 18.0 gm cm^{-3}, fission cross-section 580 barns)? How much energy is released?

19–14. A small nuclear reactor operates at a power of 50 w. How many U^{235} nuclei must fission per second to accomplish this? How much U^{235} will be used per month?

19–15. A large nuclear reactor operates at a power level of 500 megawatts. How many U^{235} nuclei must fission per second to accomplish this? How much U^{235} will be used per month?

19–16. Compute the number of fast neutrons resulting in one generation in an infinite reactor given the following data: 1000 original fast neutrons, $\epsilon = 1.03$, $p = 0.90$, $f = 0.90$, $\eta = 1.30$.

19–17. Suppose that the product of the 4 factors η, ϵ, p, and f for a homogeneous spherical reactor is 1.12. If the fraction of neutrons that escape when the radius is 30 cm is 0.20, at what radius will the reactor become critical?

19–18. If the reproduction factor k is 1.03 how many repetitions of the slowing down process are needed to (a) double, (b) quadruple the number of neutrons?

19–19. If in a breeder reactor using Th^{232} all the neutrons not producing fission were captured by the thorium, how much U^{233} would be formed for each kilogram of U^{235} that fissioned? Suppose this material were used for further breeding, how much more would be formed?

SELECTED REFERENCES

BISHOP, A. S. *Project Sherwood, The U. S. Program in Controlled Fusion.* Addison-Wesley Publishing Co., Inc., Reading, Mass., 1958.

GLASSTONE, S. *Principles of Nuclear Reactor Engineering.* D. Van Nostrand Co., Inc., Princeton, N. J., 1952. Chaps. 4 and 7.

GLASSTONE, S., and R. H. LOUBERG. *Controlled Thermonuclear Reactions.* D. Van Nostrand Co., Inc., Princeton, N. J., 1960. Chaps. 1, 2, and 3.

KAPLAN, I. *Nuclear Physics.* Addison-Wesley Publishing Co., Inc., Reading, Mass., 1955. Chaps. 19 and 20.

MURRAY, R. L. *Introduction to Nuclear Engineering.* Prentice-Hall, Inc., Englewood Cliffs, N. J., 1954. Chap. 6.

SMYTH, H. D. *Atomic Energy for Military Purposes.* Princeton Univ. Press, Princeton, N. J., 1945. Chap. 12.

SOODAK, H., and E. C. CAMPBELL. *Elementary Pile Theory.* John Wiley & Sons, Inc., New York, 1950. Chap. 12.

STEPHENSON, R. *Introduction to Nuclear Engineering.* McGraw-Hill Book Co., Inc., New York, 1954. Chap. 3.

UNITED STATES ATOMIC ENERGY COMMISSION. *The Effects of Nuclear Weapons.* U. S. Government Printing Office, Washington, D. C., 1957.

20

Cosmic Rays and
"Strange" Particles

Although there are still many mysteries regarding cosmic rays, enough is known to make it possible to present a pictorial sketch of the circumstances which lead to most of the observed effects in this field.

The first direct evidence of cosmic rays appeared in an early set of experiments by C. T. R. Wilson[1] and by Elster and Geitel[2] in 1899–1900, when it was discovered that there was a continually present source of ionization in air. In 1910, Gockel[3] showed that the effect tends to increase with altitude. This was confirmed by Hess and Kolhoerster[4] in 1911–1914. About 1925, Millikan and Cameron[5] became interested and performed experiments that further confirmed the non-terrestrial source of the radiation. They discovered that some of the radiation penetrated even deep into the ground. Since that time many people have studied a wide variety of aspects of this radiation which was called *cosmic rays* by Millikan and Cameron.

20–1. The Primary Cosmic Rays. It is now clear that the major constituent of the primary cosmic radiation consists of high energy protons. The range of energies extends from 2×10^8 ev (and possibly lower) up to 10^{19} ev with the number of protons in the lower energy range much greater than the number found in the high energy range. The spectrum above 15 Bev is given approximately by

$$\frac{dN}{dE} = \frac{C}{(E + 5.3)^{2.75}} \qquad (20\text{–}1)$$

[1] C. T. R. Wilson, *Proc. Camb. Phil. Soc.*, **11**, 32 (1900).
[2] J. Elster, and H. Geitel, *Phys. Zeit.*, **2**, 560 (1900).
[3] A. Gockel, *Phys. Zeit.*, **11**, 280 (1910); **12**, 595 (1911).
[4] V. F. Hess, *Phys. Zeit.*, **12**, 998 (1911); **13**, 1084 (1912); **14**, 610 (1913), and W. Kolhoerster, *Verhandl. deut. phys. Ges.*, **15**, 1111 (1913); **16**, 719 (1914).
[5] R. A. Millikan, and G. H. Cameron, *Phys. Rev.*, **28**, 851 (1926); **31**, 921 (1928).

where E is in Bev. (The term Bev for 10^9 ev is used here, although the prefix "giga" has been proposed for 10^9 to avoid confusion with other meanings of billion throughout the world. 1 Bev = 1 Gev.) A few alpha particles and some nuclei with Z as high as 26 (Fe) have also been found. In a rough way, the concentration of cosmic ray primaries seems to approximate the concentration of nuclei in the universe. The particles seem to come uniformly from all directions in space, although this is not certain. There can be no radioactive particles, such as neutrons, except for those originating in our own solar system. It is generally believed that the sun produces at most a small fraction of the total primary cosmic-ray flux. The actual flux is about 0.35 particles per cm^2 per sec per sterad. If one multiplies by the average energy per particle, the result is

$$4 \times 10^{-6} \text{ w m}^{-2}. \qquad [4 \times 10^{-3} \text{ erg sec}^{-1} \text{ cm}^{-2}.]$$

This is approximately equal to the radiant flux from all stars except the sun.

The earth is a magnet and its field will deflect the protons as they approach the earth. One of the two principal effects of this is that at the geomagnetic equator only particles having an energy greater than about 15 Bev can reach the earth while at the magnetic poles there are no restrictions. In Fig. 20–1 we have plotted a set of possible trajectories for different energies and directions of approach. Many of the slower ones (A and B) are deflected without striking the earth. Some with sufficient energy (C) are hardly deviated. Some have energies and directions of approach (D) that lead them to spiral around the earth's lines of force toward the earth, but then are "reflected" and spiral back out. The details of the possible trajectories have been worked out principally by Lemaitre and Vallarta[6] following the earlier work of Stormer regarding the origin of the auroras. Particles with momenta (and hence energy) large enough can reach the earth at the geomagnetic equator, but not if they have less. At higher magnetic latitudes particles with lower momenta can reach the earth. Fig. 20–2 is a plot of the limiting energy versus geomagnetic latitude (latitude based on the magnetic poles rather than geographical poles). From these curves we see that we should expect that the intensity of cosmic radiation is least in the equatorial region and that more particles will enter from the west than from the east. Both of these effects are observed. The reason for the east-west effect can be seen in Fig. 20–1.

There is some evidence that no cosmic rays of low energy (≤ 0.2 Bev) arrive. Some believe this to be due to a magnetic field belonging to the sun. The facts about this point are far from clear.

Interesting fluctuations in intensity are observed. Some are associated with variations of the earth's atmosphere and others with solar effects. For instance a solar flare is nearly always followed by a decrease in cosmic

[6] G. Lemaitre, and M. S. Vallarta, *Phys. Rev.*, **43**, 87 (1933); **74**, 1837 (1948).

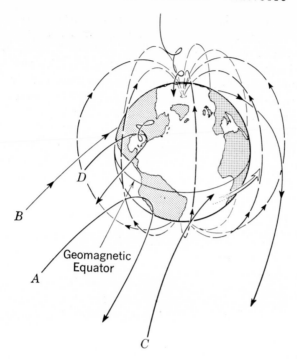

Fig. 20–1.   Trajectories (solid lines) for various cosmic rays related to the earth's magnetic field (dotted lines).

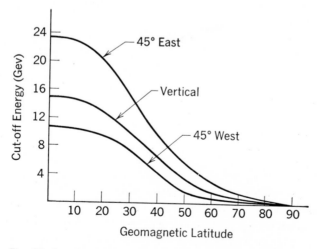

Fig. 20–2.   Cut-off energy versus geomagnetic latitude.

ray intensity. Fluctuation in the magnetic field close to the earth, within the solar system, and perhaps even beyond the solar system probably cause these effects.

Another interesting phenomenon associated with the earth's field was discovered by instruments in the early satellites launched by the United States. It was found that there are two somewhat extended bands or belts of intense radiation circling the earth at altitudes of about 2000 miles and 10,000 miles. These were believed to be somewhat "doughnut" shaped and symmetric about the geomagnetic equator as shown in Fig.

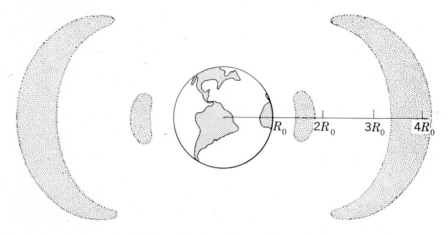

Fig. 20–3. The Van Allen radiation belts.

20–3. These belts were named the *Van Allen*[7] *belts*. Satellites launched in 1961 have shown that in fact there are not two belts but one large pulsating band of particles extending 40,000 miles from the earth, or more than twice the earlier estimate. This band of charged particles, mostly positive protons and negative electrons, trapped in the earth's magnetic field, has been named the *magnetosphere*. The charged particles spiral back and forth along the lines of force of the earth's magnetic field. They are found to range in energy from 10^4 ev to 10 Mev. The magnetosphere appears to have quite a sharp outer boundary, and is probably part of the mechanism producing auroras. It is certainly affected by magnetic storms. More details must await further experimentation.

20–2. Secondary Cosmic Radiation. Whatever radiation reaches sea level must have gone through a lot of matter (equivalent to 76 cm of mercury). Practically none of the primaries make it (the average penetration for a proton is down to a pressure of about 7 cm of mercury, which

[7] J. A. Van Allen, *Sci. Am.*, **200**, 39 (March, 1959); *Nature*, **183**, 430 (1959).

is at an altitude of about 50,000 ft). Instead, the cosmic rays observed lower down in the atmosphere are all secondary rays that are produced in a rather complex set of events.

When a high energy proton strikes a nucleus in the atmosphere, it disrupts it, forming a spray of nucleons (both protons and neutrons), and a spray of pi-mesons. The secondary nucleons will collide with other nuclei and disrupt them. Each time this happens the energy of the secondary nucleons decreases. Eventually, it loses its last kinetic energy by the regular processes of ionization of the air. On the other hand, the neutrons keep on until finally captured by a reaction such as $N^{14}(n,p)C^{14}$, the principal cause of $_6C^{14}$. This whole complex, resulting in many high energy protons and neutrons, is called a *nucleon cascade*. Almost none of these reach sea level. They are absorbed in the middle portions of the atmosphere.

However, the charged pi-mesons released by a nucleon collision have a different sort of history. Some of them strike nuclei, are absorbed, and disrupt the nucleus, but many disintegrate in flight forming mu-mesons. These interact very little with matter and form a very penetrating part of the secondary cosmic rays. About half the cosmic-ray particles at sea level are such mu-mesons. It is these mesons that continue deep into the ground.

The neutral pi-mesons are yet another case. They disintegrate almost instantly into two gamma rays. This, along with some delta rays (electrons knocked out of atoms by any of the other ionizing particles), produces the soft component of the secondary cosmic rays that makes up the other half of the total radiation at sea level.

These gamma rays may produce a process known as a *cascade shower* since close to a nucleus, a gamma ray of high energy may be converted into a high energy electron-positron pair. These particles may be accelerated by the fields of atoms and thus radiate *bremsstrahlung* (high energy photons) which may again produce electron pairs. In addition, the positrons annihilate, producing other photons to produce more pairs. (See Fig. 20–4.) The over-all result is that, starting with one photon or electron of very high energy, many electron pairs are created. The number increases as the radiation proceeds. Eventually the energy is all absorbed by ionization processes. The more dense the material in which the showers are formed, the faster they develop. In lead, a shower is likely to reach its maximum development in about 5 cm. Fig. 20–5 illustrates schematically the nature of the events initiated by a primary cosmic-ray particle.

The primary cosmic rays have been observed principally by the use of balloon and rocket flights. Photographic emulsions are particularly good for recording them and their interactions with matter. The secondary particles can also be similarly recorded, but the devices described in

Chapter 15 are all commonly used. The earliest instruments used were electroscopes and ionization chambers. A comparatively steady level of ionization results from cosmic rays. Occasionally sudden bursts of increased ionization occur when large showers pass through the ionization chamber.

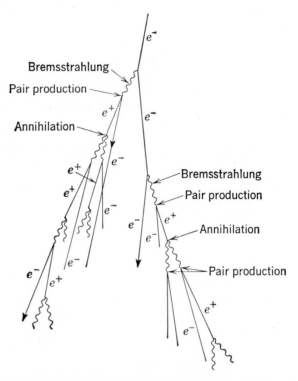

Fig. 20–4.   An electron shower.

Geiger-Muller tube counters are also useful devices. Several can be placed in various positions and coincidence counts may be used to determine the nature of various events. Thus, in Fig. 20–6a a triple coincidence identifies a particle traveling in the direction of the line of the three counters; in Fig. 20–6b a fivefold coincidence shows a shower. The high penetrating power of cosmic rays means that one need not use thin-walled counters. Another important detection device of a similar nature is the combination of a scintillator and a photomultiplier.

The use of a cloud chamber to make the tracks of cosmic-ray particles visible has been demonstrated in the illustrations. If a strong magnetic field is used at the cloud chamber, one can tell both the sign of the charge on the particle and its momentum.

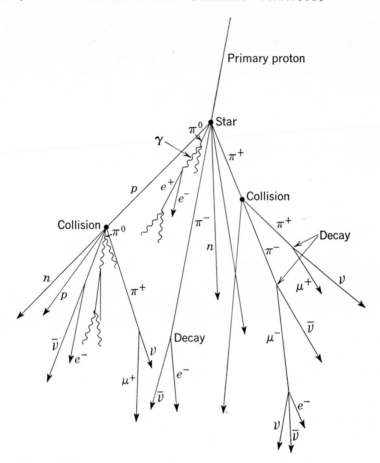

Fig. 20–5. Schematic diagram of the production of cosmic ray secondaries.

20–3. The Dirac Theory of the Electron and Positron.   The Schroedinger wave equation is changed by a Lorentz transformation. It, therefore, does not satisfy the first postulate of the special theory of relativity. This does not spoil its usefulness since so many situations involve rather slow velocities. But a truly relativistic wave equation is needed for particles with non-zero rest mass (the regular wave equation holds perfectly well for photons). In 1928, Dirac[8] found a suitable wave equation. It is really four simultaneous partial differential equations for a wave function having four components. The interpretation of these equations leads to two especially important results. The first shows that an electron has an intrinsic angular momentum described by a quantum

[8] P. A. M. Dirac, *Proc. Roy. Soc.*, **117**, 610 and **118**, 351 (1928).

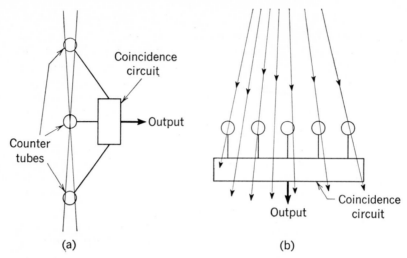

Fig. 20–6. Coincidence counting (a) cosmic-ray telescope (b) shower detector.

number $s = \frac{1}{2}$ and that there is a magnetic moment of 1 Bohr magneton associated with this spin. Thus the concept of electronic spin used so successfully in spectroscopy is a direct consequence of the special theory of relativity. The interpretation of the second result is somewhat more difficult. It was found that states are possible for which the total energy is negative (including energy of rest mass and kinetic energy).

For the problem of a free particle the Dirac wave equation permits the energy levels shown in Fig. 20–7a. One might dismiss this as simply pro-

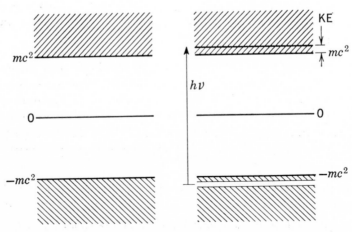

Fig. 20–7. Energy levels for a free electron in the Dirac theory.

viding an extraneous root except that the form of the theory demands that the negative energy levels be included and even predicts the transition probability for a jump from a positive state to a negative one. The whole theory would have to be rejected except for the explanation given by Dirac and others. If we claim that empty space consists of the situation in which all negative energy levels are occupied, then the exclusion principle would prevent the jump to an already occupied level. The particles with negative kinetic energy would be impossible for us to detect. But the theory permits transitions up as well as down. Suppose a gamma ray with an energy of a little more than $2m_0c^2$ is absorbed as shown in Fig. 20-7b. We then would have an ordinary electron with some kinetic energy and a vacant negative energy state. An attempt to discover what empty space with an unoccupied negative energy state would look like showed that it would be a positively charged particle having the same inertial characteristics (mass) and same spin and magnetic moment (opposite to an ordinary electron, of course) as an ordinary electron. Dirac had first hoped that it would be a proton, but such was not the case. In 1932, Anderson[9] first observed tracks of positive electrons, positrons, in cloud chamber photographs of cosmic rays. Since then, they have been observed often in cosmic-ray showers and have been produced in large numbers by artificially produced radioactive sources.

The theory predicts that if such a positron and an ordinary electron come close together the electron will drop into the unoccupied negative energy state and thus annihilate itself and the positron. If both energy and momentum are to be conserved, two photons are produced each with an energy close to $m_0c^2 = 0.511$ Mev (assuming both electrons had little kinetic energy). Thus the eventual fate of all positive electrons is annihilation. Such annihilation radiation is found in abundance around positron emitters. The creation of electron pairs (pair production) can occur only in regions of high electrical field strength, generally close to nuclei.

Similar relativistic wave equations should exist for protons, neutrons, and perhaps other particles. Thus we should expect antiparticles for each. There should be negative protons and antineutrons. The latter has no charge but its magnetic moment should be the reverse with respect to spin as compared to the ordinary neutron. Both particles have been created by the Berkeley Bevatron[10] and other accelerators and have been studied in some detail. Neutrinos and antineutrinos are also believed to make up such a pair.

20-4. Unusual Particles. A large number of interesting particles have been discovered in the study of cosmic rays. The first observations of

[9] C. D. Anderson, *Science*, **76**, 238 (1932); *Phys. Rev.*, **43**, 491 (1933).

[10] S. Chamberlain, Y. Wiegand, *Phys. Rev.*, **100**, 947 (1955); B. Cork, G. R. Lambertson, O. Piccioni, W. A. Wentzel, *Phys. Rev.*, **104**, 1193 (1956).

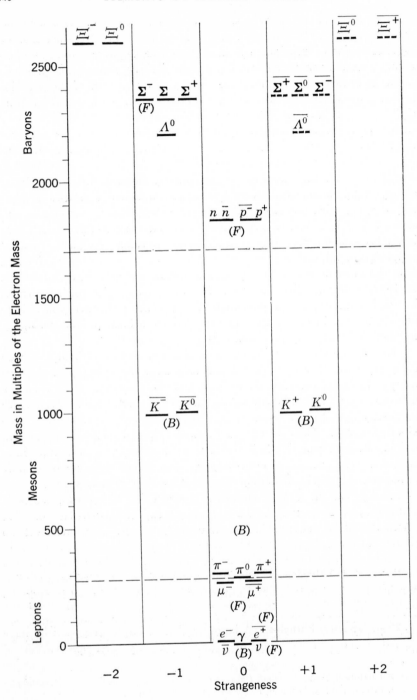

Fig. 20–8. Fundamental particles as a function of strangeness and mass.

positrons were made in cosmic ray studies. The next new particle found was the mu-meson. Pi-mesons were also found. All of these are now considered to have a definite place in the pattern that describes the behavior of matter. But recently, some other particles have been observed. As yet, their full nature and roles are not understood. We shall only list the major properties of the particles that have been discovered by this time.

The known particles divide (see Fig. 20–8) into three major classes— *leptons* (light particles), *mesons* (medium particles), and *baryons* (heavy particles).

Photons, electrons, neutrinos, and mu-mesons (muons) are leptons. Of these, photons and electrons are familiar, while neutrinos arise in beta decay, and mu-mesons (muons) seem to be just the decay product of pi-mesons and may be simply "heavy" electrons. Since these mu-mesons do not really fit into the meson class, the name *muon* has been suggested as more appropriate.

Pi-mesons and the heavier *K*-mesons make up the meson class. Pi-mesons probably are the particles analogous to photons in that pi-mesons play the same role in nuclear forces as photons do in electromagnetic forces. They were first observed in cosmic ray studies at high altitudes, but now are made in large quantities by powerful accelerators. The heavy mesons, originally called τ, θ, and *K*-mesons, have so nearly the same mass that it is now clear that they are probably all the same particle and are now known as $K^{\pm,0}$-mesons. The original names were based on their different decay schemes first observed in cosmic rays. They are now produced by the very large accelerators.

Neutrons and protons and the hyperons (non-nucleon particles) are baryons. The hyperons were first seen in cosmic ray studies and were called *V*-particles because of the characteristic tracks they left in photographic plates. They are now designated Λ, Σ, and Ξ particles.

The relations among all of these particles are still not well understood. In any case, it is clear that there is an abundance of opportunity for the investigator in this field. However, certain regularities appear which may help to understand them.

20–5. The Systematics of Particles. The many particles just mentioned have made the understanding of nature more complicated. The original observations seemed to indicate a multiplicity of particles in excess of what are now known to exist. Of course, there may still be many particles as yet undetected. Order has been obtained out of the confusion by noting that the following features are all required to describe particles.

1. Electrical Charge:
   positive, neutral, negative

2. Spin:

$s = \frac{1}{2}$—such particles obey Fermi-Dirac statistics and are called *fermions*

$s = 0$ or 1—such particles obey Einstein-Bose statistics and are called *bosons*

3. Mass:

very light—rest mass $= 0$ or about $1m_0$—Leptons

intermediate—rest mass ~ 300 or $900m_0$—Mesons

heavy—rest mass ~ 2000 or greater m_0—Baryons

4. Strangeness:[11]

a label which cannot be identified with familiar quantities but which limits the possible particle transformations; it can be 0, ± 1, or -2.

Fig. 20–8 shows a plot of the particles known or expected. A bar above the label indicates an antiparticle. The statistics, Fermi-Dirac (F) or Einstein-Bose (B) are shown beside the particle. The statistics of the Ξ particles are not known. The mu-mesons are usually classed as leptons in spite of the fact that they have a mass of 206 electronic units. The evidence tends to indicate that they are really only another form of electron, one with 105.2 Mev extra energy. They have even the same anomalous magnetic moment of $1.00116\mu_B$.

Another representation is given in Table 20–1 which has been adapted from Lee[12] and a table compiled by the Brookhaven Laboratory. For each of the particles there is an antiparticle. In general, the antiparticle has opposite charge and opposite strangeness. Thus $e^{\pm}$, $\mu^{\pm}$, $\pi^{\pm}$, $p^{\pm}$, and $\nu\bar{\nu}$ are all particle-antiparticle pairs all with strangeness zero; K^- of strangeness -1 is the antiparticle of K^+ with strangeness $+1$. Presumably, there may exist three antiparticles $\bar{\Sigma}^+$, $\bar{\Sigma}^0$, and $\bar{\Sigma}^-$ all of strangeness $+1$; and it is inferred that $\bar{\Xi}^+$ and $\bar{\Xi}^0$ with strangeness $+2$ are the only antiparticles for the Xi particles. These are shown in dotted lines in Fig. 20–8 since they have not yet been observed.

One can also classify the interaction between particles into four major groups:

1. strong—nuclear, i.e., nucleon-nucleon; also interaction with pi-mesons and other strange particles
2. electromagnetic—Coulomb forces—emission and absorption of photons
3. weak—beta decay—decay of pi- and mu-mesons and of strange particles
4. gravitation—gravitational forces.

In transformations involving strong interactions, strangeness is conserved along with charge, energy, etc. So too is intrinsic parity (right or left handedness of a particle). Typical strong interactions which can

[11] Introduced by M. Gell-Mann, *Phys. Rev.*, **93**, 933 (1953).
[12] T. D. Lee, *Physics Today*, **13** (10) 30 (1960).

TABLE 20-1

A Table of Fundamental Particles

Particle		Spin	Rest mass (electron masses)	Mean life (seconds)	Decay products	Strangeness
Xi	Ξ^-	$\frac{1}{2}$	2585	10^{-10} to 10^{-9}	$\Lambda^0 + \pi^-$	-2
	Ξ^0	$\frac{1}{2}$	2570	10^{-10}	$\Lambda^0 + \pi^0$	-2
Sigma	Σ^+	$\frac{1}{2}$	2325	0.7×10^{-10}	$p + \pi^0 \quad n + \pi^+$	-1
	Σ^-	$\frac{1}{2}$	2341	1.5×10^{-10}	$n + \pi^-$	-1
	Σ^0	$\frac{1}{2}$	2324	Not measured	$\Lambda^0 + \gamma$	-1
Lambda	Λ^0	$\frac{1}{2}$	2182	2.7×10^{-10}	$p + \pi^- \quad n + \pi^0$	-1
Proton	p	$\frac{1}{2}$	1836.1	Stable		0
Neutron	n	$\frac{1}{2}$	1838.6	About 10^3	$p + e^- + \bar{\nu}$	0
K-meson	K^+	0	966.5	1.2×10^{-8}	$\mu^+ + \nu \quad \pi^+ + \pi^0$ $\pi^+ + \pi^+ + \pi^- \quad \pi^+ + \pi^0 + \pi^0$ $\mu^+ + \nu + \pi^0 \quad e^+ + \nu + \pi^0$	$+1$
	K^-	0	966.5	1.2×10^{-8}	$\mu^- + \bar{\nu} \quad \pi^- + \pi^0$ $\pi^- + \pi^- + \pi^+ \quad \pi^- + \pi^0 + \pi^0$ $\mu^- + \bar{\nu} + \pi^0 \quad e^- + \bar{\nu} + \pi^0$	-1
	K_1^0	0	965	1×10^{-10}	$\pi^+ + \pi^- \quad \pi^0 + \pi^0$	-1
	K_2^0	0	965	3×10^{-8} to 10^{-6}	$\pi^+ + e^- + \bar{\nu} \quad \pi^- + e^+ + \nu$ $\pi^+ + \mu^- + \bar{\nu} \quad \pi^- + \mu^+ + \nu$ $\pi^+ + \pi^- + \pi^0 \quad \pi^0 + \pi^0 + \pi^0$	$+1$
Pion	π^+	0	273.2	2.6×10^{-8}	$\mu^+ + \nu$	0
	π^-	0	273.2	2.6×10^{-8}	$\mu^- + \bar{\nu}$	0
	π^0	0	264.2	10^{-16} to 10^{-15}	$\gamma + \gamma$	0
Muon	μ^-	$\frac{1}{2}$	206.7	2.2×10^{-6}	$e^- + \nu + \bar{\nu}$	0
Electron	e^-	$\frac{1}{2}$	1	Stable		0
Neutrino	ν	$\frac{1}{2}$	0	Stable		0
Photon	γ	1	0	Stable		0

occur in 10^{-18} sec are

$$K^- + p \rightarrow \Sigma^- + \pi^+$$

$$\Xi^- + p \rightarrow \Lambda^0 + \Lambda^0$$

$$\pi^+ + p \rightarrow \pi^+ + \pi^0 + p$$

$$\pi^- + p \rightarrow \Lambda^0 + K^0$$

$$p + n \rightarrow \Lambda^0 + K^+.$$

In weak interactions strangeness is not conserved and neither is parity, but charge, energy, momentum, and angular momentum are. Typical weak interactions besides ordinary beta decay and the decay of pi- and mu-

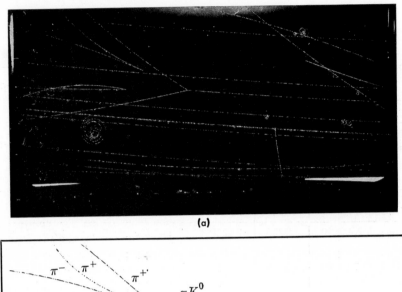

(a)

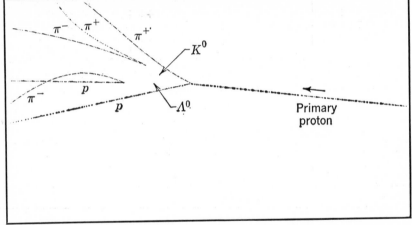

(b)

Fig. 20-9. Hyperon reactions in a liquid hydrogen bubble chamber. (a) Photograph. (b) Sketch for identification. A 2.85 Bev proton collides with a proton producing a Λ^0 and a K^0 particle by the reaction $p + p \rightarrow \Lambda^0 + p + K^0 + \pi^+$. The Λ^0 particle decays by the process $\Lambda^0 \rightarrow p + \pi^-$, and the K^0 particle decays by the process $K^0 \rightarrow \pi^+ + \pi^-$ (Brookhaven National Laboratory).

mesons are the decay of strange particles like:

$$K^+ \rightarrow \pi^+ + \pi^+ + \pi^-$$
$$\Lambda^0 \rightarrow p + \pi^-$$
$$\Sigma^\pm \rightarrow n + \pi^\pm$$
$$\Xi^- \rightarrow \Lambda^0 + \pi^-$$
$$K^\pm \rightarrow \pi^\pm + \pi^0$$

$$K^{\pm} \to \mu^{\pm} + \nu$$
$$K^0 \to \pi^+ + \pi^-.$$

All reactions such as these have been observed and are consistent with half lives of the order of 10^{-10} sec.

Both a strong force reaction and a weak force reaction are illustrated in Fig. 20-9. The production of a Λ^0 baryon and a K^0 meson is shown. These two particles then decay within the field of the photograph. The formation of the particles involves strong interactions, and the decay reactions result from weak interactions.

20-6. Elementary Particles. The bewildering array of particles described in previous articles in this chapter has grown from what a few years ago was called the elementary particles, that is, the electron, proton and perhaps neutron. The latest experimental evidence now shows that these particles are not at all elementary. Both the proton and the neutron appear to be collections of pi-mesons. A dense core of mesons of radius 2×10^{-16} m appears to be surrounded by two concentric shells of mesons. In the proton the charge is the same in core and shells while the neutron cancels its positive core and outer shell with a negative inner shell. Recent experiments[13] indicate that two other mesons, the ω-meson and ρ-meson with masses of about 1500 m_0, participate in the structure of the proton and neutron. They are not shown in Table 20-1 or Fig. 20-8.

As nuclear machines and techniques improve, a deeper probe is made into the particles which make up matter. The truly elementary particle seems more remote than ever.

PROBLEMS

20-1. An *ion pair* is formed when an electron is completely removed from an atom. Measurements show that 34 ev of energy are required on the average to form an ion pair. How many ion pairs might a cosmic proton of 10 Bev of energy create?

20-2. Cosmic-ray background produces 8.1 ion pairs $cm^{-3} sec^{-1}$ in an ionization chamber at sea level. What current per cubic centimeter is produced?

20-3. Since Eq. 20-1 is a distribution function, employ the methods of Chapter 5 to compute the average energy of high-energy range cosmic-ray protons.

20-4. Plot dN/dE versus E for the spectrum of primary cosmic rays given in Eq. 20-1. Choose the most appropriate type of graph paper.

20-5. Calculate the velocity of a proton with a kinetic energy of 200 Mev, 10 Bev, 10^{10} Bev.

20-6. Calculate the kinetic energy of a proton with a speed 0.2c, 0.9c, 0.999c, 0.99999c.

[13] B. C. Maglic, L. W. Alverz, A. H. Rosenfeld, and M. L. Stevenson, *Phys. Rev. Letters*, **7**, 178 (1961).

20–7. Calculate the momenta and wavelength of the protons of Problem 20–5.

20–8. Calculate the momenta and wavelength of the protons of Problem 20–6.

20–9. What will be the radius of the path of protons having the energies specified in Problem 20–5 in a magnetic flux density of 3×10^{-5} weber m^{-2} if the protons are moving in a plane perpendicular to the field?

20–10. Calculate the radius of the path of the protons having the speed specified in Problem 20–6 in a magnetic flux density of 2×10^{-5} weber m^{-2} if the protons are moving in a plane perpendicular to the field.

20–11. What energy proton would just circle the earth in a plane containing the geomagnetic equator? (Earth's radius $= 6.37 \times 10^6$ m; B at surface of earth at magnetic equator $= 3 \times 10^{-5}$ weber m^{-2}.)

20–12. Because of the earth's magnetic field only about 10% of the total cosmic ray flux strikes the earth. What is the total number striking the earth per second? If these are all protons, what electric current does this amount to? How fast would this current increase the earth's potential?

20–13. If cosmic-ray background amounts to 1400 particles cm^{-2} hour^{-1}, what current would this amount to if all particles were singly charged?

20–14. If cosmic particles have an average energy of 5 Bev, use the data of Problem 20–13 to compare the energy delivered to the earth's surface by cosmic rays to that delivered by the sun and the stars. The solar constant is 2 cal cm^{-2} min^{-1}, the starlight constant is approximately 4×10^{-9} cal cm^{-2} min^{-1}.

20–15. What is the greatest number of electron pairs that could be formed in an electron shower by a 15 Bev proton primary?

20–16. What angle should separate the two photons when a 0.5 Mev positive electron annihilates an electron originally at rest?

20–17. What must be the energy of the photon that will just produce a proton pair?

20–18. Check the conservation of strangeness for all the strong reactions listed in Art. 20–5.

20–19. In weak interactions, strangeness is not conserved but changes by ± 1. Can a Ξ decay to a nucleon directly? Find a suitable chain of events.

SELECTED REFERENCES

HEISENBERG, W. *Cosmic Radiation*. Dover Publishers, Inc., New York, 1946. Chap. 1.
LEIGHTON, R. B. *Principles of Modern Physics*. McGraw-Hill Book Co., Inc., New York, 1959. Chaps 20 and 21.
MONTGOMERY, D. J. X. *Cosmic Ray Physics*. Princeton Univ. Press, Princeton, N. J., 1949. Chaps. 3 and 4.
TH. R DIKE, A. M. *Mesons*. McGraw-Hill Book Co., Inc., New York, 1952. Chaps. 1, 2, and 3.

APPENDIX

A

Units

The choice of a set of units is usually a very personal matter. All the different sets have certain advantages over the others, at least in the eyes of some. The British Engineering System (foot, slug, second, pound force) is favored by British and U. S. engineers because materials are generally purchased in such units and manufacturers are accustomed to specifications in this set. Physicists and chemists tend to prefer the more universal metric sets because of their more general use and the convenience of the decimal feature. The choice between the cgs (centimeter, gram, second, dyne) and mks (meter, kilogram, second, newton) set is usually determined by custom or personal preference regarding the location of certain constants in the formulas used. At the present time there is a tendency to use mks units, probably because of the increased interest in electrical phenomena and a greater familiarity with the so-called practical units, ampere, volt, ohm, etc. But much of the literature is written using cgs units and the reader should at least know how to convert formulas and measurements from one system to another even though he may prefer to do his calculating and thinking in one particular set.

There should be no need to reproduce here the standard conversions between the mechanical units of the various systems. Most elementary textbooks in physics provide this information. The formulas for force, energy, etc., are the same regardless of the units used. The problems that require clarification are nearly all in the field of electromagnetism. Since the reader who has been "raised" on the mks system is particularly likely to need a description of the cgs system, the following is phrased from that point of view.

The mks system provides a single consistent set of formulas and units for computing electromagnetic effects. All of the interrelations between electrical and magnetic effects are accommodated by two basic constants ϵ_0, the permittivity of free space and μ_0, the permeability of free space. The factor 4π needs to be inserted in various formulas because the complete solid angle around a point is 4π steradians. Those preferring mks units have agreed to insert it in the elementary force equations while the cgs proponents usually leave it out of the force equations and insert it in other places. When the 4π is inserted in the force equations the system of units is called a *rationalized* set, thus in this text the mks system is a rationalized mks system.

The chain of reasoning leading to the definition of electrical units proceeds as follows: a current balance is used (see Fig. A–1) to define a unit

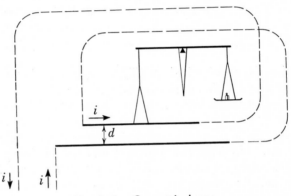

Fig. A–1.   Current balance.

of current, the *ampere*. It is that current which passing through two parallel wires d meters apart leads to a force of $(2/d) \times 10^{-7}$ newtons on each meter of one wire. This new unit can then be used to define the unit of charge; 1 coulomb = 1 ampere-second. It is also the unit from which the magnetic field intensity unit is derived, namely, an ampere per meter, by the formula

$$dH = \frac{1}{4\pi} \frac{i \, ds \times r}{r^3} \tag{A-1}$$

(see Eq. 3–24).

We can define the unit of potential difference (volt) as that potential difference which requires 1 joule of work to carry 1 coulomb across it. The familiar units of ohm and farad follow. The unit of magnetic flux is the weber. If the magnetic flux Φ through a circuit is given in webers, then the emf developed in the circuit as Φ changes is, according to Faraday's law of electromagnetic induction

$$V = \frac{d\Phi}{dt} \qquad \text{(A-2)}$$

with V in volts. The flux density B is then in webers per square meter. One can show that Faraday's law and Eq. 3–28,

$$\mathbf{dF} = i\,\mathbf{ds} \times \mathbf{B}, \qquad \text{(A-3)}$$

are consistent. But now one can compare $\mathbf{H}$ and $\mathbf{B}$, and in free space it turns out that

$\mathbf{B}$ (webers per square meter) $= 4\pi \times 10^{-7}\mathbf{H}$ (ampere per meter)

$$= \mu_0\mathbf{H}. \qquad \text{(A-4)}$$

In fact the definition of the ampere and the combination of Eq. A–1 and Eq. A–2 are based upon the choice of $\mu_0 = 4\pi \times 10^{-7}$. This quantity is in weber per ampere-meter. An equivalent unit is a henry per meter. A henry is the unit of inductance such that if the current in one part of a circuit is changing at the rate of 1 ampere per second, the emf produced in another (or same) part of the circuit is 1 volt.

Next, one can experimentally evaluate the constant in Coulomb's law. It is convenient to write this in the form

$$F = \frac{1}{4\pi\epsilon_0}\,\frac{q_1 q_2}{r^2}. \qquad \text{(A-5)}$$

(see Eq. 1–17). The experiments show that $\epsilon_0 = 8.854 \times 10^{-12}$ f m^{-1} and $1/4\pi\epsilon_0 = 8.988 \times 10^9$ ($\simeq 9.0 \times 10^9$). Theory and experiment show that the velocity of light

$$c = 1/\sqrt{\mu_0\epsilon_0} = 2.997 \times 10^8 \text{ m sec}^{-1}.$$

Two separate cgs systems were developed to handle electrical and magnetic problems. One of these is particularly useful when magnetic effects are involved. For that system, a current balance with wires d centimeters apart is used to define the electromagnetic unit of current (emu of current or abampere). It is that current for which the force on one wire is $2/d$ dynes per centimeter of its length. This corresponds to

$$dH = i\,\mathbf{ds} \times \frac{\mathbf{r}}{r^3}, \qquad \text{(A-6)}$$

$$\mathbf{B} = 1\mathbf{H} \quad \text{(for free space)}, \qquad \text{(A-7)}$$

and

$$\mathbf{dF} = i\,\mathbf{ds} \times \mathbf{B}. \qquad \text{(A-8)}$$

The unit of magnetic field intensity is the oersted and that for flux density is the gauss. The unit of magnetomotive force (an oersted-centimeter) is a gilbert. The unit of flux (a gauss-cm^2) is a maxwell. From an abampere, the abcoulomb (electromagnetic unit of charge) is defined in an obvious way. From this is defined the unit of potential difference, the abvolt (emu of potential difference), as that potential difference which requires 1 erg of work to carry 1 abcoulomb across it, and we have for an emf induced by a flux change $V = d\Phi/dt$ in these units. This set of units does not furnish a convenient set of formulas for electrostatics experiments. In fact the force between two charges expressed in ab units is

$$F = 9 \times 10^{20} \frac{q_1 q_2}{r^2} .$$

A more satisfactory set of units was developed to treat such systems.

The electrostatic units are based on Coulomb's law, choosing the constant to be unity. Thus, if the charges are measured in electrostatic units of charge (esu of charge or statcoulombs),

$$F = \frac{q_1 q_2}{r^2} . \qquad (A\text{--}9)$$

An electrostatic unit of potential difference (esu of P.D., statvolt) is that potential difference for which one erg of work must be done to carry 1 statcoulomb across it. The unit of electric field intensity is the dyne per statcoulomb or statvolt per centimeter. The electrostatic unit of current (statampere) is inappropriate for the calculations of H or determination of forces on currents.

The abcoulomb is large—the statcoulomb is small.

$$1 \text{ abcoulomb} = 3 \times 10^{10} \text{ statcoulomb};$$

$$1 \text{ abampere} = 3 \times 10^{10} \text{ statampere}.$$

The statvolt is large—the abvolt is small.

$$1 \text{ statvolt} = 3 \times 10^{10} \text{ abvolts}.$$

The ratio between the size of units of charge or potential difference is $c = 2.998 \times 10^{10} \simeq 3 \times 10^{10}$ and is theoretically and experimentally the velocity of propagation of an electromagnetic wave in free space in centimeters per second.

The existence of two sets of cgs units has been handled by various authors in a number of ways. Some shift back and forth without much concern in showing which they used since it is usually clear to anyone familiar with the field. One commonly followed procedure (and the one used in this book) uses esu for all electrical units such as charge current, electric field intensity, potential difference, capacitance, etc., and emu for all magnetic units such as magnetic field intensity, flux, flux density. In this system, the Gaussian system, Eq. A–6 and Eq. A–8 become,

$$dH = \frac{i}{c} \, ds \times \frac{r}{r^3}$$

and

$$dF = \frac{i}{c} \, ds \times B$$

since the current in emu is i/c if i is in statamperes.

A table of relations is given in Table A–1. There are gaps where the quantity is practically never used. The asterisk(*) is used to mark the Gaussian system.

TABLE A–1

Table of Equivalents

Quantity	mks	cgs stat	cgs ab
Charge	1 coulomb	is 3×10^9 statcoul*	or $\frac{1}{10}$ abcoul
Current	1 ampere	is 3×10^9 statamp*	or $\frac{1}{10}$ abamp
Potential difference	1 volt	is $1/300$ statvolt*	or 10^8 abvolt
Electric field	1 volt per meter	is $1/30{,}000$ statvolt cm^{-1}*	or 10^6 abvolt cm^{-1}
Magnetomotive force	1 ampere	is	$4\pi/10$ gilbert*
Magnetic field	1 ampere per meter	is	$4\pi \times 10^{-3}$ oersted*
Magnetic flux	1 weber	is	10^8 maxwell*
Flux density	1 weber per square meter	is	10^4 gauss*
Magnetic moment	1 ampere-square meter	is	10^3 erg gauss^{-1}
Capacitance	1 farad	is 9×10^{11} cm (statfarad)*	or 10^{-9} abfarad
Inductance	1 henry	is $\dfrac{1}{9 \times 10^{11}}$ stathenry	or 10^9 abhenry*
Resistance	1 ohm	is $\dfrac{1}{9 \times 10^{11}}$ statohm*	or 10^9 abohm

* Gaussian system.

Table A–2 consists of commonly used formulas in the different unit systems. The column on Gaussian units has the appropriate units indicated. In the other cgs systems all units in a formula belong to that system. Several formulas given are rarely used, if ever.

TABLE A–2

Some Formulas in Different Units

Formula for	mks	cgs (esu)	cgs (emu)	cgs Gaussian
Coulomb's law	$F = \dfrac{q_1 q_2}{4\pi\epsilon_0 r^2}$	$F = \dfrac{q_1 q_2}{r^2}$	$F = c^2 \dfrac{q_1 q_2}{r^2}$	$F = \dfrac{q_1 q_2}{r^2}$
Force on a charge	$\mathbf{F} = \mathbf{E}q$	$\mathbf{F} = \mathbf{E}q$	$\mathbf{F} = \mathbf{E}q$	$\mathbf{F} = \mathbf{E}q$
Potential due to point charge	$V = \dfrac{q}{4\pi\epsilon_0 r}$	$V = \dfrac{q}{r}$	$V = \dfrac{c^2 q}{r}$	$V = \dfrac{q}{r}$
Electric field between paralle plates	$E = \dfrac{\Delta V}{d}$	$E = \dfrac{\Delta V}{d}$	$E = \dfrac{\Delta V}{d}$	$E = \dfrac{\Delta V}{d}$
Magnetic field in a solenoid	$H = i\dfrac{n}{l}$	$H \text{ (esu)} = 4\pi \dfrac{n}{l} i \text{ (esu)}$	$H \text{ (oersted)} = 4\pi \dfrac{n}{l} i \text{ (emu)}$	$H \text{ (oersted)} = 4\pi \dfrac{ni}{lc} \text{ (esu)}$
Magnetic field around a wire	$H = \dfrac{i}{2\pi R}$	$H \text{ (esu)} = \dfrac{2i \text{ (esu)}}{R}$	$H \text{ (oersted)} = \dfrac{2i \text{ (emu)}}{R}$	$H \text{ (oersted)} = \dfrac{2i \text{ (esu)}}{cR}$
Force on wire	$F = iLB$	$F = \dfrac{i \text{ (esu)} LB \text{ (esu)}}{c^2}$	$F = i \text{ (emu)} LB \text{ (gauss)}$	$F = \dfrac{i \text{ (esu)} LB \text{ (gauss)}}{c}$
Magnetic moment of current loop	$M = iA$	$M \text{ (esu)} = i \text{ (esu)} A$	$M \text{ (emu)} = i \text{ (emu)} A$	$M \text{ (emu)} = \dfrac{i \text{ (esu)} A}{c}$
Bohr magneton	$\mu_B = \dfrac{e\hbar}{2m}$	$\mu_B \text{ (esu)} = \dfrac{e \text{ (esu)} \hbar}{2m}$	$\mu_B \text{ (emu)} = \dfrac{e \text{ (emu)} \hbar}{2m}$	$\mu_B \text{ (emu)} = \dfrac{e \text{ (esu)} \hbar}{2mc}$

B

Complex Numbers

As an introduction to complex numbers consider the roots of a quadratic equation such as

$$x^2 - 6x + 13 = 0. \tag{B-1}$$

The quadratic formula leads to two roots

$$x_1 = 3 + \sqrt{-4}$$

and

$$x_2 = 3 - \sqrt{-4}.$$

These are often written in the form

$$x_1 = 3 + 2i \tag{B-2}$$

and

$$x_2 = 3 - 2i,$$

where

$$i = \sqrt{-1}. \tag{B-3}$$

Quantities such as these roots are called *complex numbers*. They have a *real part*, 3, and an *imaginary part*, 2 or -2.

The rules of addition and subtraction for complex numbers are

$$(a + ib) + (c + id) = a + c + (b + d)i, \tag{B-4}$$
$$(a + ib) - (c + id) = (a - c) + (b - d)i. \tag{B-5}$$

The commutative and associative laws hold.

The rules of multiplication seem more arbitrary, but are the only ones that are useful. The product is

$$(a + ib)(c + id) = ac - bd + (ad + bc)i. \tag{B-6}$$

You will note that ordinary algebraic multiplication plus the property

453

$i^2 = -1$ has been used. Here the usual commutative and distributive
laws hold.

If we represent the complex number $a + ib$ by k, that is

$$k = a + ib,$$

the quantity

$$k^* = a - ib \tag{B-7}$$

is called the *complex conjugate* of k. You will note that the complex conjugate of k^* is $(k^*)^* = k$. You will also note that the two roots of a
quadratic such as Eq. B–1 are complex conjugates of each other. The
product $kk^* = a^2 + b^2$ is always real. Its positive square root is called
the *modulus* or *absolute value of k* and is written

$$\sqrt{kk^*} = |k|. \tag{B-8}$$

Division of complex numbers must have the usual property that if

$$\frac{a + ib}{c + id} = e + if \tag{B-9}$$

then

$$(e + if)(c + id) = a + ib.$$

The usual way to find this ratio is to multiply numerator and denominator
by the complex conjugate of the denominator, thus

$$\frac{a + ib}{c + id} \cdot \frac{c - id}{c - id} = \frac{ac + bd}{c^2 + d^2} + \frac{bc - ad}{c^2 + d^2} i. \tag{B-10}$$

Another form for designating a complex number makes use of an
exponential with an imaginary exponent. The complex number can be
written in the two equivalent ways (the first is called the *Cartesian* form
and the second is called the *Euler* form),

$$z = x + iy$$

$$z = r \exp i\theta = r \cos \theta + ir \sin \theta. \tag{B-11}$$

[In this text we have used exp (for exponential) in place of the natural
log base e with superscripts. Thus, $\exp u = e^u$.]

That this is so can be seen by noting that the infinite series that represents $\exp u$ is

$$\exp u = 1 + u + \frac{u^2}{2!} + \frac{u^3}{3!} + \frac{u^4}{4!} + \cdots + \frac{u^n}{n!} + \cdots, \tag{B-12}$$

and the series for $\sin \theta$ and $\cos \theta$ are respectively

$$\sin \theta = \theta - \frac{\theta^3}{3!} + \frac{\theta^5}{5!} - \frac{\theta^7}{7!} + \cdots, \tag{B-13}$$

and

$$\cos\theta = 1 - \frac{\theta^2}{2!} + \frac{\theta^4}{4!} - \frac{\theta^6}{6!} + \cdots. \qquad \text{(B–14)}$$

Thus

$$\exp i\theta = 1 + i\theta + \frac{i^2\theta^2}{2!} + \frac{i^3\theta^3}{3!} + \frac{i^4\theta^4}{4!} + \cdots$$

$$= 1 + \frac{i^2\theta^2}{2!} + \frac{i^4\theta^4}{4!} + \cdots + i\theta + \frac{i^3\theta^3}{3!} + \frac{i^5\theta^5}{5!} + \cdots$$

$$= 1 - \frac{\theta^2}{2!} + \frac{\theta^4}{4!} - \cdots + i\left(\theta - \frac{\theta^3}{3!} + \frac{\theta^5}{5!} - \cdots\right)$$

$$= \cos\theta + i\sin\theta.$$

Multiplication and division are particularly easy in the Euler form.

$$z_1 z_2 = r_1 \exp(i\theta_1) r_2 \exp(i\theta_2)$$

$$= r_1 r_2 \exp i(\theta_1 + \theta_2), \qquad \text{(B–15)}$$

and

$$\frac{z_1}{z_2} = \frac{r_1}{r_2} \exp i(\theta_1 - \theta_2). \qquad \text{(B–16)}$$

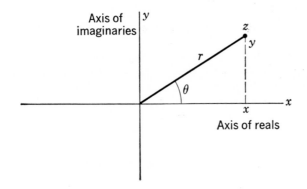

Fig. B–1. Argand diagram.

The complex conjugate also has a simple form.   If

$$z = r \exp i\theta$$

then

$$z^* = r \exp -i\theta. \qquad \text{(B–17)}$$

Both the Cartesian form $z = x + iy$ and the Euler form can be represented graphically in what is called an Argand diagram. See Fig. B–1. It is seen that the polar coordinates r and θ and the Cartesian coordinates

x and y have the proper relation to be expected from the Cartesian form and the Euler form for z, namely,

$$x = r \cos \theta$$

$$y = r \sin \theta.$$

Since

$$r^2 = x^2 + y^2 = r^2 (\cos^2 \theta + \sin^2 \theta),$$

r is the modulus or absolute value of z. The angle θ is called the phase of z.

It will be noted that addition of two complex numbers corresponds to the addition of two vectors in a plane. See Fig. B–2.

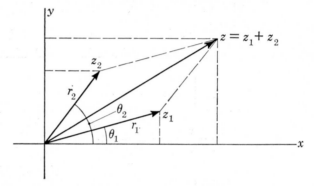

Fig. B–2. Addition of complex numbers graphically on Argand diagram.

All normal algebraic and geometric processes can be carried out with such quantities. One need only remember that

$$i^2 = -1.$$

C

Fourier Series, Fourier Integrals,
Wave Packets

One of the important applications of sinusoidal functions is the representation of other functions by an expansion in a series of sinusoidal functions, or by an expansion in an integral of sinusoidal functions. The series is used for periodic functions and the integral for aperiodic functions. There are limitations on the behavior of the functions that can be represented by such a Fourier analysis, but at least any continuous function, or one with a finite number of finite discontinuities, can be represented, if the function is properly defined at the discontinuities.

A function $f(t)$ that is periodic with period τ [so that $f(t + \tau) = f(t)$] can be written

$$f(t) = \frac{1}{2} a_0 + \sum_{n=1}^{\infty} \left(a_n \cos \frac{2\pi n}{\tau} t + b_n \sin \frac{2\pi n}{\tau} t \right). \qquad \text{(C-1)}$$

The constant coefficients a_0, a_n, and b_n are determined by the integrals

$$a_0 = \frac{2}{\tau} \int_0^\tau f(t) \, dt,$$

$$a_n = \frac{2}{\tau} \int_0^\tau f(t) \cos \frac{2\pi n}{\tau} t \, dt, \qquad \text{(C-2)}$$

$$b_n = \frac{2}{\tau} \int_0^\tau f(t) \sin \frac{2\pi n}{\tau} t \, dt.$$

Since each term of the series may be thought of as having a frequency that is an integral multiple of $\nu = 1/\tau$ these coefficients may be thought of as the amplitudes of the various harmonics. How such a series represents a function may be illustrated by Fig. C–1 in which a fundamental

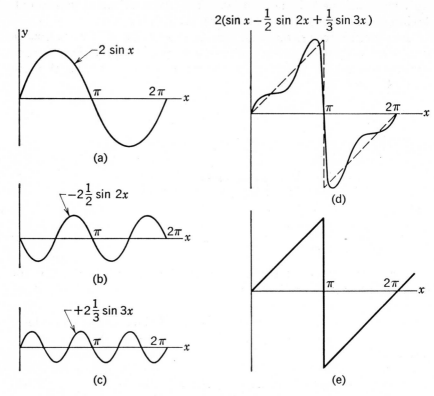

Fig. C–1.   The combination of harmonics to form a periodic function.

(a) and two harmonics (b) and (c) are added (d) to give a function ap-
proximating the saw-tooth form (e).   As more terms are included the
approximation becomes better.

That the coefficients given by Eq. C–2 are the proper ones can be
verified by multiplying Eq. C–1 by $\cos (2\pi m/\tau)t$ and then integrating from
0 to τ.   Since

$$\int_0^\tau \cos \frac{2\pi n}{\tau} t \cos \frac{2\pi m}{\tau} t \, dt = 0, \; n \neq m,$$

$$\int_0^\tau \cos \frac{2\pi n}{\tau} t \sin \frac{2\pi m}{\tau} t \, dt = 0, \qquad\qquad \text{(C–3)}$$

and

$$\int_0^\tau \cos^2 \frac{2\pi m}{\tau} t \, dt = \int_0^\tau \sin^2 \frac{2\pi m}{\tau} t \, dt = \frac{1}{2} \tau.$$

Only one term, the mth term, remains from which a_n can be determined. Multiplication by $\sin (2\pi m/\tau)t$, similarly leads to b_n.

It is possible to generalize the infinite series of Eq. C–1 by passing to a limit in which the frequency difference between adjacent Fourier components becomes infinitesimal and the series becomes an integral which may have the form,

$$f(t) = \frac{1}{\sqrt{2\pi}} \left[\int_{-\infty}^{\infty} a(\omega) \cos \omega t \, d\omega + \int_{-\infty}^{\infty} b(\omega) \sin \omega t \, d\omega \right], \quad \text{(C–4)}$$

with

$$a(\omega) = \frac{1}{\sqrt{2\pi}} \int_{-\infty}^{\infty} f(y) \cos \omega y \, dy \quad \text{(C–5)}$$

and

$$b(\omega) = \frac{1}{\sqrt{2\pi}} \int_{-\infty}^{\infty} f(y) \sin \omega y \, dy. \quad \text{(C–6)}$$

This is called a Fourier integral. It is often more convenient to use the complex exponential. In this case

$$f(t) = \frac{1}{\sqrt{2\pi}} \int_{-\infty}^{\infty} g(\omega) \exp (i\omega t) \, d\omega \quad \text{(C–7)}$$

where

$$g(\omega) = \frac{1}{\sqrt{2\pi}} \int_{-\infty}^{\infty} f(s) \exp (-i\omega s) \, ds. \quad \text{(C–8)}$$

The functions $a(\omega)$ and $g(\omega)$ may be thought of as the amplitude of the component of angular frequency $\omega = 2\pi\nu$ in analogy to a_n and b_n of Eq. C–1.

An example is the case in which $b(\omega) = 0$ for all values of ω and in which $a(\omega) = 0$ except between $\omega = -\Omega$ and $\omega = +\Omega$ where it is $\sqrt{2\pi}/2\Omega$. Then

$$f(t) = \frac{1}{2\Omega} \int_{-\Omega}^{\Omega} \cos \omega t \, d\omega = \frac{1}{2\Omega t} \int_{-\Omega'}^{\Omega'} \cos \omega t \, d(\omega t)$$

$$= \frac{\sin \Omega t}{\Omega t}. \quad \text{(C–9)}$$

A plot of the function and the spectrum of the Fourier transform $a(\omega)$ is shown in Fig. C–2. This plot shows that if the spectrum is made narrower, by making Ω smaller, the function spreads out and becomes more nearly like a pure sinusoidal wave. On the other hand, it is possible to limit the region in which $f(t)$ is appreciable by letting Ω become large.

In fact the product of the "width" $2\pi/\Omega$ of $f(t)$ and Ω is of the order of 2π.

Sinusoidal waves can also be combined in a similar way. Consider a monochromatic wave, $\cos(kx - \omega t)$ in which k, the propagation constant, is $2\pi/\lambda$. The ratio

$$\frac{\omega}{k} = \frac{2\pi\nu}{\dfrac{2\pi}{\lambda}} = \nu\lambda = V \tag{C-10}$$

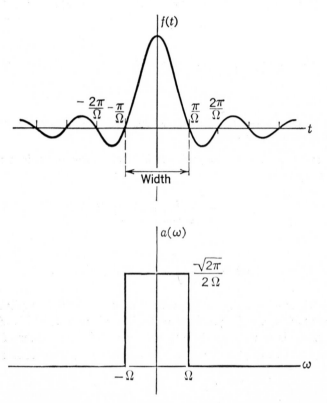

Fig. C–2. Fourier integral representation and spectrum of Fourier transform.

is the phase velocity. This may be constant or may be a function of either k or ω (λ or ν). Next, consider a combination of many such waves of different k's summed over k. At any moment, this represents a particular function of x and as t progresses the wave is propagated. If V is a constant, the shape of the wave is unchanged and the propagation velocity is V. If, on the other hand, V is a function of k, then the pattern will change and the main features will be propagated at a speed, $u = d\omega/dk$, the group velocity.

An illustration of this behavior is to be found in the wave,

$$f(x,t) = \int_{k_0 - \Delta k}^{k_0 + \Delta k} a(k) \cos(kx - \omega t)\, dk \qquad \text{(C–11)}$$

where $a(k)$ is a very slowly varying function of k and where

$$\omega(k) = \omega(k_0) + (k - k_0)\left(\frac{d\omega}{dk}\right)_0.$$

For any time t, the evaluation of Eq. C–11 is

$$f(x,t) = 2a(k_0)\, \Delta k \cos(k_0 x - \omega_0 t)\, \frac{\sin \Delta k\left[x - \left(\dfrac{d\omega}{dk}\right)_0 t\right]}{\Delta k\left[x - \left(\dfrac{d\omega}{dk}\right)_0 t\right]}. \qquad \text{(C–12)}$$

It will be seen that this is a modulated monochromatic wave with a wavelength $\lambda_0 = 2\pi/k_0$ whose envelope is

$$\frac{\sin \Delta k(x - ut)}{\Delta k(x - ut)}, \qquad \text{(C–13)}$$

where $u = (d\omega/dk)_0$. This envelope is small everywhere except where the denominator of the fraction is small, that is, except near $x = ut$. Therefore the region where $f(x,t)$ is appreciably different from zero moves along at the speed, $u = (d\omega/dk)_0$, the group velocity. This type of wave is called a *wave packet*.

D

The Solution of the Problem of the Hydrogen Atom

The proper form for the Schroedinger wave equation is determined by the expression for the potential energy of the electron in the field due to the nucleus. The potential energy is

$$V = \frac{-e^2}{4\pi\epsilon_0 r}. \qquad \left[V = -\frac{e^2}{r}. \right] \qquad \text{(D–1)}$$

Thus the Schroedinger wave equation is

$$\left(\frac{\partial^2\psi}{\partial x^2} + \frac{\partial^2\psi}{\partial y^2} + \frac{\partial^2\psi}{\partial z^2} \right) + \frac{2\mu}{\hbar^2}\left[W + \frac{e^2}{4\pi\epsilon_0\sqrt{x^2+y^2+z^2}} \right]\psi = 0, \qquad \text{(D–2)}$$

where μ is the mass of the electron. This equation is not in an easy form to find its well-behaved solutions. Because V has radial symmetry we are led to try the equation in spherical coordinates, r, θ, and ϕ. The equation then becomes

$$\frac{1}{r^2}\left[\frac{\partial}{\partial r}\left(r^2 \frac{\partial\psi}{\partial r} \right) + \frac{1}{\sin\theta}\frac{\partial}{\partial\theta}\left(\sin\theta \frac{\partial\psi}{\partial\theta} \right) + \frac{1}{\sin^2\theta}\frac{\partial^2\psi}{\partial\phi^2} \right]$$

$$+ \frac{2\mu}{\hbar^2}\left[W + \frac{e^2}{4\pi\epsilon_0 r} \right]\psi = 0. \qquad \text{(D–3)}$$

Let us now separate variables by assuming that

$$\psi(r,\theta,\phi) = R(r)\,\Theta(\theta)\Phi(\phi). \qquad \text{(D–4)}$$

We put this into Eq. D–3 (note that we now have ordinary derivatives) and divide by $\psi/(r^2 \sin^2\theta)$ to get

$$\frac{\sin^2\theta}{R}\frac{d}{dr}\left(r^2 \frac{dR}{dr} \right) + \frac{\sin\theta}{\Theta}\frac{d}{d\theta}\left(\sin\theta \frac{d\Theta}{d\theta} \right)$$

462

$$+ \frac{2W\mu r^2 \sin^2 \theta}{\hbar^2} + \frac{2e^2 \mu r \sin^2 \theta}{4\pi\epsilon_0 \hbar^2} = -\frac{1}{\Phi}\frac{d^2\Phi}{d\phi^2}. \quad \text{(D-5)}$$

Both sides are independent and hence can be set equal to a constant, here m^2. The right-hand side gives

$$\frac{d^2\Phi}{d\phi^2} + m^2\Phi = 0. \quad \text{(D-6)}$$

The left-hand side can be written

$$\frac{1}{R}\frac{d}{dr}\left(r^2\frac{dR}{dr}\right) + \frac{2W\mu r^2}{\hbar^2} + \frac{2e^2\mu r}{4\pi\epsilon_0\hbar^2} = -\frac{1}{\Theta \sin\theta}\frac{d}{d\theta}\left(\sin\theta\frac{d\Theta}{d\theta}\right) + \frac{m^2}{\sin^2\theta}. \quad \text{(D-7)}$$

Again we have two independent expressions which must be constant. We set these equal to $-l(l+1)$; and get

$$\frac{1}{\sin\theta}\frac{d}{d\theta}\left(\sin\theta\frac{d\Theta}{d\theta}\right) + \left[l(l+1) - \frac{m^2}{\sin^2\theta}\right]\Theta = 0, \quad \text{(D-8)}$$

and

$$\frac{1}{r^2}\frac{d}{dr}\left(r^2\frac{dR}{dr}\right) + \frac{2\mu}{\hbar^2}\left[W + \frac{e^2}{4\pi\epsilon_0 r} - \frac{\hbar^2 l(l+1)}{2\mu r^2}\right]R = 0. \quad \text{(D-9)}$$

The solutions of Eq. D-6 are

$$\Phi_m(\phi) = A \exp \pm im\phi. \quad \text{(D-10)}$$

If Φ is to be well behaved, it must be single valued; so m must be a real integer. The double sign in the exponential may be dropped by writing

$$\Phi_m(\phi) = A \exp im\phi \quad \text{(D-10')}$$

where m is a positive or negative real integer, $\cdots -2, -1, 0, 1, 2, \cdots$. Eq. D-8 can be rewritten

$$\frac{d}{du}\left[(1-u^2)\frac{dP}{du}\right] + \left[l(l+1) - \frac{m^2}{1-u^2}\right]P = 0, \quad \text{(D-11)}$$

where $u = \cos\theta$ and hence $du = -\sin\theta\,d\theta$. This is the associated Legendre equation. The only well-behaved solutions are the associated Legendre polynomials

$$P = P_l^{|m|}(u)$$

which are obtained only if l is a positive integer and $|m| \leq l$. A few of these polynomials are:

$$P_0^0(u) = 1; \quad P_1^0(u) = u; \quad P_1^1(u) = (1-u^2)^{1/2};$$

$$P_2^0(u) = \tfrac{1}{2}(3u^2 - 1); \quad P_2^1(u) = 3u(1-u^2)^{1/2}; \quad P_2^2(u) = 3(1-u^2).$$

Thus we set

$$\Theta(\theta) = B_{m,l}P_l^m(\cos\theta). \quad \text{(D-12)}$$

The solution of the radial equation requires more manipulation. It is convenient to introduce a new variable $\rho = 2r/na_0$ where $a_0 = 4\pi\epsilon_0\hbar^2/\mu e^2 = 0.529$ Å, the radius of the first Bohr orbit. One then discovers that the resulting equation can have a well-behaved solution only if

$$W_n = \frac{-\mu e^4}{32\pi^2\epsilon_0^2\hbar^2 n^2} \qquad \left[W_n = \frac{-\mu e^4}{2n^2\hbar^2} \right] \tag{D-13}$$

with n any integer greater than zero. These are the same energy levels predicted by Bohr. The solutions of the radial equation are

$$R_{nl} = C_{nl} \exp\left(\frac{-\rho}{2}\right) \rho^l \, L_{n+l}^{2l+1}(\rho) \tag{D-14}$$

where L_{n+l}^{2l+1} is an associated Laguerre polynomial with $l < n$.

Note that W_n is independent of l and m. Thus there are n^2 different solutions for the same energy level W_n (n values of l, and $2l + 1$ values of m for each value of l). The degeneracy is n^2-fold. The usual normalization constants are

$$A_m = \frac{1}{\sqrt{2\pi}},$$

$$B_{ml} = \sqrt{\frac{(2l+1)(l-m)!}{2(l+m)!}}, \tag{D-15}$$

and

$$C_{ln} = \sqrt{\left(\frac{2}{na_0}\right)^3 \frac{(n-l-1)!}{2n(n+l)!^3}}.$$

These make

$$\int_0^{2\pi} \int_0^{\pi} \int_0^{\infty} \psi_{nlm}{}^* \psi_{nlm} r^2 \sin\theta \, dr \, d\theta \, d\phi = 1. \tag{D-16}$$

One can calculate many properties of the hydrogen atom knowing these wave functions. Two important examples are (a) the z-component of the angular momentum and (b) the square of the angular momentum. To determine whether we may expect to be able to measure either of these we need to construct an operator for each. Quantum rules say that in case (a) we have

$$(J_z)_{\text{op}} = -i\hbar \frac{\partial}{\partial\phi}. \tag{D-17}$$

Since

$$(J_z)_{\text{op}}\psi = -i\hbar \frac{\partial}{\partial\phi} R_{nl}\Theta_{lm}\Phi_m$$

$$= -i\hbar R_{nl}\Theta_{lm} \frac{\partial (A \exp im\phi)}{\partial \phi}$$

$$= \hbar m R_{nl}\Theta_{lm}\phi_m = m\hbar\psi, \qquad (D-18)$$

we know (see Art. 11–7) that we can measure the z-component of $\mathbf{J}$ and that our answer will be $m\hbar$. In case (b)

$$(J^2)_{op} = \frac{1}{\sin\theta}\frac{\partial}{\partial\theta}\left(\sin\theta\frac{\partial}{\partial\theta}\right) - \frac{m^2}{\sin^2\theta}, \qquad (D-19)$$

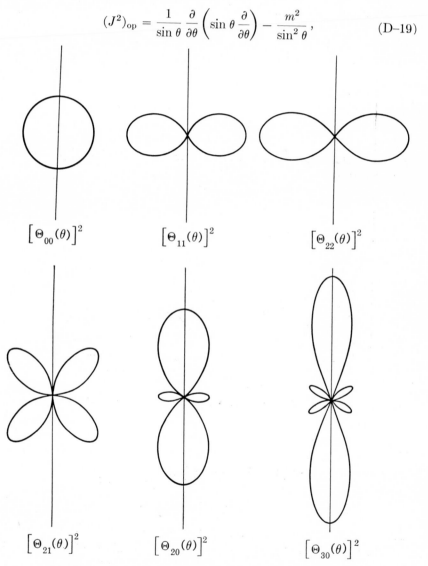

$$\left[\Theta_{00}(\theta)\right]^2 \qquad \left[\Theta_{11}(\theta)\right]^2 \qquad \left[\Theta_{22}(\theta)\right]^2$$

$$\left[\Theta_{21}(\theta)\right]^2 \qquad \left[\Theta_{20}(\theta)\right]^2 \qquad \left[\Theta_{30}(\theta)\right]^2$$

Fig. D–1. Angular dependence of the wave functions.

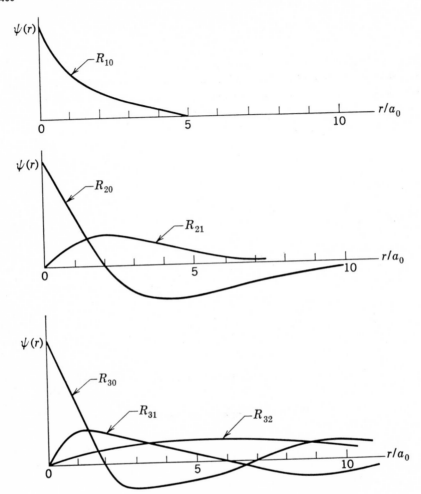

Fig. D–2.   The r-dependence of the wave functions.

and

$$(J^2)_{op}\psi = R\Phi \frac{1}{\sin\theta} \frac{d}{d\theta}\left(\sin\theta \frac{d\Theta}{d\theta}\right) - \frac{m^2\Theta}{\sin^2\theta}$$

$$= l(l+1)\hbar^2 R\Phi\Theta = l(l+1)\hbar^2\psi. \qquad (D\text{–}20)$$

Thus one can measure J^2 and the result will be $l(l+1)\hbar^2$.

The simplest of the states of hydrogen is the ground state.   It is the state for which $n = 1$, hence $l = 0$ and $m = 0$, and we have

$$\psi_{100} = \frac{1}{\sqrt{\pi}} \left(\frac{1}{a_0}\right)^{3/2} \exp -r/a_0.$$

The variation with ϕ of all states is sinusoidal (or independent of ϕ), but the charge or probability density is independent of ϕ. In Fig. D–1 we plot the variation of ψ with θ for several cases and in Fig. D–2 we plot the variation with r. The variation of $\psi^*\psi r^2\, dr$ (the probability of finding the electron between r and $r + dr$) is shown in Fig. D–3.

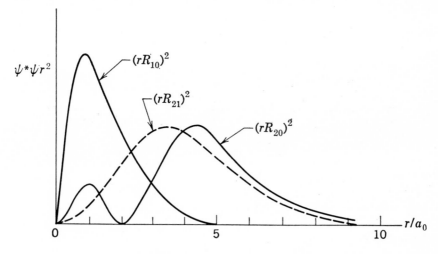

Fig. D–3.   The probability density.

E

Angular Momentum and Spectroscopy

In Chapter 12 it was pointed out that the angular momenta associated with various portions of the atom serve as very good labels for the various energy levels of an atom. The reason for this, of course, is that the angular momentum is constant unless some torque acts on the atom. Unless some external field, such as a magnetic field or an electric field, acts on the atom there will be no change in angular momentum. Even if such fields are applied, the component of the angular momentum along the field will be constant, since there will be no component of the torque parallel to the field.

Another fact which makes the study of angular momentum important is that, if the angular momentum is changed in some respect or other, it does influence the energy of the system. If it did not, its value (even though constant) would really be of little significance. For example, the penetration of the orbit depends upon the eccentricity of the orbit and this depends upon the angular momentum (in the language of wave mechanics—the probability density depends upon l). This means that the value of l does matter in the determination of the energy (except for hydrogen). Similarly the relative arrangements of several l's into L will affect the probability distribution and hence the energy. Another example is that the relative orientation of the spin angular momenta and orbital angular momenta affects the energy because of magnetic effects.

We shall, therefore, be interested in seeing what quantum mechanics demands regarding the behavior of angular momenta, and what the consequences are so far as spectroscopy is concerned.

E–1. Quantum Rules About Angular Momentum. The rules of quantum mechanics concerning angular momentum are arrived at by following the usual procedures of quantum mechanics, namely, by looking for eigenfunctions and eigenvalues for operators formed by the rules of Art. 11–7. The x-, y-, and z-components of the angular momentum $\mathbf{j}^1$ are

$$j_x = yp_z - p_y z,$$
$$j_y = zp_x - p_z x, \qquad \text{(E–1)}$$
$$j_z = xp_y - p_x y.$$

The proper operators for these are then formed.   For example,

$$(j_z)_{\text{op}} = -i\hbar \left(x \frac{\partial}{\partial y} - y \frac{\partial}{\partial x} \right)$$
$$= -i\hbar \frac{\partial}{\partial \phi}, \qquad \text{(E–2)}$$

where the z-axis is the polar axis of a set of spherical coordinates as in Fig. E–1.   The manipulation of the expression from rectangular coordi-

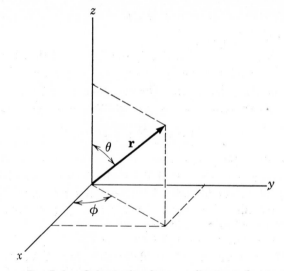

Fig. E–1.   Spherical polar coordinates r, θ, ϕ.

nates x, y, z to spherical coordinates r, θ, ϕ depends upon the fact that

$$\frac{\partial}{\partial x} = \frac{\partial r}{\partial x} \frac{\partial}{\partial r} + \frac{\partial \phi}{\partial x} \frac{\partial}{\partial \phi} + \frac{\partial \theta}{\partial x} \frac{\partial}{\partial \theta}, \qquad \text{(E–3)}$$

[1] The use of $\mathbf{j}$ to stand for angular momentum and j for a quantum number representing the magnitude of the angular momentum should cause no trouble if the reader pays close attention to the words used along with the expressions.

and similar expressions for $\partial/\partial y$ and $\partial/\partial z$; and that

$$\frac{\partial r}{\partial x} = \sin \theta \cos \phi; \qquad \frac{\partial r}{\partial y} = \sin \theta \sin \phi; \qquad \frac{\partial r}{\partial z} = \cos \theta;$$

$$\frac{\partial \theta}{\partial x} = \frac{1}{r} \cos \theta \cos \phi; \qquad \frac{\partial \theta}{\partial y} = \frac{1}{r} \cos \theta \sin \phi; \qquad \frac{\partial \theta}{\partial z} = -\frac{1}{r} \sin \theta; \quad \text{(E–4)}$$

$$\frac{\partial \phi}{\partial x} = -\frac{1}{r}\frac{\sin \phi}{\sin \theta}; \qquad \frac{\partial \phi}{\partial y} = \frac{1}{r}\frac{\cos \phi}{\sin \theta}; \qquad \frac{\partial \phi}{\partial z} = 0.$$

We now look for well-behaved solutions of

$$-i\hbar \frac{\partial \psi}{\partial \phi} = j_z \psi. \tag{E–5}$$

The eigenfunctions are

$$\psi = A \exp im\phi, \tag{E–6}$$

and the eigenvalues of j_z are

$$j_z = m\hbar, \tag{E–7}$$

where m must be an integer.

When we write the equations for j_y and j_x we find they have no eigenvalues (the reason for the special preference for the z-axis is that it has been chosen for the polar axis). The equation for $|\mathbf{j}|^2 = j_x{}^2 + j_y{}^2 + j_z{}^2$, however, does have eigenvalues and eigenfunctions. The eigenvalues of $|\mathbf{j}|^2$ are

$$|\mathbf{j}|^2 = j(j+1)\hbar^2 \tag{E–8}$$

where j is a positive integer or zero.

Other considerations show that the limitations on m and j just given are too stringent except for orbital type angular momenta. Intrinsic or spin type can include half integral values such as $\frac{1}{2}$, $\frac{3}{2}$, $\frac{5}{2}$, etc., but a given sequence must have integral differences.

The results are now summarized.

Rule 1. It is never possible to determine more than the magnitude and one component of the angular momentum of the whole of a system or any part of it at any one time.

Rule 2. The magnitude and one component of the angular momentum of a system can be described by using certain quantum numbers. These numbers may be integers, including zero, or half integers. No other numbers can be used.

Rule 3. In a sequence of permitted values of angular momentum, each quantum number must differ from its neighbor by 1.

Rule 4. The magnitude of the angular momentum described by a quantum number j is

$$|\mathbf{j}| = \hbar \sqrt{j(j+1)}. \tag{E–9}$$

Rule 5. The projection of the angular momentum in a certain direction (one component) is

$$j_z = m\hbar, \tag{E–10}$$

where $-j \leq m \leq j$.

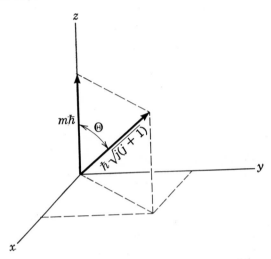

Fig. E–2.   Angular momentum diagram—the vector and its z-component.

Each of these rules is interesting in itself, but we want to comment especially upon two of them. The first is Rule 2. The surprising point here is that half integers are permitted as well as whole integers, even though Rule 3 keeps the half integral and whole integral values completely separated. The half integral values are rather special and will be discussed later in connection with the spin. The second is Rule 4. The value for $|\mathbf{j}|$, which may seem strange, is purely a quantum mechanical result, but has been found to give an accurate value while

$$|\mathbf{j}| = j\hbar$$

will not. This gives for the cosine of the angle Θ between the angular momentum and the z-axis

$$\cos \Theta = \frac{m}{\sqrt{j(j+1)}}. \tag{E–11}$$

See Fig. E–2 which shows how an angular momentum might be represented. Remember that j must be an integer or a half integer. The sum of two angular momenta $\mathbf{j}_1$ and $\mathbf{j}_2$, having quantum numbers j_1 and j_2 may be found as shown in Fig. E–3 where only the quantum numbers are written alongside of the vectors representing the angular momenta.

In this case, the quantum rules give the following expression for the angle α between $\mathbf{j}_1$ and $\mathbf{j}_2$:

$$\cos \alpha = \frac{J(J+1) - j_1(j_1+1) - j_2(j_2+1)}{2\sqrt{j_1(j_1+1)}\sqrt{j_2(j_2+1)}}. \qquad \text{(E–12)}$$

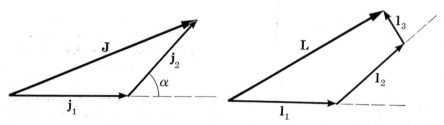

Fig. E–3.   Vector addition of angular momenta.   Fig. E–4.   Vector addition of several orbital angular momenta.

E–2. Electronic Spin and Adding Angular Momenta.

Around 1925, it was suggested by Uhlenbeck and Goudsmit that many of the peculiarities of optical spectra could be explained by postulating that each electron has an intrinsic angular momentum of its own, a spin $\mathbf{s}$, and that the quantum number describing it should be $s = \frac{1}{2}$. Note that the quantum mechanics includes this as a possibility. The quantum mechanical rules then say that

$$|\mathbf{s}| = \sqrt{\tfrac{1}{2} \cdot \tfrac{3}{2}}\, \hbar, \qquad \text{(E–13)}$$

and

$$s_z = +\tfrac{1}{2}\hbar \quad \text{or} \quad -\tfrac{1}{2}\hbar. \qquad \text{(E–14)}$$

The notation commonly used regarding these and other angular momenta is as follows: The letter l stands for the quantum number representing the orbital angular momentum of an individual electron (the angular momentum due to the motion of the electron in its orbit). The letter L stands for the resultant of several orbital angular momenta. We can, in fact, draw vector additions of orbital angular momenta using only the quantum numbers as we did in Fig. E–3. Thus, to find the total orbital angular momenta we use a figure such as Fig. E–4, which is appropriate to three electrons. We shall use s for the quantum number of each separate electronic spin (even though we know $s = \frac{1}{2}$) and S for the resultant. The figure showing a possible summing of spins for three electrons is Fig. E–5.

The total angular momentum of the atom, of course, is the sum of orbital *and* spin angular momenta. We will use J for the quantum number representing it. Fig. E–6 shows how L and S might be added. Under

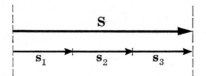

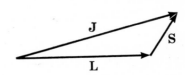

Fig. E–5.   Resultant spin angular momentum.

Fig. E–6.   The resultant angular momentum J is the vector sum of the resultant orbital and resultant spin angular momenta.

some circumstances, the spin and orbital angular momenta of each electron are added first, and the resultant, then, is represented by **j**. See Fig. E–7. The separate **j**'s may then be added to obtain **J** as shown in Fig. E–8.

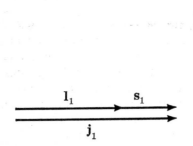

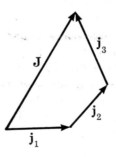

Fig. E–7.   The total angular momentum due to a single electron.

Fig. E–8.   The total angular momentum of the unpaired electrons.

The reason for going into all this, of course, is that each different combination of l's, s's, L's, S's, and J's give different energy levels as we have pointed out before. In Chapter 12 we have discussed the reasons for some of these effects. The details for complex atoms, of course, can be found in more advanced treatments.

Whether $\mathbf{L} = \mathbf{l}_1 + \mathbf{l}_2 + \mathbf{l}_3 + \cdots$, $\mathbf{S} = \mathbf{s}_1 + \mathbf{s}_2 + \mathbf{s}_3 + \cdots$ and $\mathbf{J} = \mathbf{L} + \mathbf{S}$ are all suitable for describing a state depends upon the relative importance of the electrostatic interaction between electrons and the magnetic interaction between the spin and orbital magnetic momenta. If the electrostatic interaction is most important, $\mathbf{L}$ and $\mathbf{S}$ are suitable and one says the atom has *Russell-Saunders coupling*. This is usually the case for atoms of low atomic number. If the spin-orbit interaction is more important, $\mathbf{L}$ and $\mathbf{S}$ no longer have a meaning. Instead $\mathbf{j}_1 = \mathbf{l}_1 + \mathbf{s}_1$, $\mathbf{j}_2 = \mathbf{l}_2 + \mathbf{s}_2$, etc. are the proper quantum numbers along with $\mathbf{J} = \mathbf{j}_1 + \mathbf{j}_2 + \mathbf{j}_3 + \cdots$. The atom is then said to have *j-j coupling*. Atoms with high Z and especially ionized atoms have strong tendencies toward j-j coupling. It is possible to find many cases in which neither $\mathbf{L}$ and $\mathbf{S}$ nor $\mathbf{j}_1$, $\mathbf{j}_2$, etc., have meaning. But in such cases of intermediate coupling $\mathbf{J}$ is still a good number and people often use either Russell-Saunders notation or j-j notation to label terms even though they are not really appropriate.

E–3. Russell-Saunders Term Designation. We shall now make use of the quantum laws for angular momentum to determine what terms are possible for atoms with various electron configurations. Actually, we shall present a number of examples to illustrate the rules. The problem is to determine the possible values of L, S, and J for the given configuration. Before doing so, we remind you that a configuration is determined when n and l for each electron is determined and that the standard notation calls for the representation of each l by a small letter s, p, d, f, g, h, etc., according as l is 0, 1, 2, 3, 4, 5, etc. and each L by the corresponding capital letters S, P, D etc. A presuperscript equal to $2S + 1$ is used to tell the multiplicity and a post-subscript gives the value of J. See Art. 12–4.

The exclusion principle limits the number of possibilities to some extent in the case of equivalent electrons (two electrons are said to be equivalent if they have the same values of n and of l). In fact a closed shell can only have $L = 0$, $S = 0$, and $J = 0$. We can disregard, therefore, any closed shells in a configuration. Our first examples also will consider only non-equivalent electrons to avoid the complications introduced by the exclusion principle.

In order to enumerate the possible values of L, S, and J one can use the following rules which result from the quantum rules for angular momentum:

1. For L: add all l's arithmetically. This gives the biggest value of L. See what is the shortest integral value of the resultant of the l's. This gives the smallest value of L. (In the case of two electrons $L_{\text{smallest}} = l_1 - l_2$, where l_1 is the larger of the two.) All values lying between these and differing by one are permitted.
2. For S: proceed as with L, but use s's. (Each $s = \frac{1}{2}$). All values lying between these and differing by one are permitted ones.
3. For J:

$$J_{\max} = L + S \qquad (E\text{–}15)$$

$$J_{\min} = |L - S|. \qquad (E\text{–}16)$$

All values differing by one between these are possible. We now put these rules to work.

EXAMPLE 1. One electron outside of a closed shell.

We see immediately that $L = l$, $S = \frac{1}{2}$, $J = L \pm \frac{1}{2}$.

Configuration				Terms
ns	$L = 0$	$S = \frac{1}{2}$	$J = \frac{1}{2}$	$^2S_{1/2}$
np	$L = 1$	$S = \frac{1}{2}$	$J = \frac{1}{2}, \frac{3}{2}$	$^2P_{1/2}\ ^2P_{3/2}$
nd	$L = 2$	$S = \frac{1}{2}$	$J = \frac{3}{2}, \frac{5}{2}$	$^2D_{3/2}\ ^2D_{5/2}$
nf	$L = 3$	$S = \frac{1}{2}$	$J = \frac{5}{2}, \frac{7}{2}$	$^2F_{5/2}\ ^2F_{7/2}$

EXAMPLE 2. Two electrons outside of a closed shell.

Configuration				Terms
$ns\ ms$	$L = 0$	$S = 0, 1$	$J = 0, 1$	$^1S_0\ ^3S_1$
$ns\ mp$	$L = 1$	$S = 0, 1$	$J = 0, 1, 2$	$^1P_1\ ^3P_0\ ^3P_1\ ^3P_2$
$ns\ md$	$L = 2$	$S = 0, 1$	$J = 1, 2, 3$	$^1D_2\ ^3D_1\ ^3D_2\ ^3D_3$
$np\ mp$	$L = 0$	$S = 0, 1$	$J = 0, 1$	$^1S_0\ ^3S_1$
	$L = 1$	$S = 0, 1$	$J = 0, 1, 2$	$^1P_1\ ^3P_0\ ^3P_1\ ^3P_2$
	$L = 2$	$S = 0, 1$	$J = 1, 2, 3$	$^1D_2\ ^3D_1\ ^3D_2\ ^3D_3$
$np\ md$	$L = 1$	$S = 0, 1$	$J = 0, 1, 2$	$^1P_1\ ^3P_0\ ^3P_1\ ^3P_2$
	$L = 2$	$S = 0, 1$	$J = 1, 2, 3$	$^1D_2\ ^3D_1\ ^3D_2\ ^3D_3$
	$L = 3$	$S = 0, 1$	$J = 2, 3, 4$	$^1F_3\ ^3F_2\ ^3F_3\ ^3F_4$

EXAMPLE 3. Three electrons outside of a closed shell.

Configuration				Terms
$ns\ ms\ rs$	$L = 0$	$S = \frac{1}{2}, \frac{3}{2}$	$J = \frac{1}{2}, \frac{3}{2}$	$^2S_{1/2}\ ^4S_{3/2}$
$ns\ ms\ rp$	$L = 1$	$S = \frac{1}{2}, \frac{3}{2}$	$J = \frac{1}{2}, \frac{3}{2}, \frac{5}{2}$	$^2P_{1/2}\ ^2P_{3/2}\ ^4P_{1/2}\ ^4P_{3/2}\ ^4P_{5/2}$
$ns\ ms\ rd$	$L = 2$	$S = \frac{1}{2}, \frac{3}{2}$	$J = \frac{3}{2}, \frac{5}{2}, \frac{7}{2}$	$^2D_{3/2}\ ^2D_{5/2}\ ^4D_{1/2}\ ^4D_{3/2}\ ^4D_{5/2}\ ^4D_{7/2}$
$ns\ mp\ rp$	$L = 0$	$S = \frac{1}{2}, \frac{3}{2}$	$J = \frac{1}{2}, \frac{3}{2}$	$^2S_{1/2}\ ^4S_{3/2}$
	$L = 1$	$S = \frac{1}{2}, \frac{3}{2}$	$J = \frac{1}{2}, \frac{3}{2}, \frac{5}{2}$	
	$L = 2$	$S = \frac{1}{2}, \frac{3}{2}$	etc.	

Surely no further elaboration is required except to point out that where there are equivalent electrons certain states are impossible. The ones permitted for certain cases are:

Configuration	Terms								
ns^2	$^1S_0$								
np^2	$^1S_0$	$^3P_0$	$^3P_1$	$^3P_2$	$^1D_2$				
nd^2	$^1S_0$	$^3P_0$	$^3P_1$	$^3P_2$	$^1D_2$	$^3F_2$	$^3F_3$	$^3F_4$	$^1G_4$
ns^3	$^2S_{1/2}$								
$ns^2\ mp$	$^2P_{1/2}$	$^2P_{3/2}$							
$ns\ mp^2$	$^2S_{1/2}$	$^2P_{1/2}$	$^4P_{1/2}$	$^2P_{3/2}$	$^4P_{3/2}$	$^2P_{5/2}$	$^4P_{5/2}$	$^2D_{3/2}$	$^2D_{5/2}$

E–4. The Landé g Factor. The quantum theory of the Zeeman effect would agree with the classical theory if it were not for the anomolous magnetic moment of the spinning electron. That this is so can be seen since the magnetic moment of the whole atom would be $\mu_B \sqrt{J(J+1)}$. The component parallel to the field would be $-\mu_B M$. The energy would differ from the no field case by $-\mu B \cos \theta = \mu_B BM$. Since the selection rule for M is $\Delta M = 0, \pm 1$, the frequency difference for any line produced by the field will be

$$\Delta \nu = \frac{\mu_B B\, \Delta M}{h} = \frac{\mu_B}{h},\ 0,\ \frac{-\mu_B}{h}$$

$$= 0,\ \pm \frac{\omega_p}{2\pi} \qquad\qquad (\text{E-17})$$

where ω_p is the Larmor precession angular rate.

But, the magnetic moment due to the spin is

$$\mu_s = 2\mu_B \sqrt{s(s+1)}. \qquad\qquad (\text{E-18})$$

The effect of this can be seen by drawing a vector diagram illustrating the adding of the angular momenta and also the adding of the magnetic moments. This is done in Fig. E-9. One can think of the motions in the atom as making the triangle $l_1 l_2 L$ rotate about L, triangle $s_1 s_2 S$ rotate about S, and triangle LSJ rotate about J. The corresponding magnetic moments rotate with the result that μ rotates about the line opposite to J in such a way that there is a constant J-component μ_{eff}. This is the effective magnetic moment of the atom. The figure and quantum mechanical rules show that

$$
\begin{aligned}
\mu_{\text{eff}} &= \mu_L \cos{(L,J)} + \mu_s \cos{(S,J)} \\
&= \mu_B \sqrt{L(L+1)} \cos{(L,J)} + 2\mu_B \sqrt{S(S+1)} \cos{(S,J)} \\
&= \mu_B \left\{ \sqrt{L(L+1)}\, \frac{J(J+1) + L(L+1) - S(S+1)}{2\sqrt{J(J+1)}\sqrt{L(L+1)}} \right. \\
&\qquad \left. + 2\sqrt{S(S+1)}\, \frac{J(J+1) + S(S+1) - L(L+1)}{2\sqrt{J(J+1)}\sqrt{S(S+1)}} \right\} \\
&= \mu_B \sqrt{J(J+1)} \left\{ \frac{J(J+1) + L(L+1) - S(S+1)}{2J(J+1)} \right. \\
&\qquad \left. + \frac{2J(J+1) + 2S(S+1) - 2L(L+1)}{2J(J+1)} \right\} \\
&= \mu_B \sqrt{J(J+1)} \left\{ \frac{2J(J+1) + J(J+1) + S(S+1) - L(L+1)}{2J(J+1)} \right\} \\
&= \mu_B \sqrt{J(J+1)} \left\{ 1 + \frac{J(J+1) + S(S+1) - L(L+1)}{2J(J+1)} \right\} \\
&= \mu_B \sqrt{J(J+1)}\, g. \qquad\qquad (\text{E-19})
\end{aligned}
$$

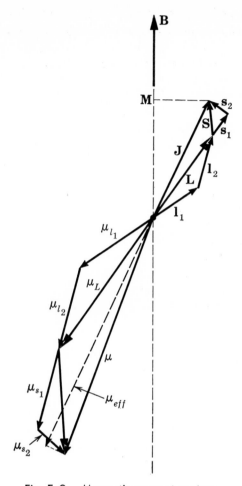

Fig. E–9. Magnetic moment vectors.

The factor

$$g = 1 + \frac{J(J+1) + S(S+1) - L(L+1)}{2J(J+1)} \qquad \text{(E–20)}$$

is called the Landé g factor. This calculation leads to an energy shift due to the field of

$$\Delta E = -\mu_B B g \cos \theta = \mu_B B g M.$$

If the non-field energy difference for a given transition is E the effect of the field will be to give transition energies

$$E + \mu_B B (g_i M_i - g_f M_f)$$

where g_i, M_i, g_f, and M_f are the g factors and magnetic quantum numbers of the initial and final states. The frequency shifts due to the field are

$$\Delta \nu = \frac{\mu_B B}{h} (g_i M_i - g_f M_f).$$

Since g_f and g_i are not likely to be the same, the Zeeman effect can become quite complicated. A typical case is shown in Chapter 12 in Fig. 12–10.

Of course, if each state is a singlet state ($S = 0$), then $J = L$ and $g = 1$. The Zeeman effect will then be a normal Zeeman effect.

F

Answers to Even-Numbered Numerical Problems

CHAPTER 1

1-2. 10, 0, 541, -1000
1-4. 500 j
1-6. 3200 newtons
1-8. (a) 49 newtons m^{-1}; (b) 0.157 j
1-10. 17.9 ft sec^{-1}
1-12. (a) 4.2×10^{-26} j; (b) 2.38×10^{-21} j; (c) 45 j; (d) 4.5×10^8 j
1-14. (a) $V = -GMm/R$; (b) $V = -gRm$
1-18. (a) 1.25×10^{-49} j; (b) 1.54×10^{-13} j
1-20. 9.21×10^{-18} j
1-22. 3.2×10^{-16} j; 2.66×10^7 m sec^{-1}
1-24. 1.13×10^{-12} j
1-26. 4.82 ev
1-30. (c) $2a/b$
1-32. 1, 0, 1, 0
1-36. Yes

CHAPTER 2

2-2. 0.27 m sec^{-1}; 0.80 newton-sec
2-4. 90 cm sec^{-1}
2-6. 148 lb
2-8. -3.0 m sec^{-1}; $+1.2$ m sec^{-1}
2-10. (a) 0, K; (b) $9/25\,K$, $16/25\,K$; (c) $9/25\,K$, $16/25\,K$; (d) $0.67K$, $0.33K$; (e) $0.96K$, $0.04K$
2-12. 1.66×10^4 m sec^{-1}
2-16. $\theta_L \simeq \theta_c$; $\theta_L \simeq \dfrac{\theta_c}{2}$; $\theta_L \simeq \dfrac{m_2}{m_1}\sin\theta_c$
2-20. 71° 25′

2-22. $\phi_L = 80°$; $\theta_L = 15° \, 40'$; $V'_1 = 7$ m sec^{-1}; $V'_2 = 2$ m sec^{-1}; $v'_1 = 8.90$ m sec^{-1}; $v'_2 = 0.70$ m sec^{-1}

2-24. 9.8 ev

2-26. 3.93 amu $= 6.53 \times 10^{-27}$ kg

CHAPTER 3

3-2. 0.66 newton-m

3-4. w at rim

3-8. (a) 8.2 kg-m sec^{-1}; (b) 2.1 radians sec^{-1}; (c) 3.84 kg-m^2; (d) 8.05 kg-m^2 sec^{-1}; (e) 17.2 newtons

3-10. 175 newtons; 1.78×10^6 j

3-12. (a) $2mv_0/Mr$; (b) $4\pi m/(2m + M)$; (c) $4\pi m/M$

3-14. 8.85 rev sec^{-1}; 128 j

3-16. (a) 17.1 sec; (b) 12.8 sec

3-20. 4.13×10^{-4} gm

3-22. Doubled

3-24. $i/(4\sqrt{2} \, R)$ (mks)

3-26. 4.5×10^{-17} newton

3-28. 4.64×10^{16} radians sec^{-1}

3-30. 1.85×10^{-23} j

3-32. 1.76×10^{11} radians sec^{-1}

CHAPTER 4

4-2. 29.2 m sec^{-1}

4-4. 7.77×10^{-13} sec

4-8. -56.1 m; 17 m; -1.5 m; 1.605×10^{-6} sec

4-10. 1.67×10^{-11} sec

4-12. 93.4 m; 8.67×10^{-7} sec; yes

4-14. 1.2×10^{11} m; 300 sec

4-16. 1.005 sec

4-18. 4.58×10^{-8} sec

4-20. (a) 14.29 m; (b) $0.89c$; (c) 2.52×10^{-7} sec; (d) 67.5 m; (e) 52.9 m

4-22. $x' = (5/13)ct'$

4-24. (a) 110 mph; (b) 109.99999999999926 mph

4-26. $0.55c$

4-28. 2.63×10^8 m sec^{-1}

4-32. 129%

4-34. 9×10^{13} j; 2.5×10^7 kwhr

4-36. 0.889 gm

4-38. 0.996; 0.103; 0.073

CHAPTER 5

5-2. (a) 404 liter; (b) 1.33×10^4 newtons m^{-2}

5-4. 2.98×10^{-5} gm

5–6. 1.39×10^{-15} dyne cm^{-2}
5–8. (a) 32; (b) 460 m sec^{-1}
5–10. 516 m sec^{-1}; 806 m sec^{-1}
5–12. 2.07×10^{-22} j; 1.29×10^{-3} ev; etc.
5–14. (a) 3.41×10^3 j; (b) 1.31×10^3 m sec^{-1}
5–16. 920
5–20. kT/m
5–26. $0.775v_m$
5–30. 2.08×10^{-2}; 0.979
5–32. (a) 4; (b) 3; (c) 1

CHAPTER 6

6–2. 3.29×10^{-4} gm coulomb^{-1}
6–4. 2.66×10^{-14} newton; 4.52×10^{-10} sec; 1.89×10^{-2} sec or 4.7×10^{-2} sec; 16.2 sec or 98 sec
6–6. 1.4×10^{-2} cm sec^{-1}
6–8. 2.59×10^{-14} kg
6–10. 3
6–12. 2.82 Å
6–14. 87.9
6–16. 3.62 Å; 178
6–18. 1.63×10^{-19} kg-m sec^{-1}
6–20. (a) 7.68×10^{-24} kg-m sec^{-1}; (b) 202 v; (c) 3.24×10^{-17} j
6–22. 9.24 gauss, 9.24×10^{-4} weber m^{-2}
6–24. 8.80×10^5 m sec^{-1}

CHAPTER 7

7–2. 382 newtons; 5.71×10^{28} m sec^{-1}; etc.
7–4. 1.70×10^7 m sec^{-1}; 1.20×10^7 m sec^{-1}; 1.30×10^{-16} j
7–6. 4.73×10^7 m sec^{-1}
7–8. (c) $(\pm 4, 0)$; $(\pm 4.48, 0)$; $\epsilon = 1.12$, $y = \pm 0.50x$
7–10. 127°
7–12. 2.68 Mev
7–14. 1.68×10^{-33} kg-m^2 sec^{-1}
7–16. 9.35×10^{-35} kg-m^2 sec^{-1}
7–18. (a) 0.27 Mev; (b) 1.17×10^{-33} kg-m^2 sec^{-1}; (c) 1.14×10^{-14} m
7–20. (a) 5.92×10^{18} cm^{-2}; (b) 3.57×10^{-4}
7–22. 1.75 cm^2; 1.25 cm^2; 1.53×10^{-2} cm^2
7–24. (a) 3.12×10^{17} cm^{-2}; (b) 3.53×10^{-7} cm^2; (c) 3.53×10^{-7}
7–26. 53° 14′
7–28. $9.34 \times 10^{-8}n$
7–30. 0.172 min^{-1}
7–32. 1×10^{12} gm cm^{-3}

CHAPTER 8

8–2. 616 w
8–4. 96,600 Å, a; 48,300 Å, 32a; etc.
8–6. 0.576
8–8. 9660 Å; yes
8–10. 1.81×10^{-18} w cm^{-2}
8–12. 6.70 ev
8–14. 1.26×10^{29} sec^{-1}; 2.52×10^{19} sec^{-1}; 7.05×10^{12} sec^{-1}
8–16. (a) 5.16×10^{-12} erg, 3.23 v; (b) 1.66 v
8–18. 3740 Å
8–20. 1.83 v
8–22. 2.71 v; magnesium
8–24. 0.25 Å
8–26. (a) 0.630 Å, 580 ev; (b) 0.618 Å, 180 ev

CHAPTER 9

9–2. 1.05×10^{-34} kg-m^2 sec^{-1}
9–4. -4.35×10^{-18} j; 2.17×10^{-18} j
9–6. -1.51 ev
9–8. 6562, 4861, 4340, 4101 Å, etc.
9–10. (a) 3650 Å; (b) 1216 Å
9–14. 1.78 Å
9–16. 6
9–18. 1.6×10^{14} sec^{-1}; 1.03×10^{14} sec^{-1}; etc.
9–20. 137
9–22. 4.53×10^{-5} ev; 0.367 cm^{-1}
9–24. 1.05×10^{-34} kg-m^2 sec^{-1}
9–26. -2530 ev; -633 ev; -281 ev; -158 ev
9–28. 2.22×10^{-3} Å
9–30. 0.0525 ev; 236,000 Å; some will be

CHAPTER 10

10–2. 5.12×10^5 dynes cm^{-1}
10–4. (a) 5.3×10^{-3} cm; (b) 6 sec^{-1}; (c) 1.67 sec; (d) zero
10–8. $x = -3 \cos 8t$ in.; $v = 24 \sin 8t$ in. sec^{-1}
10–10. $x = 1.5 \times 10^{-4} \cos(83.6t - \pi/6)$; etc.
10–12. 4.72×10^{-9} j
10–14. (a) 3.55×10^{-10} newton-m radian^{-1}; (b) 2.76×10^2 radians sec^{-1}; (c) 1.36×10^{-8} j
10–16. 0.242 dyne-cm
10–18. 16 cm sec^{-1}
10–20. (a) 2 cm; (b) 6 sec; (c) 0.167 sec^{-1}; (d) 4 cm; (e) 0.667 cm sec^{-1}

10-22. (a) negative x-direction; (b) 5 cm; (c) $100 \sec^{-1}$; (d) 600 cm; (e) 6×10^4 cm $\sec^{-1}$

10-24. 1.57×10^{-2} radian; 0.0995 radian

10-26. 0.833 in. $\sec^{-1}$

10-30. $34.2n \sec^{-1}$; $68.4n \sec^{-1}$

10-32. $y_n = 2C \sin 68.4n\pi t \sin 1.25n\pi x$

10-34. 1.17×10^5 newtons m^{-2}

10-36. 7:34 P.M.

CHAPTER 11

11-2. 1.096

11-4. (a) 2.21×10^{-31} m; (b) 1.82×10^{-38} m; (c) 2.24×10^{-11} m

11-6. 1.66×10^{-10} m

11-8. 1.61 Å

11-12. 0.687 Å; 43°

11-14. 1.6×10^{-10} m

11-16. 1.05×10^{-24} kg-m $\sec^{-1}$; 3.8 ev

11-18. $hk/2\pi m$

11-22. 2.04 Mev; 8.16 Mev; 18.4 Mev

11-26. 0.0166 ev

11-30. $W_n = n^2 \hbar^2/(2I)$

CHAPTER 12

12-2. 9.27×10^{-24} amp-m^2; 1.05×10^{-34} kg-m $\sec^{-1}$

12-4. 7702 Å; 4049 Å; 3448 Å; 3218 Å

12-6. -4.34 ev; -2.73 ev; -1.28 ev; -0.75 ev; -0.49 ev

12-8. 16,900 cm^{-1}; 16,980 cm^{-1}; 18,310 cm^{-1}; 39,420 cm^{-1}

12-10. 16,900 cm^{-1}; 5900 Å

12-12. 2.70

12-16. 1, 1, 2; 0, 2, 2; 3/2, 1, 3/2; 5/2, 3, 9/2; 0, 0, 0

12-18. $S = 1, 0$; $L = 1, 2, 3, 4, 5$; For $S = 0$, $J = L$; For $S = 1$, $J = L - 1, L, L + 1$, etc.

12-20. $j_1 = 5/2, 3/2$; $j_2 = 7/2, 5/2$; J's the same as in 12-18

12-22. $^1P_1$, $^3P_{0,1,2}$; $^1P_1$, $^1D_2$, $^1F_3$, $^3P_{0,1,2}$, $^3D_{1,2,3}$, $^3F_{2,3,4}$

12-24. 74° 30'; 37°, 74° 30', 105° 30', 143° 30'

12-26. 1.61×10^{-23} newton-m

12-28. 2; 3/2; nine equally spaced lines

12-30. 1.296×10^{-23} j; 9.75×10^{-24} j

12-32. 0.186 cm^{-1}; 5580 mc; 0.0623 Å

CHAPTER 13

13-4. Argon 15.6 v; $K_\alpha = 4.21$ Å, $K_\beta = 3.89$ Å; etc.

13-8. 1.24×10^4 ev

13-10. 3.61×10^4 v

13–12. $1° 56'$
13–14. 0.50 Å
13–16. 56
13–18. 14.1 cm^{-1}
13–20. 5.23 cm^2 gm^{-1}
13–22. 5.27×10^4 ev

CHAPTER 14

14–2. 0.35 ev; 0.70 ev
14–4. Parabolic, $V = 21.2x^2$
14–6. 6.4 Å, 3.2 Å; 4.53 Å, 2.26 Å
14–8. Insulator, intrinsic semiconductor, semiconductor, semiconductor, metal
14–10. 3.56 ev
14–12. $17,200$ Å; of the order of $8000°$K
14–14. (b) of the order of $550°$K
14–16. (a) $1/2$; (b) exp $(-E/kT)$
14–18. 5.53 ev
14–20. 2.82 Å
14–22. 1.12×10^{-2} m sec^{-1}; 1.08×10^6 m sec^{-1}
14–24. 1.0×10^{-5} amp
14–26. 0.0205 cm sec^{-1}
14–28. p-type

CHAPTER 15

15–2. $2/3$
15–4. (a) 4.52×10^{17}; (b) 1.36×10^{18}
15–6. 1.70×10^{-4} cm^3
15–10. 1.01×10^{-12} gm; 1.03×10^{-10} cm^3
15–12. 32.4 sec; 46.8 sec; 2.14×10^{-2} sec^{-1}
15–18. 1.62×10^{-4} gm; $0.330, 0.550, 0.982$, etc.
15–20. 4.73×10^{-7} gm; 4.95×10^{-11} gm
15–22. $12,380$ yr
15–24. 1.35×10^9 yr
15–28. 3.75×10^{-13} amp
15–30. $0.693/\mu$

CHAPTER 16

16–4. (a) 3.12×10^{15}; (b) 1.92×10^{-12} j
16–6. 2.67×10^{-5} coulomb m^{-2}; 0.685 sec
16–8. 4.18 Mev
16–10. 1.44×10^{-14} m
16–12. 9.15 mc
16–14. 41.6 cm

16–16. 13.6 mc; 194 Mev; 7.81×10^{14} sec^{-1}
16–18. 186 Mev
16–20. 12.2 mc; 11.6 mc; 11.1 mc; 10.6 mc
16–22. 0.107 weber m^{-2}; 1.79×10^5 rev
16–24. 4.10×10^6 w; 18.5 kw

CHAPTER 17

17–2. 0.30; 0.98; 2.36
17–6. 0.260 cm
17–8. 1.16 amu
17–10. 0.30 Mev
17–14. 14.1 Mev
17–16. 44.2 rev sec^{-1}
17–18. $_{11}\text{Na}^{24}$; $_0 n^1$; etc.
17–20. -3.16 Mev; -4.75 Mev
17–22. 1.92×10^{-3} cm; 1.97×10^{-2} cm
17–24. $_{14}\text{Si}^{28}$
17–26. 66%
17–28. Yes; $_{15}P^{31}$; 1.48 Mev

CHAPTER 18

18–2. 4.97×10^{-15} m
18–4. $3/2$; 0; $7/2$; $9/2$
18–6. $_2\text{He}^3$, $_1\text{H}^3$; $_6\text{C}^{11}$, $_5\text{B}^{11}$; $_7\text{N}^{13}$, $_6\text{C}^{13}$; and others
18–8. 3
18–10. 1.09×10^{17} j m^{-2}
18–12. 21 Mev; 29 Mev
18–14. 26.98189 amu
18–16. 1.03×10^{21}; 1.02×10^{-27}
18–18. 4.32×10^{10} neutrino sec^{-1}

CHAPTER 19

19–2. If all collisions are head on, 56; on the average, 115 (see Kaplan, *Nuclear Physics* p. 453)
19–4. 3.12×10^3 m sec^{-1}; 1.27 Å
19–6. 1.42×10^9 cm^{-3} (2.84×10^9 cm^{-3} assuming an isotropic flux)
19–8. Mfp $= 1/N\sigma$
19–10. (a) 1.30 gm; (b) 8000 kwhr
19–12. 44.5 gm; 49 kg; 11.8 kg
19–14. 1.63×10^{12} sec^{-1}; 1.65×10^{-3} gm
19–16. 1085
19–18. (a) 23.6; (b) 47.2

CHAPTER 20

20–2. 1.30×10^{-18} amp cm^{-3}

20–6. 18.8 Mev; 1.22 Bev; 20 Bev; 207 Bev

20–8. 6.63×10^{-15} m; 6.45×10^{-16} m; 5.94×10^{-17} m; 5.92×10^{-18} m

20–10. 3.12×10^4 m; 3.24×10^5 m; 3.45×10^6 m; 3.50×10^7 m

20–12. 5.6×10^{17}; 0.09 amp; 127 v sec^{-1}

20–14. 4.5×10^{-9} cal cm^{-2} min^{-1}; about the same

20–16. 89° 20′

Index